D1221431

RECENT DEVELOPMENTS IN GENERAL RELATIVITY

RECENT DEVELOPMENTS IN GENERAL RELATIVITY

[redacted]

A Pergamon Press Book

THE MACMILLAN COMPANY
NEW YORK

RC6
.R34
1962

PERGAMON PRESS INC.
122 East 55 th Street, New York 22, N. Y.
1404 New York Avenue, N.W.
Washington 5 D.C.

PERGAMON PRESS LTD.
Headington Hill Hall, Oxford
4 & 5 Fitzroy Square, London W. 1

PERGAMON PRESS S. A. R. L.
24 Rue des Écoles, Paris Ve

PERGAMON PRESS G. m. b. H.
Kaiserstrasse 75, Frankfurt am Main

Copyright 1962
by
PAŃSTWOWE WYDAWNICTWO NAUKOWE
PWN – Polish Scientific Publishers
WARSZAWA

Library of Congress Card Number
62–9878

Printed in Poland
to the order of PWN–Polish Scientific Publishers
by Wrocławska Drukarnia Naukowa

44851

THIS BOOK IS DEDICATED TO
LEOPOLD INFELD
IN CONNECTION WITH HIS 60TH BIRTHDAY.

FOREWORD

In spite of its comparatively "old age" general relativity is developing again quite rapidly. Its beautiful and profound mathematical and physical structure attracts even physicists from other branches of physics. Very many of them believe that the period of separation of general relativity from the quantum physics is coming to an end. Several physicists are looking just here for the solution of some basic difficulties encountered in quantum field theories. They think that the general, and not the special, relativity ought to be used as a framework for the future theory of elementary particles. Whether or not this is so we have to record the rapidly growing interest in general relativity.

In such a period of growing interest and fast development many people need a book informing them not only about recent developments and achievements, but also about main trends, main ways of thought, and problems to be solved. The lack of such a book covering at least the period of the last few years was felt by many physicists whom we asked for their opinion. Of greatest value would be probably a comprehensive edition of many volumes reviewing in a synthetic manner our present knowledge on the subject. However, it would be rather hard to convince the physicists to write a synthetic handbook just now in the period of extensive scientific activity.

Therefore, what we present here to the reader is not a synthetic and complete review, for which the time may not be ripe enough. It is rather a comprehensive collective book comprising articles written by many physicists active in general relativity. But we hope that it will stimulate in the future, further, more synthetic and more complete reviews. The book is divided into two parts. Part I consists of 7 longer review articles presenting the actual status of such basic problems as: gravitational radiation, problem of motion, experimental tests, quantization, unified theories, cosmology, and mathematical problems of general relativity. Part II consists of 38 original contributions which present a fairly good survey of different schools of thought, different mathematical methods, and different scientific approaches to various problems of general relativity.

The idea of the edition of this book was originated in Warsaw by a group of Prof. L. Infeld's collaborators and students, who would like to take the opportunity to dedicate this book to him in connection with his 60th birthday. This explains also why his name does not occur on the list of contributors.

The editorial committee is very much indebted to all contributors from so many different countries for their helpful response. We were very sorry for being forced by the limited scope of the book to ask some contributors to shorten their articles. We should like to express our gratitude to the Polish Scientific Publishers and the Pergamon Press for the careful preparation of this book.

Editorial Committee

CONTENTS

PART ONE

THE PROBLEM OF MOTION*

S. Bażański

Institute of Physics, Polish Academy of Sciences, Warsaw

1. EQUATIONS OF MOTION

The problem of the motion of bodies in the general theory of relativity, as in every field theory, is a problem of basic importance, since motion is primarily a physical phenomenon by means of which the field discloses its existence. In the initial formulation of the general theory of relativity the equations of motion of test bodies (equations of geodesic lines) moving in a gravitational field that is given *a priori* were postulated independently, alongside the field equations. On the other hand, the problem of the motion of heavy bodies, i.e. bodies of comparable mass, was not posed. In 1927, Einstein and Grommer [1] showed that it was sufficient to postulate only the field equations, because the equations of motion of the test bodies follow from the field equations of the general theory of relativity (see also [11]). The possibility of eliminating the equations of motion as an independent postulate is due to two features of general relativity theory: its nonlinearity; and its covariance with respect to arbitrary transformations of the frames of reference, which leads to the vanishing of the covariant divergence of the Einstein tensor (Bianchi identity). The work of Einstein and Grommer introduced a simplification of the logical structure of the theory, but the problem of the equations of motion of heavy bodies was still not solved. The solution of this difficult problem was given for the first time only in 1938 by Einstein, Infeld, and Hoffmann [2].

* The Editorial Committee, wishing to give, in the first part of this book, a survey of all fields of gravitation theory, recommended that an article be prepared which would present only a general outline of the problem of motion. This problem has been presented rather exhaustively in the published monograph of L. Infeld and J. Plebański [58]. The reader who is particularly interested in this problem is referred to that monograph.

It was then shown that the equations of motion of heavy bodies (with spherical symmetry) were also contained in the field equations of general relativity. The method of obtaining the equations of motion given in this work were subsequently perfected from the mathematical viewpoint in [6] and [10].

Einstein, Infeld, and Hoffmann assumed that the bodies under consideration are described by point singularities of the gravitational field. This very convenient assumption makes it possible to avoid the choice of some special form for the energy-momentum tensor. Physically, this does not mean that the bodies must be limited to those having small dimensions, provided that (as in Newtonian physics) the field outside spherically symmetric extended bodies is identical with the field of appropriately chosen point singularities. In accordance with this assumption, the equations of the gravitational field in the regions outside the bodies go over into the equations

$$G^{\mu\nu} \equiv R^{\mu\nu} - \tfrac{1}{2}g^{\mu\nu}R = 0 \tag{1.1}$$

(the Greek indices run over 0, 1, 2, 3 and the Latin indices, over 1, 2, 3), where the gravitational field that is a solution to the above equations, $g_{\mu\nu}$, depends not only on x^{μ}, but also on the coordinates of the singularities $\overset{A}{\xi}{}^{k}(x^0)$ ($A = 1, 2, \ldots, N$; N is the number of singularities; $\overset{A}{\xi}{}^{0} = x^0$). It is assumed here that the system is always in a finite region of space. Then at infinity in space (i.e. for $|\underline{x}| = (x^k x^k)^{1/2} \to \infty$) the curvature tensor vanishes, and one may choose at infinity a frame of reference such that

$$\lim_{|\underline{x}|\to\infty} g_{\alpha\beta} = \eta_{\alpha\beta}, \tag{1.2}$$

where $\eta_{00} = 1$, $\eta_{0m} = 0$, $\eta_{mn} = -\delta_{mn}$. As quantities describing the field one may take the quantities

$$h_{\mu\nu} = g_{\mu\nu} - \eta_{\mu\nu} \tag{1.3}$$

or the quantities

$$\gamma^{\mu\nu} = \mathfrak{g}^{\mu\nu} - \eta^{\mu\nu} = \sqrt{-g}\,g^{\mu\nu} - \eta^{\mu\nu}. \tag{1.4}$$

These quantities are related to each other in the following way:

$$\gamma^{\mu\nu} = h^{\mu\nu} - \tfrac{1}{2}\eta^{\mu\nu}\eta_{\alpha\beta}h^{\alpha\beta} + \text{nonlinear expressions}. \tag{1.5}$$

The left-hand side of Eqs (1.1) (see Infeld [51]) may be written in the form

$$\sqrt{-g}\,G^{\mu\nu} = K^{\mu\alpha\nu\beta}{}_{|\alpha\beta} + \Lambda^{\mu\nu} \tag{1.6}$$

where

$$K^{\mu\alpha\nu\beta} = \tfrac{1}{2}(\gamma^{\mu\beta}\eta^{\nu\alpha} + \gamma^{\nu\alpha}\eta^{\mu\beta} - \gamma^{\alpha\beta}\eta^{\mu\nu} - \gamma^{\mu\nu}\eta^{\alpha\beta})$$

has the same symmetry properties as the Riemann tensor and $\Lambda^{\mu\nu}$ contains only expressions nonlinear in the $\gamma_{\alpha\beta}$ and their derivatives (also second derivatives). If we consider a two-dimensional surface Σ_A enclosing only the Ath singularity and calculate the integral

$$\int_{\Sigma_A} G^{m\nu} d_2\sigma$$

then, by the field equations and the symmetry properties of the quantity $S^{\mu\alpha\nu\beta}$ one obtains

$$\frac{d}{dt}\int_{\Sigma_A} K^{m0\nu\beta}{}_{|\beta} n_m d_2\sigma + \int_{\Sigma_A} \Lambda^{m\nu} n_m d_2\sigma = 0. \tag{1.7}$$

From the symmetry properties of the quantity $K^{mk\nu\beta}$ we have $K^{mn\nu\beta}{}_{|\varrho km} = 0$, from which, by the field equations and by formula (1.6) it follows that Eqs (1.7) do not depend on the choice of the surface Σ_A as long as it contains only one singularity. Therefore, the $4N$ equations (1.7) cannot be relations among the coordinates x^μ. They can only be relations among the coordinates of the singularities $\overset{A}{\xi}{}^k(x^0)$, and therefore, if they are not satisfied trivially, they must be the equations of motion of the bodies described by the singularities ($3N$ equations of motion for $\nu = 1, 2, 3$, and N equations of the conservation of mass for $\nu = 0$). In the works of Einstein and collaborators Eqs (1.7) were taken as the definition of the equations of motion. In order to write Eqs (1.7) in explicit form, Eqs (1.1) should be solved and the function that is found should be inserted into (1.7). This cannot be done, however, since the satisfying of the equations of motion (1.7) is precisely the condition of integrability of the field equations (1.1). This difficulty is by-passed by the approximation method proposed by Einstein, Infeld, and Hoffmann (hereafter referred to as the EIH method). This method acts in such a way as to permit the writing of the equations of motion in the kth order of approximation (and therefore the conditions of integrability of the field equations in this order) by means of fields that are already known (of order $< k$) (cf. [20], [58]). In that work [2] the non-trivial equations of motion were determined in the post-Newtonian order. The relativistic corrections of this order are fully sufficient for the experimental confirmation of the theory; higher orders would already give small corrections. An analysis of the physical content of the EIH equations of motion was made by H. P. Robertson [3], who, by means of these equations of motion, determined the motion of periastron of double stars.

Alongside with the direction of development of the problems of motion presented above, another direction, initiated by the work of V. A. Fock [5] has been developed (see also [28], [40]). Independently of Einstein and co-workers, Fock derived from the equations of the gravitational field the equations of motion of heavy bodies in the Newtonian approximation. The starting point of Fock was the field equations with the energy-momentum tensor of extended bodies; the bodies were therefore described by a continuum of degrees of freedom. In the case of nonrotational motion of bodies with a central symmetry this difference in the description is not essential. (The difference in the views of the Einstein and Fock schools on the role of coordinate systems is, however, essential. See also [17], [18], [19], [23], [24], [26], [28], [40], [44], [59].) Using Fock's method, Petrova [12] derived the post-Newtonian equations identical to the EIH equations. The conservation laws resulting from these equations were given by Fichtenholz [14]. Also belonging to this direction, to a certain degree, is the work of Papapetrou [16], [17] which is a modification of Fock's method.

In Fock's method the equations of motion are defined by means of the energy-momentum tensor, while the EIH equations of motion were defined by means of the tensor $G^{\mu\nu}$. A certain kind of synthesis of these definitions is introduced in the work of Infeld [21]. In this work the bodies are also described by means of the singularities of the gravitational field, but these singularities are introduced into the energy-momentum tensor by means of the Dirac δ function:

$$\boldsymbol{T}^{\alpha\beta} \equiv \sqrt{-g}\,T^{\alpha\beta} = \sum_{A=1}^{N} \overset{A}{m}(t)\,\delta_3(x-\overset{A}{\xi})\,\overset{A}{\xi}{}^{\alpha}{}_{|0}\,\overset{A}{\xi}{}^{\beta}{}_{|0} \tag{1.8}$$

where $\overset{A}{\xi}{}^{0}_{|0} = 1$ and $\delta_3(x-\overset{A}{\xi}) = \prod_{k=1}^{3}\delta(x^k-\overset{A}{\xi}{}^k)$. In the work of Infeld referred to above [21] this form of the energy-momentum tensor was assumed; it however results, as Tulczyjew showed [38], from the field equations if it is required that $\boldsymbol{T}^{\alpha\beta}$ describe singularities of the polar structure.

From the field equations one obtains the symbolic equation

$$\boldsymbol{T}^{\alpha\beta}{}_{;\beta} = 0. \tag{1.9}$$

If this equation is integrated over the three-dimensional region $\overset{A}{\Omega}$ containing only one singularity, then one obtains the equations

$$\int\limits_{\overset{A}{\Omega}} \boldsymbol{T}^{\alpha\beta}{}_{;\beta} d_3 x = 0, \tag{1.10}$$

which are relations between the coordinates $\overset{A}{\xi}{}^k$ of the singularities and their derivatives. Infeld [21] took them as the definition of the equations of motion (they are, by the field equations, equivalent to the relations (1.7)) and using the EIH approximation method, he calculated them to the accuracy of the post-Newtonian approximation. From the viewpoint of computational technique, this method is considerably simpler than the previous methods given in [2], [6], [10].

In the post-Newtonian equations of motion derived by Infeld [21] there appear infinities which were removed by the renormalization of the mass in the post-Newtonian approximation (see Infeld [21], Plebański and Bażański [54]). The renormalization can be avoided by means of the formalism of generalized $\hat{\delta}$ functions worked out by Infeld and Plebański [31], [37] (see Appendix). The introduction of these functions into the energy-momentum tensor (1.8) leads to equations of motion not containing infinities. In fact, the main advantage of the $\hat{\delta}$ functions is the possibility of defining a finite value of the fields on the world lines of particles (see (A.1)). With their help, some of the properties of the equations of motion may be discussed without resorting to the approximation method (cf. [32]).

If it is assumed that the δ function occurring in the energy-momentum tensor is the $\hat{\delta}$ function, then we can transform Eq. (1.10) by making use of the definition of finite values of the tensors on the world lines. Thus we have

$$\begin{aligned}\boldsymbol{T}^{\alpha\beta}{}_{;\beta} &= \boldsymbol{T}^{\alpha s}{}_{|s} + \boldsymbol{T}^{\alpha 0}{}_{|0} + \left\{ {\alpha \atop \mu\nu} \right\} \boldsymbol{T}^{\mu\nu} \\ &= \boldsymbol{T}^{\alpha s}{}_{|s} + \sum_{A=1}^{N} [\overset{A}{m}(t) \overset{A}{\xi}{}^{\alpha}{}_{|0} \hat{\delta}_3(x - \overset{A}{\xi})]_{|0} + \left\{ {\alpha \atop \mu\nu} \right\} \sum_{A=1}^{N} \overset{A}{m}(t) \overset{A}{\xi}{}^{\mu}{}_{|0} \overset{A}{\xi}{}^{\nu}{}_{|0} \hat{\delta}_3(x - \overset{A}{\xi}).\end{aligned}$$

Integrating this over the region $\overset{A}{\Omega}$ of the Ath singularity, we find that the integral with $\boldsymbol{T}^{\alpha s}{}_{|s}$ vanishes, while

$$\int\limits_{\overset{A}{\Omega}} \boldsymbol{T}^{\alpha 0}{}_{|0} d_3 x = [\overset{A}{m}(t) \overset{A}{\xi}{}^{\alpha}{}_{|0}]_{|0}$$

and

$$\int\limits_{\overset{A}{\Omega}} \left\{ {\alpha \atop \mu\nu} \right\} \boldsymbol{T}^{\mu\nu} d_3 x = \overset{A}{m}(t) \overline{\left\{ {\alpha \atop \mu\nu} \right\}}^{A} \overset{A}{\xi}{}^{\mu}{}_{|0} \overset{A}{\xi}{}^{\nu}{}_{|0} = 0 .$$

Hence Eqs (1.10) take the form

$$[\overset{A}{m}(t) \overset{A}{\xi}{}^{\alpha}{}_{|0}]_{|0} + \overset{A}{m}(t) \overline{\left\{ {\alpha \atop \mu\nu} \right\}}^{A} \overset{A}{\xi}{}^{\mu}{}_{|0} \overset{A}{\xi}{}^{\nu}{}_{|0} = 0 . \tag{1.11}$$

When the above equations are multiplied by $\overline{g_{\alpha\beta}}^{A}$ and use is made of (A.4), we have

$$[\overset{A}{m}(t) \overline{g_{\alpha\beta}}^{A} \overset{A}{\xi}{}^{\alpha}{}_{|0}]_{|0} - \tfrac{1}{2} \overset{A}{m}(t) \overline{g_{\mu\nu|\beta}}^{A} \overset{A}{\xi}{}^{\mu}{}_{|0} \overset{A}{\xi}{}^{\nu}{}_{|0} = 0 . \tag{1.12}$$

The above system of $4N$ equations is equivalent to the system (1.11). In Eqs (1.12) appear the unknown functions $\overset{A}{m}(t)$, $\overset{A}{\xi}{}^{k}(t)$ (with the assumption that $\overset{A}{\xi}{}^{0}{}_{|0} = 1$) and the unknown fields $g_{\alpha\beta}(x^\mu)$. The equations of motion of bodies containing the unknown fields whose sources are the bodies under consideration are called, following the terminology of Infeld and Plebański [58], equations of motion of the *second kind*. (In this terminology, the equations of motion of the first kind denote the equations of motion of test particles in an external field.) If by means of the field equations it would be possible to determine the field $g_{\mu\nu}(x^\mu, \xi^k, \xi^k{}_{|0})$ dependent also on the world lines of the field source, then, after substituting this field into the equations of motion (1.12), one would obtain $4N$ equations in which there occur only the variables $\overset{A}{m}(t)$, $\overset{A}{\xi}{}^{k}(t)$, and their time derivatives. Such equations from which the field is eliminated are called by Infeld and Plebański equations of motion of the *third kind*. The transition from the equations of motion of the second kind to the equations of motion of the third kind in the general theory of relativity is possible only by means of the approximation method.

From Eqs (1.12) it is easy to determine the mass $\overset{A}{m}(t)$. Multiplying (1.12) by $\overset{A}{\xi}{}^{\beta}{}_{|0}$, we obtain

$$\tfrac{1}{2} \overset{A}{m}(t) [\overline{g_{\alpha\beta}}^{A} \overset{A}{\xi}{}^{\alpha}{}_{|0} \overset{A}{\xi}{}^{\beta}{}_{|0}]_{|0} - \overset{A}{m}(t)_{|0} \overline{g_{\alpha\beta}}^{A} \overset{A}{\xi}{}^{\alpha}{}_{|0} \overset{A}{\xi}{}^{\beta}{}_{|0} = 0$$

from which we obtain

$$[\log \overline{m(t)}^{A}]_{|0} = [\log (\overline{g_{\alpha\beta}}^{A} \overset{A}{\xi}{}^{\alpha}{}_{|0} \overset{A}{\xi}{}^{\beta}{}_{|0})^{-\frac{1}{2}}]_{|0}$$

or

$$\overset{A}{m}(t) = \overset{A}{m}_0 [\overset{A}{g}_{\alpha\beta} \overset{A}{\xi}{}^{\alpha}{}_{|0} \overset{A}{\xi}{}^{\beta}{}_{|0}]^{-1/2} = \overset{A}{m}_0 \frac{dt}{\overset{A}{ds}} \tag{1.13}$$

where $\overset{A}{m}_0$ are constants of integration (rest masses) and

$$\overset{A}{ds}{}^2 = \overset{A}{g}_{\alpha\beta} d\overset{A}{\xi}{}^{\alpha} d\overset{A}{\xi}{}^{\beta}.$$

The $4N$ equations (1.12) will be equivalent to the system of equations composed of N equations (1.13) and $3N$ equations

$$\left[\frac{dt}{\overset{A}{ds}} \overset{A}{g}_{\alpha k} \overset{A}{\xi}{}^{\alpha}{}_{|0}\right]_{|0} - \frac{1}{2} \frac{dt}{\overset{A}{ds}} \overset{A}{g}_{\mu\nu|k} \overset{A}{\xi}{}^{\mu}{}_{|0} \overset{A}{\xi}{}^{\nu}{}_{|0} = 0 \tag{1.14}$$

obtained from the elimination of the mass $\overset{A}{m}(t)$ from Eqs (1.12) for $\beta = k$.

The equations of motion may also be obtained from the so-called "geodesic method" (see Bertotti [22]), equivalent to Eqs (1.11). Still other methods of obtaining the equations of motion may be found in [54], [55], [56], [57], [44], [45]. The considerations presented here may also be generalized to the case in which, apart from the gravitational field, there occur other additional fields (e.g. an electromagnetic field) (see [8], [29], [34], and [41]). The use of these methods in special relativity theory is discussed in [25] and in [7].

2. EIH APPROXIMATION METHOD

This method is a powerful (and thus far, in principle, the only) tool in the problem of the motion of bodies in the general theory of relativity. It is used in the case in which the bodies producing the gravitational field execute finite motion. The mathematical counterpart of this is the assumption that, at infinity, space is asymptotically flat. It is then most convenient to assume that the coordinate system is defined by (1.2). (It is also possible to introduce curvilinear systems at infinity; see [30].) Characteristic of this method is the assumption that the quantities describing the field are analytic functions of the parameter $\lambda = c^{-1}$ (c is the velocity of light). These quantities may then be expanded in a power series in λ. Thus e.g. for $h_{\alpha\beta}$ (1.3) we have

$$h_{\alpha\beta} = \underset{1}{h}_{\alpha\beta}\lambda + \underset{2}{h}_{\alpha\beta}\lambda^2 + \underset{3}{h}_{\alpha\beta}\lambda^3 + \ldots, \tag{2.1}$$

where $\underset{i}{h}_{\alpha\beta}$ does not depend on c. The approximation procedure does not differ from that adopted in other approximation methods; thus e.g. it is assumed that the product $\underset{i}{h}\underset{k}{h}$ is of the order $i+k$, and that the derivative with respect to the space coordinates $\frac{\partial}{\partial x^k}\underset{i}{h}_{\alpha\beta} = \underset{i}{h}_{\alpha\beta|k}$ is of the same order as $\underset{i}{h}_{\alpha\beta}$. Introduced here, however, is one essential assumption which distinguishes this method from others. It is connected with the distinct character of time in the problem of motion. Thus it is assumed that the time

$$t = \frac{x^0}{c} = \lambda x^0$$

does not depend on c (and therefore that it is a quantity of the order zero, just as $\eta_{\alpha\beta}$). This means that

$$\underset{i}{h}_{\alpha\beta|0} = \frac{1}{c}\frac{\partial}{\partial t}\underset{i}{h}_{\alpha\beta} = \lambda\frac{\partial \underset{i}{h}_{\alpha\beta}}{\partial t} \tag{2.2}$$

is a quantity of the order $i+1$; this is frequently indicated by writing 1 under the index zero, e.g. $\underset{i}{h}_{\alpha\beta|\underset{1}{0}}$. The method formulated in this way is useful in practice (i.e. reality is already described well by several of its first approximations) for relatively slow motions ($v \ll c$) and for distances greater than the Schwarzschild radius of the individual singularities and less than wavelength that is characteristic for the field (see [46]). (It is not useful in the wave radiation zone.).

If it is required that the equations of motion of the test bodies in the general theory of relativity for $c \to \infty$ go over into the Newtonian equations, then it can be shown [58] that in the expansion (2.1) $\underset{1}{h}_{00} = \underset{1}{h}_{0m} = 0$. In accordance with the principle of relativity, the quantities $h_{\alpha\beta}$ are not uniquely defined by the field equations, but to an accuracy of arbitrary transformations of the coordinate system $x^{\alpha'} = x^{\alpha'}(x^\mu)$. In the EIH approximation method, owing to the assumptions on which it is based, one considers the class of transformations which

(1) preserve the condition $\lim\limits_{|x|\to\infty} g_{\alpha\beta} = \eta_{\alpha\beta}$ and go over at infinity into the identity

(2) do not change the orders of the expansion of the quantity $h_{\alpha\beta}$.

Writing the transformation $x^{\alpha'} = x^{\alpha'}(x^\mu)$ in the form

$$x^{\alpha'} = x^\alpha + a^\alpha(x^\mu),$$

we may formulate conditions 1 and 2 as follows:

$$(1') \qquad \lim_{|x|\to\infty} a^{\alpha}(x^{\mu}) = 0,$$

$$(2') \qquad a^{0} = \underset{2}{a^{0}}\lambda^{2} + \underset{3}{a^{0}}\lambda^{3} + \ldots,$$

$$a^{k} = \underset{1}{a^{k}}\lambda + \underset{2}{a^{k}}\lambda^{2} + \ldots$$

($\underset{1}{a^{0}} = 0$ if it is desired to preserve the relation $\underset{1}{h_{00}} = \underset{1}{h_{0m}} = 0$). If we consider the transformation of the coordinate system generated only by $\underset{i+1}{a_{0}}$ and $\underset{i}{a_{k}}$ ($a_{\alpha} = \eta_{\alpha\beta}a^{\beta}$), then the quantities $h_{\alpha\beta}$ will transform beginning with the orders $\underset{i}{h_{mn}}$, $\underset{i+1}{h_{0n}}$, $\underset{i+2}{h_{0n}}$. Here a necessary and sufficient condition for the group of transformed quantities $\underset{i}{h'_{mn}}$, $\underset{i+1}{h'_{0n}}$, $\underset{i+2}{h'_{00}}$ to equal zero is the vanishing of the following components

$$\underset{i}{S_{manb}} = 0, \qquad \underset{i+1}{S_{m0nb}} = 0, \qquad \underset{i+2}{S_{m00b}} = 0$$

of the linearized curvature tensor

$$S_{\mu\alpha\nu\beta} = \tfrac{1}{2}(h_{\alpha\beta,\mu\nu} + h_{\mu\nu,\alpha\beta} - h_{\mu\beta,\nu\alpha} - h_{\alpha\nu,\mu\beta})$$

(cf. [46], [47], [58]).

Using this condition, one may show ([4], [13], [15], [58]) that by a suitable choice of $\underset{2}{a_{0}}$, $\underset{1}{a_{k}}$ and $\underset{4}{a_{0}}$, $\underset{3}{a_{k}}$ the group of quantities $\underset{1}{h_{mn}}$, $\underset{2}{h_{0n}}$, $\underset{3}{h_{00}}$ and $\underset{3}{h_{mn}}$, $\underset{4}{h_{0n}}$, $\underset{5}{h_{00}}$ can be eliminated from the expansion (2.1) ($\underset{1}{h_{00}}$ and $\underset{1}{h_{0n}}$ can be eliminated by using the correspondence principle mentioned above); as a result, the expansion, takes the form

$$\begin{aligned} h_{00} &= 0 + \underset{2}{h_{00}}\lambda^{2} + 0 + \underset{4}{h_{00}}\lambda^{4} + 0 + \underset{6}{h_{00}}\lambda^{6} + \underset{7}{h_{00}}\lambda^{7} + \ldots, \\ h_{0n} &= 0 + 0 + \underset{3}{h_{0n}}\lambda^{3} + 0 + \underset{5}{h_{0n}}\lambda^{5} + \underset{6}{h_{0n}}\lambda^{6} + \ldots, \\ h_{mn} &= 0 + \underset{2}{h_{mn}}\lambda^{2} + 0 + \underset{4}{h_{mn}}\lambda^{4} + \underset{5}{h_{mn}}\lambda^{5} + \ldots; \end{aligned} \tag{2.3}$$

the remaining groups $\underset{i}{h_{mn}}$, $\underset{i+1}{h_{0m}}$, $\underset{i+2}{h_{00}}$ cannot, in general, be eliminated. (One may, of course, always eliminate 9 components of such a group, e.g. $\underset{5}{h_{mn}}$, $\underset{6}{h_{0n}}$, $\underset{7}{h_{00}}$ can be replaced by $0, 0, \underset{7}{h_{00}}$, etc.) Using the expansion (2.3) instead of (2.1) is equivalent to narrowing the allowable frames of reference (by establishing the "generators" of the transformation: $\underset{2}{a_0}$, $\underset{1}{a_k}$ and $\underset{4}{a_0}$, $\underset{3}{a_k}$). In the expansion (2.3) there still remains the arbitrariness of the choice of $\underset{3}{a_0}, \underset{5}{a_0}, \underset{6}{a_0}, \ldots$ and $\underset{2}{a_k}, \underset{4}{a_k}, \underset{5}{a_k}, \ldots$ (in specific cases one still establishes $\underset{2}{a_k}$ by setting $\underset{2}{h_{mn}} = \delta_{mn} \underset{2}{h_{00}}$). One may, of course, always return from the form (2.3) to the form (2.1) by means of the transformation generated by $\underset{2}{a_0}, \underset{4}{a_0}$ and $\underset{1}{a_k}, \underset{2}{a_k}$.

In the original EIH method the expansions corresponding to the standing potential in electrodynamics (cf. Infeld [4]) were assumed:

$$h_{\alpha\beta} = \sum_{i=1}^{\infty} \underset{2i}{h_{\alpha\beta}} \lambda^{2i}, \qquad \alpha\beta = 00 \text{ and } \alpha\beta = mn,$$

$$h_{0n} = \sum_{i=1}^{\infty} \underset{2i+1}{h_{0n}} \lambda^{2i+1}. \tag{2.4}$$

Up to the order $\underset{6}{h_{00}}, \underset{5}{h_{0n}}, \underset{4}{h_{mn}}$ the above expansions are identical to the expansion (2.3). The procedure based on Eqs (2.3) or (2.4) will therefore not differ up to the order in which one may obtain the post-post-Newtonian equations of motion (equations of the eighth order). (In the original EIH method the approximation procedure was combined with the so-called dipole method; see [10], [33], [58], [48]-[50].)

Besides the expansion of the field (2.1) the EIH method also takes the expansions of the dynamical variables occurring in the tensor $T^{\alpha\beta}$. A suitable choice of the coordinate system corresponding to the transition from (2.1) to (2.3) can annihilate some terms in the expansions for the dynamical variables. Thus, for the mass $\overset{A}{m} = \overset{A}{m}(t)$ we have from Eq. (1.13)

$$\overset{A}{m} = \underset{2}{\overset{A}{m}}\lambda^2 + \underset{4}{\overset{A}{m}}\lambda^4 + \underset{6}{\overset{A}{m}}\lambda^6 + \ldots$$

(the variables $\overset{A}{\xi}{}^k$ have expansions of the form $\overset{A}{\xi}{}^k = \sum_{i=0}^{\infty} \underset{i}{\overset{A}{\xi}}{}^k \lambda^i$).

By putting the expansions (2.3) into the field equations, the latter may be solved successively. In fact, the field equation in the lowest order (Poisson's equation) defining $\underset{2}{h_{00}}$ is solvable for any arbitrary motion $\overset{A}{\xi}{}^k$. Inserting the field $\underset{2}{h_{00}}$ that was found into (1.14), we obtain the Newtonian equations of motion (equations of the fourth order). In order to find the post-Newtonian equations

(equations of the sixth order) $\underset{3}{h}_{0n}$ and $\underset{4}{h}_{00}$ should be determined (if one takes as the point of departure a variational principle, then it is sufficient to know only $\underset{3}{h}_{0n}$; see [54], [62]). The condition of integrability of the field equations determining $\underset{3}{h}_{0n}$ and $\underset{4}{h}_{00}$ are the Newtonian equations of motion. Thus $\underset{3}{h}_{0n}$ and $\underset{4}{h}_{00}$ will depend on the world line of the singularity established with the accuracy of the Newtonian approximation; in the opposite case, the field equations will not be satisfied. Inserting the fields $\underset{3}{h}_{0n}$ and $\underset{4}{h}_{00}$ into Eqs (1.14), we obtain the post-Newtonian equations of motion found in [2]. These equations, in turn, are a condition of integrability of the field equations defining the quantities $\underset{4}{h}_{mn}$, $\underset{5}{h}_{0m}$, $\underset{6}{h}_{00}$ necessary to determine the post-post Newtonian equations (equations of the eighth order). Generally, the equations of motion for a given step of the approximation are the conditions of integrability of the field equations in the next step of the approximation (cf. [20], [39]).

The expansion (2.3) begins to differ from the expansion (2.4) starting with the expressions $\underset{5}{h}_{mn}$, $\underset{6}{h}_{0m}$, $\underset{7}{h}_{00}$ determining equations of the ninth order. These equations contain expressions similar to the expressions describing damping in electrodynamics (cf. [4], [9], [27], [56], [47]). This result does not necessarily mean that the motion is damped and that the bodies fall on to one another. For it should be remembered that to see the character of the motion in general relativity theory it is not, in general, sufficient to know only the world lines of the singularities (or equations of motion). The physical effects are obtained from the theory by considering together the motions $\overset{A}{\xi}{}^k = \overset{A}{\xi}{}^k(t)$ and the metric field. In particular, the given expression in the equations of motion may be transformed away (or it may be added), but the physical effect associated with it cannot be annihilated, since the corresponding transformation of the field must always be taken into account (cf. Infeld [19]). In any case, the occurrence of expressions describing "damping" in the higher orders is evidence of the fact that to a given Newtonian motion it corresponds, in the higher orders of the approximation method, more gravitational fields, namely, a field of the standing potential type (2.4) and fields such as $\underset{5}{h}_{0m}$, $\underset{6}{h}_{0n}$, $\underset{7}{h}_{00}$ resembling retarded or advanced potentials. In order to investigate the physical significance of such fields one should investigate whether they cause secular changes in the motion of bodies constituting the sources of these fields.

In the case when space at infinity is flat (as is the case in the problem of motion) one may, in the physical interpretation of the results, use the method formulated by Infeld and Plebański [58]. In this method the motion of the bodies is projected by means of light rays onto the plane at infinity which is "parallel" to the plane of the motion (in case the motion is not planar, the projection should be made on two planes at infinity). The world lines of the light rays, being zero geodesic lines, are well defined geometrically. If, therefore, the coordinate system is changed by means of a transformation satisfying condition (1′) then the functions describing the world lines of the bodies and the world lines of the light rays will change; on the other hand, the projection of the motion on the above-mentioned plane at infinity will not change. In particular, physical effects described by the post-Newtonian equations of motion will not depend on which of the generators a_a were chosen in deriving these equations. The above or similar constructions may be considered as a proof that in the problem of motion one may, in a unique way, obtain physical results without resorting to preferred classes of reference frames proposed by some authors [28], [17], [18].

3. EQUATIONS OF MOTION OF ROTATING BODIES

In the EIH method in its initial formulation only the nonrotational motion of bodies possessing spherical symmetry was considered. Likewise in the first papers of Fock [5] and Papapetrou [16] only nonrotating bodies were considered. The equations of motion of rotating bodies can be given by making use of the description of the bodies either by means of singularities or by means of a continuous distribution of matter. In the case of a continuous distribution of matter the equations were given by Fock [28], but in a form that is not suitable for integration. Fock's method was developed by Kalitzin [53], who also determined the motion of bodies in the more important cases. Haywood [35] used Papapetrou's method, but he neglected some essential terms, so that the final equations do not basically differ from the equations of nonrotating bodies. Infeld's method was applied by Tulczyjew [52] to the case of rotating bodies, and independently, also by Ryabushko [43]. In his work, however, Ryabushko took an energy-momentum tensor whose form was not consistent with the conditions of integrability of the field equations.

In Tulczyjew's paper, an energy-momentum tensor of the form

$$\boldsymbol{T}^{\alpha\beta} = \sum_{A=1}^{N} [\overset{A}{t}{}^{\alpha\beta}\hat{\delta}(x-\overset{A}{\xi}) - t^{r\alpha\beta}\hat{\delta}(x-\overset{A}{\xi})_{|r}, \tag{3.1}$$

where $t^{\alpha\beta}$ and $t^{r\alpha\beta}$ are symmetric with respect to α and β, is introduced into the field equations. The equations of motion of matter described by (3.1), which are conditions of integrability of the field equations, take the form

$$\int_{\overset{A}{\Omega}} \boldsymbol{T}^{\alpha\beta}{}_{;\beta} d_3 x = 0 \tag{3.2}$$

$$\int_{\overset{A}{\Omega}} (x^r - \overset{A}{\xi}{}^r)\boldsymbol{T}^{\alpha\beta}{}_{;\beta} d_3 x = 0 \tag{3.3}$$

$$\int_{\overset{A}{\Omega}} (x^r - \overset{A}{\xi}{}^r)(x^s - \overset{A}{\xi}{}^s)\boldsymbol{T}^{\alpha\beta}{}_{;\beta} d_3 x = 0 \tag{3.4}$$

(The equations of the higher "momenta" in the case of tensor (3.1) are satisfied identically.)(1) Eqs (3.2)–(3.4) constitute a system of 40 N equations with 43 N unknowns $\overset{A}{t}{}^{\alpha\beta}$, $\overset{A}{t}{}^{r\alpha\beta}$, $\overset{A}{\xi}{}^s$. In order for this system to uniquely determine the motion further information about tensor $\boldsymbol{T}^{\alpha\beta}$ is necessary. Such information may be obtained from the condition of correspondence of the coordinates $\overset{A}{\xi}{}^k$ with the coordinates of the center of mass of continuous bodies (see Michalska [60]). From this condition we obtain in the lowest order of the approximation

$$\underset{4}{\overset{A}{t}}{}^{r00} = \tfrac{1}{2}\overset{A}{\xi}{}^i{}_{|0}\,\underset{3}{\overset{A}{S}}{}^{ri}, \tag{3.5}$$

where $\overset{A}{S}{}^k = \frac{1}{2}\varepsilon^{kri}\overset{A}{S}{}^{ri}$ is the intrinsic angular momentum of the Ath body (ε^{kri} is the permutation symbol). From the viewpoint of Eqs (3.2)–(3.4), Eqs (3.5) are a supplementary assumption.(2) Using

(1) In the case of nonrotating bodies the conditions of integrability are Eqs (3.2) and (3.3). In Section 1 only Eqs. (3.2) were discussed. Equation (3.3) is, in this case, a condition limiting the form of the energy-momentum tensor; tensor (1.8) is in agreement with this equation (cf. [38]).

(2) This viewpoint presented here is not generally adopted. For instance, Tulczyjew [52] claims that solely equations (3.2)–(3.4) (when there are taken the usual assumptions about the field $g_{\alpha\beta}$) are sufficiant to define in a unique way all physical effects associated with the motion. This statement is true for simple cases discussed in [52].

the EIH method, one may, by means of the field equations, Eqs (3.2), and (3.3) for $\alpha = 0$, the symmetrical part of Eqs (3.3), and Eqs (3.4) together with condition (3.5), obtain the quantities $t^{\alpha\beta}$ and $t^{r\alpha\beta}$ in the order necessary to determine the post-Newtonian equations of motion $(\underset{2}{t}^{00}, \underset{4}{t}^{00}, \underset{3}{t}^{0k}, \underset{5}{t}^{0k}, \underset{3}{t}^{r0s}, \underset{4}{t}^{rst})$. Eqs (3.2) for $\alpha = k$ define the progressive motion of the bodies. The physical contents of these equations was discussed by Tulczyjew. In the particular case in which the motion takes place in a plane perpendicular to the vector s^k determined by the intrinsic angular momenta $\overset{1}{S}{}^k$ and $\overset{2}{S}{}^k$ of both bodies, the motion obtained is that along a rotating ellipse. In the general case it turns out that the vector of the orbital angular momentum L^k precesses about the vector $\vec{s}$ (motion of the line of nodes). From the antisymmetric part of Eqs (3.3) and from the equations of progressive motion the law of conservation of total angular momentum is obtained (see [60]).

The equations of motion derived under assumption (3.1) describe the motion of bodies possessing a spherical symmetry. It seems that the motion of bodies having a more complex structure could be obtained by introducing further multipole expressions (containing higher derivatives of the δ functions). A countable set of all multipoles forms the so-called gravitational skeleton of the body. Such a skeleton always exists in classical potential theory. Thus far, it has not been known whether it also exists in general relativity theory. The recently obtained results show that here the situation seems to be more complicated.

Michalska [61], starting out from the method of the action principle [54] and describing the bodies as the limiting case of a drop of ideal liquid, derived the post-Newtonian Lagrangian for the motion of rotating bodies. In this Lagrangian, the bodies are described not only by means of multipole momenta, but also by means of some structural constants which have their origin in the non-linearity of the equations. This result indicates that, for the model discussed there, no gravitational skeleton exists. If, in the Lagrangian given by Michalska, terms describing the departure of the bodies from spherical symmetry are neglected, then Tulczyjew's results are obtained. In Michalska's paper [62], which uses the above-mentioned Lagrangian as a point of departure, the secular changes of all parameters determining the orbits of the rotating bodies are found.

Acknowledgement. The author is very indebted to Dr R. Michalska for her helpful discussion in elaborating the third section of this review.

APPENDIX

Infeld and Plebański [31], [37] (cf. also [39]) have shown that one can construct a $\hat{\delta}$-function fulfilling the following conditions:

1. $\hat{\delta}_3(\underline{x})(\underline{x} = x^1, x^2, x^3)$ is a spherically symmetric quantity which, from the formal point of view, can be considered as a function possessing derivatives of any order.

2. $\hat{\delta}_3(\underline{x}) = 0$ for $\underline{x} = 0$.

3. For any continuous function $f(\underline{x})$:

$$\int_{\Omega(\underline{x}_0)} \hat{\delta}_3(\underline{x}-\underline{x}_0) f(\underline{x}) d_3 x = f(\underline{x}_0)$$

where the three-dimensional region $\Omega(\underline{x}_0)$ is an arbitrary neighbourhood of the point $\underline{x}_0$.

4. For any neighbourhood $\Omega(0)$ of the point $x = 0$:

$$\int_{\Omega(0)} \hat{\delta}_3(\underline{x}) \underline{x}^{-p} d_3 x = 0 \qquad p = 1, 2, \ldots, k$$

where k is an arbitrary but fixed integer; $\underline{x} = (x^s x^s)^{1/2}$.

The first three conditions are characteristic of the usual Dirac δ-function. The fourth condition is a generalization of the third for discontinuous functions $f(\underline{x}) = \underline{x}^{-p}$. This new $\hat{\delta}$-function makes it possible to define the finite part of fields at the world lines of particles treated as singularities of these fields. When $\overset{A}{\xi}{}^k(x^0)$ is a world line of the Ath particle and $\varphi(x^a, \overset{A}{\xi}{}^k, \overset{A}{\xi}{}^k{}_{|0})$ is a given solution of the field equations, then

$$\overset{A}{\tilde{\varphi}} = \int_{\overset{A}{\Omega}} \varphi \hat{\delta}_3(x - \overset{A}{\xi}) d_3 x \tag{A.1}$$

($\overset{A}{\Omega}$ is a neighbourhood of $\overset{A}{\xi}{}^k$) is a well-defined function of x^0, $\overset{A}{\xi}{}^k$, and $\overset{A}{\xi}{}^k{}_{|0}$ not only in the case of a continuous φ but also when φ contains singularities of the type $(x - \overset{A}{\xi})^{-p}$. Besides the $\overset{A}{\tilde{\varphi}}$ have the same transformations properties as the φ. From (A.1) we can easily deduce that the operation which establishes a correspondence between φ and $\overset{A}{\tilde{\varphi}}$ has the following properties:

$$\frac{\partial \overset{A}{\tilde{\varphi}}}{\partial \overset{B}{\xi}{}^k} = \overset{A}{\overline{\varphi_{\overset{B}{|\xi^k}}}} + \overset{A}{\overline{\varphi_{|k}}}\, \delta_{AB} \quad \text{(do not sum over index } A\text{);} \tag{A.2}$$

$$\overset{A}{\tilde{\varphi}}_{|0} = \overset{A}{\overline{\varphi_{|0}}} + \overset{A}{\overline{\varphi_{|s}}}\, \overset{A}{\xi}{}^s{}_{|0} = \overset{A}{\overline{\varphi_{|a}}}\, \overset{A}{\xi}{}^a{}_{|0}. \tag{A.3}$$

(A.2) means that this operation in general does not commute with differentiation with respect to $\overset{A}{\xi^k}$. Generally the distributive law of multiplication is not valid for this operation. However, when two functions φ and ψ have an expansion in the neighbourhood of $\overset{A}{\xi^k}$ into a series of the form: $\sum_{m=-k}^{0} a_{(2m-1)}|x-\xi|^{2m-1}+\sum_{m=1}^{\infty} a_{(m)s}(x^s-\overset{A}{\xi^s})^m$ i.e. the singular parts of this series are odd powers of $(x-\xi)^{2m-1}$; then we have the distributive property

$$\overline{\varphi\psi}^{A} \equiv \overset{A}{\tilde{\varphi}}\,\overset{A}{\tilde{\psi}}. \tag{A.4}$$

This property we assume for the fields used in the problem of motion since, in general, they have series of the form mentioned.

REFERENCES

[1] A. Einstein and J. Grommer, *S. B. Berl. Akad. Wiss.* p. 2 (1927).
[2] A. Einstein, L. Infeld and B. Hoffmann, *Ann. Math.* **39**, 65 (1938).
[3] H. P. Robertson, *Ann. Math.* **39**, 101 (1938).
[4] L. Infeld, *Phys. Rev.* **53**, 836 (1938).
[5] V. A. Fock, *J. Phys. Moscow* **1**, 81 (1939).
[6] A. Einstein and L. Infeld, *Ann. Math.* **41**, 455 (1940).
[7] L. Infeld and P. R. Wallace, *Phys. Rev.* **57**, 797 (1940).
[8] P. R. Wallace, *Amer. J. Math.* **63**, 729 (1941).
[9] N. Hu, *Proc. R. Irish. Acad.* **51**A, 87 (1947).
[10] A. Einstein and L. Infeld, *Canad. J. Math.* **1**, 209 (1949).
[11] L. Infeld and A. Schild, *Rev. Mod. Phys.* **21**, 408 (1949).
[12] N. Petrova, *J. Eksp. Teor. Phys.* **19**, 989 (1949).
[13] A. E. Scheidegger and L. Infeld, *Phys. Rev.* **79**, 201 (1950).
[14] I. G. Fichtenholz, *J. Eksp. Teor. Phys.* **20**, 233 (1950).
[15] L. Infeld, and A. E. Scheidegger, *Canad. J. Math.* **3**, 195 (1951).
[16] A. Papapetrou, *Proc. Phys. Soc.* A**64**, 57 (1951).
[17] A. Papapetrou, *Proc. Phys. Soc.* A**64**, 302 (1951).
[18] J. H. Haywood, *Proc. Phys. Soc.* A**65**, 170 (1952).
[19] L. Infeld, *Canad. J. Math.* **5**, 17 (1953).
[20] A. E. Scheidegger, *Rev. Mod. Phys.* **25**, 451 (1953).
[21] L. Infeld, *Acta Phys. Polon.* **13**, 187 (1954).
[22] B. Bertotti, *Nuovo Cim.* **12**, 226 (1954).
[23] R. Teisseyre, *Acta Phys. Polon.* **13**, 47 (1954).
[24] L. Infeld, *Bull. Acad. Polon. Sci.* Cl III, **2**, 163 (1954).
[25] L. Infeld, *Bull. Acad. Polon. Sci.* Cl III, **3**, 213 (1955).
[26] H. J. Meister and A. Papapetrou, *Bull. Acad. Polon. Sci.* Cl III, **3**, 163 (1955).
[27] J. N. Goldberg, *Phys. Rev.* **99**, 1873 (1955).
[28] V. A. Fock, *Theory of Space, Time and Gravitation* (In Russian), Moscow 1955.

[29] B. Bertotti, *Nuovo Cim.* **2**, 231 (1955).
[30] A. Trautman, *Bull. Acad. Polon. Sci.* Cl III, **4**, 439 (1956).
[31] L. Infeld and J. Plebański, *Bull. Acad. Polon. Sci.* Cl III, **4**, 687 (1956).
[32] L. Infeld and J. Plebański, *ibid.* **4**, 757 (1956).
[33] L. Infeld and J. Plebański, *ibid.* **4**, 763 (1956).
[34] S. Bażański, *Acta Phys. Polon.* **15**, 363 (1956).
[35] J. H. Haywood, *Proc. Phys. Soc.* A**69**, 2 (1956).
[36] B. Bertotti, *Nuovo Cim.* **4**, 898 (1956).
[37] L. Infeld and J. Plebański, *Bull. Acad. Polon. Sci.* Cl III, **5**, 51 (1957).
[38] W. Tulczyjew, *Bull. Acad. Polon. Sci.* Cl III, **5**, 297 (1957).
[39] L. Infeld, *Rev. Mod. Phys.* **29**, 398 (1957).
[40] V. A. Fock, *Rev. Mod. Phys.* **29**, 325 (1957).
[41] S. Bażański, *Acta Phys. Polon.* **16**, 423 (1957).
[42] B. Bertotti, *Nuovo Cim.* **6**, 755 (1957).
[43] A. P. Ryabushko, *J. Eksp. Teor Phys.* **33**, 1387 (1957).
[44] P. T. Hoang, *C. R. Acad. Sci., Paris* **246**, 61 (1958).
[45] P. T. Hoang, *Nuovo Cim.* **9**, 647 (1958).
[46] A. Trautman, Lectures on General Relativity, King's College, London (1958).
[47] A. Trautman, *Bull. Acad. Polon. Sci.* Cl III, **6**, 627 (1958).
[48] J. Moffat, *Nuovo Cim.* **7**, 107 (1958).
[49] J. Moffat and R. Kerr, On the Dipole Method in the Problem of Gravitational Motion, *preprint.*
[50] J. Moffat, *J. Math. Mech.* **8**, 771 (1959).
[51] L. Infeld, *Ann. Phys. Lpz.* **6**, 341 (1959).
[52] W. Tulczyjew, *Acta Phys. Polon.* **18**, 37 (1959).
[53] S. Kalitzin, *Nuovo Cim.* **11**, 178 (1959).
[54] J. Plebański and S. Bażański, *Acta Phys. Polon.* **18**, 307 (1959).
[55] A. Peres, *Nuovo Cim.* **11**, 617 (1959).
[56] A. Peres, *ibid.* **11**, 644 (1959).
[57] A. Peres, *ibid.* **13**, **439** (1959).
[58] L. Infeld and J. Plebański, *Motion and Relativity*, Warszawa 1960.
[59] V. A. Fock, *J. Eksp. Teor. Phys.* **38**, 108 (1960).
[60] R. Michalska, *Bull. Acad. Polon. Sci.* Cl III, **8**, 233 (1960).
[61] R. Michalska, *ibid.* **8**, 237 (1960).
[62] R. Michalska, *ibid.* **8**, 247 (1960).

STATUS REPORT ON THE QUANTIZATION OF THE GRAVITATIONAL FIELD*

PETER G. BERGMANN and ARTHUR B. KOMAR**

Syracuse University, Syracuse, New York, U. S. A.

1. INTRODUCTION

EFFORTS to subject the general theory of relativity to field quantization date back at least to 1930 [1]. They were resumed almost twenty years later [2], and today this problem occupies the attention of several groups [3]–[11].(1) In this article we shall review primarily one facet of this search, the present status of the search for *observables*.

In the most common approach to the quantization of classical field theories, the point of departure is the group of canonical transformations that map the phase space of the classical theory on itself. The infinitesimal group of canonical transformations may be represented by its generators, the canonical field variables and their functionals, which are thereby endowed with a commutator algebra, the Poisson brackets. In field quantization, one endeavors to match this classical infinitesimal group to a similar group of infinitesimal unitary transformations that map the Hilbert space of possible quantum states on itself. These infinitesimal unitary transformations are generated by Hermitian operators, called the observables of the quantized theory, which are assumed to correspond to the classical canonical field variables. The relationship between the two infinitesimal groups and their commutator algebras is not one-to-one. Rather, the classical group is a homomorphism of

* Our work has been supported by the National Science Foundation and by the Wright Air Development Center, both agencies of the United States Government.

** This report is dedicated to our colleague, Professor Leopold Infeld, and to the remarkable group of workers in general relativity that has emerged under his leadership.

(1) Many further references are listed in [4].

the group of unitary transformations in Hilbert space, which maps into the identity the invariant subgroup of all those unitary transformations whose generators tend to zero for $\hbar = 0$. This approach does not apply to the quantization of fermion fields, which are believed not to possess a classical counterpart. As the field of gravitation is undoubtedly a boson field, we shall restrict ourselves to boson quantization in all that follows.

General-relativistic theories differ in important respects from other field theories commonly dealt with in theoretical physics. Not only are they invariant with respect to a transformation group whose members represent a function space whose functions are defined on the four-dimensional spacetime manifold (they share this property with gauge-invariant theories), but the resulting system of first-class constraints includes the Hamiltonian constraint, that is to say, the invariance group includes the transformations that correspond to the mapping of three-dimensional space-like hypersurfaces ("instants in time") on each other; these mappings correspond to what ordinarily would be called the unfolding of the physical situation in time. This circumstance, along with the considerable complexity of the arithmetic involved, has led to a number of perplexing conceptual problems in the construction of observables, which form the subject of this paper. As far as possible we shall avoid the "technology" of actual methods of construction and concentrate instead on group-theoretical considerations.

2. THE PHASE SPACE OF GENERAL RELATIVITY

General relativity may be cast into a Hamiltonian formalism in several different ways. Rosenfeld [1] employed a "vierbein" formalism involving 16 field variables and 16 canonically conjugate momentum densities, along with 14 first-class constraints. Pirani and Schild [2] and Bergmann *et al* [10] started with the 10 variables $g_{\mu\nu}$ and their 10 canonically conjugate momentum densities, leading to 8 first-class constraints. Recently Dirac [11] introduced coordinate conditions as constraints. In his formalism the number of canonically conjugate field variables is 12, and the number of second-class constraints 8. All these approaches have in common that twice the number of degrees of freedom, minus twice the number of first-class constraints, and minus the number of second-class constraints, equals 4. Accordingly, it is generally believed that the number of "dynamical" degrees of freedom of the gravitational field is 2, the same as the number of degrees of freedom of the electromagnetic field. This conjecture is in line with the conclusion reached by Pauli and Fierz [12] concerning linear fields of all non-zero spins propagating with the speed of light.

We shall first discuss the approaches involving only first-class constraints. In all these formulations the original number of canonical field variables is restricted by a number of constraints. Some of the constraints arise because the defining equations

$$\pi^A = \frac{\partial L}{\partial y_{A,0}} \tag{2.1}$$

cannot be solved with respect to the time derivatives $y_{A,0}$. Instead, there exist relations between the π^A completely independent of all $y_{A,0}$. These are the *primary constraints.* Under the canonical field equations, some of the time derivatives of the primary constraints do not vanish identically, but must be set zero as additional requirements; these are the *secondary constraints.* If we substitute the expressions (2.1) for π^A into the primary constraints, we obtain identities, whereas the secondary constraints turn out to represent those combinations of Euler-Lagrange field equations that are free of any second-order time derivatives $y_{A,00}$. The combinations of canonical field variables y_A, π^A that satisfy all constraints form a subspace of the phase space of the theory, which we call the *constraint hypersurface.*

Because the constraints are all of the first class (i.e. they have Poisson brackets that vanish if the constraints themselves are satisfied), the infinitesimal mappings generated by them do not lead off the constraint hypersurface. They do, however, map the points on the constraint hypersurface on each other. In order to have a standardized terminology, we shall call a representative point on the constraint hypersurface a *permissible field.* Its components are, of course, defined only on a three-dimensional hypersurface of physical space-time. If a permissible field is followed, by means of the field equations of general relativity, through some ength of ti me, we shall call the resulting set of functions on a four-dimensional domain a *solution of the field equations.* We shall call two *solutions equivalent* if they can be carried over into each other by means of a coordinate transformation. Likewise, we shall call two permissible *fields equivalent* if they lead to equivalent solutions.

Within the compass of these definitions, infinitesimal mappings generated by linear combinations of the constraints (with variable coefficients) map permissible fields on equivalent fields. The constraint generators thus enable us to cover the whole constraint hypersurface with mutually exclusive *equivalence classes* of permissible fields. These equivalence classes are the points of a new phase space, the *reduced phase space*.

Retaining the original meaning of canonical transformations and of generators (i.e., the original definition of Poisson brackets), we assert that any generator of an infinitesimal canonical transformation which maps each equivalence class intact on another equivalence class is a function(al) defined on the reduced phase space. Stated differently, we assert that each such generator has a constant value within one equivalence class. The proof is straightforward: Assume that the infinitesimal mapping maps a point a in one equivalence class on a point b in another equivalence class, and another point a', in the same class as a, on a point b'. By assumption, b and b' lie in the same equivalence class. Now, to get from a' to b', we could have gone from a' to a, thence to b, and finally to b'. The generators for the first and the third mapping vanish; hence the two generators $a \to b$, $a' \to b'$ have the same value.

It is appropriate to call a variable that is defined on the reduced phase space a *constant of the motion*. This definition includes both the usual requirement that the variable in question does not change its value in the course of time, but also the further requirement that it is invariant with respect to coordinate transformations. In view of the fact that in general relativity the change in the course of time is defined only up to a coordinate transformation, only invariant functionals can be constants of the motion in every possible coordinate system. Our result is then that constants of the motion (used as generators) map equivalence classes on each other, that is to say, they generate infinitesimal canonical transformations in the reduced phase space.

The structure of the reduced phase space is independent of the chosen initial phase space, plus first-class constraints. To this extent the reduced phase space represents the intrinsic structure of the theory, stripped of the accident of the point of departure. It might be mentioned parenthetically that the Lagrangian approach [13], [14] leads to the same reduced phase space, including the Lie algebra of its mappings.

3. COORDINATE CONDITIONS

The construction of constants of the motion in general relativity, in sufficient numbers that they span the reduced phase space, has not yet been accomplished in a completely satisfactory manner.

A number of workers [7], [11], [15], [16] have approached the quantization problem of general relativity by means of coordinate conditions, in analogy to the imposition of gauge conditions on the electromagnetic field. Coordinate conditions in general relativity have been proposed in widely different forms. Examples are the De Donder conditions,

$$(\sqrt{-g}\, g^{\mu\varrho})_{,\varrho} = 0\,, \tag{3.1}$$

algebraic conditions, such as

$$g_{\mu 0} = \delta_{\mu 0}\,, \tag{3.2}$$

and the introduction of so-called intrinsic coordinates, which will be discussed in Section 4. The motivation for introducing coordinate conditions is to reduce the number of equivalent solutions, either by restricting the number of equivalent permissible fields, or by eliminating the arbitrary functions that appear in the Hamiltonian [2], [10] (and thereby rendering the dynamics of the theory formally unique), or both. Conditions of the type (3.1) merely fix the arbitrary functions in the Hamiltonian, whereas conditions of the type (3.2) in addition restrict the variety of permissible fields. Coordinate conditions that eliminate any equivalence classes entirely are, of course, to be rejected. Trite as this restriction appears to be, it may be extremely difficult, in particular cases, to assure oneself on that score. In fact, in the following section we shall point out that the intrinsic coordinates proposed by ourselves exclude, at least in the original form of our proposal, some solutions of the field equations; we shall argue that the excluded set is in a certain sense a set of zero measure.

Coordinate conditions of the type (3.2), or more generally, coordinate conditions that can be expressed in terms of canonical field variables (without requiring time derivatives of canonical field variables) are admissible if no functional of the coordinate conditions has vanishing Poisson brackets with all the constraints. The De Donder coordinate conditions (3.1) cannot be stated entirely in terms of canonical field variables ($g^{0\mu}{}_{,0}$ cannot be expressed in terms of canonical momentum densities). In the presence of conditions of this type it is to be examined first whether it is perhaps possible to form functionals of the conditions which are expressible in terms of the canonical field variables; if so, these functionals must be examined as regards their Poisson brackets with the constraints, just as in the previous case. The remaining coordinate conditions will then restrict the arbitrary functions in the Hamiltonian, and may determine them entirely, or only in part. They restrict the direction in which any given permissible field may propagate, within its equivalence class, in the course of time. At least locally such conditions cannot lead to the exclusion of any equivalence class. The consideration of the global question is, as always in general relativity, an extremely difficult problem, and certainly not solved with any degree of generality.

Let us consider first the coordinate conditions that set up restrictions between the canonical field variables on one space-like hypersurface. These coordinate conditions single out a subdomain on the constraint hypersurface. The conditions (3.2) belong to this type, as do the conditions proposed by Dirac [11] and by Arnowitt, Deser, and Misner [6]–[8].[1] Conditions of this type are permissible only if the sets of Poisson brackets that each condition forms with all the constraints are linearly independent of each other. In that case it follows that some canonical transformations generated by the constraints map permissible fields which obey the coordinate conditions on fields that do not. Likewise, if we consider the coordinate conditions themselves as additional constraints and accordingly consider the canonical mappings generated by them, then each coordinate condition maps at least some of the permissible fields on points of the phase space that lie outside the constraint hypersurface. At the outset this situation is unsatisfactory. It appears to prevent us from introducing that portion of the constraint hypersurface that obeys the coordinate conditions as a new space that can be divided up naturally into equivalence classes.

The remedy lies in a modification of the Poisson brackets due to Dirac [17] (cf. also Bergmann and Goldberg [18]). Dirac's procedure may be explained as follows. We shall call that portion of the constraint hypersurface selected by the coordinate conditions the *restricted domain* of the phase space. Now consider some generator A, which maps the restricted domain (partially) outside itself. We shall add to A a linear combination of constraints and coordinate conditions (whose coefficients may be variable) so that the modified generator A^* will map the restricted domain on itself. Such an operator A^* always exists; within the restricted domain we have $A^* = A$. It will be unique only if, with the addition of the coordinate conditions to the constraints, all the constraints (both old and new) are second-class. Otherwise A^* will be determined only up to an

---

[1] Cf. also several preprints by these authors.

arbitrary linear combination of those constraints that have remained first-class.

The modification of Poisson brackets according to Dirac is then simply a device for reducing the number of generating constraints to those that map the restricted domain of the phase space on itself. It is clear that this diminished number of generating constraints reduces the size of an equivalence class to that portion of the original equivalence class that is compatible with the chosen coordinate conditions. There remains the question whether the reduced number of constraints leads to the emergence of new constants of the motion—variables that commute with the smaller number of constraints that remain as generators of equivalence mappings [15]. The answer depends on our definition of "constants of the motion". According to the definition adopted in Section 2 (which implies the invariant character of constants of the motion with respect to whatever invariant transformation group may be left after the adoption of coordinate conditions), no new constants of the motion arise.

Anderson [15], using the conventional definition of constants of the motion, has obtained new constants of the motion, which commute with the Hamiltonian but not with the remaining constraints. For instance by requiring in electrodynamics

$$\varphi = 0 \tag{3.3}$$

he finds

$$\frac{\partial}{\partial t}(\nabla \cdot \mathbf{A}) = 0 \tag{3.4}$$

Hence div**A** is constant in the course of time, but it does not commute with the secondary constraint

$$\nabla \cdot \pi = 0 \tag{3.5}$$

By introducing the further coordinate condition

$$\nabla \cdot \mathbf{A} = 0 \tag{3.6}$$

and thus restricting the electromagnetic field variables to A_{trans}, π_{trans}, he has reduced his phase space essentially to the equivalence classes under gauge transformations.

Coordinate conditions that involve time derivatives restrict the range of directions in which a representative point on the constraint hypersurface may move within its equivalence class. This requirement is formally identical with a restriction on the arbitrary functions in the Hamiltonian of the theory. With our definition of constants of the motion in Section 2, restrictions on the form of the Hamiltonian do not lead to new constants of the motion. Hence the structure of the reduced phase space is not affected by such coordinate conditions.

4. INTRINSIC COORDINATES

Various sets of coordinate conditions reduce the remaining choice of coordinate system in varying degree. If there is precisely one possible coordinate system left in each equivalence class, we shall call that coordinate system *intrinsic*. The reduced equivalence class then consists of a one-parametric set of permissible fields, the parameter being the intrinsic time coordinate x^0. If the canonical field variables are independent of x^0 (i.e. if there is but one permissible field left), we shall call the intrinsic coordinate system *co-moving*. (*Co-moving* coordinate systems are those in which the Hamiltonian vanishes *strongly* in the sense in which Dirac uses this term. A co-moving coordinate system is not necessarily intrinsic.) Experience has shown that it is insufficient to count the number of coordinate conditions imposed in order to decide whether a given set of restrictions leads to intrinsic coordinates or not. The construction of intrinsic coordinate systems is at least one possible approach, and so far the only successful one, for constructing the reduced phase space of general relativity. If it is possible to specify a coordinate system in such a manner that in every Riemann–Einstein manifold there is exactly one (four-dimensional) coordinate system having the properties specified by the chosen coordinate conditions, then every component of any geometric object at a specified world point in that coordinate system has an invariant significance; that is to say, its numerical value is determined uniquely for each solution, regardless of the coordinate system in which this solution is originally presented.

The existence of intrinsic coordinate systems has now been established [19]. Whether they must be specified by local properties of a Riemann–Einstein manifold, or whether they may instead be introduced by the appeal to global characteristics (e.g. the solution of differential equations with boundary conditions at spatial infinity) remains, in our opinion, an open question. It has been suggested that there may exist coordinate systems specified not uniquely but up to a transformation group isomorphic with the Lorentz group [7], [20]. This proposition also has not as yet been proven.

For purposes of illustration, let us return once more to electrodynamics. The radiation gauge conditions, (3.3) together with (3.6), are preserved by gauge conditions of the form

$$\mathbf{A}^* = \mathbf{A} + \nabla \Lambda \tag{4.1}$$

$$\nabla^2 \Lambda = 0, \qquad \frac{\partial \Lambda}{\partial t} = 0$$

In a finite spatial domain, and in the absence of boundary conditions, the Laplace equation for Λ has an infinity of solutions. In the presence of the usual boundary conditions, however, there is only the trivial solution $\Lambda = \text{const}$ if we exclude solutions with singularities in a three-dimensional space that is topologically Euclidean. Finally, in a metrically flat but topologically closed or multiply connected manifold there are non-singular gauge transformations that preserve the gauge conditions (4.1) throughout the manifold.

Using purely local characteristics a set of intrinsic coordinate conditions can be devised [19]. If the field equations of Einstein are satisfied throughout a Riemannian space, there remain of the twenty components of the Riemann–Christoffel curvature tensor only 10 algebraically independent components, the components of the so-called Weyl tensor. Of these one can form precisely four algebraically independent scalars [21]. Provided that the Jacobian between arbitrary coordinates and these four scalar fields is non-zero (i.e. the four gradients of these scalars are not coplanar), the scalars may be adopted as intrinsic coordinates. Any world point may be identified by the numerical values of these four scalars, and this characterization of a world point is quite independent of the choice of original coordinate system. This scheme breaks down if the four gradient fields are coplanar, e.g. in the presence of a group of "motions" of the manifold (i.e. when a Killing field exists). Such special manifolds presumably represent a set of zero measure among all Riemann–Einstein manifolds, but all known closed-form solutions of the field equations belong to this degenerate type!

In what follows we shall assume consistently that the manifolds considered are non-degenerate in the sense that these intrinsic coordinates span the manifold, at least in pieces. Under this assumption, the existence of intrinsic coordinates proves that the world points of a Riemann–Einstein manifold are not only distinct but inequivalent in terms of local geometric properties. For our present discussion it is not essential whether the adoption of our coordinates is the most practical intrinsic coordinate system that can be devised. It is sufficient that there exists a method of unique local identification, regardless of whether alternative approaches are available as well.

In Section 2 we established the existence of constants of the motion, a set of field variables whose numerical values uniquely identify a whole equivalence class of solutions of Einstein's field equations. The existence of intrinsic coordinates shows that these constants of the motion do not describe the geometry in the vicinity of a world point completely, but that within a given Riemann–Einstein manifold some aspects of the geometry change from world point to world point. Accordingly, to determine the geometry on a given three-dimensional hypersurface completely we must know both the values of the intrinsic coordinates on that hypersurface and the values of the complete set of constants of the motion that identifies the solution of the field equations.

This situation has been known, at least partly, for some time. Dirac [11] showed that for the determination of the intrinsic nature of a solution from data given on a space-like hypersurface with normal n^ϱ, knowledge of the four components of the metric tensor $g_{\mu\varrho}n^\varrho$ is not required. On the other hand, these components and their derivatives enter the expressions for the Weyl tensor and its four scalars.(1) It appears now that the constants of the motion are indeed independent of $g_{\mu\varrho}n^\varrho$, but the intrinsic coordinates are not.(1)

It is perhaps pertinent to inquire into the possible relationships between two intrinsic coordinate systems, in view of the likelihood that additional intrinsic coordinate systems will be discovered in time. An intrinsic coordinate system identifies world points in different (=inequivalent) Riemann–Einstein manifolds, that is to say, any intrinsic coordinate system provides for a one-to-one mapping of two inequivalent manifolds on each other. This mapping is, of course, not unique. Accordingly we shall call two different intrinsic coordinate systems *similar* if they provide identical mappings, *dissimilar* if their associated mappings are different. Formally similar intrinsic coordinates are functions of each other, dissimilar coordinates are functions of each other as well as of the constants of the motion.

5. TIME-DEPENDENT SOLUTIONS

The construction of the reduced phase space leads automatically to a representation of general relativity purely in terms of constants of the motion, and of the commutator algebra connecting the con-

---

(1) But see Bergmann and Komar, *Phys. Rev. Letters* **4**, 432 (1960). [Note added in proof.]

stants of the motion. In such a representation the Hamiltonian vanishes strongly, and there does not appear to be any room for the concept of energy. The question has been frequently asked whether from the standpoint of the physicist such a representation is "natural", or whether perhaps some other representation has a stronger intuitive appeal.

In the preceding section we have established that there are two types of variables in general relativity, the constants of the motion, which characterize equivalence classes, are the generators of a transformation group, and possess a commutator algebra, and the intrinsic coordinates, which tell us at which world point we are within a given manifold. By combining these two types of variables into new quantities, we can construct new variables which combine some of the characteristics of both [7], [11], [22]. Without attempting a value judgment, for which in our opinion at present there is not enough known about either type of representation, we shall in this section indicate some of the properties of canonical variables that are not constants of the motion.

We shall start again with a formulation of general relativity in which the Hamiltonian is a combination of first-class constraints and hence vanishes weakly (in the sense of Dirac's definition of that term). We shall now choose one of the (infinitely many) constants of the motion, C, and one variable to be denoted by Θ, whose Poisson bracket with the chosen constant of the motion equals 1. (Even after the choice of the constant of the motion the choice of the second variable is still possible in an infinity of ways). Of Θ we shall require, moreover, that it is not a constant of the motion, as it will eventually serve as our "time". Finally we shall choose a canonical transformation which leads from the original canonical field variables to a new set in which Θ and C appear as canonically conjugate variables. It is now possible to adopt $-C$ as the Hamiltonian of the theory.

To this end we use the algebraic relationship implied by the original (weakly vanishing) Hamiltonian H of the theory to express C in terms of the remaining canonical variables of the theory. We are assured that in H the "time" Θ does not occur (or occurs at most multiplied by constraints), because it is canonically conjugate to a constant of the motion. We thus obtain a relationship of the form

$$C + h(\varphi, \pi) = 0. \tag{5.1}$$

where the arguments on the right do not include Θ. The original Hamiltonian constraint of the theory, H, was determined only up to an arbitrary, locally variable factor. We shall fix that factor now by adopting as our Hamiltonian constraint the expression

$$H \equiv h(\varphi, \pi) + C = 0. \tag{5.2}$$

We shall distinguish between the original phase space with the canonical field variables $(\varphi, \Theta; \pi, C)$, and a new phase space possessing as canonical variables only $(\varphi; \pi)$. Let us denote the Poisson brackets with respect to the former phase space by the symbol $\{,\}$, those with respect to the latter by $[\,,]$. Then, obviously, we have, for any two functionals A and B,

$$\{A, B\} = [A, B] + \left(\frac{\partial A}{\partial \Theta}\frac{\partial B}{\partial C} - \frac{\partial A}{\partial C}\frac{\partial B}{\partial \Theta}\right) \tag{5.3}$$

and in particular,

$$\{A, H\} = [A, h] + \frac{\partial A}{\partial \Theta}. \tag{5.4}$$

Hence the functional h will serve adequately as the new Hamiltonian. It does not contain Θ among its arguments; it is thus manifestly a constant of the motion. Likewise it follows from Eq. (5.4) that with the adoption of the Hamiltonian h the rate of change of the variable Θ equals unity.

The transcription of the original theory into the form (5.4) has manifestly eliminated two canonically conjugate "coordinates" from the infinite-dimensional original phase space, and one from among the infinite number of first-class constraints. From our method of construction it is clear that the initial choice of C determines the value of the "energy" (i.e. the Hamiltonian h) for any equivalence class; in fact, this value can be chosen at will, as any functional of equivalence classes is *ipso facto* a constant of the motion, both in our sense and in the conventional sense. By the same token, whatever choice we make, the Hamiltonian h is an invariant, that is to say, its value cannot change within one equivalence class. Even with the choice of C, the time coordinate is not uniquely determined; given some particular choice of Θ any functional Θ' having the form

$$\Theta' = \Theta + g(\varphi, \pi) \tag{5.5}$$

is equally admissible. From these considerations it would appear that a choice of "energy" and "time" must be based on stronger criteria than merely the conditions that the energy be conserved and that it be capable of serving as a Hamiltonian.

What about the remaining constraints? Before the elimination of C and Θ from among the canonical variables, all the remaining constraints had vanishing Poisson brackets with each other and with H. As a first step in the reduction of the canonical variables, we shall eliminate the variable C, wherever it may occur in one of the remaining constraints, with the help of the relationship (5.2). This elimination is equivalent to the replacement of the original constraints by algebraic combinations with H, and it should not destroy their property of being first-class, i.e. of having vanishing $\{,\}$ brackets with each other and with H. If follows immediately that none of the constraints can depend on Θ, because otherwise the Poisson brackets with C would not vanish. We conclude that as far as the Poisson bracket of the constraints other than H are concerned, they will remain first-class under the $[,]$ Poisson brackets. Moreover, as the constraints are independent of Θ they have vanishing $[,]$ Poisson brackets with h, because of Eq. (5.4). Hence the remaining constraints and h form a function group under the new definition of Poisson brackets. We have at this stage achieved the same form of theory that is familiar from studies of gauge-invariant theories such as electrodynamics.

In the reduced theory we may again define equivalence classes among all the fields of canonical variables that obey the remaining constraints. Fields are to be considered equivalent if they can be mapped on each other by a continuous canonical mapping generated by linear combinations of the remaining constraints only. The infinitesimal transformation generated by the Hamiltonian h leads outside the equivalence class. The corresponding transformation in the original phase space also leads to another equivalence class; it differs from the transformation generated by H in that $\delta\Theta = 0$ instead of $\delta\Theta = 1$. In establishing then the correspondence between equivalence classes in the original and in the time-dependent formulations of general relativity, we must distinguish between *permissible fields* and *solutions* (the latter representing whole histories). The correspondence between equivalence classes of solutions in the two kinds of formalism is perfect; the correspondence between equivalence classes of fields is imperfect, in that a one-parametric set of inequivalent fields (those that belong to one solution, for different values of Θ) in the "time"-dependent formalism corresponds to fields in the same equivalence class in the original formulation of the theory.

With the help of the new equivalence classes we may again seek to map the remaining phase space on a reduced phase space of equivalence classes. In the new formalism there exist invariants that are not necessarily constants of the motion. They generate mappings of *equivalence classes of permissible fields* on each other; but they will map *equivalence classes of solutions* on each other only if they are constants of the motion as well. An invariant that is a constant of the motion in the new formalism is also a constant of the motion (in the sense defined in Section 2) in the original formalism.

If we wish to retain the pecularities of the "time"-dependent formalism, but eliminate all the remaining first-class constraints, we shall consider the reduced phase space of equivalence classes of fields, and the canonical mappings generated by variables defined on that reduced phase space. The number of independent canonical variables in the reduced phase space will again be four variables for each three-dimensional space point.

6. CONSTRUCTION OF CONSTANTS OF THE MOTION

The availability of intrinsic coordinates makes it possible, at least in principle, to construct constants of the motion. Given an arbitrary solution of the field equations, then for any particular intrinsic coordinate system the component of a chosen geometric object (such as the metric tensor, the affine connection, or the Weyl tensor) at a fixed world point is determined uniquely. Accordingly, the value of such a quantity is a functional of data defined on a three-dimensional space-like surface in arbitrary coordinates, provided only that the data are sufficient to characterize the solution uniquely, (and independent of each other, so that they may not contain internal inconsistencies under the constraints of the theory). Such a functional is then a constant of the motion in every sense of the word; its dependence on the arguments contains no explicit reference to the conventional coordinates employed.

If in this manner we should succeed in constructing all components of the metric tensor at all the world points with respect to some particular intrinsic coordinate system, then obviously we should have sufficient data to determine the solution uniquely; however, this information is highly redundant. The amount of data actually required equals four per point on a three-dimensional hypersurface [19]. Beyond these general observations, the actual construction of constants of the motion remains to be greatly improved before it becomes a practical scheme.

7. CONCLUDING REMARKS

Assuming we should have overcome all the difficulties as yet in front of us and succeed in constructing a complete and non-redundant set of observables, including their Lie algebra, in the non-quantum general theory of relativity, how should we proceed toward the construction of the q-number theory? We do not believe that this question can now be answered with complete assurance, and we should like merely to make some comments, which may turn out to become obsolete even sooner than the preceding discussion.

If we formulate the c-number theory in terms of a time-dependent formalism, we obtain a Hamiltonian which is some functional of the canonical coordinates of the theory. Assuming we have already eliminated the constraints, then we shall have a theory closed within itself provided we can determine the factor sequences of the arguments of the Hamiltonian functional according to some heuristic point of view—there appears to be no logically compelling manner in which to make that determination. This *embarras de richesse* is avoided in a Lie algebra dealing exclusively with constants of the motion, as the Hamiltonian in such a theory vanishes identically.

This apparent advantage of the "frozen" over the "time-dependent" theory is, however, probably minor at best. If we construct all the constants of the motion available according to the arguments presented in Section 6, we must eliminate most of them before the remainder becomes non-redundant. Even if we were to require that the remainder consist of canonically conjugate pairs, this requirement is not unique. The choice of variables to be retained as the basic variables of the "frozen" q-number theory probably is almost as arbitrary as the corresponding choices to be made in the "time-dependent" version.

This uncertainty in the construction of the quantized theory, which in our opinion has not yet been overcome successfully in any of the schemes proposed in recent years, reminds us forcefully of a comment made by many thoughtful physicists, most eloquently perhaps by W. Pauli. The history of Dirac's quantum theory of the electron shows that the transition from c-number theory to q-number theory need not be straightforward. The correct quantum theory may well contain formal and physical elements that have no counterpart in the non-quantum theory. Because of the complete absence of experimental information on gravitational waves we cannot hope for the kind of experimental evidence that indicated the existence of electronic spin long before Pauli and Dirac constructed a quantum-theoretical model. Unless we dare to hope that the quantum theory of gravitation will present us with a theory of elementary particles, or the like, we must continue to hope that appropriate clues will unfold in the course of the formal elaboration of the theory.

REFERENCES

[1] L. Rosenfeld, *Ann. Phys., Lpz.* **5**, 113 (1930); *Ann. Inst. H. Poincaré* **2**, 25 (1932).
[2] F. A. E. Pirani and A. Schild, *Phys. Rev.* **79**, 986 (1950).
[3] J. L. Anderson and P. G. Bergmann, *Phys. Rev.* **83**, 1018 (1951).
[4] P. G. Bergmann, *Helv. Phys. Acta* Suppl. IV, 79 (1956).
[5] B. S. DeWitt, *Rev. Mod. Phys.* **29**, 377 (1957).
[6] S. Deser, *Rev. Mod. Phys.* **29**, 417 (1957).
[7] R. Arnowitt and S. Deser, *Phys. Rev.* **113**, 745 (1959).
[8] C. W. Misner, *Rev. Mod. Phys.* **29**, 497 (1957).
[9] F. J. Belinfante, D. I. Caplan and W. L. Kennedy, *Rev. Mod. Phys.* **29**, 518 (1957).
[10] P. G. Bergmann, R. Penfield, R. Schiller and H. Zatzkis, *Phys. Rev.* **80**, 81 (1950).
[11] P. A. M. Dirac, *Phys. Rev.* **114**, 924 (1959).
[12] W. Pauli and M. Fierz, *Helv. Phys. Acta* **12**, 297 (1939).
[13] P. G. Bergmann and R. Schiller, *Phys. Rev.* **89**, 4 (1953).
[14] P. G. Bergmann, I. Goldberg, A. Janis and E. Newman, *Phys. Rev.* **103**, 807 (1956).
[15] J. L. Anderson, Generation of coordinate conditions and the construction of invariants in covariant theories, *preprint*.
[16] P. G. Bergmann and A. Janis, *Phys. Rev.* **111**, 1191 (1958).
[17] P. A. M. Dirac, *Canad. J. Math.* **2**, 129 (1950); 3, 1 (1951).
[18] P. G. Bergmann and I. Goldberg, *Phys. Rev.* **98**, 531 (1955).
[19] A. Komar, *Phys. Rev.* **111**, 1182 (1958).
[20] V. Fock, *Rev. Mod. Phys.* **29**, 325 (1957).
[21] J. Géhéniau and R. Debever, *Helv. Phys. Acta* Suppl. IV, 101 (1956).
[22] J. L. Anderson, Absolute change in General Relativity, an article in this book.

RELATIVITY AND COSMOLOGY

H. Bondi

King's College, London

The connection between the two subjects of relativity and cosmology is old and close; but the strength of the links is not always clearly understood. From the earliest days of scientific cosmology, the assumption of uniformity has been fertile and fundamental. At first uniformity was essentially a convenient assumption, and observational support was slight. Nowadays we have reached the position where, whatever other interpretation may be put on the observational data, their support of the assumption of uniformity is extremely strong. As soon as attempts were made in the nineteenth century to link the idea of an infinite uniform populated universe with Newtonian gravitational theory, difficulties arose; for, fundamentally, these two notions are incompatible. Even in the most modern form of Newtonian cosmology, due to McCrea, the notion of complete uniformity had to be replaced by the notion of uniformity within an arbitrarily large sphere with empty space beyond it. Of course, there can be no conflict between observation and the notion of uniformity within an arbitrarily large sphere; but, nevertheless, there is something slightly artificial about this concept. There is, accordingly, a distinct suggestion that the theory of gravitation ought to be modified. One modification was suggested by Neumann and Seeliger many years ago, the idea being essentially to replace the Newtonian potential by a meson potential, though, of course, with an enormous range of force. This idea did not gain much support owing to the fact that it was completely unconnected with anything else in physics, a pure *ad hoc* assumption to get out of a difficulty. A second approach of a more refined character can be made on the following lines, lines that are not unconnected with the foundations of General Relativity. We may state Newton's First and Second Laws of Motion, in the form:

1. There is a standard motion of matter. As long as matter follows this standard pattern of behaviour it is a waste of time to look for a physical force that keeps the matter on the standard, as this is its undisturbed motion.

2. Deviations from the standard are measured in terms of acceleration relative to the standard, and the product of mass and this acceleration gives us the physical force that is in some way the cause of the deviation from the standard.

The nature of the standard motion has been deliberately left undefined in this formulation. Newton, from observations of his day, assumed the standard to be motion in a straight line with constant velocity. General Relativity, basing itself on the equality of inert and gravitational masses, uses as the standard the motion of matter under gravitation and inertia. However, from a cosmological point of view we could argue differently. Noting the remarkable uniformity of the universe, we could take the motion of matter in a smeared-out uniform universe that would keep it uniform as the standard, and ascribe only deviations from this standard motion of the universe to forces. In this case the gravitational effect of the smeared-out universe is part of the standard, and we would naturally ascribe gravitational forces only to concentrations of matter different in density from the uniform density of the smeared-out universe. The basis of this approach is the idea that dynamics, like other branches of physics, is essentially concerned with repeatable experiments; repeatable, that is to say, at least in principle. The universe as a whole is unique; there is no point in looking for forces that keep the universe moving; the concept of force does not belong to the unique universe, but to the enormous multiplicity of deviations from the uniform background of the smeared-out universe. Alternatively, we may try to resolve the conflict between uniformity and Newtonian gravitational theory by having a new gravitational theory based on local phenomena, and then to hope that somehow or other this gravitational theory will be able to be applied to the universe as a whole.

In many ways it may be said that the greatest and most lasting contribution of relativity to cosmology does not arise directly from its discussion of gravitation; but from its adoption of a Riemannian geometry. Few steps in physics have had as utterly irrevocable a character as Einstein's abandonment of Euclidean geometry, and his adoption of the Riemannian map. Whereas originally this may have seemed to some of the contemporaries an arbitrary step, it now becomes clear to us that almost any serious consideration, whether of local phenomena or of cosmology, leads directly to the Riemannian geometry. The most beautiful derivation of this in the cosmological field is due to Robertson and to Walker, and in their work, which was inspired (or provoked?) by Milne's proposals, it is shown beautifully and in an utterly compelling fashion how the cosmological notion of uniformity combined with the most elementary and qualitative facts of local physics, such as the uniqueness of the paths of light, leads to a special type of Riemannian geometry. It is doubtful whether, even nowadays, there is sufficient awareness of the fundamental nature of this proof. The future of cosmology is full of question marks; but only the complete reversal of our physical knowledge is ever likely to lead to an abandonment of the Riemannian map of Robertson and Walker. Their work has suffered the fate reserved for the most successful papers: it has become so much the background of everybody's work that the magnitude of the original step has been forgotten. Whenever a cosmological theory is being discussed, it is one that refers to a Robertson–Walker Riemannian map. It is essentially through this work, through the adoption of Riemannian geometry and the investigation of the consequences of uniformity in geometry, that the most lasting contribution of relativity to cosmology lies. However, General Relativity does not only show that the effects of gravitation can be most successfully and clearly mapped in Riemannian space, it also shows how gravitational fields arise through the action of its field equations. While the field equations for empty space are extremely plausible (though not quite as compelling as the adoption of the Riemannian map) the field equations involving the energy tensor were felt by many, including Einstein himself, to be of a much less satisfactory kind. To a considerable extent, it was this dissatisfaction with the energy tensor that led to the theory of the equations of motion by Einstein, Infeld and Hoffman. All the experimental tests of General Relativity rely on the field equations in empty space. The step from the empty space field equations to those in the presence of matter have a considerable mathematical attractiveness about it, but little physical basis. It is important to realise that relativistic cosmology in the narrow sense depends entirely and completely on the field equations with the energy-momentum tensor, and thus on the least well founded part of the theory. It must be admitted that virtually no proposal has been made that amends the field equations radically, but only a very small change by terrestrial standards is required to make the significance of the field equations in the cosmological subject change utterly and completely.

One modification of the field equations was indeed proposed by Einstein, shortly after they were first propounded. This is the well known addition of the cosmological term. It is also known that this term had a somewhat chequered history, and that Einstein himself completely abandoned it a few years after its conception. However, only a small minority, led by Pauli, followed him in this step, and numerous other relativists still regard the cosmological term as an essential part of the theory, a view particularly forcefully put forward by Eddington some twenty odd years ago. As a result of historical developments, Einstein's attitude has received particularly little attention in cosmology. From fairly early on relativistic cosmology was beset by the time-scale difficulty, the fact that the expansion constant of the universe seemed to indicate a short time compared with those obtained from astrophysical and geophysical measurements. Owing to the gravitational influence of the matter of the universe, the expansion of a model not involving the cosmological term is necessarily slowing down. Therefore such a model of the universe is younger than is indicated by Hubble's constant. This difficulty can be avoided only by adopting a positive value for the cosmological constant. Of all the beautiful variety of Friedmann universes only those with a positive value of lambda were given close attention before 1952, that is, during all the most formative and fruitful years in the development of relativistic cosmology. None of these models has received more attention than that due to Lemaitre. Whatever the future role of this model, it has given us a clear indication of how much a model of the universe is only an outline drawing, and how compelling physical considerations can fill in the outlines of this drawing and release a wealth of information, implicit in the adoption of a particular model.

Now that, thanks to the work of Baade and Sandage, the time-scale difficulty is no longer an oppressive factor in the development of relativistic cosmology, the time has come when a thorough examination of other models of the Friedmann variety is greatly overdue. In particular there is now every reason to come back to Einstein's view that the cosmological constant vanishes. The simplest model that can be constructed on this basis is the famous model of Einstein and de Sitter, which in sheer simplicity is far ahead of any of the others. It also has the unique property that the product of the gravitational constant, the density of the universe and the square of the inverse of the Hubble constant is unchanging in time. One may well argue that, on the basis of Mach's principle, a constant gravitational constant presupposes a constancy of this number, and General Relativity certainly presupposes such a constancy. Thus, in many ways this is the most intriguing of all the Friedmann models. The time elapsed since the initial explosion is only two thirds of the reciprocal of the Hubble constant, a situation that led to the rejection of this model in the days before 1952. Now, however, it would be most interesting if this model, too, could be filled with physical content in the way that Lemaitre has shown possible for his own model.

One of the most important problems facing any theory of the universe is that of the formation of galaxies. It is generally taken for granted that in any evolutionary universe there was a stage before there were any galaxies. The problem of how these may have condensed all over the universe in such a way as to leave the system with the degree of uniformity we know it to possess is an interesting and important problem. The formation of any galaxy out of a less differentiated medium was first tackled by Jeans and his work has recently been improved upon very much by Bonnor and others. However, a great deal of work remains to be done before all this is in a satisfactory state.

For many years General Relativity was taken to be an extremely rigid theory, giving little leeway to the investigator. Partly for this reason the freedom afforded by the cosmological term was regarded as so desirable by many authors. The cosmological term is the most obvious extension of the original field equations on a purely mathematical basis. It must, however, be doubted very much indeed whether a purely mathematical basis is the right way to proceed in these circumstances. There is a great deal to be said for attempting to explore the universe on the basis of the usual formulation of purely locally established laws of physics, although these require to be extrapolated to very much lower densities, larger distances, and longer times. Once, however, one abandons the usual formulation of the locally established laws, and is willing to consider an amendment to them which will leave them locally the same as before, but will make considerable differences to the universe at large, it seems very doubtful indeed whether then one should be guided by mathematical arguments. One would rather think that, in those circumstances, one ought to be guided by the outcome; in other words, one ought to devise a cosmology that is exceptionally simple, in agreement with current observations, and vulnerable to as many future observations as possible, and then attempt to link such a picture of the universe at large to the locally established theories. This is the procedure adopted by the Steady State theory of cosmology. The universe is supposed not merely to be uniform in space, but unchanging in time. Nevertheless, it is supposed to be expanding as only in this way can the flood of radiation predicted by Olber's paradox be avoided. As is well known, this approach leads to the continual creation of matter, and thus to a conflict with the usual formulation of the laws of conservation of mass, momentum and energy. At first the conflict with General Relativity was taken to be absolute and complete. It is true that, as in all cosmological theories, the Riemannian map was taken over as this follows from the elementary cosmological assumptions in the Robertson–Walker manner. The unchanging nature of the model then immediately confines one to the de Sitter model. Various more or less artificial attempts were made to get this notion of continual creation into relativistic form; but the most promising step forward was taken by McCrea when, instead of changing the mathematical structure of the field equations, he proceeded to change the interpretation of the energy momentum tensor. He suggested that the vacuum should not correspond to a vanishing of the energy momentum tensors. We know from quantum physics that the vacuum is a very complicated system with its own state of strain and stress. McCrea suggests, then, that in relativity, too, we should have non-zero properties of the vacuum. With suitable assumptions about the state of strain of the vacuum, the expansion of the universe then leads automatically to the required continual creation of matter. This most ingenious approach has been taken somewhat further by Davidson. But there is still a difficulty present. What one requires, strictly speaking, is not an assignment of special values for the vacuum so much as an equation of state for it, and no proposals for this have been made that are at all compelling. Nevertheless, McCrea's bold step has, for the first time, linked the Steady State theory with General Relativity in a simple and straightforward manner that would have been regarded as impossible before.

Another approach in relativistic cosmology has become much talked about in recent years. With the Baade–Sandage revision of the time-scale, the objections to decelerating universes have disappeared, as we mentioned earlier. One is then led to consider the oscillating class of Friedmann universes. It will be remembered that, on the basis of a pressure that is vanishingly small compared with the density of matter, an oscillating class of models arises which contracts periodically to zero size, then expands to a maximum, and contracts again, repeating the cycle endlessly. The contraction to zero size corresponds to a singularity of the equations. However, this singularity is due to the total neglect of the pressure. As soon as pressures are introduced, or even without pressures, some local angular momentum, as in the work of Heckmann, the singularity disappears, and one is left with a model of the universe oscillating between a minimum and a maximum size. This model has been considered as being interesting and worthy of investigation on the ground that it combines some of the best features of the Steady State theory and of ordinary relativistic cosmology. It does not violate any of the basic relativistic equations, and can be set up even with vanishing cosmological constant. On the other hand, owing to the endless repetition of the contraction-expansion cycle, the universe has, on the large time scale, an unchanging property that is much in line with its uniformity which, after all, also shows itself only in the large. Unfortunately, no detailed investigation of the physical character of such an oscillating universe appears to have been made so far. Several questions of great difficulty and importance arise. First, on the question of the unchanging nature of the universe. Let us consider what the uniformity — the spatial uniformity — of the universe actually means. The usual statement "uniformity in the large" does not seem to be sufficiently clear-cut. What one wishes to say is that, if we consider large enough portions of the universe, then irrespective of at what point they are centred the physical mean values of density temperature, etc., will tend to be the same. But here the question arises of just how large the pieces have to be before this uniformity becomes apparent. The effectively accessible part of the universe is limited in size by the expansion. The observable region of the universe, while not necessarily finite, is yet limited in the sense that if we go to regions of large red shift a doubling, say, of telescope power, will lead to only a very small increase in the volume surveyed. In other words, a law of sharply diminishing returns will set in, so that one can speak of the effectively observable portion of the universe without having to be precise about the power of the telescope that one is considering. Clearly, the uniformity postulate loses meaning if, in order to get uniformity, one has to consider regions of a size not markedly smaller than the effectively surveyable universe. Fortunately, this does not seem to be so in the case of the actual universe. Taking the large clusters of galaxies as the units, one still finds that there are thousands and tens of thousands of them in the effectively surveyable region. In other words, the distance within which uniformity applies is very markedly smaller than the velocity of light times the reciprocal of Hubble's constant. This is certainly quite different from the unchanging aspect of an oscillating universe, where the period over which one has to average to obtain any sort of degree of uniformity is a multiple of the reciprocal of Hubble's constant. Naturally, this is only a minor objection, an objection that indicates that the oscillating universe is in a different class from the Steady State model. A much more serious criticism arises from a consideration of the propagation of light. It is well known that, in a static universe, thermodynamic equilibrium obtains and one reaches Oblers' paradox according to which the night sky should be intensely brilliant. This is avoided in an expanding universe because the light from the distant sources is greatly weakened by the red shift. The universe in which we live is one in which the sky is very dark indeed. This is a most fundamental property that runs through the whole of physics. All our physics has been established on the basis that radiation is gratefully swallowed up by space, that there is an extreme paucity of radiation, and that matter enormously preponderates over it. This is entirely due to the expansion. In an oscillating universe, the light that now reaches us would in part come from contracting periods. If the sources of light in the contracting periods were anything like what they are now, then we should be receiving a flood of light from them. It may, of course, be that these were entirely different periods when stars were not sending radiation into the universe, but were absorbing radiation from the universe; assuming, that is to say, that there were stars in those periods. What is quite clear is that these periods of contraction must have been utterly and completely different from anything that we know. This is not to say that a picture of these situations cannot be made. But until the physical conditions in a contracting phase have been thoroughly examined no serious consideration can be given to the suggestion of an oscillating universe. If and when it is shown that a physical content of an oscillating universe can be conceived in such a way as not to lead to a bright sky, and yet to be compatible with what we know of physics, then oscillating universes can and will deserve serious consideration. At present, this is not so. What is demanded in cosmology — possibly even more than in other fields of science — is that a theory that wants to be taken seriously must be vulnerable to observations that are practicable in the immediate future. It is on this basis that the absence of any knowledge of physical content for relativistic models, other than Lemaitre's, must be regretted particularly much. It is for these reasons that, at present, only Lemaitre's model and the Steady State theory can be considered as fruitful guides for critical examination by observers and theorists and not just as amusing mathematical constructions.

EXPERIMENTAL VERIFICATIONS OF THE GENERAL THEORY OF RELATIVITY

V. L. Ginzburg

U. S. S. R. Academy of Sciences, Moscow

CONTENTS

INTRODUCTION

At the very beginning of the General Theory of Relativity Einstein put forward the problem of its experimental verifications [1]–[4]. Then he pointed to three effects: the precession of the perihelion of planets, the deflection of light rays passing near a body of large mass (the Sun) and the gravitational shift of spectral lines. All these effects (and some others found later) are quite small both in our solar system and near the other stars. This is due to the weakness of the gravitational fields of all the stars (except neutron stars), i.e. to the condition

$$\frac{|\varphi|}{c^2} \sim \frac{v^2}{c^2} \ll 1 \tag{1}$$

where φ — gravitational (Newtonian) potential, v — velocity of a test particle (a planet) which moves in a potential φ, and c — the speed of light in vacuum.

At the surface of the Sun (mass $M_\odot = 1{\cdot}991 \times 10^{33}$ g, radius $r_\odot = 6{\cdot}960 \times 10^{10}$ cm)

$$\frac{|\varphi|}{c^2} = \frac{\varkappa M_\odot}{r_\odot c^2} = \frac{\varrho_\odot}{r_\odot} = 2{\cdot}12 \times 10^{-6}, \qquad \varrho_\odot = 1{\cdot}47 \times 10^5 \text{ cm} \tag{2}$$

where: $\varrho = \varkappa M/c^2$ — gravitational radius and $\varkappa = 6{\cdot}67\times10^{-8}$ dyne$\times$ $\times$cm^{2}g^{-2} the gravitational constant. On the Earth's surface ($M_♁ = 5{\cdot}98\times10^{27}$ g, $r_♁ = 6{\cdot}37\times10^8$ cm) if we take into consideration only its own field, we have

$$\frac{|\varphi|}{c^2} = 7\times10^{-10}, \qquad \varrho_♁ = 0{\cdot}43 \text{ cm}. \tag{3}$$

On the Earth's orbit $|\varphi|/c^2 \simeq v^2/c^2 \simeq 10^{-8}$ (the velocity of the Earth $v_♁ \simeq 30$ km/sec), and even on the surface of white dwarf stars $|\varphi|/c^2 \sim 10^{-4}$. Thus in all these cases the field is not only weak but even very weak.

The situation changes for large parts of the universe (for average density of the matter $\mu_0 \sim 3\times10^{-29}$ g$\times$cm^{-3} the gravitational radius $\varrho = \varkappa M/c^2 \sim 4\varkappa\mu_0 R^3/c^2 \sim R/10$ for $R \sim 3\times10^{27} \simeq 3\times10^9$ light years). However we should put aside all cosmological problems when we are discussing the experimental verifications of General Relativity Theory (G.R.T.). (It is enough to mention that for the most generally used cosmological models we have to assume isotropy, the non-existence of the cosmological term in the gravitational equations, etc.)

Thus we must take into consideration the observation of quite small effects for the experimental verification of G.R.T. This fact, however, should not lessen our interest in the theory and its experimental tests as we cannot "measure" the importance of G.R.T. by the magnitude of the parameter $|\varphi|/c^2$, for instance, inside the solar system. On the other hand the solution of this problem is delayed by the necessity of measuring very small effects and, because of this, some questions about an experimental test of G.R.T. have not yet been answered. Nevertheless we have now gained new possibilities for experimental confirmation of G.R.T. with the new technical devices (such as artificial satellites of the earth, molecular and atomic clocks, etc.), and the progress here is definite, although relatively slow.

In this paper we shall speak about results attained as well as about further possible tests of G.R.T.

1. THE MOTION OF PLANETS AND THEIR SATELLITES

We can consider the influence of G.R.T. effects in a weak field as a perturbation. Then, there exists only one secular (that is growing up with time) perturbation for a non-rotating central body. That is the relativistic motion of a planet differs from the classical only because the elliptical orbit moves very slowly within its plane in the direction of the motion of the planet (satellite). From this follows the precession of the perihelion of the planet (the point of its orbit nearest to the Sun) and it is, in radians per revolution:

$$\varepsilon = \frac{24\pi^3 a^2}{c^2 T^2 (1-e^2)} = \frac{6\pi \varkappa M_\odot}{c^2 a (1-e^2)}, \tag{4}$$

where $2a$ — is the major axis, $e = \sqrt{a^2-b^2}/a$ — the eccentricity, $2b$ — the minor axis, T — the period of one revolution in seconds. To find the last expression we made use of Kepler's third law: $a^3 = (\varkappa M_\odot/4\pi^2)T^2$.

Effect (4) is obviously of the order: $\varkappa M_\odot/ac^2 \sim |\varphi|/c^2 \sim v^2/c^2$ and for $e \ll 1$ the value of the precession of the perihelion is $\varepsilon/2\pi \simeq 3v^2/c^2$.

The precession of a perihelion is, in seconds per century:

$$\Psi = \frac{5\pi^2 a^2 Y}{24 c^2 T^3 (1-e^2)} = 8{\cdot}35 \times 10^{-19} \frac{a^2}{T^3(1-e^2)} = \frac{3{\cdot}34\times 10^{33}}{a^{5/2}(1-e^2)} \tag{5}$$

where $Y = 365{\cdot}25$ is the number of days in a year. We measure period T in seconds and the major axis $2a$ in centimetres.

The accuracy of the measurement of the precession does not depend only on the angle Ψ but also on other factors, namely on the eccentricity. This is quite clear since for a circular orbit we cannot speak at all about perihelion. Then the magnitude of this effect is characterized by the product $e\Psi$ even better than by the angle Ψ itself. We can introduce some other expressions which show us the possible precision of the measurement of the precession, besides having $e\Psi$ as a parameter [5], [6]. However we shall make use only of Ψ and $e\Psi$, the values of which are given in Table I.

TABLE I[(1)]

The Precession of the Perihelion of the Planets

(in seconds per century)

Planet	Ψ from formula (5)	$e\Psi$	Ψ experimental
Mercury	43″·03	8″·847	42″·56 ± 0″·94
Venus	8″·63	0″·059	
Earth	3″·84	0″·064	4″·6 ± 2″·7
Mars	1″·35	0″·126	
Jupiter	0″·06	0″·003	

(1) The values are taken from [6].

We must note that the precession of the perihelion of a planet is due not only to the relativistic effect but also to the perturbing influence of other planets. Together with this the full perturbation for Mercury is 532″ that is 12·5 times as great as the effect of G.R.T. alone. The perturbation of other planets and the Moon leads to the Earth's precession of the perihelion of 1154″ per century while the relativistic effect is 3″·8. It is clear that the separation of the relativistic effect is very complicated but it is accomplished for Mercury. Thus, it can be seen that the precession of the perihelion (shown in the last column of Table I), which would be inexplicable by the influence of other planets, agrees perfectly with that predicted by G.R.T.(1) Nevertheless it is interesting to study further the relativistic effects in the motion of planets and their satellites. (It suffices to say that it is always desirable to confirm the theory for more than one case.) In this field there are three interesting possibilities.

The first is to make precise the data for the Earth and other planets (see Table I)(2) and to study the motion of the small planet Icar. In this case [5] $a = 1{\cdot}6\times10^{13}$ cm, $e = 0{\cdot}8265$, $T = 408{\cdot}67$ days and the theoretical values of Ψ and $e\Psi$ are: $\Psi = 10''{\cdot}05$, $e\Psi = 8''{\cdot}3$. (A more precise analysis shows that the possible accuracy in the case is Icar is 4–5 times better than in the case of Mercury.)

The second possibility is to observe an artificial planet which has a large eccentricity [7]. It was estimated that the maximum possible value is $\Psi \sim 1000''$ per century; the experimental error in this case is not yet known.

The third method of verifying G.R.T. is to make use of the artificial satellites of the Earth.

The precession of the perigees of these satellites is $1''{\cdot}9$ per century because of the influence of the Sun and this can be neglected. We shall discuss only the effect caused by the Earth's field. For this we have (in seconds per century):

$$\Psi' = \frac{5\pi^2 a^2 Y}{24c^2T^3(1-e^2)} = 8{\cdot}35\times10^{-19}\frac{a^2}{T^3(1-e^2)} = \frac{1{\cdot}74\times10^{25}}{a^{5/2}(1-e^2)}. \quad (6)$$

(1) Leverrier had already noticed that the precession of the perihelion of Mercury is inexplicable by the perturbation of other planets. Einstein in his paper [3] in which he derived formula (4) gave for the observed value of Ψ: $45''\pm5''$. From Table I it can be seen how much more accurate are the results we obtain nowadays. About some unsuccessful attempts to explain the abnormality in relation of the motion of Mercury before G. R. T., see [7a].

(2) Thanks to the kindness of Professor M. F. Subbotin the author can report that the motion of Venus has been investigated in detail in a not yet published

It is clear from this formula and from the very essence of the problem that those parts of formulae (4)–(5) in which the period T is expressed by a are valid also for the satellites. In other words, only the last parts in (4) and (5) apply only to the Sun or the Earth; in these parts a is measured in centimetres.

For the Moon $\Psi' = 0''{\cdot}06$ per century but for the nearer satellites it is as much as 1700″.(1) The values of Ψ' and $e\Psi'$ for some satellites are given for instance, in [10]. Here we can give an example of a satellite with eccentricity $e = 0{\cdot}25$ and an average distance from the Earth of 10,000 km; for this case, $\Psi' = 584''$ and $e\Psi' = 146''$. The accuracy of the measurement of the satellites orbit may be good enough to measure the quantities of the same order as Ψ'. The main difficulty, however, lies in the fact that we must take into account the perturbations caused by air resistance and chiefly by the deviation of the earth's field from $\varphi = -\varkappa M_{\male}/r$. As far as we know the error in the measurement of the precession of the perigees of artificial satellites when the nonspherical shape of the Earth is taken into account, has not yet been analysed in detail in any literature. Thus we cannot show any concrete possibilities in this field; it is rather difficult to expect success here in the near future. Nevertheless we shall emphasize the new possibilities gained in principle, by the use of the sputniks [9], [10] in the observation of such an interesting fourth effect of G.R.T. (the "rotation effect"), i.e. the influence of the rotation of a central body on the motion of a planet or a satellite [11], [12], [12a]. The corresponding precession of a perihelion or a perigee (in seconds per century) is

$$\Psi_{\text{rot}} = -\frac{\pi^2 r_0^2 Y \cos i}{6c^2 \tau T^2 (1-e^2)^{3/2}}, \tag{7}$$

where i is the angle between the plane of the orbit and the equatorial plane of a central rotating body; r_0 — is its radius (in centimetres);

---

paper by R. L. Duncombe. The experimental datum for the relativistic effect is $e\Psi = 0''{\cdot}057 \pm 0''{\cdot}033$ which agrees well with the theoretical value $0''{\cdot}059$ (see Table I).

(1) The velocity of the satellites is $v \lesssim 8$ km/sec, thus it is less than the velocity of the Earth. Because of this the precession of the perigees of the satellites is less, per revolution, than the precession of the perihelion of the Earth. For a given period of time, however, that precession is quite large for the nearer satellites, as their period of revolution T is comparatively small (for the nearer satellites $T \sim 1{\cdot}5$ hour). Relativistic corrections to the theory of the motion of the Moon are fully examined in [10a]; these results can obviously find an application for the investigation of artificial satellites.

τ — the period of its revolution (in days); all the other symbols have the same meaning and are in the same units as in formulae (5)–(6). We observe that besides the precession of the perihelion we have also the precession of the nodes of the orbit; for this the angle is one third as great and has the opposite sign to that from formula (7) with $i = 0$ (with $i = 0$ we regard a central body and a satellite at its orbit as rotating in the same direction).

The sum of (6) and (7) gives the full relativistic effect for a satellite. The minus in (7) shows us that for $\cos i > 0$ the rotation of a body lessens the precession of its perigee (perihelion).

The role of the "rotation effect" we determine by the ratio (see (5), (6) and (7) with $i = 0$)

$$\Delta = \frac{|\Psi_{rot}|}{\Psi} = \frac{4}{5}\left(\frac{r_0}{a}\right)^2 \frac{T}{\tau(1-e^2)^{1/2}}\,. \tag{8}$$

For Mercury $\Delta \simeq 4\times 10^{-4}$ and $|\Psi_{rot}| \simeq 0''\cdot 02$; but at the same time the experimental error is $\sim 1''$ (see Table I). Thus we cannot measure the "rotation effect" for planets nowadays; it is due to the slow rotation of the Sun ($T \sim 25$ days) and to the great distance of even the nearest planet (for Mercury $r_0/a \sim 10^{-2}$). For the fifth satellite of the quickly rotating Jupiter the value of Ψ_{rot} is $\sim 5'$ while $\Psi = 36''\cdot 37$ (see [11]) but it is extremely difficult to measure. For artificial satellites of the earth which move at a distance of some hundreds of kilometres $\Delta \sim 4\times 10^{-2}$ and $\Psi_{rot} \sim -60''$, the rotation effect is of the same order as the whole relativistic effect for Mercury. As has already been said, the problem of choosing that effect is still open. We should only like to emphasize the great importance of the measuring influence of the rotation of the central body from the point of view of a thorough test of G.R.T. (see Section 4 and the note added in proof).

2. THE DEFLECTION OF LIGHT RAYS PASSING NEAR THE SUN

According to G.R.T. the deflection of a light ray passing at a distance R from the centre of the Sun is

$$\alpha = \frac{4\varkappa M_{\odot}}{c^2 R} = 1''\cdot 75\,\frac{r_0}{R} \tag{9}$$

where by using the second expression we measure the angle α in seconds. It is obvious that for a light ray which passes at the very edge of the Sun $\alpha_{max} = 1''\cdot 75$; this corresponds approximately to an angle at which one centimetre is seen from a distance of one kilometre.

We note that in 1801 Soldner predicted a deflection half as great as that in formula (9) on the basis of the corpuscular theory of light and classical mechanics. (His paper is reprinted in [13] and the derivation of this formula is given, for instance, in [10].) It is interesting that Einstein obtained the same result in his early works [1], [2]; it doubled only when computed on the basis of the completed formulae of G.R.T. [3], [4].

The experimental verification of formula (9) occurred during the total eclipses of the Sun since 1919. A summary of some results is given in Table II and they do not leave any doubt either as to the reality of the effect or as to the close agreement α_{max} with the theoretical value $\alpha_{max} = 1''\cdot 75$ and not with the classical $\alpha_{max} = 0''\cdot 87$.

TABLE II

The Deflection of the Light Rays passing near the Edge of the Sun

(the theoretical value $\alpha_{max} = 1''\cdot 75$)

Year of observation	Angle of deflection (according to the data in the literature given in the next column).	Reference to the literature	Angle of deflection as worked out in [16]
1919	$1''\cdot 98 \pm 0''\cdot 18$	[14]	$2''\cdot 07 \pm 0''\cdot 13$
1919 (the second place of observations)	$1''\cdot 61 \pm 0''\cdot 45$	[14]	
1922	$1''\cdot 78 \pm 0''\cdot 17$	[14]	$1''\cdot 83$
1922 (the second place of observations)	$1''\cdot 77$	[15]	
1929	$2''\cdot 24$	[15]	$1''\cdot 96$
1936	$2''\cdot 70$	[16]	$2''\cdot 70$
1947	$2''\cdot 01 \pm 0''\cdot 27$	[17]	$2''\cdot 20$
1952	$1''\cdot 7 \pm 0''\cdot 10$	[18]	$1''\cdot 43$
Mean value	$1''\cdot 97$	—	$2''\cdot 03$

We can say even more: within the limits of the experimental error (10–20%) the mean experimental value $\alpha_{max} = 2''\cdot 0$ also agrees with that predicted by theory (the sign of the effect is, of course, the same as in the theory). However, we cannot yet speak of a check on the law $\alpha = \dfrac{\text{const}}{R}$, i.e. about finding the dependence of α

on the distance R [16] although we know that α decreases when R increases.

There have been only 11 observations [16a] of the deflection of light rays in the Sun's field during the last 40 years, thus the low degree of accuracy is not surprising. Taking into account the possibility of carrying out such an experiment nowadays on a higher technical level [16], [16a] we can hope to check formula (9) with an experimental error of not more than a few percent during 2–3 eclipses.

At the end of this section we shall note that the rotation of a central body (the Sun) should affect the deflection of light rays and turn the polarization plane of the light [19]. This effect can be expressed by the parameter $\xi = 4\varkappa K/c^3R^2$ where K is the angular momentum of the central body. On a surface of a sphere with radius r_0 we can write down this parameter as $\frac{|\varphi|}{c^2}\times\frac{v_0}{c}$ where $\frac{|\varphi|}{c^2} = \frac{\varkappa M}{r_0c^2}$ and $v_0 = \omega r_0$ is the velocity of the rotation at the equator (see [10]). For the Sun with $R = r_0$ parameter $\xi \sim 5\times10^{-6}$ seconds and the influence of the rotation on the propagation of light is negligible.

3. THE GRAVITATIONAL SHIFT OF SPECTRAL LINES

In a weak field (i.e., as in Sections 1 and 2, neglecting all terms of order higher than φ/c^2) the change in the frequency ν, when the light passes between two points with potentials φ_1 and φ_2 respectively, is

$$\frac{\Delta\nu}{\nu} = \frac{\nu_2-\nu_1}{\nu_1} = \frac{\varphi_1-\varphi_2}{c^2}, \tag{10}$$

where ν_2 and ν_1 — frequency at points 2 and 1.

We can put $\varphi_2 = 0$ for the spectrum emitted by the atoms of a star or the Sun observed from the Earth (i.e. we neglect the Earth potential). Then

$$\frac{\Delta\nu}{\nu} = -\frac{\Delta\lambda}{\lambda} = \frac{\varphi_1}{c^2} = -\frac{\varkappa M}{rc^2}. \tag{11}$$

Here $\lambda = c/\nu$ is the wave length and r the radius of the photosphere of a star. For the Sun, $\Delta\nu/\nu = -2{\cdot}12\times10^{-6}$ (see (2)); for observations on the Earth of a radiation emitted at a great distance $\varphi_1 = 0$ and $\Delta\nu/\nu = \varkappa M_♁/r_♁c^2 = 7\times10^{-10}$ (see (3)). We see that the sign of the shift depends on the conditions of the observation and thus it should be called the gravitational shift rather than the red shift.

In practice we use only the simple formula (10); it can be obtained in a quite elementary way from the principle of equivalence [1], [2]; the same result, on the basis of quantum notions, follows at once from the fact that a quantum with mass $h\nu/c^2$ in the gravitational field performs the work $(h\nu/c^2)(\varphi_1-\varphi_2) = h\Delta\nu$. We also note that the gravitational shift (10) does not depend on the acceleration of the source and always remains the same (in particular the source can freely fall; for more details see [10]).

Attempts to determine out experimentally the gravitational shift of the spectral lines of the Sun and stars have been made for a long time; however, as the effect by itself is so small and the Doppler effect is present, there are great difficulties in this work. The weight of the Doppler effect becomes quite evident if we measure the gravitational shift in the effective velocities:

$$v_{\text{eff}} = c\frac{\Delta\nu}{\nu} = \frac{\varphi_1-\varphi_2}{c}. \tag{12}$$

For the Sun $v_{\text{eff}} = -0{\cdot}636$ km/sec and for the Earth (see (3)) $v_{\text{eff}} = 21$ cm/sec. At the same time the radial velocities of the stars reach tens of km/sec and the velocity of currents in the Sun's atmosphere is of the same order as v_{eff}. There is no doubt that for white dwarfs the gravitational (red) shift is ascertained, the effect in this case is extremely great as the mass $M \sim M_\odot$ and radius $r \sim 10^{-2} r_\odot$; because of this $|\varphi|/c^2 \sim 10^{-4}$ or $v_{\text{eff}} \sim 30$ km/sec. Nevertheless the radii of these stars (white dwarfs) are not known accurately enough to use known data for a reliable quantitative testing of formula (11). We can also report the results of the statistical analysis of the red shift in the spectrum of some stars (the K-effect) [20]. The red shift has also been discovered for the Sun but the use of these observations to verify the theory is complicated; here we must take into acount the motion of the gas in the photosphere and the existence of the shift of spectral lines because of the interaction of atoms, ions and electrons. The observed red shift in the Sun's spectrum depends on the emission spot of the Sun's disk [21], [22], but at the edge of the disk it tends ot the theoretical value $\Delta\lambda/\lambda = 2{\cdot}12\times10^{-6}$. Such a picture is explained by the role of the motion in the rotating reversing layer which is in a state of convectional motion (granulation). As a result we have the violet shift in the central part of the disk which partly compensates for the relativistic effect (for further details see [21], [23]). The presence of the radial motion in the Sun's atmosphere does not give any additional shift of the spectral lines at the edge of the disk (the

Doppler effect of the first order is eliminated when we observe the radiation perpendicular to the velocity of the source). Thus the data on the shift of the spectral lines of the Sun not only do not contradict the conclusions of G.R.T. but even confirm them. But also in this case, from the point of view of strict quantitative testing of formulae (10)–(11), we might wish for much better accuracy and clarity.

There are attractive perspectives for the study of the gravitational shift, besides further investigations of the spectra of the Sun and stars, in connection with the artificial satellites and the development of radiophysics. The minimal observable shift of the frequency does not surpass $(\Delta\nu/\nu)_{\min} \sim 10^{-7}$ in optics. In radiodiapason the picture changes and, in principle, a shift of frequency equal to a part of a hertz can be observed; so that even the value $\Delta\nu/\nu \sim 10^{-13}$ for $\nu \sim 10^{10}$ ($\lambda = c/\nu \sim 3$ cm) is probably not the maximum possible. The stability of the sources also can go as high as $\Delta\nu/\nu \sim 10^{-12}$–$10^{-13}$ (see [24]–[26]). In the case of measurements of the frequency carried out with an accuracy of $\Delta\nu/\nu \sim 10^{-13}$ the gravitational effect can be observed even directly on the Earth. It is easy to place the receiver and the transmitter on the Earth with a difference in altitude of, let us say, 3 km. Then, according to (10)

$$\left|\frac{\Delta\nu}{\nu}\right| = \frac{gH}{c^2} = 1{\cdot}09\times10^{-18}h \simeq 3\times10^{-13} \tag{13}$$

(here $g = 981$ cm/sec is the accelaration of gravity and H is the difference in altitudes). It is rather difficult to attain the accuracy required in (13); thus we turn our attention to the use of artificial satellites ([23], [9], [10], [27]–[30]). The violet shift can reach the value already mentioned, of $\Delta\nu/\nu = 7\times10^{-10}$ for a very distant satellite and it can be measured by known methods (here we have in mind only the principle of measurement and set aside all technical difficulties). For a satellite which is at the altitude H above the level of the Earth, for $H \ll r_{♁}$:

$$\frac{\Delta\nu}{\nu} = 1{\cdot}09\times10^{-18}H\left(1-\frac{H}{r_{♁}}\right)$$

and for instance for $H = 800$ km $\Delta\nu/\nu = 7{\cdot}7\times10^{-11}$ i.e. the gravitational shift is one order less than for a distant satellite. Besides the gravitational we have also the Doppler shift of the spectral lines, so that the full effect is:

$$\left(\frac{\Delta\nu}{\nu}\right)_t = \frac{v_1}{c}\cos\theta - \frac{v_1^2}{2c^2}(1-2\cos^2\theta) + \frac{\varphi_1-\varphi_2}{c^2}, \tag{14}$$

where $\Delta\nu = \nu_{\text{Earth}} - \nu_{\text{sat}}$, v_1 — velocity of a satelite, θ — the angle between $\vec{v}_1$ and the ray of observation. On a circular orbit $v_1^2 = -\varphi_1$ where φ_1 is the potential of the Earth's field at the satellite's orbit. (φ_2 is the potential on the Earth's surface where there is an observer.) It is clear from (14) that for near satellites (for $|\varphi_1 - \varphi_2| \ll |\varphi_2|$) even the Doppler effect of the second order with respect to v_1/c is higher than the gravitational shift, not to mention the linear Doppler effect. The latter vanishes for $\theta = \pi/2$; it can also be eliminated by measuring not the frequency but the difference in the indications of two clocks: one on a satellite and the other on the Earth. The ratio of this difference $\Delta\tau = \tau_{\text{sat}} - \tau_{\text{Earth}}$ and the time $\tau \approx \tau_{\text{sat}} \approx \tau_{\text{Earth}}$, for a circular orbit ($r_{\oplus} + H$ — radius of the orbit), is

$$\frac{\Delta\tau}{\tau} = \frac{\varphi_1 - \varphi_2}{c^2} - \frac{v_1^2}{2c^2} = \frac{\frac{3}{2}\varphi_1 - \varphi_2}{c^2} = \frac{\varkappa M_{\oplus}}{r_{\oplus} c^2}\left(1 - \frac{3}{2}\frac{r_{\oplus}}{r_{\oplus} + H}\right). \quad (15)$$

It is obvious that the difference in the rate of the clocks and in the shifts of spectral lines are simply two aspects of the same phenomenon and for distant satellites

$$\left(\frac{\Delta\tau}{\tau}\right)_{\max} = \left(\frac{\Delta\nu}{\nu}\right)_{\max} = \frac{\varkappa M_{\oplus}}{r_{\oplus} c^2} = 7\times 10^{-10},$$

where $\Delta\tau = \tau_{\text{sat}} - \tau_{\text{Earth}}$, $\Delta\nu = \nu_{\text{Earth}} - \nu_{\text{sat}}$. At the same time we measure frequency and time in different ways and at present it is difficult to say which is more convenient. It is easy to see from (15) that for a distant satellite we have, per year ($H \gg r_{\oplus}$) $\Delta\tau = \tau_{\text{sat}} - \tau_{\text{Earth}} \simeq 2\times 10^{-2}$ sec, and for a near-by satellite ($H \ll r_{\oplus}$) $\Delta\tau \simeq -10^{-2}$ sec. In the latter case we have the effect of the special theory of relativity namely the dependence of the rate of clocks on time (in other words, on a near-by satellite the often discussed "travelling in time", is realized). For $H = 1/2 r_{\oplus} \simeq 3200$ km, $\Delta\tau = 0$ i.e. the two effects are compensated.

Unlike the use of satellites for the measurement of the relativistic precession of their perihelions it is already quite possible to use them to test formula (10). We can hope then that in the next few years the gravitational shift on satellites will be measured with sufficient accuracy.

4. SOME ADDITIONAL REMARKS AND CONCLUSIONS

Before summing up, we should make a general remark on the testing of a theory. It is obvious that disagreement between theory and experiment decides against the theory. It is much more difficult to conclude that a theory is true because it is confirmed by experiment. We cannot strictly deduce the applicability of a theory to more general cases than those for which it has been tested. Concretely, in the verification of G.R.T. we must remember that all the effects discussed are for a weak field and thus the agreement between theory and experiment does not guarantee the correctness of the rigorous equations of the gravitational field. Here we should notice the attempts to develop a linear theory of gravitation ([31]–[34]) in which we can get the same results as in Einstein's G.R.T. for the three so called "critical" effects (see Sections 1–3). We cannot dwell on these linear theories here and we shall only mention that they encounter essential difficulties ([32], [34]) and we believe that they cannot compare with G.R.T. for consistency, clarity and conviction (1). We can notice that in the experiments which take into account the "rotation effect" (see Sec. 1) there is a disagreement [35] between the results of G.R.T. and the theories [31], [33]. It is a pity that the possibility of observing the "rotation effect" is still problematical. If the agreement between the consequences of G.R.T. and experiment for the three critical effects does not prove the truth of the whole theory it does decisively testify for it. From this point of view, as is usual in comparing theory with experiment, we can say:

There exist no experimental data against G.R.T.

All three of the effects pointed out by Einstein have been observed. For the precession of the perihelion of Mercury the agreement with theory is very good (see Table I), the deflection of light rays in the Sun's field agrees with the theoretical value within the limits of experimental error amounting to 10–20% (see Table II) and the gravitational shift is of the same order and sign as the theoretical.

Thus we can already say that G.R.T. on the whole has stood experimental testing very well and there is no reason to doubt its truth when applied to the corresponding phenomena.

At the same time, if we remember the fundamental character of G.R.T. it is fully justified to test it further. Here there are possibilities of using both the old (astronomical) methods and also radio methods and artificial satellites of the Earth etc.

Note added in proof. After this paper had been written about eighteen months ago (September 1959) many papers have appear-

---

(1) Attempts are made to substitute for G. R. T. If the problem is one of the linear approximation of G. R. T. only, then we have hardly any problems which are not methodological.

red about the experimental verification of the General Theory of Relativity. Here we can point out only the most important ones (for more details see [36]).

The use of the Mössbauer effect enables us to measure very small changes of the frequency of γ rays. In this way it was possible to measure [37] the gravitational shift of the frequency of γ rays; the obtained result, with the accuracy up to $4\,^0/_0$, well agrees with the theoretical value. The carrying out of the measurements in a radiodiapason (as well as in an optical diapason with the help of "lasers" — optical masers) has not become needless, although it is now less interesting.

A project was proposed [38] of measuring the deflection of light rays in the field of the Sun with the accuracy up to some hundredth of a second with the help of an apparatus installed on an artificial satellite or on a balloon. This discussed the possibility of discovering gravitational waves of cosmic origin [39].

Not dwelling on some other proposals (see [36] and the references given there) we only notice here an extremely interesting possibility of observing the precession of an axis of a gyroscope which is on an artificial satellite or on the Earth [40]. If the centre of mass of the gyroscope rests with respect to the Earth, the precession of its axis caused by the rotation of the Earth reaches 6×10^{-9} radian/day $\simeq 0.4$ sec/year. The precession of a gyroscope on a satellite reaches 6×10^{-9} radians per rotation (the magnitude of the effect depends on the orbit and on the direction of the gyroscope axis); it is caused by the rotation of the Earth as well as by the motion of the mass centre of the gyroscope. The carrying out of such an experiment (e.g. with a superconductive gyroscope) would be very important from the point of view of the further verification of the General Theory of Relativity.

Finally, we mention that lately there has been broadly discussed in the literature the problem of the significance of these or other experiments from the point of view of the testing of Einstein's General Theory of Relativity in the whole or in just some of its parts (e.g. the principle of equivalence). To complete what has been said in Sec. 4 of this paper, we mention only that contrasting the General Theory of Relativity with the principle of equivalence combined with the Special Theory of Relativity seems artificial (for more details see [36]). Because of this we have not analysed in this paper this side of the problem of the experimental verification of the General Theory of Relativity.

REFERENCES

[1] A. Einstein, *Jb. Radioakt.* **4**, 441 (1907).
[2] A. Einstein, *Ann. Phys., Lpz.* **35**, 898 (1911).
[3] A. Einstein, *S. B. Preuss. Akad. Wiss.* p. 831 (1915).
[4] A. Einstein, *Ann. Phys. Lpz.* **49**, 760 (1916).
[5] J. J. Gilvary, *Publ. Astron. Soc. Pacific.* **65**, 173 (1953); *Phys. Rev.* **89**, 1046 (1953).
[6] G. M. Clemence, *Rev. Mod. Phys.* **19**, 361 (1947); *Astron. Papers* **13**, p. V, 367 (1954).
[7] J. J. Gilvary, *Nature, Lond.* **183**, 666 (1959).
[7a] M. F. Subbotin, *Astron. Z.* **33**, 251 (1956).
[8] L. La Paz, *Publ. Astron. Soc. Pacific* **66**, 13 (1954).
[9] V. L. Ginzburg, *J. Eksp. Teor. Phys.* **30**, 213 (1956).
[10] V. L. Ginzburg, *Usp. Fiz. Nauk* **59**, 11 (1956); **63**, 119 (1957); *Fortschr. Physik* (Berlin) **5**, 16 (1957).
[10a] W. A. Brumberg, *Bul. Inst. Teor. Astr.* **6**, N 10, 733 (1958).
[11] J. Lense and H. Thirring, *Phys. Z.* **19**, 156 (1918).
[12] N. St. Kalitzin, *Nuovo Cim.* **9**, 365 (1958).
[12a] L. Landau and E. Lifshiz, *Theory of Fields*, § 101, Moscow, 1960.
[13] J. Soldner, *Ann. Phys., Lpz.* **65**, 593 (1921).
[14] S. I. Vavilov, *Experimental Bases of the Theory of Relativity*, GIZ, 1928.
[15] *Irish Astron. J.* **3**, 58 (1954).
[16] A. A. Mihailov, *Astron. Z.* **33**, 912 (1956).
[16a] H. v. Klüber, *Vistas in Astronomy* Vol. **3**, p. 47, London 1960.
[17] G. Van Biesbroeck, *Astron. J.* **55**, 49 (1950).
[18] G. Van Biesbroeck, *Astron. J.* **58**, 57 (1953).
[19] G. W. Skrotzky, *Dokl. Akad. Nauk SSSR* **114**, 73 (1957).
[20] P. P. Parenago, *Stellar Astronomy*, § 25, GIZ, 1954.
[21] M. G. Adam, *Mon. Not. R. Astr. Soc.* **108**, 446 (1948).
]22] E. F. Freundlich, A. V. Broun and H. Brück, *Z. Astrophys.* **1**, 43 (1950).
[23] V. L. Ginzburg, *Dokl. Akad. Nauk SSSR* **91**, 617 (1954).
[24] C. H. Townes, *J. Appl. Phys. Moscow.* **22**, 1365 (1951).
[25] J. P. Gordon, H. J. Zeiger and C. H. Townes, *Phys. Rev.* **99**, 1264 (1955).
[26] N. G. Basov and A. M. Prohorov, *Usp. Fiz. Nauk* **57**, 485 (1955).
[27] F. Wittenberg, *Astronautica Acta* **2**, 25 (1956).
[28] S. F. Singer, *Phys. Rev.* **104**, 11 (1956).
[29] B. Hoffmann, *Phys. Rev.* **106**, 358 (1957).
[30] C. Møller, *Nuovo Cim.* Suppl. **6**, No. 1, 381 (1957).
[31] G. D. Birkhoff, *Proc. Nat. Acad. Sci. USA* **29**, 231 (1943); **30**, 1324 (1944).
[32] S. N. Gupta, *Rev. Mod. Phys.* **29**, 334 (1957).
[33] F. J. Belinfante and I. C. Swihart, *Ann. Phys., Paris* **1**, 168 (1957); **2**, 88 (1957).
[34] W. Thirring, *Fortschr. Physik*, (Berlin) **7**, 79 (1959).
[35] W. I. Pustovoit, *J. Eksp. Teor. Phys.* **37**, 870 (1959).
[36] V. L. Ginzburg, Collection: "*Einstein and the Development of the Physico-Mathematical Thought*" (in Russian). Edited by U. S. S.R. Acad. of Sci., Moscow 1961.

[37] R. V. Pound and G. A. Rebka, *Phys. Rev. Letters* **4**, 337 (1960); R. V. Pound, *Usp. Fiz. Nauk* **72**, 673 (1960).

[38] R. L. Lillestrand, American Astronautical Society, *Preprint* 60–61 (1960).

[39] J. Weber, *Phys. Rev.* **117**, 306 (1960).

[40] L. I. Schiff, *Phys. Rev. Letters* **4**, 215 (1960); *Proc. Nat. Acad. Sci. Amer.* **46**, 871 (1960).

PROBLÈMES MATHÉMATIQUES EN RELATIVITÉ

A. LICHNEROWICZ et Y. FOURÈS-BRUHAT

Institut Henri Poincaré, Paris

DANS cet article, nous nous proposons d'indiquer l'état de certains des principaux problèmes mathématiques posés par la théorie relativiste de la gravitation. Beaucoup de ces problèmes apparaissent, aujourd'hui encore, difficiles à aborder et nos connaissances restent relativement limitées.

L'étude de la structure mathématique des équations de champ conduit à partager le problème de l'intégration locale des équations d'Einstein en deux problèmes: le problème de l'évolution dans le temps qui a pu être résolu dans les cas extérieur et intérieur et en coordonnées isothermes, le problème de la recherche des données de Cauchy auquel les A. ont apporté différentes contributions et qui est fondamental pour l'élaboration de modèles d'univers. On se trouve ainsi conduit à l'étude de problèmes globaux auxquels il a été possible d'apporter une solution dans le cas stationnaire ou dans le cas périodique. Récemment l'étude de problèmes physiques ou celle de la quantification des champs a conduit B. DeWitt et l'un de nous à introduire en relativité générale des propagateurs tensoriels qui semblent devoir jouer un rôle important dans certains développements de la théorie.

Nous nous sommes limités en général au champ gravitationnel et à la relativité générale. Seules quelques brèves indications sont consacrées au cas où un champ électromagnétique est présent. Les problèmes concernant les solutions gravitationnelles radiantes ne sont pas abordés ici.

I. LA STRUCTURE DES ÉQUATIONS DU CHAMP

1. *La variété espace temps.* Dans toute théorie relativiste du champ gravitationnel l'élément primitif est constitué par une variété à quatre dimensions, l'espace temps, V_4 douée d'une struc-

ture de variété différentiable: pour des raisons étroitement liées à la covariance du formalisme et qui apparaîtraient en détail par l'analyse des équations du champ gravitationnel, nous sommes amenés à supposer que dans l'intersection des domaines de deux systèmes de coordonnées admissibles, les coordonnées d'un point dans l'un des systèmes sont des fonctions quatre fois différentiables, à jacobien non nul, des coordonnées de ce point dans l'autre système, les dérivées premières et secondes étant continues, les dérivées troisièmes et quatrièmes étant seulement continues par morceaux: nous traduirons ceci en disant que la variété est C^2, C^4 *par morceaux*.

Sur V_4 est définie une métrique riemannienne ds^2 de type hyperbolique normal à un carré positif et trois carrés négatifs. L'expression locale de cette métrique, dans un système de coordonnées admissibles est:

$$ds^2 = g_{\alpha\beta} dx^\alpha dx^\beta \qquad (\alpha, \beta \text{ et tout indice grec} = 0, 1, 2, 3).$$

Le "tenseur de gravitation" $g_{\alpha\beta}$ est supposé C^1, C^3 par morceaux ce qui est strictement compatible avec la structure imposée à V_4. Toute précision supplémentaire de la structure différentiable de la variété ou de la métrique doit être considérée comme dépourvue de sens physique: on montre d'ailleurs que les équations d'Einstein ne peuvent avoir de solutions, même faibles (dans le cadre de la théorie des distributions de Schwartz) discontinues à la traversée d'une hypersurface non caractéristique.

La métrique ds^2, hyperbolique normale, admet en chaque point la décomposition:

$$ds^2 = (\omega_0)^2 - \sum_{i=1}^{3} (\omega_i)^2$$

où les ω_α sont des formes linéaires des différentielles des coordonnées. A cette décomposition corespond un système de quatre vecteurs $\mathbf{e}_\alpha$ tangents à la variété V_4, orthogonaux et de longueur ± 1 au sens de la métrique (repère lorentzien). L'équation $ds^2 = 0$ définit en chaque point un cône réel C_x, le *cône élémentaire* ou *isotrope* en ce point. Une direction dx tangente en x à V_4 est orientée dans le temps si elle est intérieure à C_x ($g_{\alpha\beta} dx^\alpha dx^\beta > 0$), orientée dans l'espace dans le cas contraire.

Un système de coordonnées locales est admissible si une des variables, soit x^0, est temporelle et les trois autres spatiales: la ligne x^i = const (i et tout indice latin = 1, 2, 3) est temporelle. On a alors $g_{00} > 0$ et les formes quadratiques duales

$$\hat{g}_{ij} = g_{ij} - \frac{g_{0i}g_{0j}}{g_{00}}, \qquad \hat{g}^{ij} = g^{ij}$$

sont définies négatives. La métrique associée à $\hat{g}_{ij}$ sera désignée par $d\hat{s}^2$.

2. *Topologie de V_4*: la variété V_4, admettant une métrique hyperbolique, possède un champ de vecteurs partout orienté dans le temps: elle admet donc un système global de lignes de temps, mais généralement n'admet pas de système global d'hypersurfaces orientées dans l'espace. En fait on suppose fréquemment, dans les problèmes globaux, que V_4 est topologiquement le produit d'une variété V_3 par la droite réelle R. Les sections d'espace, correspondant à V_3 sont généralement, soit des variétés closes, soit des variétés riemanniennes complètes pour la métrique $d\hat{s}^2$.

Dans le cas où V_4 admet un domaine à l'infini on suppose généralement que la métrique admet un „comportement asymptotique minkowskien" à l'infini [13].

Toutes ces hypothèses ne s'imposent pas a priori et ne peuvent être justifiées que par des considérations physiques, avec recours possible à l'expérience, ou mathématiques, pour assurer l'existence ou l'unicité des solutions.

3. *Structure des équations d'Einstein.* Dans la relativité générale la métrique ds^2 satisfait aux équations d'Einstein:

$$S_{\alpha\beta} = R_{\alpha\beta} - \tfrac{1}{2}g_{\alpha\beta}R = \chi T_{\alpha\beta} \qquad (\alpha, \beta = 0, 1, 2, 3) \tag{3-1}$$

où $R_{\alpha\beta}$ est le tenseur de Ricci associé au ds^2, χ une constante; $T_{\alpha\beta}$ est le tenseur d'impulsion énergie; il définit les sources du champ et satisfait aux conditions de conservation

$$\nabla_\alpha T^{\alpha\beta} = 0, \tag{3-2}$$

conséquences des identités de Bianchi $\nabla_\alpha S^{\alpha\beta} \equiv 0$. $T_{\alpha\beta}$ est continu par morceaux; dans les régions où $T_{\alpha\beta} = 0$ on a le cas „extérieur", dans les autres le cas „intérieur".

Soit Σ une hypersurface locale de V_4 qui n'est pas tangente aux cônes $ds^2 = 0$. Si $x^0 = 0$ définit Σ localement on a, sur Σ, $g^{00} \neq 0$. Les équations d'Einstein peuvent s'écrire [10]:

$$R_{ij} \equiv \tfrac{1}{2}g^{00}\partial_{00}g_{ij} + F_{ij} = \chi(T_{ij} - \tfrac{1}{2}g_{ij}T); \qquad (i, j = 1, 2, 3), \tag{3-3}$$

$$S^0_\alpha \equiv G_\alpha = \chi T^0_\alpha; \tag{3-4}$$

où F_{ij} et G_α sont des fonctions connues sur Σ si l'on connait les valeurs des $g_{\alpha\beta}$ et de leurs dérivées premières ("données de Cauchy"). Les équations (3–4) relient les données de Cauchy aux sources. Les équations (3–3) donnent les valeurs sur Σ des six dérivées secondes $\partial_{00} g_{ij}$ (dérivées "significatives"). Les quatres autres dérivées secondes restent inconnues et peuvent être discontinues sur Σ (même avec $T_{\alpha\beta}$ continue) mais de telles discontinuités sont dépourvues de signification physique et peuvent être annulées par un changement de coordonnées compatible avec la structure différentiable de V_4: la liaison entre nos hypothèses sur cette structure et la covariance du formalisme apparaît ici [10].

Dans le cas extérieur on voit sur les équations (3–3) que les dérivées significatives sur Σ peuvent être discontinues seulement si Σ est tangente au cône élémentaire. Les fronts d'onde gravitationnelle sont donc les hypersurfaces tangentes en chacun de leurs points à ce cône.

Dans le cas intérieur hydrodynamique les variétés exceptionnelles sont les mêmes fronts d'onde gravitationnelle, les variétés engendrées par les lignes de courant et les fronts d'onde hydrodynamique.

Ou déduit, d'autre part, des conditions de conservation le caractère involutif du système des équations d'Einstein: si une métrique satisfait (3–3) et, sur Σ seulement (3–4), elle satisfait aussi à ces équations en dehors de Σ. Ainsi l'intégration des équations d'Einstein conduit à deux problèmes différents:

I. Recherche de données de Cauchy satisfaisant au système

$$S_\alpha^\beta \partial_\beta f = \chi T_\alpha^\beta \partial_\beta f \quad \text{sur } \Sigma \quad (f = 0):$$

c'est le *problème des conditions initiales* [10].

II. *Problème d'évolution* ou problème de Cauchy: intégration, avec les données de Cauchy satisfaisant sur Σ aux conditions du premier problème, du système

$$S_{\alpha\beta} = \chi T_{\alpha\beta};$$

$$\nabla_\alpha T^{\alpha\beta} = 0.$$

II. EXISTENCE ET UNICITÉ POUR LE PROBLÈME D'ÉVOLUTION

4. *Coordonnées isothermes.* Une famille d'hypersurfaces locales d'équation $f =$ const est dite *isotherme* si f est harmonique dans la métrique ds^2, c'est à dire si

$$\Delta f = 0;$$

un système de coordonnées (x^ϱ) locales est isotherme si les

$$F^\varrho = \Delta x^\varrho = -g^{\lambda\mu}\Gamma^\varrho_{\lambda\mu}$$

sont nuls pour tout ϱ.

Les quantités F^ϱ interviennent d'une manière simple dans l'expression du tenseur de Ricci. On a identiquement

$$R_{\alpha\beta} = R^{(i)}_{\alpha\beta} + L_{\alpha\beta}$$

avec

$$R^{(i)}_{\alpha\beta} \equiv -\tfrac{1}{2}g^{\lambda\mu}\partial_{\lambda\mu}g_{\alpha\beta} + f_{\alpha\beta}(g_{\lambda\mu}, \partial_\gamma g_{\lambda\mu});$$

$$L_{\alpha\beta} \equiv -\tfrac{1}{2}g_{\alpha\mu}\partial_\beta F^\mu - \tfrac{1}{2}g_{\beta\mu}\partial_\alpha F^\mu.$$

Nous résoudrons le problème de Cauchy pour le système d'équations

$$R^{(i)}_{\alpha\beta} = \chi(T_{\alpha\beta} - \tfrac{1}{2}g_{\alpha\beta}T); \qquad (4\text{–}1)$$

$$\nabla_\alpha T^{\alpha\beta} = 0. \qquad (4\text{–}2)$$

Si les données de Cauchy vérifient sur Σ $(x^0 = 0)$ les conditions nécessaires

$$S^0_\alpha = \chi T^0_\alpha \qquad (4\text{–}3)$$

et les conditions d'isothermie initiale:

$$F^\mu = 0 \qquad (4\text{–}4)$$

on constate qu'elles vérifient aussi sur Σ:

$$\partial_0 F^\mu = 0. \qquad (4\text{–}5)$$

La solution correspondante $g_{\alpha\beta}$ des équations (4–1) (4–2) vérifie alors les équations tensorielles

$$R_{\alpha\beta} = \chi(T_{\alpha\beta} - \tfrac{1}{2}g_{\alpha\beta}T),$$

$$\nabla_\alpha T^{\alpha\beta} = 0.$$

Construisons en effet le tenseur $S_{\alpha\beta} \equiv R_{\alpha\beta} - \frac{1}{2}g_{\alpha\beta}R$ relatif à cette solution. Il vérifie les identités $\nabla_\alpha S^{\alpha\beta} \equiv 0$; $g_{\alpha\beta}$ vérifie donc, compte tenu de (4–1), (4–2) les équations

$$\nabla_\alpha(L^{\alpha\beta} - \tfrac{1}{2}g_{\alpha\beta}L) = 0,$$

qui s'écrivent

$$\tfrac{1}{2}g^{\alpha\lambda}\partial_{\alpha\lambda}F^\mu + P^\mu(\partial_\alpha F^\lambda) = 0, \qquad (4\text{–}6)$$

[redacted]

[redacted]

système d'équations du second ordre hyperbolique pour les inconnues F^μ, pour lequel est valable un théorème d'unicité [3] d'où, d'après (4-4), (4-5),

$$F^\lambda = 0$$

dans le domaine d'existence de la solution $g_{\alpha\beta}$.

5. *Solution élémentaire d'un système d'équations hyperboliques du second ordre. Problème d'évolution cas extérieur.* Les équations (4–6) et les équations d'Einstein du cas extérieur en coordonnées isothermes, ont la forme:

$$A^{\lambda\mu}\partial_{\lambda\mu}W_S + f_S = 0, \qquad S = 1, 2, \ldots, N \text{ (pair)} \tag{5-1}$$

où les W sont des fonctions inconnues de 4 variables indépendantes x^α, les $A^{\lambda\mu}$ et f_S des fonctions données des W_R, $\partial_\alpha W_R$ et des x^α, la forme quadratique $A^{\lambda\mu}x_\lambda x_\mu$ étant du type hyperbolique normal. La résolution du problème de Cauchy pour un tel système peut se faire par approximations successives à partir de la résolution du même problème pour les équations linéaires obtenues en remplaçant, dans les coefficients, les inconnues par leur valeur obtenue à l'approximation précédente.

La résolution du système d'équations linéaires du type (5–1) est donnée par sa solution élémentaire, $E(x, x')$, matrice $N\times N$ dont les éléments sont des distributions au sens de Schwartz, dépendant du point x où elle est calculée et d'un point courant x'. Le support de $E(x, x')$ si x est fixé, est la surface et l'intérieur du demi-conoïde caractéristique rétrograde Γ_x engendré par les géodésiques de longueur nulle (rayons lumineux) aboutissant en x. On obtient ainsi, sous de simples hypothèses de différentiabilité, une solution du problème d'évolution pour les équations d'Einstein ne dépendant en un point x que des donnés de Cauchy intérieures à Γ_x. On montre que cette solution est physiquement unique (c'est à dire unique à un changement de coordonnées près) [3].

6. *Le cas intérieur.* Dans le cas "matière pure" $T_{\alpha\beta} = \varrho u_\alpha u_\beta$ (ϱ densité, u_α vitesse unitaire) ou "fluide parfait" $T_{\alpha\beta} = (\varrho + p)u_\alpha u_\beta - p g_{\alpha\beta}$ (p pression relié à ϱ par une équation d'état $\varrho = \varrho(p)$) on obtient encore un théorème d'existence local, sous de simples hypothèses de différentibilité, pour le problème d'évolution de l'ensemble des inconnues $g_{\alpha\beta}$, ϱ, p, u_α. Le domaine de dépendance de la solution en un point x est toujours le demi-conoïde lumineux rétrograde de sommet x. Dans le cas où interviennent des phénomènes de dissipation (échanges thermodynamiques, fluides visqueux) il n'a

pas été possible d'obtenir un tel théorème, qui serait pourtant bien en accord avec la conception déterministe de la relativité générale.

Pour démontrer l'existence d'une solution du problème d'évolution à l'intérieur d'une matière incohérente (matière pure) ou d'un fluide parfait adiabatique on utilise les coordonnées isothermes et les théorèmes généraux de J. Leray sur les systèmes hyperboliques [9].

Dans le cas matière pure les conditions de conservation sont équivalentes à

$$u^\alpha \nabla_\alpha u_\beta = 0, \qquad \nabla_\alpha(\varrho u^\alpha) = 0; \tag{6–1}$$

on montre directement que le système des équations

$$S^{(i)}_{\alpha\beta} = \varkappa T_{\alpha\beta} \tag{6–2}$$

et des équations (6–1) est hyperbolique au sens de Leray. Dans le cas fluide parfait on démontre l'hyperbolicité par l'intermédiaire d'équations donnant l'évolution de "tourbillons" et de relations liant les tourbillons aux vitesses dont les caractéristiques sont les fronts d'onde hydrodynamique. Les conditions de conservation sont en effet équivalentes à

$$\nabla_\alpha[(\varrho+p)u^\alpha] - u^\alpha\partial_\alpha p = 0, \quad \text{équation de continuité,} \tag{6–3}$$

$$u^\alpha \nabla_\alpha u_\beta - \frac{\partial_\alpha p}{\varrho+p}(g^\alpha_\beta - u^\alpha u_\beta) = 0, \quad \text{équations du mouvement,} \tag{6–4}$$

Posons $f = \exp \int\limits_{p_0}^{p} \frac{dp}{\varrho+p}$ (indice du fluide), $C_\alpha = f u_\alpha$ et définissons le tourbillon $\Omega_{\alpha\beta}$ comme rotationnel de la pseudo-vitesse C_α [12] (voir aussi [19])

$$\Omega_{\alpha\beta} = \partial_\alpha C_\beta - \partial_\beta C_\alpha. \tag{6–5}$$

Les équations (6–3), (6–4) s'écrivent alors:

$$C^\alpha \Omega_{\alpha\beta} = 0, \qquad \nabla_\alpha C^\alpha = -C^\alpha \partial_\alpha \log[f^{-2}(\varrho+p)].$$

Des premières, et du fait que la différentielle de la forme extérieure $\Omega_{\alpha\beta}dx^\alpha \wedge dx^\beta$ est nulle on déduit les équations de Helmholtz relativistes donnant l'évolution des tourbillons

$$C^\alpha \nabla_\alpha \Omega_{\beta\gamma} = \Omega_{\alpha\beta}\nabla_\gamma C^\alpha + \Omega_{\gamma\alpha}\nabla_\beta C^\alpha; \tag{6–6}$$

de la dernière, et de l'expression (6–4) de $\Omega_{\alpha\beta}$ on tire les relations entre tourbillons et vitesses [6]

$$\{g^{\alpha\beta} + 2C^\alpha C^\beta \Phi'\}\nabla_\alpha\nabla_\beta C_\gamma + 2C^\alpha\Phi'\{\nabla_\beta C_\gamma \nabla_\alpha C^\beta + \nabla_\gamma C^\beta \nabla_\beta C_\alpha\} +$$
$$+ 4\Phi'' C^\alpha C^\beta \nabla_\gamma C_\beta C^\lambda \nabla_\alpha C_\lambda + R^\alpha_\gamma C_\alpha - \nabla_\alpha \Omega^\alpha_\gamma = 0 \tag{6–7}$$

où Φ est une fonction déterminé par l'équation d'état

$$\Phi(f^2) = \operatorname{Log}[f^{-2}(\varrho+p)], \qquad \Phi' = 2\left(\frac{d\varrho}{dp}-1\right)f^{-2}.$$

Les termes du second ordre des équations (6–6) déterminent le cône des ondes hydrodynamiques, dual du cône

$$\{g^{\alpha\beta}+2c^\alpha c^\beta \Phi'\}\chi_\alpha\chi_\beta \equiv \left\{g^{\alpha\beta}+u^\alpha u^\beta\left(\frac{d\varrho}{dp}-1\right)\right\}\chi_\alpha\chi_\beta$$

le carré de la vitesse de propagation de ces ondes est $dp/d\varrho$ si la vitesse de la lumière est prise pour unité. Le cône hydrodynamique est intérieur au cône de lumière si $dp/d\varrho < 1$. Si $dp/d\varrho = 1$ les deux cônes sont confondus, c'est le cas des fluides *incompressibles*.

Le système des équations (6–2), (6–6), (6–7) est un système hyperbolique au sens de Leray pour lequel le problème de Cauchy a une solution et une seule.

III. PROBLÈME DES CONDITIONS INITIALES

7. *Cas d'une hypersurface minima.* Soit Σ une hypersurface d'espace, d'équation locale $x^0 = 0$, prenons pour lignes de temps au voisinage de Σ des courbes orthogonales à Σ. Le ds^2 prend la forme:

$$ds^2 = V^2(dx^0)^2 + g_{ij}dx^i dx^j \qquad (i, j = 1, 2, 3).$$

Posons

$$\Omega_{ij} = \tfrac{1}{2}\partial_0 g_{ij}, \qquad K = \Omega_i^i, \qquad H^2 = \Omega_{ij}\Omega^{ij};$$

dans le cas extérieur, pour Σ minima, les conditions initiales s'écrivent:

$$\bar{\nabla}_j\Omega^{ij} = 0, \qquad \bar{R}+H^2 = 0, \qquad K = 0$$

où $\bar{\nabla}$ est l'opérateur de dérivation covariante et $\bar{R}$ la courbure scalaire de Σ. Si on pose

$$g_{ij} = \exp(2\theta)g^*_{ij}$$

et qu'on suppose la métrique $ds^{*2} = g^*_{ij}dx^i dx^j$ connue sur Σ on peut introduire les fonctions:

$$\varphi^2 = e^\theta, \qquad \pi^{ij} = e^{5\theta}\Omega^{ij}, \qquad L^2 = g^*_{ik}g^*_{jl}\pi^{ij}\pi^{kl};$$

on trouve pour ces fonctions le système simple, linéaire

$$g^*_{ij}\pi^{ij} = 0, \qquad \nabla^*_j \pi^{ij} = 0$$

et l'équation elliptique

$$-8\Delta^*_2\varphi + R^*_2\varphi = -\frac{L^2}{\varphi^7}. \tag{7-1}$$

Le problème de Dirichlet pour (7–1) admet une solution si le domaine de Σ est suffisamment petit, ou si L^2 est petit et $R^* \leqslant 0$. Cette étude peut être étendue à certains cas intérieurs hydrodynamiques: on montre précisément que les sections d'espace orthogonales aux lignes de courant d'un fluide parfait en mouvement irrotationnel sont minima dans la métrique d'espace temps. Il est ainsi possible de construire des exemples de données de Cauchy correspondant au mouvement des corps. Pour le problème des deux corps on obtient en première approximation la loi de Newton [11].

8. *Cas général*. Prenons en chaque point de Σ (hypersurface d'espace d'équation locale $x^0 = 0$) un repère orthonormé dont le vecteur e_0 soit orthogonal à l'hypersurface initiale. La métrique ds^2 s'écrit $ds^2 = \Sigma\omega_a^2$ avec

$$\omega_0 = V\,dx^0$$

$$\omega_i = a_{ij}\,dx^j + \lambda_i\,dx^0$$

les équations du problème des conditions initiales s'écrivent alors:

$$S_{0k} = \overline{\nabla}_h P_{hk} - \overline{\nabla}_k P,$$

$$S_{00} = \bar{R} + H^2 - P^2, \qquad P = P_{hh}, \qquad H^2 = P_{hk}P_{hk}$$

où $\overline{\nabla}$ désigne une dérivée covariante dans la métrique $\overline{ds}^2 = \sum_i a_{ij}a_{ik}\,dx^j\,dx^k$ de Σ et où les P_{hk} sont les coefficients de la deuxième forme quadratique fondamentale de Σ par rapport à l'espace temps. Dans des coordonnées orthogonales $P_{hk} = \frac{1}{2V}\,\partial_0 g_{hk} = \frac{1}{V}\Omega_{hk}$.

Prenons pour repère en un point de Σ trois vecteurs propres du tenseur P_{hk}, alors:

$$P_{hk} = 0 \quad \text{pour} \quad h \neq k.$$

Posons encore

$$\overline{ds}^2 = e^{2\theta} ds^{*2}$$

où ds^{*2} est une métrique donnée. Les inconnues θ, P_{11}, P_{22}, P_{33} satisfont dans le cas extérieur au système

$$-4\Delta_2^*\theta - 2(\partial_i^*\theta)^2 + Le^{2\theta} + R^* = 0, \tag{8-1}$$

$$\partial_1^* u_1 - \partial_1^*\theta(u_2 + u_3 - 2u_1) - \gamma_{1kk}^* u_1 = 0 \tag{8-2}$$

et à deux autres équations déduites de la précédente par permutation circulaire des indices 1, 2, 3 (on a posé $u_1 = P_{22} + P_{33}$, $L = H^2 - P^2$, Δ_2^* est l'opérateur de Beltrami du second ordre dans la métrique ds^{*2}).

Les équations (8–1), (8–2) sont linéaires par rapport aux dérivées d'ordre le plus élevé. On peut en obtenir la solution rigoureuse, dans un domaine suffisamment petit de Σ à partir des données de θ sur la frontière (à deux dimensions) du domaine et des u sur une partie de cette frontière: la méthode consiste à transformer, en utilisant la fonction de Green, le système (8–1), (8–2) en un système d'équations intégrales que l'on résoud par approximations successives. On peut obtenir dans certains cas, des solutions sans restriction sur la dimension du domaine [4].

9. *Méthode des coordonnées isothermes.* Nous avons vu en II que le système des conditions initiales $S_\alpha^0 = 0$ sur Σ ($x^0 = 0$) jointes à la condition $F^\mu = 0$ entrainait, pour toute solution des équations $R_{\alpha\beta}^{(i)} = 0$, $\partial_0 F^\mu = 0$ sur Σ. Ceci suggère de prendre, pour conditions initiales, les équations $F^\mu = 0$ et celles obtenues par élimination des dérivées secondes par rapport à x^0 entre $R_{\alpha\beta}^{(i)} = 0$ et $\partial_0 F^\mu = 0$. Toute solution de $R_{\alpha\beta}^{(i)} = 0$ vérifiera alors, sur Σ, $F^\mu = 0$ et $\partial_0 F^\mu = 0$ donc vérifiera partout $F^\mu = 0$ et les équations tensorielles d'Einstein, en particulier les conditions initiales primitives.

Prenons pour inconnues les densités tensorielles $G^{\alpha\beta} = \sqrt{-g}\, g^{\alpha\beta}$, les équations $F^\mu = 0$, $\partial_0 F^\mu = 0$ s'écrivent alors, sur Σ:

$$\left.\begin{aligned} &\partial_\lambda G^{\lambda\mu} = 0, &(9\text{-}1)\\ &\partial_0(\partial_\lambda G^{\lambda\mu}) = 0, &(9\text{-}2) \end{aligned}\right\} \text{pour } x^0 = 0.$$

Pour satisfaire à (9–1) on peut prendre arbitrairement, sur Σ, $G^{i\mu}$. Les $\partial_0 G^{0\mu}$ sont alors déterminés.

On trouve, d'autre part, dans le cas extérieur:

$$S_{(i)}^{\alpha\beta} \equiv \frac{1}{2\sqrt{-g}}(g^{\lambda\mu}\partial_{\lambda\mu}G^{\alpha\beta} + H^{\alpha\beta}) = 0 \tag{9-3}$$

où $H^{\alpha\beta}$ ne contient les dérivées des inconnues que d'ordre $\leqslant 1$.

L'élimination des $\partial_{00}G^{0\mu}$ entre les équations (9–2) et (9–3) donne les équations du problème des conditions initiales pour les inconnues restantes G^{00} et $\partial_0 G^{ij}$.

On trouve, sur Σ ($x^0 = 0$):

$$\Delta G^{00} = A, \qquad A \equiv g^{00}\partial_{0i}G^{i0} - 2g^{i0}\partial_{i0}G^{00} - H^{00}; \tag{9–4}$$

$$g^{00}\partial_{i0}G^{ij} = g^{00}B^j, \qquad g^{00}B^i \equiv 2g^{j0}\partial_{j0}G^{0i} + \Delta G^{0i} + H^{0i}. \tag{9–5}$$

Nous poserons sur Σ:

$$\partial_0 G^{ij} = g^{jk}\frac{\partial V^i}{\partial x^k} + Q^{ij} \tag{9–6}$$

où les V^i sont des fonctions satisfaisant à

$$\Delta V^i = B^i - \partial_k V^i \partial_j g^{jk}.$$

Les équations (9–4) et (9–5) sont un système elliptique quasi linéaire pour les inconnues G^{00}, V^i que l'on peut résoudre par approximations successives dans un domaine convenable avec des données frontières régulières. Il correspondra à ces fonctions G^{00}, V^i une solution du problème des conditions initiales si les Q^{ij} sont tels que

1° $\partial_j Q^{ij} = 0$: la solution générale de ces équations est donnée localement par la formule classique de l'analyse vectorielle à trois dimensions (Q^{ij} j^{eme} composante du rotationnel d'un vecteur arbitraire $\boldsymbol{u}^{(i)}$)

2° le deuxième membre de (9–6) est symétrique en i et j: cette condition s'exprime, V^i étant donné, par trois équations du premier ordre pour les composantes des $\boldsymbol{u}^{(i)}$. Leur écriture montre qu'on peut choisir arbitrairement six d'entre elles, les trois autres sont déterminées par une quadrature [5].

IV. MODÈLES D'UNIVERS ET PROBLÈMES GLOBAUX

10. *Solutions globales.* Résoudre un problème de mécanique relativiste c'est lui faire correspondre une métrique regulière solution des équations d'Einstein sur une variété V_4. Si $T_{\alpha\beta}$ est discontinu à travers une hypersurface Σ ($f = 0$) nous supposerons toujours que le ds^2 est C^1, C^3 par morceaux dans le voisinage de Σ. Le raccordement des différents champs intérieurs et du champs extérieur cause l'interdépendance des mouvements. Les classiques équa-

tions du mouvement sont dues à la continuité à travers Σ des quatre quantités [10], [1]

$$V_\alpha = S_\alpha^\beta \partial_\beta f.$$

Dans le cas où V_4 est borné, ou admet un domaine à l'infini, les conditions aux limites imposées à la métrique doivent être précisées.

Le problème que nous avons à résoudre est donc l'intégration globale, avec conditions de régularité et conditions aux limites, d'un système d'équations aux dérivées partielles non linéaires: la solution générale est hors de notre portée pour l'instant. Il semble donc important de construire et d'étudier des modèles dont on peut a posteriori (comme en hydrodynamique) chercher l'interprétation physique.

11. *Problèmes globaux.* La cohérence interne de la théorie et la recherche de solutions globales générales conduisent à l'étude de théorèmes globaux d'existence et d'unicité. En particulier se posent les deux problèmes fondamentaux [10]:

A. Est-il possible d'introduire dans un univers de nouvelles distributions d'énergie, telles que leur champ intérieur soit compatible avec le champ extérieur préexistant?

B. Si un modèle d'univers est extérieur et régulier partout (donc vide) est-il localement euclidien?

Des réponses satisfaisantes à ces questions ne sont connues que dans le cas stationnaire. Rappelons brièvement les résultats obtenus (la régularité est celle définie en I) [10], [2], [13], [14].

(1) Un champ extérieur stationnaire régulier partout est localement euclidien si $V_4 = V_3 \times R$ et si

(*a*) V_3 est compacte,

(*b*) V_3 est complète et admet un comportement asymptotique minkowskien.

(2) Dans un univers stationnaire le champ extérieur étendu, avec continuité des dérivées secondes, à l'intérieur des masses, est singulier dans cet intérieur.

(3) Un univers stationnaire qui admet un domaine à l'infini, et dans ce domaine un comportement asymptotique minkowskien, et pour lequel les lignes de courant sont les lignes de temps, est statique. Il existe des sections d'espace orthogonales aux lignes de temps. Ceci conduit à une réduction des hypothèses nécessaires à la construction du ds^2 de Schwarzschild.

M. Avez a recemment étendu le résultat (1) (a) à un espace temps périodique. Des recherches dans cette voie ont été faites également par Papapetrou.

V. EQUATIONS DE MAXWELL–EINSTEIN ET THÉORIES UNITAIRES

12. La plupart des résultats précédents s'étendent sans difficulté au cas où il existe un champ électromagnétique, que l'on prenne les équations "primitives" de l'électromagnétisme relativiste (équations de Maxwell–Einstein) ou celles de la théorie unitaire pentadimensionnelle de Jordan–Thiry. Le potentiel électromagnétique joue dans les équations, un rôle tout à fait analogue aux potentiels de gravitation, la condition usuelle de normalisation de Lorentz tient la place d'une condition d'isothermie.

Dans la théorie unitaire asymétrique d'Einstein–Schrödinger l'étude du problème de Cauchy permet encore de montrer le caractère involutif du système des équations et de mettre en évidence les caractéristiques (tangentes en chaque point à l'un ou l'autre de trois cônes du second ordre) [15], [17].

VI. PROPAGATEURS ET QUANTIFICATION

13. Un problème essentiel pour la quantification du champ électromagnétique dans un espace temps riemannien et pour la quantification du champ de gravitation lui-même, est la construction de propagateurs tensoriels généralisant le propagateur défini par Jordan et Pauli dans l'espace-temps de Minkowski.

Sur une variété riemannienne V_4 de métrique hyperbolique normale $(g_{\alpha\beta})$ on est amené à introduire des propagateurs tensoriels: $G^{(p)}(x, x')$ sera une bi-p-forme extérieure $(0 \leqslant p \leqslant 4)$ dont les composantes sont des tenseurs antisymétriques d'ordre p en x et des tenseurs antisymétriques d'ordre p en x', à valeurs distributions (au sens de Schwartz). Ces propagateurs sont antisymétriques en x et x', ont pour support les conoïdes isotropes et leur intérieur et vérifient

$$\Delta' G^{(p)}(x, x') = 0 \tag{13–1}$$

où Δ' est l'opérateur laplacien de G. de Rham dans la métrique $(g_{\alpha\beta})$, par rapport au point x' $(\Delta' = d'\delta' + \delta' d'$; d différentiation extérieur, δ codifférentiation) [16], [23].

Pour les composantes de $G^{(p)}$, les équations (13–1) sont un système hyperbolique linéaire du second ordre, du type étudié en (II–4). Ces équations admettent une solution élémentaire, définissant une bi-p-forme $G^{(p)-}(x, x')$ dont le support est la surface et l'intérieur du demi-conoïde rétrograde, elles admettent aussi une solution élémentaire $G^{(p)+}(x, x')$ dont le support est la surface et l'intérieur du demi-conoïde direct. Δ' étant autoadjoint on montre que

$$G^{(p)+}(x, x') = G^{(p)-}(x', x).$$

La différence $G^{(p)} = G^{(p)+} - G^{(p)-}$ est une solution des équations (13–1) correspondant aux conditions requises. Ce sera par définition le propagateur d'ordre p.

14. *Relations entre les propagateurs des divers ordres.* Les bi-p-formes $G^{(p)\pm}$ vérifient

$$\Delta' G^{(p)\pm} = D^{(p)}, \qquad D^{(p)} = t^{(p)}\bar{\delta}(x, x')$$

où $\bar{\delta}(x, x') = |g|^{-\frac{1}{2}}\delta(x, x')$, $\delta(x, x')$ étant la densité de Dirac de poids 1/2 en x, 1/2 en x' et où $t^{(p)}$ est une bi-p-forme dont les composantes ont pour valeur pour $x' = x$ celles du tenseur de Kronecker

$$\varepsilon_{\alpha_1 \dots \alpha_p, \lambda'_1 \dots \lambda'_p}.$$

On montre que

$$\delta' D^{(p)} = dD^{(p-1)}$$

or, puisque Δ' commute avec δ' et d:

$$\Delta'\delta' G^{(p)\pm} = \delta' D^{(p)}, \qquad \Delta' dG^{(p-1)\pm} = dD^{(p-1)}.$$

Donc

$$\Delta'(\delta' G^{(p)\pm} - dG^{(p-1)\pm}) = 0.$$

Mais une solution-distribution de l'équation homogène $\Delta' u = 0$ dont le support est dans un demi-conoïde est nécessairement nulle, d'où la relation

$$\delta' G^{p\pm} = dG^{(p-1)\pm}$$

et la relation entre propagateurs

$$\delta' G^{(p)} = dG^{(p-1)}.$$

L'égalité précédente permet de montrer la compatibilité avec les équations du champ électromagnétique en relativité générale des relations de commutation adoptées par l'un de nous [16] pour ce champ sur une variété riemannienne V_4:

$$[F(x), F(x')] = \left(\frac{\hbar}{i}\right) dd' G^{(1)}.$$

Des propagateurs tensoriels (symétriques dans ce cas) interviennent aussi dans la quantification du champ de gravitation et dans beaucoup de problèmes physiques.

BIBLIOGRAPHIE

[1] G. DARMOIS, Les équations de la gravitation einsteinienne, *Mem. Sci. Math.* 1927.
[2] A. EINSTEIN and W. PAULI, *Ann. Math.* **44**, 131–138 (1943).
[3] Y. FOURÈS-BRUHAT, *Acta Matem.* 1952, 141–225.
[4] Y. FOURÈS-BRUHAT, *J. Rat. Mech. Anal.* **5**, (1956.)
[5] Y. FOURÈS-BRUHAT, *C. R. Acad. Sci,. Paris* **245**, 1384–1386 (1957).
[6] Y. FOURÈS-BRUHAT, *Bull. Soc. Mat. France* **86**, 155–175 (1958).
[7] F. HENNEQUIN, *Bull. Sci. Canad. Hist.* **1**, 2-ème partie, Mathématiques p. 73–154 (1956).
[8] P. JORDAN, *Ann. Phys., Lpz.* 1947, p. 219.
[9] J. LERAY, *Hyperbolic differential equations*, Princeton, 1951–52.
[10] A. LICHNEROWICZ, *Problèmes globaux en mécanique relativiste*, Hermann, Paris 1939.
[11] A. LICHNEROWICZ, *J. Math. Pures Appl.* (9) **23**, 37–63 (1944).
[12] A. LICHNEROWICZ, *Ann. Sci. Éc. Norm. Sup., Paris* **8**, 285–304 (1941).
[13] A. LICHNEROWICZ, *C. R. Acad. Sci., Paris* **222**, 432–434 (1946).
[14] A. LICHNEROWICZ, *Théories relativistes de la gravitation et de l'électromagnétisme*, Masson, Paris, 1955.
[15] A. LICHNEROWICZ, *J. Rat. Mech. Anal.* **3**, 487–922 (1954).
[16] A. LICHNEROWICZ, *C. R. Acad. Sci., Paris* **249**, 1329–1331 (1959).
[17] F. MAURER-TISON, Thèse Sc. Math. Paris, 1957.
[18] PHAM-MAU QUAN, *Ann. Mat. Pura Appl.* (4) **38**, 121–204 (1955).
[19] J. L. SYNGE, *Proc. Lond. Math. Soc.* **43**, 376–416, (1937).
[20] J. L. SYNGE, *Relativity, The general theory*, Amsterdam, 1960.
[21] A. H. TAUB, *Illinois J. Math.*, 1957.
[22] Y. THIRY, *J. Math. Pures Appl.* (9) **30**, 375–96 (1951).
[23] B. DEWITT, *Phys. Rev. Letters*, **4**, 317 (1960).

SURVEY OF GRAVITATIONAL RADIATION THEORY

F. A. E. PIRANI

King's College, London

Abstract—A survey, to early 1960, of the *covariant* part of gravitational radiation theory, aimed at those with a working knowledge of general relativity. Approaches to gravitational radiation problems through weak field and other approximation methods and through the use of special coordinate conditions are not discussed. Most attention is given to (1) the theory of gravitational wave-fronts; (2) the algebraic and differential properties of the Riemann tensor and their implications for wave propagation; (3) exact vacuum metrics representing gravitational waves. It is to be concluded that the present theory gives a good understanding of wave propagation in a wide class of somewhat idealized situations, and some strong indications of the behaviour of actual gravitational radiation fields. The satisfactory development of the theory awaits the discovery of exact vacuum metrics representing radiation from isolated finite systems.

1. INTRODUCTION

THIS brief review is confined to a discussion of gravitational radiation within the framework of general relativity theory. On the whole, few technical details are given, and therefore the survey is not "elementary" in the sense of being technically selfcontained. The details may be found in the cited papers. Nor are any new results presented. The writer's intention is only to give some perspective of the subject from a particular point of view.

The study of gravitational radiation was initiated by Einstein [1] from the point of view of the weak field approximation. For two reasons, radiation will not be discussed here from this point of view or from any of those which developed out of it. One reason is mathematical: nobody knows whether the approximation methods developed up to now are convergent or not. The other reason is physical: all these methods depend to some extent on particular prescriptions of the metric or the coordinate system or both, and the physical significance of such prescriptions is not yet at all clear.

The Einstein–Infeld–Hoffmann method, which has proved its worth in the study of the problem of motion, does not come into question here, because it is designed for situations where the time rate of change of the gravitational field is small compared to the space rate of change, and of course this is not the case in the presence of radiation.

For the reasons given, it has proved very difficult to settle any arguments about gravitational radiation from the point of view of the approximation methods.(1) Therefore this survey is restricted to those aspects of the radiation theory which are independent of such methods. In the past few years there have been several developments of which this is true; those which will be mentioned particularly are:

the theory of gravitational *wave-fronts*,
the algebraical and differential properties of the *Riemann tensor*. and
the existence of *exact solutions* representing gravitational waves.

2. BASIC IDEAS

We begin with the point of view that the theory of gravitational radiation, like other parts of general relativity theory, must be formulated in a covariant way if it is to make any sense physically. This does not mean that one should never use a particular coordinate system in solving a particular problem — of course one should — but it does mean that the general formulation should not depend on a particular choice of coordinate system, nor on the use of a particular approximation procedure.

This demand for covariance leads one to the idea that the field quantities describing radiation should be covariant quantities. However, a difficulty soon presents itself. Starting from the metric tensor components, which may be regarded as the gravitational potentials, the first *covariant* quantities which one reaches by differentiation are the components of the Riemann curvature tensor, which depend on the *second* derivatives of the potentials. But in electromagnetic theory and other Lorentz-invariant field theories, through which the concept of radiation has become familiar, energy and momentum and other dynamical quantities are always defined

(1) *Note added in proof:* Recently Bondi [66] and his co–workers have developed approximation methods, involving expansion in negative powers of distance from a finite source, which are free from the objections raised above. Bondi's results accord beautifully with the Riemann tensor theory of propagation of radiation [67].

in terms of the *first* derivatives of the potentials. Therefore one cannot from this point of view expect all the familiar attributes of electromagnetic radiation to have analogues in the case of gravitational radiation. *Some* analogy has to be sought, because the concept of radiation is until now largely familiar through electromagnetic theory, and one cannot define gravitational radiation sensibly without some appeal to electromagnetic theory for guidance.

One should not expect, for example, to be able to deal very directly with the transfer of energy from the covariant point of view. Energy has been discussed extensively from the point of view of the various canonical formalisms. The expressions for energy which come out are, naturally, non-covariant expressions quadratic in the Christoffel symbols. One cannot regard such discussions as quite satisfactory, because of the lack of covariance. It is likely that such considerations can be thrown into covariant form, probably by the introduction of additional geometrical elements into Riemannian space-time.(1) It might be necessary to introduce a complete Vierbein field for this purpose, but it is more likely that for the discussion of energy alone a timelike vector field would suffice. Such a timelike vector field would represent a preferred class of observers, not necessarily a class introduced *a priori* into the space-time, but rather one defined intrinsically by a suitable mathematical and physical property (a discussion along these lines has been given recently by the writer [2]). A complete Vierbein field would no doubt be necessary for discussion of momentum transfer. A formulation in such terms if carried out intrinsically would have close connection with the formulation in terms of the Riemann tensor which is to be outlined here, because the differential properties of vector fields are related to the properties of the Riemann tensor.

From the physical point of view, the Riemann tensor might be called the "field variation" tensor. The way in which it characterizes variations in the gravitational field is seen most readily in the equation of geodesic deviation, which describes the relative accelerations of neighbouring particles (Pirani [3], [4]). Many other early ideas on the subject (cf. Pirani [5]) need revision, but the essential idea, which still stands, is that the Riemann tensor, which charac-

---

(1) *Note added in proof:* Some progress in this direction has been made by Arnowitt, Deser, and Misner in their series of papers on canonical formulations of gravitation theory in asymptotically flat spaces, with asymptotically rectangular coordinate systems. The geometrical significance of the conditions imposed by these authors is not, however, always entirely clear.

terizes variations in the gravitational field generally, in particular characterizes the presence of radiation.

Now consider a gravitational wave-front. Across a wave-front one expects, generally speaking, that some field quantities will be discontinuous. It is natural to suppose that across a gravitational wave-front, the Riemann tensor will be discontinuous. From this assumption, and from Einstein's field equations, it may be shown that a gravitational wave-front moves in vacuum with the fundamental velocity. That is, the characteristic hypersurfaces of the vacuum field equations are *null* hypersurfaces. These ideas will be discussed at greater length in the next section.

One naturally wishes to form some idea of how the Riemann tensor characterizes radiation fields of all kinds, not only in the special case of wave-fronts. Also one does not wish to consider only pure radiation fields, but also fields with sources. Here the analogy with the electromagnetic field is a helpful guide.

In the electromagnetic case, one may in the first place distinguish algebraically between null fields and non-null fields. A null field is characterized by $\boldsymbol{E}^2-\boldsymbol{H}^2=\boldsymbol{E}\cdot\boldsymbol{H}=0$ (that is,(1) by $F^{mn}F_{mn}=F^{mn}\varepsilon_{mnrs}F^{rs}=0$). The distinction is a purely algebraic one, depending on the values of the field strengths at a single space-time event. A null field, (for example a plane-wave field) represents pure radiation, without any Coulomb field being present (in discussing general ideas, let us disregard the exceptional case of crossed electric and magnetic fields of equal strength, which is not important and confuses the issue unnecessarily). The field of any system of charges, stationary or moving, is non-null. One cannot pick out the radiation part of the field of a system of accelerated charges in a Lorentz-invariant way by purely algebraical considerations on the field strengths. In order to make such distinctions one must in effect consider the space-dependence of the field:(2) for large $\boldsymbol{r}$ the radiation part goes like r^{-1}. Alternatively one may pick it out by considering the algebraical properties of the field strengths and their derivatives together, which amounts to the same thing.

In the case of vacuum gravitational fields one may, by local algebraic considerations, distinguish not two but three types of fields—Petrov's types I, II and III (Petrov [6](3)). This classification may

(1) Latin letters range and sum over 1, 2, 3, 4.

(2) The question of Lorentz-invariance of the concept for "large $\boldsymbol{r}$" does not arise because the radiating system automatically defines a standard of rest.

(3) It must be noted that the classification is purely local and it is possible for the type of the field to vary from one region to another in space-time.

be slightly refined, the first two types each being split into two; the five resulting types are denoted I, D (or I_e) II, N (or II_0), and III. This more refined language will be used throughout what follows. The hierarchy of specialization leading from type I, the most general, to 0 (denoting flat space-time) is conveniently indicated in a Penrose diagram (Penrose [7]):

$$\begin{array}{ccccc} & & \mathrm{I} & & \\ & \swarrow & \downarrow & & \\ & \mathrm{II} & \rightarrow & \mathrm{D} & \\ \swarrow & \downarrow & & \downarrow & \\ \mathrm{III} & \rightarrow & \mathrm{N} & \rightarrow & \mathrm{O} \end{array}$$

The details of this classification are given in Section 4. The greater richness of this classification, compared to the null–non-null dichotomy in the electromagnetic case, is of course explained mathematically by the greater complexity of the Riemann tensor. The algebraic distinction drawn originally (Pirani [5]) between types I and D representing no radiation, and types II, III, and N, representing radiation, is a rather crude one, corresponding to the distinction between non-null and null fields in the electromagnetic theory. A much more subtle analysis has been carried out by Sachs (Ehlers and Sachs [8], Sachs [9]), who reports part of his work in the present volume (see also Section 4 below).

The first Coulomb-like term in the Riemann tensor goes like r^{-3} (because it represents the variation in the field, not the field itself); such terms are typically of Petrov type D. The far radiation field is of type N, and goes like r^{-1}. Between these falls Sachs's "semi-far" field, which is of type III and goes like r^{-2}.

Sachs has given an extensive analysis of type D, II, III and N space-times. He has also discussed in the linear approximation a more general situation in which the field is linked explicitly to its sources.

Of course, all real fields must be of type I, just as all real electromagnetic fields are non-null. However, the analysis of the fields lower down the Penrose diagram is very valuable as a guide both to the structure of the gravitational radiation field generally and to the understanding of type I fields.

In this analysis, the consideration of particular examples, though it may smack slightly of botany, is also useful to fix one's ideas. The Schwarzschild field is of type D, while the axi-symmetric fields of Weyl and Levi-Cività, which appear to have been the next exact vacuum solutions to be discovered, are of type I. A type N field was probably first discovered by Brinkmann [10], but its discoverer was concerned with tensor-analytic characterization and it did not occur to him to identify his solution with radiation. A special case of this was rediscovered by Rosen [11], in a different coordinate system and identified as radiative, but rejected by physical arguments which later proved groundless. Brinkmann's solutions, now called "plane-fronted" waves (Robinson [12b]), were rediscovered independently by Robinson [12], who first gave them physical significance, and pointed out the position of the Rosen solution among them. They have now been classified in terms of their symmetry properties by Kundt [13]. Some of them were discovered independently by Petrov [14], who has also found some type III metrics, by Bondi [15], Peres [16], and others. Exact solutions of types N are discussed in Section 5.

An interesting class of solutions of various types, representing radiation expanding from a finite source distribution (but apparently containing a line singularity leading from the source to infinity) has recently been discovered by Robinson and Trautman [17] (see Section 5).

3. GRAVITATIONAL WAVE-FRONTS

The first discussion of Einstein's field equations from the point of view of the theory of characteristics appears to have been that by Vessiot [18]. An important paper is that by Stellmacher [19], who showed that the characteristics were null hypersurfaces, and derived the algebraic form of discontinuities in the second derivatives $g_{mn,rs}$ of the metric tensor and an equation for their propagation along a bicharacteristic (namely, a null geodesic). Stellmacher's work was overlooked, and the theory of discontinuities was later reinvestigated independently by Finzi [20], Trautman [21], [22], [23], Lichnerowicz [24], Bel [25] and the writer [5]. The work of the last five authors named begins from the discussion of differentiability properties of the metric (namely g_{rs} to be C^1, piecewise C^3) in Lichnerowicz's book [26] (referred to below as "Lichnerowicz's conditions"), and is formulated entirely in terms of the Riemann tensor. Stellmacher's work was subsequently rediscovered, and reformulated in the same covariant way by Treder [27], who also with Papapetrou [28], developed the consequences of some weaker differentiability assumptions (namely g_{rs} to be C^0, piecewise C^2).

The main results of the theory of discontinuities which are of interest in discussing gravitational wave-fronts are the following (and here all attempts at attribution of priority are given up):

The characteristics of Einstein's field equations are null hypersurfaces, and the bicharacteristics are null geodesics lying in these hypersurfaces. Let $[F]$ denote the discontinuity in any function $F(s)$ across a hypersurface S: $\varphi(x^m) = 0$. Then Lichnerowicz's conditions and a convenient, but not important, restriction of the coordinate system, require $[g_{mn}] = [g_{mn,r}] = 0$, $[g_{mn,rs}] = h_{mn}\varphi_{,r}\varphi_{,s}$, where h_{mn} is a tensor on S (and the comma denotes partial differentiation). Hence $[R_{mnrs}] = -\frac{1}{2}\delta^{pq}_{mn}\delta^{tu}_{rs}h_{pt}\varphi_{,q}\varphi_{,u}$. If the matter tensor is continuous across S: $[T_{rs}] = 0$, then $[R^s{}_{nrs}] = 0$, which implies that $[R_{mnrs}] = 0$ unless S is null. If S is null, then $h_{mn} = \sigma(v_m v_n - w_m w_n)$ where σ is a scalar on S and v_m and w_m are vectors on S, orthogonal to $\varphi_{,m}$ and to each other. Moreover, $[R_{mn[rs}\varphi_{,t]}] = [R^m{}_{nrs}\varphi_{,m}] = 0$. Along a bicharacteristic, $dx^m/du = g^{mn}\varphi_{,m}$ and $[R_{mnrs}]$ is propagated according to $\frac{\delta}{\delta s}[R_{mnrs}]+\frac{1}{2}[R_{mnrs}]\,\Box\varphi = 0$, where $\frac{\delta}{\delta s}$ denotes the absolute derivative and $\Box$ the covariant d'Alembertian. If S is a spherical shell expanding from the centre of a Schwarzschild space-time, then in a set of frames of reference representing observers at rest relative to the central mass, the physical components (Vierbein components) of $[R_{mnrs}]$ decrease like r^{-1}.

These results have been extended to the case where an electromagnetic field is present, and, as mentioned above, to the case $[g_{mn,r}] \neq 0$.

The scalar σ represents, roughly speaking, the strength of the discontinuity. However, at a given space-time point it may be given an arbitrary non-zero value by a local Lorentz transformation in the 2-space (containing $\varphi_{,m}$) orthogonal to $v_{[m}w_{n]}$. For a system of observers with definite velocities, σ is well-defined. The vectors v_m and w_n determine the polarization of the radiation. The form of the discontinuity is precisely the same as the form of a type N field. In fact, in a type N field whose field of propagation vectors k_m (the vectors corresponding to $\varphi_{,m}$) is hypersurface-orthogonal, all the equations for $[R_{mnrs}]$ given above will hold for R_{mnrs} itself, and all except the propagation equation (in which an additional term must be included) hold whether or not the propagation vector field is hypersurface-orthogonal.

A visual representation of the Riemann tensor which takes full advantage of its symmetry properties and gives some ready insight into its local character is provided by the six-dimensional notation.

In this notation, each skewsymmetric index pair mn is replaced by a single index M running from 1 to 6, according to the scheme

mn	23	31	12	14	24	34
M	1	2	3	4	5	6

The Riemann tensor then becomes a symmetric 6-tensor R_{MN} which may conveniently be written as a matrix. In general, the physical components may be written

$$R_{AB} = \begin{bmatrix} M & N \\ N^t & P \end{bmatrix}$$

where M and P, which are symmetric, and N, which is trace-free, are 3×3 matrices (and t denotes the transpose). In vacuum, Einstein's field equations are equivalent to $P = -M$, $\operatorname{tr} M = 0$, and $N = N^t$, so that

$$R_{AB} = \begin{bmatrix} M & N \\ N & -M \end{bmatrix}$$

with M and N symmetric and trace-free.

In this notation, this permissible discontinuity across a null surface in vacuum is given by

$$[M] = \begin{array}{c} \begin{matrix} x & y & z \end{matrix} \\ \begin{bmatrix} 0 & 0 & 0 \\ 0 & \sigma & 0 \\ 0 & 0 & -\sigma \end{bmatrix} \end{array} \begin{matrix} x \\ y, \\ z \end{matrix} \qquad [N] = \begin{array}{c} \begin{matrix} x & y & z \end{matrix} \\ \begin{bmatrix} 0 & 0 & 0 \\ 0 & 0 & \sigma \\ 0 & \sigma & 0 \end{bmatrix} \end{array} \begin{matrix} x \\ y. \\ z \end{matrix}$$

Here the frame of reference has been chosen so that the x-axis is the direction of propagation, and the y and z axes are the directions of polarization.

The relative acceleration of neighbouring particles, in a reference frame in which they are momentarily at rest, is given by the matrix $-M$. The form of discontinuity of M shows clearly the transverse character of gravitational radiation: the passing of a gravitational wave-front produces no jump in the relative acceleration in the direction in which the wave-front is travelling, but only in transverse directions. The polarization phenomenon is simply that the transverse acceleration in a direction making angle θ with a given direction (in this case the z-axis) jumps by $\sigma \cos 2\theta$.

Thus the consideration of wave-fronts gives a good deal of insight into the properties which gravitational waves may be expected to possess. With this background, we proceed to consideration of gravitational fields in general, and radiation fields in particular, in terms of the Riemann tensor.

4. RIEMANN TENSOR ANALYSIS OF RADIATION

Petrov's classification of gravitational fields [6], referred to earlier, may be given very simply in terms of the 3×3 matrics M and N, introduced in the previous section, which characterize a vacuum gravitational field. Consider the traceless symmetric complex matrix $R = M+iN$. If it has respectively 3, 2 or 1 independent eigenvectors, then the Petrov type is respectively I, II or III. In each case the sum of the eigenvalues is zero. In type I, there are two independent complex eigenvalues, therefore four independent parameters. If two eigenvalues are equal, then the Petrov type is D ("type I degenerate"). In type II, there is one independent complex eigenvalue, therefore two independent parameters. If the eigenvalue vanishes, then the Petrov type is N ("type II null").

The hierarchy of increasing specialization is elegantly summarized by the Penrose diagram, shown earlier and now repeated:

$$\begin{array}{ccccc} & & \mathrm{I} & & \\ & \swarrow & \downarrow & & \\ & \mathrm{II} & \rightarrow & \mathrm{D} & \\ \swarrow & \downarrow & & \downarrow & \\ \mathrm{III} \rightarrow & \mathrm{N} & \rightarrow & \mathrm{O} & \end{array}$$

By suitable choice of reference frame, one may put the physical components of the metric tensor into canonical form; canonical forms for the various types are as follows:

Type I.

$$M = \begin{bmatrix} m_1 & \cdot & \cdot \\ \cdot & m_2 & \cdot \\ \cdot & \cdot & m_3 \end{bmatrix}, \quad N = \begin{bmatrix} n_1 & \cdot & \cdot \\ \cdot & n_2 & \cdot \\ \cdot & \cdot & n_3 \end{bmatrix},$$

$$\sum m_i = 0, \qquad \sum n_i = 0.$$

Type D (or I_e). As type I, but with $m_2 = m_3$, $n_2 = n_3$ (or type II with $\sigma = 0$).

Type II.

$$M = \begin{bmatrix} -2m & \cdot & \cdot \\ \cdot & m+\sigma & \cdot \\ \cdot & \cdot & m-\sigma \end{bmatrix}, \quad N = \begin{bmatrix} -2n & \cdot & \cdot \\ \cdot & n & \sigma \\ \cdot & \sigma & n \end{bmatrix}.$$

Type N, (or II_0). As type II, but with $m = n = 0$.

Type III.

$$M = \begin{bmatrix} \cdot & -\sigma & \cdot \\ -\sigma & \cdot & \cdot \\ \cdot & \cdot & \cdot \end{bmatrix}, \quad N = \begin{bmatrix} \cdot & \cdot & \sigma \\ \cdot & \cdot & \cdot \\ \sigma & \cdot & \cdot \end{bmatrix}.$$

The Petrov classification may be given in a number of different ways besides the above, the most convenient form depending on the use to which the classification is being put. The existence of the above form depends essentially on the fact that the Lorentz group is isomorphic to the group of complex 3-dimensional rotations. Another form, due to Penrose, takes advantage of the spinor representations of the Lorentz group. Another form may be obtained by translating the reduced characteristic equation for $R_A{}^B$ into tensor form, for the distinction by types is just a distinction by Segré characteristic:

Type	I	D	O	II	N	III
Segré char. of $R=M+iN$	[111]	[(11)1]	[(111)]	[21]	[(21)]	[3]
Segré char. of $R_A{}^B$	$[111\overline{111}]$	$[(11)(\overline{11})1\bar{1}]$	$[(111)(\overline{111})]$	$[21\overline{21}]$	$[(21)(\overline{21})]$	$[3\bar{3}]$

The corresponding reduced characteristic equations for R are

I $[R-(m_1+in_1)][R-(m_2+in_2)][R-(m_3+in_3)] = 0,$

D $[R-(m+in)][R+2(m+in)] = 0,$

II $[R-(m+in)]^2[R+2(m+in)] = 0,$

III $R^3 = 0,$

N $R^2 = 0,$

O $R = 0.$

Earlier discussions of the geometry of the Riemann tensor and of its invariants had been given by Ruse [29], [30], [31], and by Géhéniau and Debever [32], [33], [34], [35], [36], and others (for a development of the 3×3 matrix techniques, see Jordan, Kundt and Ehlers [37]).

Tensorial characterizations of some types have been given by Lichnerowicz [24], Bel [38], [39], [40], [41], [42], Sachs [9], Takeno [43], [44] and others. From the copious algebraic results of these authors, we mention that in a type N field there exists a vector k_t (the propagation vector) such that $R_{mn[rs}k_{t]} = R^m{}_{nrs}k_m = 0$, and in a type III field a vector k_t and a tensor V_{rs} such that $R^m{}_{nrs}k_m = k_n V_{rs}$. There is a certain precise sense in which type N may be regarded as a limit of type III, in which another null vector defined by the type III Riemann tensor approaches coincidence with k_t. This kind of characterization brings out very clearly the analogy between type N fields and null electromagnetic fields, for which there exist vectors k_t such that $F_{[rs}k_{t]} = F^m{}_n k_m = 0$. Such considerations have suggested to several authors the construction out of the Riemann tensor of conserved tensors analogous to the energy tensor $T^m{}_n = F^{ms}F_{ns} - \frac{1}{4}\delta^m{}_n F_{rs}F_{rs}$ of the electromagnetic field (cf. Robinson [12], Bel [41], [45], Debever [36], Sachs [9]). A class of such tensors has been enumerated systematically by Collinson [46]. While of considerable entertainment value in their own right, such tensors are unlikely, for reasons discussed earlier, to have much to do with the energy of the gravitational field. An interesting and useful incidental result of Debever's is that in any vacuum gravitational field, there is at least one, and at most four null vectors k_a such that $k_{[d}R_{a]ij[b}k_{c]}k_i k_j = 0$. Sachs has proved that in every case except type I there must be (and in type I there may be) at least one of these Debever vector fields which is tangent field to a congruence of null geodesics.

In an earlier paper (Pirani [5]) it was stated categorically that "gravitational radiation is present if the Riemann tensor is of type II or type III, but not if it is of type I". This is a gross and misleading oversimplification of the actual physical situation as it is now understood, and should be replaced by something along the following lines (which are based on the work of Trautman [47], [48] and of Sachs [referred to below]):

The gravitational field of an actual isolated physical system is of type I. However, if the system is radiating, then at distances large compared to the dimensions of the system and the wavelength of the radiation, the field will appear to be approximately of type N, in the sense that in the frame of reference of an observer (who by radar and optical measurements or otherwise finds himself to remain roughly at a fixed distance in a fixed direction from the radiating system), terms of type N will dominate the physical components of the Riemann tensor (far-field). At distances large compared to the dimensions of the system but small compared to the wavelength of the radiation, the field will appear to be approximately of type III, in the same sense ("semi-far-fields"). Fields which are exactly of type N represent pure far-field radiation (example: plane waves). Fields which are exactly of type III represent pure semi-far field radiation.

This situation is not as clear-cut as it ought to be. There is no unambiguous criterion of a radiating system. Such a criterion will come from a study of the properties of the field over (time-like) 3-spaces surrounding sources. The basis for such a study has been laid by Bel and Lichnerowicz in Paris, and by Sachs and others at Hamburg in their elegant studies of the propagation of gravitational radiation (cf. Sachs's contribution to the present volume, and see also Ehlers and Sachs [8], Sachs [9], Jordan, Kundt and Ehlers [37], Jordan, Ehlers and Sachs [49] and the series of papers by Bel).

From the results of these authors are selected the following, mainly due to Sachs: If the gravitational field is of type D, II, III or N, then the Riemann tensor defines a congruence of null geodesics, which are the *rays* of the field (bicharacteristics), whose tangent vectors k_a may be identified as the propagation vectors of the radiation (whenever there is any; type D includes non-radiating solutions, for example the Schwarzschild solution). The propagation vector k_a satisfies the Robinson equation (Robinson [12], [12b])

$$k_{(a;b)}k^{a;b} = \tfrac{1}{2}(k^a{}_{;a})^2.$$

If the radiation spreads out, then $k^a{}_{;a} \neq 0$, and the usual definition of parallax distance r_P yields $r_P = 2/k^a{}_{;a}$. Between parallax distance, luminosity distance r_L, and preferred parameter distance s (=Whittaker distance; see Kermack, McCrea and Whittaker [50], Goldberg and Newman [51]) Sachs finds the remarkable relations

$$r_L{}^2 = r_P s = s^2[1+(\omega r_P)^2] = r_P{}^2[1+(\omega r_P)^2]^{-1},$$

where ω is the *rotation* of the rays: $\omega = (\tfrac{1}{2}k_{[a;b]}k^{a;b})^{\frac{1}{2}}$.

The most remarkable part of Sachs's work relates to the dependence of spreading-out fields on distance. He defines a complex parameter $z = r_P{}^{-1}+i\omega$, and shows that in type N fields, the Riemann tensor goes like z, that in type III fields it contains at most three covariantly distinguishable parts: of type N, going like z, of type III going like z^2, and of type N going like z^3, and in type II or D fields at most five covariantly distinguishable parts, one of type N going like z, and four higher terms (which are given in Table II of Sachs's contribution to this volume). If the rays do not rotate, then $\omega = 0$, and z is just the reciprocal parallax distance, and the Sachs decomposition shows the distance dependence of different types of fields very clearly and naturally.

Sachs's method is to write the Riemann tensor in terms of its principal vectors, and to impose the differential conditions on these vectors which are implied by the vacuum field equations and the Bianchi identities, namely $R^a{}_{bcd;\,a} = 0$ and $R_{ab[cd;\,e]} = 0$. If one might borrow from Schouten (epithet on Veblen and Thomas's development of normal tensors) to comment on his work, the way is here open for orgies of formalism, but Sachs has restricted himself in an exemplary way to those relations which are really interesting[(1)].

5. EXACT SOLUTIONS REPRESENTING RADIATION

The confused early history of type N fields was described in section 2. The Brinkmann solution and its variations comprise the "plane-fronted waves" first given an acceptable physical interpretation by Robinson (see below). The expanding waves of Robinson and Trautman include solutions of types D, II (the first of this type to be discovered?), N and III. The first type III solution seems to be that found be Petrov [14]. Solutions representing cylindrical waves, which are of type I, have been discussed by Einstein and Rosen [52], Rosen [53], Marder [54], [55], Bonnor [56], and Weber and Wheeler [57]. A large number of solutions has been found by Harrison [58]. He remarks that all of them are of type I, but observes that a number have "wave-like character". So far, the physical significance of these solutions has not been much investigated. A convenient form of the metric for type N plane-fronted waves is

$$ds^2 = 2du dv + dy^2 + dz^2 + 2H(u, y, z) du^2$$

with the single vacuum field equation

$$\frac{\partial^2 H}{\partial y^2} + \frac{\partial^2 H}{\partial z^2} = 0 .$$

The Riemann tensor is

$$R_{ijkl} = \tfrac{1}{2}\delta^{0\alpha}_{ij}\delta^{0\beta}_{kl}\frac{\partial^2 H}{\partial x^\alpha \partial x^\beta} \qquad (x^\alpha, x^\beta = y, z \text{ only})$$

and therefore vanishes if and only if H is linear in or independent of y and z. Such metrics have been classified in an invariant-theoretical manner by Kundt [13]. They are all of type N. Each admits at least one motion (because ds^2 is independent of v), and

---

(1) *Note added in proof:* Since this section was written many further results about the algebraic and differential properties of the Riemann tensor have been discovered (for example, see [68]–[72]). In particular we should mention the result of Goldberg and Sachs (not yet published), that a vacuum metric is algebraically special (below the top line in the Penrose diagram) if and only if it contains a ***shear-free*** congruence of null geodesics.

a motion group with up to six parameters is possible. The metrics with 5-parameter and 6-parameter groups constitute the so-called plane waves; they have been discussed at some length by Bondi, Robinson and the writer [59]. It is notable that the 5-parameter group is identical in structure with the motion group admitted by plane electromagnetic waves in flat space-time. One of the 6-parameter metrics was discovered by Petrov [14] in the course of a search for metrics of given type and maximum mobility (that is, admitting the largest possible motion group); all were found by Robinson. Another was found by Ozsváth and Schücking (in their contribution to this volume), who have called it an "anti-Mach metric" on the grounds that it is empty, stationary and complete, and therefore contradicts Mach's principle in the form "In the absence of matter, space-time should necessarily be Minkowskian".

Plane-waves have also been investigated by Takeno [60], [61], [62], [63], [43], [44], among whose results may be mentioned that the assumption that the vacuum metric is a function of one (null) variable and satisfies the de Donder coordinate condition leads only to the flat solution.

About cylindrical waves it should be remarked only that the consensus is that they do carry energy, but that the necessarily infinite dimensions of the source leads to great difficulties of interpretation.

The expanding metrics of Robinson and Trautman have the form $ds^2 = (K - 2Mu^{-1} - 2uq^{-1}\partial q/\partial v)dv^2 + 2du\,dv - u^2 q^{-2}(dy^2 + dz^2)$ where $M = M(v)$, $q = q(v, y, z)$, and $K = q^2[(\log q)_{yy} + (\log q)_{zz}]$. The single field equation is $K_{yy} + K_{zz} = 4q(q^{-3}M)_v$. Here subscripts denote differentiation. Further details are given in the original note (Robinson and Trautman [17]).

As remarked before, these solutions appear to contain singularities which may be interpreted as "wires" connecting the central object to infinity. The main need at the present time is for exact solutions representing radiation from an isolated finite system without singularities except at the region containing the system itself. Since such a solution can hardly admit a motion group with more than one parameter (axial symmetry), the solution of the field equations presents considerable difficulty.

6. OTHER DEVELOPMENTS

Many interesting developments, including approximation methods, have been left out of this brief survey. However, a number of other so-far isolated developments are worth mentioning:

D. R. Brill has shown [64] that the Schwarzschild mass of every time-symmetric axi-symmetric asymptotically Schwarzschildian vacuum gravitational field is positive-definite, and has given a procedure for the construction of such a metric at the moment of time-symmetry. The vacuum field considered by Brill is a more-or-less spherical wave which implodes to maximum concentration at the moment of time-symmetry, and then explodes again. Considerations of this kind support the view that gravitational waves can carry energy.

The work of Krutchkovitch [65] supplies a basis for the study of gravitational waves in matter. Such a study would naturally begin with an investigation of the Weyl conformal curvature tensor, which has the same algebraic properties as the vacuum Riemann tensor, and therefore admits a Petrov classification. It is natural to presume for example that a space-time with matter and a type N or type III Weyl tensor is pervaded by gravitational radiation (which does not, however, interact with the matter). In more complicated circumstances, investigation of the Weyl tensor will make it possible to distinguish gravitational from elastic or hydrodynamic waves. Krutchkovitch, completing the classical work of Fubini on Riemannian 4-spaces admitting groups of motions, has found those 4-spaces of indefinite signature which admit intransitive groups of motions possesing isotropic surfaces of transitivity. (Fubini found all the transitive groups.) Among these, one would expect to find, for example, solutions representing plane-fronted waves in matter and in cosmological models.

Finally should be mentioned a new approach to the problem of defining a radiation field, which has been developed by Trautman in his contribution to this volume. Starting from the idea that radiation must be able to carry information, that is, that the transmitted amplitude may be an arbitrary function of the time, he seeks solutions of the vacuum field equations containing arbitrary functions. Of course, every solution of the vacuum field equations may be made to *look* as though it contained arbitrary functions, by making an arbitrary coordinate transformation, and Trautman has devised a way of overcoming this difficulty: he finds a solution of the form $g_{mn} = \underset{0}{g}_{mn} + F(\sigma) h_m h_n$, where $F(\sigma)$ is an arbitrary function of the scalar σ. He shows *inter alia* that $\sigma =$ const must be null and that h_m must be normal to it. Other conditions and results are given in his paper. Among them is that if the "background" metric $\underset{0}{g}_{mn}$ is flat, the derived solutions are plane-fronted waves.

Acknowledgements. The writer is grateful to Dr A. Trautman and Dr R. K Sachs for their advice and encouragement during the preparation of this review, and to many colleagues for discussions and, as will appear from the list of references, for showing him their work before publication. The article suffers from the absence, as co-author, of Mr. Ivor Robinson, who was prevented by circumstances beyond his control from collaborating, and to whom the writer is indebted in all questions concerning the theory of gravitation to an extent which it is impossible to acknowledge.

REFERENCES

[1] A. Einstein, *S. B. Preuss. Akad. Wiss.* **154** (1918).
[2] F. A. E. Pirani, Report at Royaumont Conference, 1959.
[3] F. A. E. Pirani, *Acta Phys. Polon.* **15**, 389 (1956).
[4] F. A. E. Pirani, *Bull. Acad. Polon. Sci.* III, **5**, 143 (1957).
[5] F. A. E. Pirani, *Phys. Rev.* **105**, 1089 (1957).
[6] A. Z. Petrov, *Scientific Notices, Kazan State University* **114**, 55 (1954.)
[7] R. Penrose, *Ann. Phys., Princeton* **10**, 171 (1960).
[8] J. Ehlers and R. K. Sachs, *Z. Phys.* **155**, 498 (1959).
[9] R. K. Sachs, *Z. Phys.* **157**, 462 (1960).
[10] H. W. Brinkmann, *Math. Ann.* **94**, 119 (1925).
[11] N. Rosen, *Phys. Z. Sowjet.*, **12**, 366 (1937).
[12] I. Robinson, Lecture at King's College, London 1956.
[12a] I. Robinson, Lecture at King's College, London 1958.
[12b] I. Robinson, Lecture at Royaumont Conference, 1959.
[13] W. Kundt, to be published.
[14] A. Z. Petrov, *Dokl. Akad. Nauk SSSR*, **105**, 905 (1955).
[15] H. Bondi, *Nature Lond.* **179**, 1072 (1957).
[16] A. Perés, *Phys. Rev. Lett.* **3**, 571 (1959).
[17] I. Robinson and A. Trautman, *Phys. Rev. Lett.* **4**, 431 (1960).
[18] Vessiot, *C. R. Acad. Sci., Paris* **166**, 349 (1918).
[19] F. K. Stellmacher, *Math. Ann.* **115**, 740 (1938).
[20] B. Finzi, *R. C. Acad. Lincei* **6**, 18 (1949).
[21] A. Trautman, *Bull. Polon. Acad. Sci.* III, **5**, 273 (1957).
[22] A. Trautman, *C. R. Acad. Sci., Paris* **246**, 1500 (1958).
[23] A. Trautman, Lectures on General Relativity (mimeographed notes), King's College, London 1958.
[24] A. Lichnerowicz, *C. R. Acad. Sci., Paris* **246**, 983 (1958).
[25] L. Bel, *C. R. Acad. Sci., Paris* **245**, 2482 (1957).
[26] A. Lichnerowicz, *Théories relativistes de la gravitation et de l'électromagnétisme*, Paris 1955.
[27] A. Treder, *Ann. Phys., Lpz.* (7), **2**, 225 (1958).
[28] A. Papapetrou and H. Treder, *Math. Nachr.* **20**, 53 (1959).
[29] H. S. Ruse, *Proc. Roy. Soc. Edinb.* **62**, 64 (1944).
[30] H. S. Ruse, *Quart. J. Math.* (*Oxford*) **17**, 1 (1946).
[31] H. S. Ruse, *Proc. Lond Math. Soc.* **50**, 75 (1948).
[32] J. Géhéniau and R. Debever, *Bull. Acad. Belg. Cl. Sci.* (5), **42**, 114 (1956).
[33] J. Géhéniau, *Bull. Acad. Belg. Cl. Sci.* (5), **42**, 252 (1956).
[34] R. Debever, *Bull. Acad. Belg. Cl. Sci.* (5), **42**, 313 (1956).
[35] R. Debever, *Bull. Acad. Belg. Cl. Sci.* (5), **42**, 608 (1956).

[36] R. Debever, *Bull. Soc. Math. Belg.* **10**, 112 (1960).
[37] P. Jordan, W. Kundt and J. Ehlers, *Abh. Akad. Wiss. Mainz*, No. 2, 1960.
[38] L. Bel, *C. R. Acad. Sci., Paris* **246**, 3015 (1958).
[39] L. Bel, *C. R. Acad. Sci., Paris* **247**, 1094 (1958).
[40] L. Bel, *C. R. Acad. Sci., Paris* **247**, 2096 (1958).
[41] L. Bel, *C. R. Acad. Sci., Paris* **248**, 1296 (1959).
[42] L. Bel, *C. R. Acad. Sci., Paris* **248**, 2561 (1959).
[43] H. Takeno, *Tensor* (N. S.), **9**, 76 (1959).
[44] H. Takeno, *Tensor* (N. S.), **10**, in press.
[45] L. Bel, Thesis, *La radiation gravitationnelle*, Paris 1960.
[46] C. D. Collinson, to be published.
[47] A. Trautman, *Bull. Acad. Polon. Sci.* Cl III, **6**, 403 (1958).
[48] A. Trautman, *Bull. Acad. Polon. Sci.* Cl III, **6**, 407 (1958).
[49] P. Jordan, J. Ehlers and R. K. Sachs, to be published.
[50] W. O. Kermack, W. H. McCrea and E. T. Whittaker, *Proc. Roy. Soc. Edinb.* **53**, 31 (1932).
[51] J. N. Goldberg and E. T. Newman, *Phys. Rev.* **114**, 1391 (1959).
[52] A. Einstein and N. Rosen, *J. Franklin Inst.* **223**, 43 (1937).
[53] N. Rosen, *Bull. Res. Council Israel* **3**, 328 (1954).
[54] L. Marder, *Proc. Roy. Soc.* A **244**, 524 (1958).
[55] L. Marder, *Proc. Roy. Soc.* A **246**, 133 (1958).
[56] W. B. Bonnor, *J. Math. Mech.* **6**, 203 (1957).
[57] J. Weber and J. A. Wheeler, *Rev. Mod. Phys.* **29**, 509 (1957).
[58] B. K. Harrison, Exact 3-variable solutions of the field equations of general relativity, Doctoral Thesis, Princeton 1959.
[59] H. Bondi, F. A. E. Pirani and I. Robinson, *Proc. Roy. Soc.* A **251**, 519 (1959).
[60] H. Takeno, *Tensor* (N. S), **6**, 15 (1956).
[61] H. Takeno, *Tensor* (N. S), **8**, 59 (1958).
[62] H. Takeno, *Tensor* (N. S), **9**, 73 (1959).
[63] H. Takeno, *Tensor* (N. S), **9**, in press.
[64] D. R. Brill, *Ann. Phys., Princeton* **7**, 466 (1959).
[65] G. Kruchkovitch, *Mat. Sborn.* **41**, (**83**), 195 (1957).
[66] H. Bondi, *Nature, Lond.* **186**, 535 (1960).
[67] R. K. Sachs, to be published.
[68] J. Robinson, *J. Math. Phys.* **2**, 290 (1961).
[69] E. Newman, *J. Math. Phys.* **2**, 324 (1961).
[70] J. N. Goldberg and R. P. Kerr, *J. Math. Phys.* **2**, 327 (1961).
[71] R. P. Kerr and J. N. Goldberg, *J. Math. Phys.* **2**, 332 (1961).
[72] A. Z. Petrov, *Einstein Spaces* (in Russian), Moscow 1961.
[73] J. Weber, *General Relativity and Gravitational Waves*, London- New York 1961.

LES ESPOIRS ET LES DIFFICULTÉS DE LA THÉORIE DU CHAMP UNIFIÉ D'EINSTEIN

M. A. Tonnelat

Institut Henri Poincaré, Paris

I. LES PRINCIPES DE LA THÉORIE

La théorie du champ unifié développée par Einstein en 1943 [1] est l'aboutissement d'une série de tentatives proposées et modifiées à plusieurs reprises par Einstein lui-même [2]. L'intérêt exceptionnel suscité par cette théorie est dû à l'ampleur du programme qu'elle se propose et à la simplicité des moyens qu'elle met en jeu.

Einstein veut en effet représenter au moyen d'un schéma purement géométrique, un champ généralisé susceptible de décrire les phénomènes de gravitation, les phénomènes électromagnétiques et aussi les caractéristiques des particules. La réalisation de ce programme permettrait donc de considérer les particules — non pas comme des singularités du champ — mais comme des données entièrement réductibles au champ lui-même.

D'autre part, la réduction de tous les apports d'énergie "extérieurs" (énergie électromagnétique, énergie matérielle etc...) à la géométrie aurait pour effet d'assimiler les équations du champs à un unique "cas extérieur" c'est à dire à une extension des équations sans second membre de la Relativité Générale. En effet, le tenseur d'énergie-impulsion $T_{\mu\nu}$ représentait, dans les théories dites "naïves", toutes les énergies autres que celle du champ de gravitation. Il est absorbé ici par un tenseur de Ricci généralisé $R_{\mu\nu}$ et l'on devra donc toujours résoudre des équations "extérieures"

$$R_{\mu\nu} = 0.$$

Les difficultés que peut présenter cette théorie apparaissent immédiatement: Il sera nécessaire d'extraire de cette équation une représentation particulière de chaque forme d'énergie dont l'ensemble seulement est donné globalement. Une telle décomposition peut-être facilement arbitraire et l'interprétation de la théorie risque ainsi d'être ambiguë.

II. LES ÉQUATIONS FONDAMENTALES

Les bases de la théorie sont extrêmement simples et consistent à généraliser formellement la fonction d'action qu'on utilise en Relativité Générale. On substituera donc à la densité invariante

$$\mathring{\mathfrak{a}} = \sqrt{-g}\, g^{\underline{\mu\nu}} G_{\mu\nu},$$

$g_{\underline{\mu\nu}}$ = tenseur métrique fondamental symétrique, $G_{\mu\nu}$ = tenseur de Ricci formé avec les symboles de Christoffel $\left\{ {\varrho \atop \mu\nu} \right\}$, la densité invariante

$$\mathfrak{a} = \sqrt{-g}\, g^{\mu\nu} R_{\mu\nu}$$

$g_{\mu\nu}$ étant un tenseur fondamental non symétrique et $R_{\mu\nu}$ le tenseur de Ricci formé avec une connexion quelquonque $\Gamma^{\varrho}_{\mu\nu}$:

$$R_{\mu\nu} = \partial_\varrho \Gamma^{\varrho}_{\mu\nu} - \partial_\nu \Gamma^{\varrho}_{\mu\varrho} + \Gamma^{\lambda}_{\mu\nu}\Gamma^{\varrho}_{\lambda\varrho} - \Gamma^{\lambda}_{\mu\varrho}\Gamma^{\varrho}_{\lambda\nu}.$$

Dans ces conditions le principe variationnel

$$\delta \int \mathfrak{a}\, d\tau = 0$$

conduit, pour des variations indépendantes $\delta\Gamma^{\varrho}_{\mu\nu}$, $\delta\mathfrak{G}^{\mu\nu}$ – nulles aux limites du domaine d'intégration – aux équations fondamentales [1]

$$(\mathrm{I}) \begin{cases} (1) \quad \mathfrak{G}^{\overset{\mu}{+}\overset{\nu}{-}}{}_{;\varrho} \equiv \partial_\varrho \mathfrak{G}^{\mu\nu} + \Gamma^{\mu}_{\sigma\varrho}\mathfrak{G}^{\sigma\nu} + \Gamma^{\nu}_{\varrho\sigma}\mathfrak{G}^{\mu\sigma} - \mathfrak{G}^{\mu\nu}\Gamma^{\lambda}_{\underline{\varrho\lambda}} = \\ \qquad\qquad = -\tfrac{2}{3}\,\delta^{\nu}_{\varrho}\mathfrak{G}^{\mu\sigma}\Gamma_\sigma + \bar{\mathfrak{G}}^{\mu\nu}\Gamma_\varrho, \\ (2) \quad \partial_\varrho \mathfrak{G}^{\underset{\vee}{\mu\varrho}} = 0, \\ (3) \quad R_{\mu\nu}(\Gamma) = 0, \end{cases}$$

en désignant par Γ_ϱ le vecteur de torsion

$$\Gamma_\varrho = \Gamma^{\lambda}_{\underset{\vee}{\varrho\lambda}}.$$

Le changement de variable

$$L^{\varrho}_{\mu\nu} = \Gamma^{\varrho}_{\mu\nu} + \tfrac{2}{3}\,\delta^{\varrho}_{\mu}\Gamma_\nu \qquad (\text{tel que } L_\varrho = L^{\lambda}_{\varrho\lambda} = 0) \qquad (4)$$

réduit le système (I) aux expressions plus simples

$$
\text{(II)}\quad
\begin{cases}
(1) & D_\varrho \mathcal{G}^{\overset{\mu\nu}{+-}} \equiv \partial_\varrho \mathcal{G}^{\mu\nu} + L^{\mu}_{\sigma\varrho}\mathcal{G}^{\sigma\nu} + L^{\nu}_{\varrho\sigma}\mathcal{G}^{\mu\sigma} - \mathcal{G}^{\mu\nu} L^{\lambda}_{\underline{\varrho\lambda}} = 0,\\
(2) & \partial_\varrho \mathcal{G}^{\underset{\vee}{\mu\varrho}} = 0,\\
(3) & \begin{cases} \text{a)} \ W_{\underline{\mu\nu}}(L) = 0,\\[2mm] \text{b)} \ W_{\underset{\vee}{\mu\nu}}(L) = \dfrac{2}{3}(\partial_\mu \Gamma_\nu - \partial_\nu \Gamma_\mu), \end{cases}
\end{cases}
$$

$W_{\mu\nu}$ étant le tenseur de Ricci formé avec la connexion $L^{\varrho}_{\mu\nu}$.

Les équations $(\text{II})_1$ permettent de déterminer de façon univoque les 64 coefficients de connexion $L^{\varrho}_{\mu\nu}$ en fonction des $g_{\mu\nu}$ et de leurs dérivées premières. En particulier, l'association de $(\text{II})_1$ et de $(\text{II})_2$ entraîne la condition $L_\varrho \equiv L^{\lambda}_{\underset{\vee}{\varrho\lambda}} = 0$. Mais il importe de souligner que les équations (II) ne sont équivalentes aux équations (I) qu'en leur adjoignant la définition (4). Dans ces conditions, il est évident que le quadrivecteur Γ_ϱ qui reste arbitraire après résolution des équations $(\text{II})_1$ et (4) intervient néanmoins dans les équations (3) dès que l'on revient à la connexion initiale $\Gamma^{\varrho}_{\mu\nu}$.

III. SOLUTION RIGOUREUSE DES ÉQUATIONS $g_{\underset{+-}{\mu\nu};\varrho} = 0$

La résolution des 64 équations $D_\varrho \mathcal{G}^{\overset{\mu\nu}{+-}} = 0$ doit nous permettre d'exprimer les 64 coefficients de connexion affine $L^{\varrho}_{\mu\nu}$ en fonction des $g_{\mu\nu}$ et de leurs dérivées du 1er ordre. Ces équations sont équivalentes au système suivant

$$
D_\varrho g_{\underset{+-}{\mu\nu}} \equiv \partial_\varrho g_{\mu\nu} - L^{\sigma}_{\mu\varrho} g_{\sigma\nu} - L^{\sigma}_{\varrho\nu} g_{\mu\sigma} = 0. \tag{5}
$$

Nous avons calculé la solution explicite de ces équations en fonction des parties symétriques et antisymétriques du tenseur $g_{\mu\nu}$ [3].[1] La méthode consiste

(a) à déterminer la partie symétrique $L^{\varrho}_{\underline{\mu\nu}}$ de la connexion en fonction de la partie antisymétrique $L^{\varrho}_{\underset{\vee}{\mu\nu}}$,

(b) à calculer explicitement la partie antisymétrique $L^{\varrho}_{\underset{\vee}{\mu\nu}}$ de la connexion en fonction des $g_{\mu\nu}$ scindés en parties symétrique et antisymétrique et de leurs dérivées premières.

---

[1] On peut aussi développer une résolution analogue en fonction des parties symétriques et antisymétrique des composantes contravariantes $g^{\mu\nu}$ ou des densités $\mathcal{G}^{\mu\nu}$ [4].

Pour cela, il est commode de poser

$$\underline{g}_{\mu\nu} = \gamma_{\mu\nu}, \qquad g_{\underset{\vee}{\mu\nu}} = \varphi_{\mu\nu} \qquad \text{c'est à dire} \qquad g_{\mu\nu} = \gamma_{\mu\nu} + \varphi_{\mu\nu} \tag{6}$$

et de désigner par g, γ, φ et par $gg^{\mu\nu}$, $\gamma\gamma^{\mu\nu}$, $\varphi\varphi^{\mu\nu}$ les déterminants et les mineurs relatifs aux éléments $g_{\mu\nu}$, $\gamma_{\mu\nu}$, $\varphi_{\mu\nu}$.

(a) On obtient ainsi l'expression de la partie symétrique de la connexion

$$\underline{L}_{\mu\nu,\varrho} = \gamma_{\varrho\sigma}\underline{L}^{\sigma}_{\mu\nu} = [\mu\nu,\varrho]_{\gamma} - (L_{\underset{\vee}{\mu\varrho},\bar{\nu}} + L_{\underset{\vee}{\nu\varrho},\bar{\mu}}) \tag{7}$$

en désignant par $[\mu\nu,\varrho]_{\gamma}$ les symboles de Christoffel formés avec les $\gamma_{\mu\nu} = \underline{g}_{\mu\nu}$:

$$[\mu\nu,\varrho]_{\gamma} = \tfrac{1}{2}(\partial_{\mu}\gamma_{\nu\varrho} + \partial_{\nu}\gamma_{\mu\varrho} - \partial_{\varrho}\gamma_{\mu\nu}) \tag{8}$$

et en utilisant les notations

$$L_{\underset{\vee}{\mu\nu},\bar{\varrho}} = \varphi_{\varrho\sigma}\gamma^{\sigma\lambda}L_{\underset{\vee}{\mu\nu},\lambda} = \varphi_{\varrho\sigma}L^{\sigma}_{\underset{\vee}{\mu\nu}}, \qquad L_{\mu\nu,\bar{\bar{\varrho}}} = \varphi_{\varrho\sigma}\gamma^{\sigma\lambda}L_{\mu\nu,\bar{\lambda}}, \qquad \text{etc.} \tag{9}$$

(b) La substitution de (7) dans (5) scindée en parties symétriques et antisymétrique conduit alors à l'équation suivante

$$L_{\underset{\vee}{\mu\nu},\varrho} - \frac{2\sqrt{\varphi}}{\sqrt{-\gamma}}L^{*}_{\underset{\vee}{\mu\nu},\varrho} + L_{\underset{\vee}{\mu\nu},\bar{\bar{\varrho}}} = R_{\underset{\vee}{\mu\nu},\varrho}. \tag{10}$$

$R_{\underset{\vee}{\mu\nu},\varrho}$ est une expression connue en fonction des $g_{\mu\nu}$ scindés et de leurs dérivées premières (Nous l'explicitons en (17)). D'autre part, outre les notations barres définies en (9), nous utilisons les notations

$$L^{*}_{\underset{\vee}{\mu\nu},\varrho} = \frac{\sqrt{-\gamma}}{2}\varepsilon_{\mu\nu\lambda\sigma}\gamma^{\lambda\alpha}\gamma^{\sigma\beta}L_{\underset{\vee}{\alpha\beta},\varrho}. \tag{11}$$

Les expressions barres et étoiles vérifient les relations de récurrence

$$A_{\bar{\bar{\bar{\varrho}}}} = -\frac{1}{\gamma}(g-\gamma-\varphi)A_{\bar{\bar{\varrho}}} - \frac{\varphi}{\gamma}A_{\varrho}, \tag{12}$$

$$A^{**}_{\underset{\vee}{\mu\nu}} = \frac{\sqrt{-\gamma}}{2}\varepsilon_{\mu\nu\varrho\sigma}\gamma^{\varrho\alpha}\gamma^{\sigma\beta}A^{*}_{\underset{\vee}{\alpha\beta}} = -A_{\mu\nu} \tag{13}$$

valables pour tout indice ϱ et toute paire d'indices antisymétrique $\underset{\vee}{\mu\nu}$. Ces opérations "barres" et "étoiles" appliquées à (10) permettent d'obtenir trois équations analogues, linéaires en $L_{\underset{\vee}{\mu\nu},\varrho}$, $L_{\underset{\vee}{\mu\nu},\bar{\bar{\varrho}}}$, $L^{*}_{\underset{\vee}{\mu\nu},\varrho}$ et $L^{*}_{\underset{\vee}{\mu\nu},\bar{\bar{\varrho}}}$ et d'en tirer aisément $L_{\underset{\vee}{\mu\nu},\varrho}$. On obtient ainsi

$$\text{(A)} \qquad \boxed{(a^{2}+b^{2})L^{\sigma}_{\underset{\vee}{\mu\nu}} = \left(2\gamma^{\sigma\varrho} - \frac{g}{\gamma}g^{\underline{\sigma\varrho}}\right)\Sigma_{\underset{\vee}{\mu\nu},\varrho} - \frac{2\sqrt{\varphi}}{\sqrt{-\gamma}}\gamma^{\sigma\varrho}\Sigma^{*}_{\underset{\vee}{\mu\nu},\varrho}} \tag{14}$$

avec

$$\Sigma_{\underset{\vee}{\mu\nu},\varrho} = aR_{\underset{\vee}{\mu\nu},\varrho} + bR^*_{\underset{\vee}{\mu\nu},\varrho}. \tag{15}$$

On a posé

$$a = 2 - \frac{g}{\gamma} + \frac{6\varphi}{\gamma}, \qquad b = \frac{\sqrt{\varphi}}{\sqrt{-\gamma}}\left(3 - \frac{g}{\gamma} + \frac{\varphi}{\gamma}\right) \tag{16}$$

$$R_{\underset{\vee}{\mu\nu},\varrho} = -\tfrac{1}{2}\varphi_{\mu\nu\varrho} + \nabla_\varrho \varphi_{\mu\nu} + \frac{\sqrt{\varphi}}{2\sqrt{-\gamma}}\overset{*}{\varphi}_{[\mu\nu]\varrho} + \frac{\sqrt{\varphi}}{4\sqrt{-\gamma}}\overset{*}{\varphi}_{\mu\nu}\varphi^{\sigma\tau}\varphi_{\sigma\tau\varrho} -$$

$$-\varphi_{\mu\nu}\partial_\varrho \log\frac{g}{\gamma} + \frac{\sqrt{\varphi}}{2}\varepsilon_{\mu\nu\varrho\sigma}\varphi^{\lambda\sigma}\partial_\lambda \log\frac{g}{\gamma} -$$

$$-\frac{\varphi}{2\sqrt{-\gamma}}\varepsilon_{[\mu\nu]\varrho\lambda}\varphi^{\sigma\lambda}\partial_\sigma \log\frac{g}{\varphi} + \frac{\sqrt{\varphi}}{2\sqrt{-\gamma}}\overset{*}{\varphi}_{\mu\nu}\partial_\varrho \log\frac{g}{\varphi} \tag{17}$$

∇_ϱ représente la dérivation covariante écrite avec les symboles $\left\{\begin{matrix}\varrho\\ \mu\nu\end{matrix}\right\}_\gamma$ et

$$\varphi_{\mu\nu\varrho} = \partial_\mu \varphi_{\nu\varrho} + \partial_\varrho \varphi_{\mu\nu} + \partial_\nu \varphi_{\varrho\mu}. \tag{18}$$

Conditions d'existence de la solution.

Le calcul qui précède suppose essentiellement $\gamma \neq 0$. Aussi les équations

$$g_{\underset{+}{\mu}\underset{-}{\nu};\varrho} =$$

admettent une solution et une seule si

$$\gamma(a^2 + b^2) \neq 0 \tag{19}$$

c'est à dire si

$$\gamma \neq 0, \quad \left(2 - \frac{g}{\gamma} + \frac{6\varphi}{\gamma}\right)^2 - \frac{4\varphi}{\gamma}\left(3 - \frac{g}{\gamma} + \frac{\varphi}{\gamma}\right)^2 \neq 0. \tag{20}$$

Cas $\varphi = 0$.[1]

La condition

$$\varphi = (\varphi_{23}\varphi_{14} + \varphi_{31}\varphi_{24} + \varphi_{12}\varphi_{34})^2 = 0 \tag{21}$$

---

[1] Bien entendu $\varphi = 0$ entraîne $\varphi^{\mu\nu} = \frac{1}{2\sqrt{\varphi}}\varepsilon^{\mu\nu\varrho\sigma}\varphi_{\varrho\sigma}$ infini. Mais les quantités qui interviennent dans la recherche d'une solution ne sont jamais les $\varphi^{\mu\nu}$ mais les expressions $\frac{1}{2}\varepsilon^{\mu\nu\varrho\sigma}\varphi_{\varrho\sigma}$ que nous representons par $\sqrt{\varphi}\,\varphi^{\mu\nu}$ quantités finies, même pour $\varphi = 0$.

réalisée notamment si le champ $\varphi_{\mu\nu}$ est un champ "singulier" permet de ramener la solution générale des équations d'Einstein à l'expression très simple

$$\left(2-\frac{g}{\gamma}\right)^2 L^\sigma_{\underset{\vee}{\mu\nu}} = \left(2\gamma^{\sigma\varrho}-\frac{g}{\gamma}g^{\underline{\sigma\varrho}}\right)\Sigma_{\underset{\vee}{\mu\nu},\varrho} \tag{22}$$

avec

$$\Sigma_{\mu\nu,\varrho} = \frac{g}{\gamma}\left[\nabla_\varrho\left(\frac{\gamma}{g}\varphi_{\mu\nu}\right)-\frac{1}{2}\partial_{[\varrho}\frac{\gamma}{g}\varphi_{\mu\nu]}\right]. \tag{23}$$

IV. LA SOLUTION GÉNÉRALE DES ÉQUATIONS $g_{\underset{+-}{\mu\nu};\varrho}=0$ EN FONCTION DES CHAMPS ASYMÉTRIQUES $g_{\mu\nu}$ NON SCINDÉS

Le principe même de la théorie, tel que l'avait postulé Einstein, réside dans l'introduction d'un tenseur fondamental asymétrique $g_{\mu\nu}$. Il semble donc a priori plus souhaitable d'exprimer la connexion affine $\Gamma^\varrho_{\mu\nu}$ en fonction des composantes $g_{\mu\nu}$ non scindées en parties symétrique et antisymétrique. On peut penser que la forme de cette solution, plus conforme à l'esprit de la théorie, s'introduirait de façon plus naturelle et serait, finalement plus simple.

Nous avons donc cherché [5] une solution de ce type en partant des mêmes équations

$$\partial_\varrho g_{\mu\nu} = L^\sigma_{\mu\varrho}g_{\sigma\nu}+L^\sigma_{\varrho\nu}g_{\mu\sigma} = L_{\mu\varrho,\nu}+L_{\varrho\nu,\hat{\mu}} \tag{24}$$

en posant

$$L^\sigma_{\mu\varrho} = g^{\sigma\lambda}L_{\mu\varrho,\lambda}, \qquad L_{\varrho\nu,\hat{\mu}} = g_{\mu\sigma}g^{\sigma\lambda}L_{\varrho\nu,\lambda}. \tag{25}$$

Permutons dans (24) les indices μ, ϱ puis ν, ϱ puis μ, ν. Nous obtenons trois équations que nous désignerons symboliquement par $(\varrho\nu,\mu)$, $(\mu\varrho,\nu)$, $(\nu\mu,\varrho)$. Formons $(\varrho\hat{\nu},\hat{\mu})+(\mu\varrho,\nu)-(\nu\hat{\mu},\varrho)$. Nous obtenons ainsi

$$L_{\mu\nu,\varrho}+L_{\hat{\mu}\hat{\nu},\hat{\varrho}} = \partial_\nu g_{\mu\varrho}+\partial_{\hat{\mu}}g_{\varrho\hat{\nu}}-\partial_\varrho g_{\nu\hat{\mu}}. \tag{26}$$

Or, la généralisation des notations $\hat{}$:

$$A_{\hat{\varrho}} = g_{\varrho\sigma}g^{\sigma\lambda}A_\lambda, \qquad A_{\hat{\hat{\varrho}}} = g_{\varrho\sigma}g^{\sigma\lambda}A_{\hat{\lambda}}, \tag{27}$$

et

$$A_\varrho = g_{\sigma\varrho}g^{\lambda\sigma}A_\lambda, \qquad A_{\underset{\vee\vee}{\varrho}} = g_{\sigma\varrho}g^{\lambda\sigma}A_{\underset{\vee}{\lambda}} \tag{28}$$

qui vérifient

$$A_{\hat{\hat{\varrho}}}+A_\varrho = p(A_{\hat{\varrho}}+A_\varrho)+2(1-q)A_\varrho, \qquad A_\varrho = A_\varrho \tag{29}$$

avec

$$p = 4\left(\frac{\gamma}{g} - \frac{\varphi}{g}\right), \qquad q = 4\left(\frac{\gamma}{g} + \frac{\varphi}{g}\right) \tag{30}$$

permet, par application de l'opération $\hat{}$ à (26) d'introduire uniquement dans cette équation les $L_{\mu\nu,\varrho}$ dont les indices sont modifiés par l'opération $\sim$ telle que

$$A_{\tilde{\varrho}} = A_{\hat{\varrho}} + A_{\check{\varrho}}\,. \tag{31}$$

On obtient en effet

$$2(4-3q)L_{\mu\nu,\varrho} + p(L_{\tilde{\mu}\nu,\varrho} + L_{\mu\tilde{\nu},\varrho} + L_{\mu\nu,\tilde{\varrho}}) + L_{\tilde{\mu}\tilde{\nu},\tilde{\varrho}} = N_{\mu\nu,\varrho} \tag{32}$$

avec

$$N_{\mu\nu,\varrho} = K_{\mu\nu,\varrho} + K_{\hat{\mu}\check{\nu},\check{\varrho}} + K_{\check{\mu}\check{\nu},\hat{\varrho}} + K_{\check{\check{\mu}}\nu,\varrho} + K_{\check{\mu}\nu,\varrho} + K_{\mu\nu,\check{\check{\varrho}}} + K_{\check{\mu}\check{\nu},\check{\varrho}}\,. \tag{33}$$

Or, nous avons montré que l'opération $\tilde{\varrho}$ vérifie la relation de réduction plus simple

$$A_{\tilde{\tilde{\varrho}}} = pA_{\tilde{\varrho}} + 2(2-q)A_{\varrho}\,. \tag{34}$$

En appliquant cette opération à (32) on peut donc, compte tenu de (34), former 4 équations linéaires entre les 4 inconnues

$$L_{\mu\nu,\varrho}, \qquad \tilde{L}_{\tilde{\mu}\nu,\varrho} = L_{\mu\tilde{\nu},\varrho} + L_{\mu\nu,\varrho} + L_{\mu\nu,\tilde{\varrho}},$$

$$\tilde{\tilde{L}}_{\mu\nu,\varrho} = L_{\mu\nu,\varrho} + L_{\mu\nu,\varrho} + L_{\mu\nu,\varrho}, \qquad \tilde{\tilde{\tilde{L}}}_{\mu\nu,\varrho} = L_{\tilde{\mu}\tilde{\nu},\tilde{\varrho}}\,. \tag{35}$$

En reprenant ici les notations très synthétiques proposées récemment par G. Dautcourt [6], nous aurons ainsi la solution générale

$$\text{(B)} \qquad \boxed{L_{\mu\nu,\varrho} = \frac{1}{D}(D_0 N_{\mu\nu,\varrho} + D_1 \tilde{N}_{\mu\nu,\varrho} + D_2 \tilde{\tilde{N}}_{\mu\nu,\varrho} + D_3 \tilde{\tilde{\tilde{N}}}_{\mu\nu,\varrho})}\,. \tag{36}$$

D_0, D_1, D_2, D_3 sont les mineurs formés respectivement par les coefficients de $L_{\mu\nu,\varrho}$, $\tilde{L}_{\mu\nu,\varrho}$, $\tilde{\tilde{L}}_{\mu\nu,\varrho}$ et $\tilde{\tilde{\tilde{L}}}_{\mu\nu,\varrho}$. On les explicite aisément en écrivant l'équation (32) et les 3 autres équations analogues obtenues par application de (34). D est le déterminant du système formé par ces équations. On obtient

$$D = \tfrac{1}{4}(p+3-2q)(p+q)^6(a^2+b^2) =$$

$$= \frac{1}{4}\left(3 - 4\frac{\gamma}{g} - 12\frac{\varphi}{g}\right)\left(8\frac{\gamma}{g}\right)^6(a^2+b^2) \tag{37}$$

en explicitant les expressions (30) de p et de q. Le facteur (a^2+b^2) est celui que nous avons défini en (20).

Nous obtenons ainsi pour la solution exprimée en fonction des $g_{\mu\nu}$ non scindés, une condition d'existence qui se réduit en partie à celle que nous avions obtenue précédemment. Toutefois la présence du facteur

$$3 - \frac{4\gamma}{g} - \frac{12\varphi}{g} \neq 0 \tag{38}$$

semble introduire une restriction supplémentaire.

En utilisant la méthode d'Einstein et Kaufman [7], c'est à dire en considérant la solution particulière obtenue dans le système de coordonnées tel que le tenseur métrique ait une forme diagonale, G. Dautcourt a montré que la condition (38) n'est pas une condition véritable pour l'existence d'une solution [6].

Les conditions d'existence d'une solution des équations fondamentales se réduisent donc à (19) dans l'un et l'autre cas.

En considérant la forme des solutions (14) et (36) il faut avouer que les espoirs d'Einstein d'obtenir une expression plus simple des lois de la physique en utilisant toujours le tenseur fondamental non scindé ne paraît pas justifié. La solution (A) qui utilise la décomposition du tenseur $g_{\mu\nu}$ est incontestablement plus simple et plus maniable que la solution (B). Il en résulte que les équations du champ peuvent se formuler en utilisant (A) mais restent peu accessibles si l'on tient à se servir de (B).

V. LES ÉQUATIONS DU CHAMP ET LEUR INTERPRÉTATION PHYSIQUE (1)

Les équations du champ rigoureuses s'obtiennent en remplaçant dans $R_{\mu\nu}(\Gamma) = 0$ les coefficients de connexion affine $\Gamma^{\varrho}_{\mu\nu}$ par leur valeur en fonction des $g_{\mu\nu}$ et de leurs dérivées premières. On utilise dans ce but la solution rigoureuse (A).

Nous nous bornerons ici à utiliser l'approximation sur les champs antisymétriques

$$\varphi_{\mu\nu} = \varepsilon \underset{1}{\varphi_{\mu\nu}} + \varepsilon^2 \underset{2}{\varphi_{\mu\nu}} + \cdots$$

sans introduire aucune approximation sur les $\gamma_{\mu\nu}$.

Nous obtenons ainsi des équations issues de $\underset{\vee}{R_{\mu\nu}} = 0$ et des équations issues de $\underline{R_{\mu\nu}} = 0$. Nous les appellerons provisoirement équa-

(1) Cf. [8].

tions électromagnétiques (E) et équations de la gravitation (G). Ces équations sont les suivantes

$$\text{(E)} \quad \begin{cases} 1) & \nabla_\varrho \varphi^{\underset{-}{\mu}\underset{-}{\varrho}} = 0, \\ 2) & \Box \varphi_{\mu\nu} = \nabla^\varrho \varphi_{\mu\nu\varrho} = -F_{\mu\nu} - G^{r\sigma}{}_{\mu\nu}\varphi_{r\sigma} \end{cases}$$

$$\text{(G)} \quad \boxed{S_{\mu\nu} \equiv G_{\mu\nu} - \tfrac{1}{2}\gamma_{\mu\nu} G = E_{\mu\nu} + M_{\mu\nu} + X_{\mu\nu} + Y_{\mu\nu}}$$

avec

$$E_{\mu\nu} = -\tfrac{1}{2}(\varphi_{\mu r} F_\nu{}^r + \varphi_{\nu r} F_\mu{}^r) + \tfrac{1}{4}\gamma_{\mu\varepsilon}\varphi_{\lambda\varepsilon} F^{\lambda\varepsilon}, \tag{39}$$

$$M_{\mu\nu} = \tfrac{1}{4}(\varphi_{\mu r\varrho}\varphi_\nu{}^{r\varrho} - \tfrac{1}{6}\gamma_{\mu\nu}\varphi_{\varrho\sigma\lambda}\varphi^{\varrho\sigma\lambda}), \tag{40}$$

$$X_{\mu\nu} = (\nabla^\varrho \varphi_{\nu\lambda})(\nabla^\lambda \varphi_{\mu\varrho}) + \tfrac{1}{4}\nabla_\mu \nabla_\nu(\varphi_{\varrho\sigma}\varphi^{\underset{-}{\varrho}\underset{-}{\sigma}}) -$$

$$-\tfrac{1}{2}\gamma_{\mu\nu}[(\nabla_\lambda \varphi_{r\varrho})(\nabla^\lambda \varphi^{\underset{-}{r}\underset{-}{\varrho}}) - F_{\varrho\sigma}\varphi^{\underset{-}{\varrho}\underset{-}{\sigma}}], \tag{41}$$

$$Y_{\mu\nu} = -\tfrac{1}{2}[G^{\varrho\sigma}{}_{\nu r}\varphi_\mu{}^{\underset{-}{r}} + G^{\varrho\sigma}{}_{\mu r}\varphi_\nu{}^r]\varphi_{\varrho\sigma} + \tfrac{3}{4}\gamma_{\mu\nu} G^{\varrho\sigma}{}_{\lambda r}\varphi_{\varrho\sigma}\varphi^{\underset{-}{\lambda}\underset{-}{r}}. \tag{42}$$

On a posé

$$F_{\mu\nu} = -\tfrac{4}{3}(\partial_\mu \Gamma_\nu - \partial_\nu \Gamma_\mu) \tag{43}$$

et on a désigné par ∇_ϱ, $G^\varrho{}_{\mu\nu\sigma}$ la dérivée covariante et le tenseur de Riemann Christoffel formé avec les symboles $\left\{{\varrho \atop \mu\nu}\right\}_\gamma$.

(1) L'aspect immédiat des équations (G) est satisfaisant car le second membre de ces équations *fait apparaître* un tenseur électromagnétique de Minkowski formé avec les champs $\varphi_{\mu\nu} = g_{\check{\mu\nu}}$ et avec les inductions $F_{\mu\nu}$, un tenseur matériel formé avec le courant $\varphi_{\mu\nu\varrho}$ si l'on convient de lier celui-ci au quadrivecteur vitesse d'univers.

Ainsi on pourrait penser qu'on a réussi à extraire — selon le voeu d'Einstein — une représentation de l'impulsion-énergie électromagnétique et de l'impulsion-énergie matérielle à partir des seules données géométriques satisfaisant les équations du cas extérieur.

Toutefois les objections à une interprétation aussi simple et satisfaisante sont immédiates. Je signalerai seulement celle-ci:

Il est difficile de ne pas admettre en première approximation une proportionalité entre les champs $\varphi_{\mu\nu}$ et les inductions $F_{\mu\nu}$. Or la définition (43) des inductions entraîne $F_{[\mu\nu,\varrho]} = 0$ et par conséquent $\varphi_{\mu\nu\varrho} = \partial_{[\mu} g_{\check{\nu\varrho}]} = 0$. Des relations électromagnétiques (E) découle alors $F_{\mu\nu} = 0$ et l'interprétation unitaire de la théorie s'évanouit.

2) D'autre part on constate que la somme des tenseurs qui figurent au second membre de (G) vérifie *identiquement* une relation de conservation

$$\nabla_\varrho (E_\mu{}^\varrho + M_\mu{}^\varrho + X_\mu{}^\varrho + Y_\mu{}^\varrho) \equiv 0 \tag{44}$$

sans que cette équation soit déduite des équations du champ (G) (dont le premier membre satisfait $\nabla_\varrho S_\mu{}^\varrho \equiv 0$). La situation est donc ici très différente de celle qui intervient en Relativité Générale et pouvait être prévue très aisément.

On sait en effet que le tenseur d'Einstein de la théorie unitaire

$$S_\mu{}^\varrho = \tfrac{1}{2}(g^{\varrho\lambda} R_{\mu\lambda} + g^{\lambda\varrho} R_{\lambda\mu}) - \tfrac{1}{2}\delta_\mu{}^\varrho g^{\alpha\beta} R_{\alpha\beta} \tag{45}$$

satisfait des identités de conservation qu'il est possible d'écrire sous la forme suivante

$$\overset{a}{\nabla}_\varrho S_{\underline{\mu}}{}^\varrho - \tfrac{1}{2} g^{\check{\lambda\nu}} (\partial_\lambda R_{\check{\mu\nu}} + \partial_\nu R_{\check{\lambda\mu}} + \partial_\mu R_{\check{\nu\lambda}}) \equiv 0 \tag{46}$$

en posant

$$\mathcal{G}^{\mu\nu} = \sqrt{-g}\, g^{\mu\nu} = \mathcal{G}^{\underline{\mu\nu}} + \mathcal{G}^{\check{\mu\nu}}$$

$$\sqrt{-a}\, a^{\mu\nu} = \mathcal{G}^{\mu\nu} = \sqrt{-g}\, g^{\underline{\mu\nu}} \quad \text{ou} \quad a^{\mu\nu} = \sqrt{\frac{g}{\gamma}}\, g^{\underline{\mu\nu}} \tag{47}$$

$$S_\mu{}^\varrho = a^{\varrho\lambda} S_{\underline{\mu\lambda}} = a^{\varrho\lambda}(R_{\underline{\mu\lambda}} - \tfrac{1}{2} a_{\mu\lambda} a^{\alpha\beta} R_{\underline{\alpha\beta}}) \tag{48}$$

Si l'on met alors en évidence, à partir de (45), un tenseur d'Einstein Riemannien et relatif à la métrique $a_{\mu\nu}$ en posant

$$S_{\underline{\mu\nu}} = \overset{a}{S}_{\underline{\mu\nu}}(\{\ \}_a) + T_{\underline{\mu\nu}} \tag{49}$$

les identités (46) se réduisent à

$$\overset{a}{\nabla}_\varrho T_\mu{}^\varrho - \tfrac{1}{2} g^{\check{\lambda\nu}} R_{[\check{\mu\nu},\lambda]} \equiv 0. \tag{50}$$

Ainsi l'obtention *d'équations* de conservation

$$\overset{a}{\nabla}_\varrho T_\mu{}^\varrho = 0 \tag{51}$$

résulte des seules identités de conservation si l'on suppose seulement que les équations électromagnétiques

$$R_{[\check{\mu\nu},\lambda]} = 0$$

sont vérifiées. Il n'est aucunement nécessaire comme en Relativité Générale de faire appel aux équations de la gravitation

$$S_{\underline{\mu\nu}} \equiv \overset{a}{S}_{\underline{\mu\nu}}(\{\ \}_a) + T_{\underline{\mu\nu}} = 0$$

et d'appliquer à ces équations l'opération $\overset{a}{\nabla}_\mu$.

Ce privilège est dû à l'existence d'un double jeu d'identités dans la théorie: l'un s'applique au tenseur d'Einstein formé avec la connexion initiale, l'autre au tenseur d'Einstein Riemannien qu'on en peut extraire. Il en résulte évidemment que le résidu (c'est-à-dire la représentation électromagnétique et matérielle extraite ici du premier membre) vérifie aussi des identités et non des équations de conservation. Une circonstance analogue se présente dans les théories riemanniennes pentadimensionelles qui font intervenir elles aussi, un double jeu d'identités. Dans ces dernières théories on peut déduire néanmoins les équations du mouvement par la méthode du tenseur d'énergie grâce à l'intervention d'un tenseur matériel extérieur.

Ainsi, bien que l'établissement des équations du mouvement à partir des équations du champ requiert la présence d'un jeu de quatre identités, la théorie unitaire en offre un nombre surabondant et ne peut aboutir qu'à un système des relations identiquement vérifiées. Bien entendu, une méthode des singularités peut théoriquement s'appliquer. Toutefois les difficultés rencontrées par L. Infeld [9] puis par J. Callaway [10] sont connues. Les tentatives effectuées depuis par J. Treder et E. Clauser sont loin de lever, à notre avis, toutes les difficultés. Il ne faut d'ailleurs pas se dissimuler que l'application d'une méthode des singularités ne peut être tout à fait conforme au principe initial d'une théorie qui admettait les seules solutions régulières, excluant donc la présence explicite ou implicite de toute fonction δ dans les équations.

CONCLUSION

La discussion précédente nous incite à conclure que la théorie unitaire d'Einstein, sous sa forme initiale, ne permet pas de déduire des apports électromagnétiques et matériels la définition d'une force de Lorentz qui conduise — sauf intervention de singularités — à la description du mouvement d'une particule chargée.

Toutefois nous sommes persuadés qu'une modification de la généralisation proposée par Einstein peut acheminer, au moins partiellement, au but qu'Einstein lui-même s'était fixé. Les généralisations "naturelles" de la fonction d'action utilisée en Relativité Générale sont diverses. On peut donc penser qu'une fonction d'action faisant intervenir explicitement, outre le tenseur de Ricci $R_{\mu\nu}$, un autre élément de structure qui échapperait à la détermination par $g_{\underset{+}{\mu}\underset{-}{\nu};\varrho} = 0$ (par exemple le vecteur de torsion Γ_μ) permettrait de modifier le premier jeu d'identités. Une discussion des bases de cette généralisation—discussion qui dépasserait le cadre de cet exposé consacré par principe à la théorie "orthodoxe"—permettrait de préciser un autre départ. Toutefois, si l'on veut s'en tenir à la forme originale de cette théorie qui a suscité beaucoup d'espoir et provoqué un grand débordement de travaux, on ne saurait atteindre, dans le cadre strict de ses principes, les objectifs que l'on s'était tout d'abord proposés.

BIBLIOGRAPHIE

[1] A. Einstein, *Ann. Math.* **46**, 578 (1945); **47**, 731 (1946); *The Meaning of Relativity* (appendice à la 4e édition, 1953).
[2] A. Einstein, *Berlin. Sitzungsb.* 32, 76, 137 (1923).
[3] M. A. Tonnelat, *C. R. Acad. Sci., Paris* **231**, 470, 487, 512, (1950); *J. Phys. Radium* **12**, 81 (1951); **16**, 21 (1955); *J. Phys. Radium* **16**, 21 (1955).
[4] S. Mavridès, *Nuovo Cim.* X, **2**, 1141 (1955),
[5] M. A. Tonnelat, *C. R. Acad. Sci., Paris* **246**, 2277 (1958).
[6] G. Dautcourt, *C. R. Acad. Sci., Paris* **249**, 2159 (1959).
[7] A. Einstein et B. Kaufman, *Ann. Math.* **59**, 230 (1954).
[8] M. A. Tonnelat, *Nuovo Cim.* X, **3**, 902 (1956).
[9] L. Infeld, *Nature Lond.* **166**, 1075 (1950).
[10] J. Callaway, *Phys. Rev.* **92**, 1967 (1953).

PART TWO

ABSOLUTE CHANGE IN GENERAL RELATIVITY

JAMES L. ANDERSON

Stevens Institute of Technology, Hoboken, New Jersey *

Abstract—A definition of absolute change within the framework of general relativity is given. It adheres to the principle of general covariance in that it makes no reference to a particular coordinate system.

INTRODUCTION

WE would like to propose here a definition of absolute change in general relativity. This definition has arisen out of an attempt to understand one of the seeming paradoxical consequences of the principle of general covariance. On the one hand, we observe a world in which things seem to change; we feel that these changes are real in contrast to the view held by Zeno. However, a strict adherence to the principle of general covariance would require a description of this world in terms of invariants. (An invariant is any functional of the basic field variables whose Lie derivative with respect to the vector field ξ^{μ} vanishes for all such vector fields. Put another way, it is any quantity whose value is independent of the particular coordinatization of the space-time manifold.) Among other things, an invariant is a constant of the motion. This property follows directly from the definition of an invariant; it also follows from the fact that the Hamiltonian of general relativity is a linear combination of the constraints of the theory and all invariants must commute with the constraints since the latter are the generators of infinitesimal coordinate transformations. A description of the world in terms of invariants would thus appear changeless or frozen.

* This work was supported by the United States Air Force under contract HAF33(616)5556, monitored by the Aeronautical Research Laboratory, Wright Air Development Center.

Recently Dirac [1] has developed an approach which seems to result in a description wherein the basic dynamical variables are not frozen. In brief, the argument goes as follows: The Hamiltonian of general relativity is of the form

$$H = \int \{ g^{00^{-\frac{1}{2}}} \mathcal{H}_L + g_{0r} \mathcal{H}^r \} d^3x \tag{1}$$

where $\mathcal{H}_L$ and $\mathcal{H}^r$ are the Hamiltonian constraint and the longitudinal constraints respectively and are taken to vanish weakly in the sense of Dirac.

The Hamiltonian constraint is of the form

$$\mathcal{H}_L = \mathcal{H}_{\text{main}} + \{ K^{-1} (K^2 e^{uv})_{,u} \}_{,v} . \tag{2}$$

Dirac now rewrites the expression for the Hamiltonian given in (1) as

$$H = \int \{ \mathcal{H}_{\text{main}} + (g^{00^{-\frac{1}{2}}} - 1) \mathcal{H}_L + g_{0r} \mathcal{H}^r \} d^3x \tag{3}$$

where he has discarded the complete divergence occurring in $\mathcal{H}_L$ from the first term in (3) on the grounds that it does not contribute to the equations of motion. He then proceeds to solve the Hamiltonian constraint equation for $K^{1/3}$ and to insert the resultant expression for $K^{1/3}$ back into the right hand side of Eq. (3). This will cause the second term to vanish identically. Although Dirac does not proceed in this manner, one could also solve the three longitudinal constraints for three momentum densities and substitute these expressions into Eq. (3) also, thereby causing the last term to vanish as well.

Let us look at the resultant expression for the Hamiltonian. It is just

$$H = \int \mathcal{H}_{\text{main}} d^3x \tag{4}$$

where now $\mathcal{H}_{\text{main}}$ is independent of the four variables which we solved for in the constraint equations. The variables canonically conjugate to these "solved for" variables are thus constants of the motion. If we assign them values initially they will maintain them throughout the course of evolution of the world. Such an assignment amounts to the imposition of initial coordinate conditions and is completely analogous to requiring that div $A = 0$ initially as a gauge condition in electromagnetic theory.

As mentioned previously [2], the four initial coordinate conditions referred to above are not sufficient to fix completely the coordinate system, just as the requirement that initially div $A = 0$ is insufficient to fix the gauge in electromagnetic theory. We need four more conditions analogous to the requirement that $\nabla^2\varphi = -\varrho$. The procedure for obtaining them has been given elsewhere [2] so that we will only indicate the method here. Instead of considering the constraint equations as strong relations between the field variables and solving them we solve Eq. (2) (and similar expressions for the longitudinal constraints) for a suitable variable in terms of the other variables and $\mathcal{H}_L$, the latter quantity being regarded for this purpose merely as another variable. We proceed, like Dirac, to substitute the expressions for the solved-for variables into the right hand side of Eq. (3). While the solved-for variables no longer appear, the quantities $\mathcal{H}_L$ and $\mathcal{H}^r$ do occur. To eliminate these latter quantities we make use of the fact that any term which depends upon them to a power higher than the first will not contribute to the equations of motion for the remaining field variables, since their commutators will contain terms which depend upon $\mathcal{H}_L$ and $\mathcal{H}^r$ at least linearly, and hence these terms will vanish modulo the constraint equations. Thus we need only examine the terms in the right hand side of (3) which depend upon $\mathcal{H}_L$ and $\mathcal{H}^r$ linearly. Where these terms occur in $\mathcal{H}_{\text{main}}$, their coefficients will be independent of $(g^{00^{-\frac{1}{2}}}-1)$ and g_{0r} since $\mathcal{H}_{\text{main}}$ is itself independent of these latter quantities. Thus we see that the terms on the right hand side of (3) which are linear in $\mathcal{H}_L$ and $\mathcal{H}^r$ can be made to vanish by appropriate choices of $(g^{00^{-\frac{1}{2}}}-1)$ and g_{0r}. Since these quantities are completely undetermined by the field equations, as regards to their temporal evolution, we can expect these choices to be valid throughout the space-time manifold under consideration. As such they constitute the remaining four coordinate conditions needed to fix the coordinate system completely.

On the basis of the above work we see that we have succeeded in eliminating for consideration as dynamical variables a total of twelve out of the original twenty field variables and their conjugate momenta. (Four of these twelve are the solved-for variables, four their conjugate variables and the other four are the $(g^{00^{-\frac{1}{2}}}-1)$ and g_{0r}.) Four more variables are eliminated by making use of the primary constraints [3], [4] so that we are left with a total of four free variables to describe the dynamics of the gravitational field. Their evolution in time is obtained by computing their Poisson bracket with the Hamiltonian given in Eq. (4). There is of course, now no longer reason for all of these Poisson brackets to vanish. The only place where we must exercise caution in this regard is in our choice of solved-for variables. They must not be chosen in such a manner as to convert $\mathcal{H}_{\text{main}}$ into a complete divergence when the expressions for the solved-for variables are substituted into it. We can be assured that this does not happen if one of the solved-for variables is contained explicitly in the complete divergence term of Eq. (2). (As an example, suppose that the variable we choose to solve for does not appear as a factor in $\mathcal{H}_{\text{main}}$. Then clearly, substitution of this variable back into Eq. (2) will result in an identically vanishing right hand side although $\mathcal{H}_{\text{main}}$ will not be a complete divergence when expressed in terms of the free variables.)

ABSOLUTE CHANGE

It appears that the above procedure leads to a Hamiltonian which yields non-frozen motion of the gravitational field as described by the free variables. However, we cannot as yet be sure whether the physical situation described is really changing or that the change is due simply to the type of coordinate system employed. In other words, on the basis of the above work alone we cannot distinguish between an intrinsically dynamic situation and a static one which appears to change in the course of time because of the particular coordinatization employed. To remedy this situation we propose the following definition of absolute change.

DEFINITION

The geometrical structure of the world is said to be changing in an *absolute sense* if and only if there exists no coordinate system in which the free variables are all constants of the motion.

As it stands, the above definition is intrinsic and as such justifies the use of the term absolute. At the same time it is not a very practical definition since it requires that we look at the evolution of the world in all conceivable coordinate systems. One would like to be able to recast this definition in a more manageable form. Nevertheless, it does serve as a basis for further discussion of the notion of change.

Even if we overlook the above-mentioned limitations on our definition, it would be useless if the choice of the free dynamical variables as well as their evolution in time were not uniquely determined once a particular set of coordinate conditions are adopted. Thus, if there were a large class of free variables remaining after the imposition of coordinate conditions, one would never be sure that there was indeed no real change simply because a large number of them were constants of the motion. On both counts however, we can be sure that the imposition of coordinate conditions leads to unique results. First with regard to the free variables themselves, we note that, once we have chosen the variables to solve for in the constraint equations, the free variables are determined; they are just the four variables left over after eliminating the solved-for variables directly and their canonical conjugates by the imposition of the initial coordinate conditions. While the form of the initial coordinate conditions is to a large degree arbitrary, the variables appearing therein are not so that to each set of initial coordinate conditions there is one and only one set of free variables.

In addition to the question of uniqueness of the free variables we must be sure that their evolution in time is also unique. At first glance, the Dirac breakup of the Hamiltonian seems quite arbitrary. We could have just as well written $\mathcal{H}_L$ in the form

$$\mathcal{H}_L = \mathcal{H}'_{\text{main}} + \{K^{uv}\}_{,uv} \tag{5}$$

and taken the Hamiltonian to be of the form

$$H = \int \{K^{-1}\mathcal{H}'_{\text{main}} + (g^{00^{-\frac{1}{2}}} - K^{-1})\mathcal{H}_L + g_{0r}\mathcal{H}^r\}\, d^3x \tag{4}$$

in contrast to our original expression (3). Proceeding as before, we would find for our Hamiltonian

$$H = \int K^{-1}\mathcal{H}'_{\text{main}}\, d^3x. \tag{6}$$

Thus we would appear to have two different candidates for the Hamiltonian corresponding to the same set of free variables. The resolution to this seeming difficulty comes when we realize that four other coordinate conditions are needed to fix the coordinate system in addition to the initial ones; the method for constructing them was described above where we saw that it led to the setting of $(g^{00^{-\frac{1}{2}}} - 1)$ and g_{0r} equal to the coefficients of $\mathcal{H}_L$ and $\mathcal{H}^r$ in $\mathcal{H}_{\text{main}}$. If we follow the same procedure here we see that the corresponding coordinate conditions would involve the quantity $(g^{00^{-\frac{1}{2}}} - K^{-1})$ in place of $(g^{00^{-\frac{1}{2}}} - 1)$ so that we would have different coordinate conditions in the two cases and hence different coordinate systems. Thus we should be able to decide, in every coordinate system admitted by the type of coordinate conditions used here, in a unique manner whether or not there is change.

DISCUSSION

The definition given above is intimately related to the question of coordinate system. To fix the coordinate system we have made use of a number of coordinate conditions. Whether or not all conceivable coordinate systems can be realized in this manner is still an open question. There seem to be coordinate systems which can be fixed by the imposition of just four coordinate conditions while we require eight. If these systems lie outside the framework of our present treatment it would be necessary to give a separate discussion of the uniqueness of the dynamical variables and their evolution with time in these systems.

REFERENCES

[1] P. A. M. Dirac, *Phys. Rev.* **114**, 924 (1959).
[2] J. L. Anderson, Paper presented at Royaumont Conference on General Relativity.
[3] J. L. Anderson, *Phys. Rev.* **111**, 965 (1958).
[4] P. A. M. Dirac, *Proc. Roy. Soc.* **A246**, 333 (1958).

CANONICAL ANALYSIS OF GENERAL RELATIVITY*

R. L. Arnowitt**, S. Deser and C. W. Misner***

Physics Department, Brandeis University, Waltham, Massachusetts

1. INTRODUCTION

We shall give here a brief summary of the results of a program isolating the dynamical features of the gravitational field.(1) The emphasis here will be on obtaining the independent modes of the field by reformulating the theory in Hamiltonian form *in terms of four canonical variables* which completely specify the motion of the field. The difficulties in obtaining such a form explicitly reside in the general coordinate invariance and the associated intrinsic non-linearity of the theory. The disentangling of the smaller number of minimal Cauchy data from the larger number needed to satisfy coordinate invariance is achieved by means of techniques familiar from the classical dynamics of particles. As a result, the gravitational field takes on the form of a Lorentz covariant field theory. Since the physics of special relativistic fields is well understood we shall find unique and physically satisfactory definitions of such basic quantities as energy, radiation, etc. in general relativity. Further, an approach of this type should be well suited for a transition to a consistent quantum theory.

Since canonical equations of motion are first order, it is convenient to begin with a Lagrangian that is linear in the time derivatives (the "first order" Lagrangian) as the resulting equations are then closely allied to the Hamilton equations. The most important step

* Supported by the National Science Foundation and the United States Air Force.

** On leave from Syracuse University, Syracuse 10, New York.

*** Alfred P. Sloan Research Fellow on leave from Princeton University, Princeton, New Jersey.

(1) The work discussed in this article may be found in greater detail in the papers [1]–[5]. A survey of [1]–[5] is given in [6].

in this reduction of general relativity to canonical form lies in recognizing the structural identity between it and the parameterized form of particle mechanics. This parallel is also important in isolating the role of general coordinate invariance.

This analysis enables one to give explicitly two pairs of independent canonical variables (which represent the minimal Cauchy data) obeying the usual Poisson Bracket (P. B.) relations. The associated Hamiltonian affords a primary definition of the energy which has a simple, coordinate independent, expression. As in electrodynamics, the excitation of the independent canonical modes represents what one ordinarily calls waves. For radiation escaping to infinity, this criterion may be given conveniently in a coordinate independent way. The coupling to other systems does not alter the canonical analysis. Since one may recognize pure particle states by the absence of field excitations in the canonical variables, it is possible to meaningfully obtain the self-energies of single particles. For a charged *point* particle, the static self-energy is *finite* and independent of the bare mass, while for a neutral particle the gravitational self-mass cancels the bare mass, showing that a point particle (as far as the static calculations are concerned) can exist only in virtue of its interaction with non-gravitational fields. This result is in contrast with the usual infinite Newtonian–Coulomb self-energies.

2. CANONICAL FORM

We begin by discussing the parameterized form of particle mechanics. The action for a conservative system of M degrees of freedom may be written as

$$I = \int dt\, L = \int dt \Big(\sum_{i=1}^{M} p_i \dot{q}_i - H(q_j, p_j) \Big) \tag{2.1}$$

where $\dot{q}_i \equiv dq_i/dt$. This action is clearly in canonical form provided every variable in H is found in the $\Sigma p_i \dot{q}_i$ term. The variables q_i and p_i are then canonically conjugate and obey the standard P. B. relations. In order to simulate the coordinate invariance found in general relativity we may introduce an arbitrary parameter $\tau = \tau(t)$ and then treat $t = q_{M+1}(\tau)$ and $-H = p_{M+1}$ as new canonical variables. The action can then be recast into the form

$$I = \int d\tau \Big(\sum_{A=1}^{M+1} p_A q'_A - N(\tau) R(q_A, p_A) \Big) \tag{2.2}$$

where $q'_A \equiv dq_A/d\tau$. Here $N(\tau)$ is a Lagrange multiplier whose variation yields the constraint equation $R = 0$, which may be any equation with solution $p_{M+1} = -H$. Although I is now "generally covariant" with respect to arbitrary transformations $\bar{\tau} = \bar{\tau}(\tau)$, the canonical form has been lost since the Lagrange multiplier N appears in the "Hamiltonian", NR, but not in $\Sigma p_A q'_A$. Given an action in the form (2.2) one may easily recover the canonical form (2.1) by inserting the solution of the constraint equation ($p_{M+1} \to -H$) and imposing the "coordinate condition" $q_{M+1} = \tau$ (which apart from notation is identical to using q_{M+1} as an "intrinsic coordinate").

The action for general relativity,(1) $I = \int d^4x(-{}^4g)^{\frac{1}{2}}\,{}^4R$, can be put in a form analogous to Eq. (2.2) by choosing as basic variables g_{ij}, π^{ij}, N and N_i defined by

$$\pi^{ij} = -(g)^{1/2}(K^{ij} - g^{ij}K), \tag{2.3a}$$

$$N = (-g^{00})^{-1/2}, \qquad N_i = g_{0i},\ g_{ij} = {}^4g_{ij} \tag{2.3b}$$

where $K_{ij} = -N\Gamma^0_{ij}$ is the second fundamental form. One then finds(2)

$$I = \int d^4x\,[\pi^{ij}\,\partial_0 g_{ij} - (NR^0 + N_i R^i)] \tag{2.4}$$

where

$$R^0 \equiv -(g)^{-1/2}[gR + \tfrac{1}{2}\pi^2 - \pi^{ij}\pi_{ij}] = 0, \tag{2.5a}$$

$$R^i \equiv -2\pi^{ij}{}_{|j} = 0 \tag{2.5b}$$

are the constraint equations obtained by varying the Lagrange multipliers N and N_i. The other field equations obtained by varying π^{ij} and g_{ij} together with Eqs (2.5), are equivalent to the Einstein equations. In Eq. (2.4) one has four Lagrange multipliers in contrast to the one entering in the particle case. As was shown in [3]

---

(1) We use units such that $\varkappa = 16\pi\gamma c^{-4} = 1 = c$, where γ is the Newtonian gravitational constant (and rationalized electromagnetic units). Latin indices run from 1 to 3, Greek from 0 to 3. The summation convention holds even if repeated indices are both co- or contravariant. A comma or ∂_μ represents ordinary differention. All notation is three-dimensional unless a prefix "4" appears. Thus R is the scalar curvature formed from the three tensor g_{ij}, and $g^{ij} (\neq {}^4g^{ij})$ is the three matrix inverse to g_{ij}. Covariant differentiation, denoted by $|$, is with respect to the three metric.

(2) In obtaining Eq. (2.4), and subsequently, we have discarded total time derivatives and spatial divergences. In general, the addition of a time derivative leads to a change of coordinate conditions (see [4a]). There actually exist specific requirements on what spatial divergences should be dropped in the parameterized formalism (see [3a]), which have been observed here.

this is characteristic of a parameterized field theory and arises due to the fact that there are now four coordinates.

The reduction to canonical form is carried out by solving Eqs (2.5) for four appropriate variables (analogous to p_{M+1}), inserting these solutions into Eq. (2.4) and imposing coordinate conditions there. This process is best performed by making use of the linear orthogonal decomposition on the symmetric arrays g_{ij} and π^{ij}. For any $f_{ij} = f_{ji}$ we write

$$f_{ij} = f_{ij}^{TT} + f_{ij}^{T} + (f_{i,j} + f_{j,i}) \tag{2.6}$$

where each of the quantities on the right hand side is a unique linear functional of f_{ij}. The quantity f_{ij}^{TT} has two independent components and is transverse and traceless ($f_{ij}^{TT}{}_{,j} = 0$, $f_{ii}^{TT} = 0$); f_{ij}^{T} is transverse ($f_{ij}^{T}{}_{,j} = 0$) and uniquely determined by its trace $f^T \equiv f_{ii}^T$. The vector f_i can also be broken up into its transverse and longitudinal (curlless) parts

$$f_i = f_i^T + \tfrac{1}{2} f^L{}_{,i} \qquad (f_i^T{}_{,i} = 0).$$

In terms of this decomposition, one finds that the linear part of Eq. (2.5a) involves only g^T while the linear part of Eq. (2.5b) involves only π^i. Thus, Eqs (2.5) are soluble for g^T and π^i in an iteration scheme (see [3]). Inserting the orthogonal decomposition for both g_{ij} and π^{ij} into the action (2.4), one finds

$$I = \int d^4x \{ \pi^{ijTT} \partial_0 g_{ij}^{TT} - (-g^T{}_{,ii}) \partial_0 \left[-\left(\frac{1}{2} \nabla^2\right) \pi^T \right] + \\ + 2(-\pi^i{}_{,jj} - \pi^j{}_{,ij}) \partial_0 (g_i) - (NR^0 + N_i R^i) \} . \tag{2.7}$$

In obtaining Eq. (2.7), we have made use of the fact that the time derivative and the orthogonal decomposition commute. The operator $1/\nabla^2$ is the inverse of the cartesian Laplacian with appropriate boundary conditions. Inserting the solutions of the constraint equations (2.5) and imposing the coordinate conditions [(1)]

$$t = -\left(\frac{1}{2} \nabla^2\right) \pi^T , \tag{2.8a}$$

$$x^i = g_i \tag{2.8b}$$

I reduces to the canonical form

$$I = \int d^4x \{ \pi^{ijTT} \partial_0 g_{ij}^{TT} - \mathcal{H}[g_{ij}^{TT}, \pi^{ijTT}] \} \tag{2.9}$$

(1) The operator $1/\nabla^2$ may be chosen to be the Coulomb Green's function if one, for example, replaces t by $te^{-\alpha r}$ and x^i by $x^i e^{-\alpha r}$ (in Eqs (2.8)) and takes the limit $\alpha \to 0$ at the end of the calculation.

where $-\nabla^2 g^T = \mathcal{H}$ is the solution of Eqs (2.5) for g^T. (A more complete derivation of this result can be found in [3].) The central result (2.9) now allows us to write down the fundamental P. b. relations

$$[g_{ij}^{TT}(\boldsymbol{r}, t), \pi^{mnTT}(\boldsymbol{r}', t)] = \delta^{mn}{}_{ij}(\boldsymbol{r}-\boldsymbol{r}'), \tag{2.10a}$$

$$[g_{ij}^{TT}(\boldsymbol{r}, t), g_{mn}{}^{TT}(\boldsymbol{r}', t)] = [\pi^{ijTT}(\boldsymbol{r}, t), \pi^{mnTT}(\boldsymbol{r}', t)] = 0. \tag{2.10b}$$

Here $\delta^{mn}{}_{ij}$ is a Dirac δ-function modified to take into account the transverse-traceless nature of the variables on the left hand side: it is symmetric, transverse and traceless on each pair of indices. It does not depend on the metric. Further one also has the P. b. equations of motion:

$$\partial_0 g_{ij}{}^{TT} = [g_{ij}{}^{TT}, H] = \delta H/\delta\pi^{ijTT}, \tag{2.11a}$$

$$\partial_0 \pi^{ijTT} = [\pi^{ijTT}, H] = -\delta H/\delta g^{ijTT} \tag{2.11b}$$

where $H = \int d^3\boldsymbol{r}\mathcal{H}$. These are identical to the Lagrange equations in the coordinate system (2.8).

The Hamiltonian H reduces correctly to the Hamiltonian of canonical linearized theory (see [1]) in first approximation, with the same set of canonical variables and coordinate conditions. In fact, Eqs (2.8) incorporate the rectangular boundary conditions of flat space at spatial infinity. These boundary conditions provide the primary physical criterion for deciding what combinations of the field variables may be taken as coordinates. Of course, one may add into Eqs (2.8) other structures which vanish at spatial infinity. This will not affect the interpretation of any experiment where the measuring apparatus is kept at spatial infinity (1) (see [4c]).

Different coordinate conditions (obeying the boundary conditions) correspond to different canonical variables. An example that will be of use later is furnished by the coordinate conditions

$$t = -(\tfrac{1}{2}\nabla^2)(\pi^T + \nabla^2\pi^i), \tag{2.12a}$$

$$x^i = g_i - (\tfrac{1}{4}\nabla^2)g^T{}_{,i}. \tag{2.12b}$$

In this frame, the canonical variables, $g_{ij}{}^{TT}$ and π^{ijTT}, now have the transverse traceless property with respect to the new coordinates and so are different from the set previously considered. This frame

(1) Similarly, in particle mechanics one could replace the time coordinate by $t+f(q(t), p(t))$ without affecting the physics of the situation. We might also note that even properties of bound orbit states can be obtained by asymptotic measurements (J. Plebański, private communication).

is of interest since for $g_{ij}{}^{TT} = 0$, the spatial metric reduces to isotropic form, i.e., $g_{ij} = (1 + \frac{1}{2}g^T)\delta_{ij}$.

Coupling of other systems to the gravitational field leaves the canonical analysis unchanged. For the case of point charges and the electromagnetic field coupled to the Einstein field the Lagrangian density takes the form (see [4] and [5]):

$$\mathcal{L} = \pi^{ij}\partial_0 g_{ij} + A_i{}^T\partial_0\mathfrak{E}^{iT} + p_i(dr^i/dt)\delta^3(\mathbf{r} - \mathbf{r}(t)) - (N\bar{R}^0 + N_i\bar{R}^i) \tag{2.13}$$

where r^i is the position and p_i the canonical momentum of the particle, and δ^3 is invariantly defined in three space as a scalar density, i.e., $\int d^3r\,\delta^3(\mathbf{r}) = 1$ in any frame. The canonical coordinates and momenta of the electromagnetic field are the transverse parts of the vector potential A_i and the electric field vector density $\mathfrak{E}_i \equiv \mathfrak{F}^{0i} = (-{}^4g)^{1/2}\mathrm{F}^{0i}$. The constraint equations now read

$$\bar{R}^0 \equiv R^0 + \tfrac{1}{2}g^{-1/2}\mathfrak{E}^i\mathfrak{E}_i + \tfrac{1}{4}g^{1/2}B_{ij}B^{ij} + \\ + [(p_i - eA_i{}^T)(p^i - eA^{iT}) + m_0^2]^{1/2}\delta^3(\mathbf{r} - \mathbf{r}(t)) = 0\,, \tag{2.14a}$$

$$\bar{R}^i \equiv R^i - B_{ij}\mathfrak{E}^j - (p_i - eA_i{}^T)\delta^3(\mathbf{r} - \mathbf{r}(t)) = 0 \tag{2.14b}$$

where $B_{ij} \equiv A_j{}^T{}_{,i} - A_i{}^T{}_{,j}$ and $\mathfrak{E}^i{}_{,i}$ is determined by the electromagnetic constraint equation $\mathfrak{E}^i{}_{,i} = e\delta^3(\mathbf{r} - \mathbf{r}(t))$. The constraint equations are again to be solved for g^T and π^i. Inserting these solutions and imposing the coordinate conditions (2.8) leads to canonical form as before with $-\nabla^2 g^T = \mathcal{H}[g^{TT}, \pi^{TT}, A^T, \mathfrak{E}^T, \mathbf{p}, \mathbf{r}]$ now being the total Hamiltonian density of the combined system. The gravitational canonical variables are again $g_{ij}{}^{TT}$ and π^{ijTT}.

3. ENERGY AND RADIATION

The canonical formalism developed in the previous section brought out the features of general relativity that have their counterpart in usual Lorentz covariant field theories. As a result, we can carry out the physical interpretation of the theory in terms of the same quantities that characterize Lorentz covariant physics.

The energy of the gravitational field is just the numerical value of the Hamiltonian for a particular solution of the field equations. In obtaining the energy, it is not necessary to express the Hamiltonian as a function of the canonical variables. Thus the energy E is given by

$$E = -\int d^3\mathbf{r}\,\nabla^2 g^T = -\oint g^T{}_{,i}\,dS_i = \oint (g_{ij,j} - g_{jj,i})\,dS_i \tag{3.1}$$

where dS_i is a two dimensional surface element at spatial infinity. Since it turns out that $\mathcal{H}$ does not depend explicitly on the coordinates x^μ (see [3]) the energy is a constant of the motion.

In evaluating the surface integrals of Eq. (3.1) it is not necessary to use the canonical frame in which Eq. (3.1) was derived: at spatial infinity, where linearized theory may rigorously be used, and hence coordinate transformations are infinitesimal, g^T, π^i, and the canonical variables are invariant. Thus E is independent of the frame and may be evaluated by the last member of Eq. (3.1) in any asymptotically rectangular coordinate system where $g_{\mu\nu,\alpha} \sim r^{-2}$ (see [4c]).

The energy and the momentum[1] P_i depend only on g_{ij} and π^{ij} at a given time. In the absence of coordinate conditions these are appropriate initial Cauchy data for relativity. When coordinate conditions are imposed, E and P_i depend only on the canonical variables, which represent the minimal Cauchy data.

As in electrodynamics, excitations of the canonical variables may be used to define waves. When sources are present, this definition is unchanged. Strictly speaking, of course, one can only separate radiation from induction effects in the "wave zone" but also as in electrodynamics, this definition may be employed consistently near the sources (but then in a non-unique fashion). For radiation escaping to infinity, the Poynting vector provides a measure of the flux of radiation. It can be shown (see [4b]) that the Poynting vector is $-2(\pi^i{}_{,jj} + \pi^j{}_{,ij}) = -2\pi^{ij}{}_{,j}$ at least asymptotically, and so is coordinate invariant since it depends only on π^i. Similarly, the existence of $g_{ij}{}^{TT}$ and π^{ijTT} provides a coordinate-invariant local specification of a wave in the asymptotic region.

For the coupled situation, Eq. (3.1) represents the energy of the total system. It states that the coefficient of $1/r$ in the asymptotic form of the metric is the total gravitational mass of the system.[2]

4. APPLICATION TO THE SELF-ENERGY PROBLEM

The canonical treatment allows us to deal rigorously with some problems involving coupled systems. In particular, we shall examine the initial value problem for point charges interacting with the

---

[1] The field momentum density may be shown to be (see [3]) $-2\pi^{ij}{}_{,j}$.

[2] Our expression (3.1) for the energy turns out to be equal to those arising from the Einstein pseudotensor and the Landau–Lifshitz expression in their surface integral forms where only the leading linearized terms need be retained since the metric is asymptotically rectangular at spatial infinity (and the $g_{0\mu}$ do not contribute). See [4c].

Einstein and Maxwell fields. The application of interest here is to the static self-energy of such particles. The canonical formalism allows us to isolate those situations which are pure particle states (i.e., states in which no canonical excitation of either field is initially present).

For the case of a point charge, we work in the coordinate frame (2.12) which, with initial conditions $g_{ij}^{TT} = \pi^{ijTT} = A^T{}_i = \mathfrak{E}^{iT} = p_i = 0$, reduces the metric to isotropic form ($g_{ij} = \chi^4 \delta_{ij}$). Eq. (2.14a) becomes simply

$$-8\chi \nabla^2 \chi = m_0 \delta^3(\boldsymbol{r}) + \tfrac{1}{2}\chi^{-2} \mathfrak{E}^i \mathfrak{E}^i \tag{4.1}$$

where $\mathfrak{E}^i$ is fully determined by the Maxwell constraint $\mathfrak{E}^i{}_{,i} = e\delta^3(\boldsymbol{r})$ (since $\mathfrak{E}^{iT} = 0$). Eq. (4.1) has a solution of the form $\chi^2 = \psi^2 - \varphi^2$ where $\psi = 1 + (a/32\pi r)$, $\varphi = (e/16\pi r)$ and a is given by

$$a = \lim_{\varepsilon \to 0} 16\pi[-\varepsilon + \{\varepsilon^2 + (e/8\pi)^2 + m_0 \varepsilon/8\pi\}^{1/2}]. \tag{4.2}$$

The parameter ε is essentially the radius of the δ-function source term.(1) From Eq. (3.1) we see that $E = a$ where E now represent the total mass, m (bare mass m_0 plus self-mass δm), of the static particle. From Eq. (4.2) one has $m = 2|e|$ (or in conventional rationalized units, $m = e/(4\pi\gamma)^{1/2}$). Thus the self-mass is finite in contrast to the usual infinite Newtonian $(-\gamma m_0^2/2\varepsilon)$ and Coulomb $(\frac{1}{2}e^2/4\pi\varepsilon)$ self-energies. Note that m is independent of m_0 and so the self-mass cancels out the bare mechanical mass. For a neutral particle one has $m = 0$, showing that the mass of a particle arises from its interaction with non-gravitational fields(2) and is rendered finite by the gravitational effects. (The result (4.2), expanded in a "dilute" limit, m_0, $e \ll \varepsilon$, gives rise to the standard Newtonian result $m = m_0 + \frac{1}{2}(e^2/4\pi - \gamma m_0^2)/\varepsilon + o(1/\varepsilon^2)$ showing how the divergences arise from an incorrect perturbation expansion.)

Our one-particle metric differs strikingly from the conventional ones of Schwarzschild and Reissner–Nordstrom. These metrics do not satisfy their respective field equations at the origin and hence the arbitrary parameter m appearing in them cannot be related to the source strengths m_0 and e. Further, the canonical formalism

---

(1) That is, in solving Eq. (4.1), an extended distribution of radius ε was used as a model of the δ-function. In the limit $\varepsilon \to 0$ the results are model-independent (see [5]).

(2) The bare mechanical mass density is a source of zero range and therefore gives no contribution to the energy. The reason a non-vanishing mass is obtained from coupling to non-gravitational fields is that the field energy term is spread out in a non-zero region.

determines uniquely the dependence of the matter stress tensor on the metric. In contrast, in the usual discussion of, say, the interior Schwarzschild solution, the bare rest mass density is never even introduced, while the "proper rest-mass density" includes clothing effects in an unanalyzed manner.

We have also been able to find a pure particle solution for two point charges of like sign. Here (for equal charges) $E = 4|e| = 2m$ again independent of the bare masses. The absence of an interaction energy (i.e., E is independent of the inter-particle separation) is consistent with the single particle result above, which determines a charge to mass ratio leading to complete cancellation between electrostatic repulsion and gravitational attraction. The lack of interaction is further borne out by the fact that this two body solution is actually static [7]. (For further details of the above calculations see [4] and [5].)

5. OUTLOOK

We have seen that a complete canonical formalism may be established for general relativity on the classical level. This canonical analysis has allowed us to define such things as energy and radiation in a physically unique fashion, in direct correspondence with the definitions for these quantities in all other fields. The classical theory has turned out to yield results of interest to elementary particle physics in that self-energies arising from point interactions have turned out to be finite at least in the static case. This may be traced to the special form of gravitational interactions which modify the free Lagrangians of all fields (in a non-linear fashion) rather than merely add an interaction term. To be realistic, the classical suppression of divergences must ultimately be tested in the quantum domain. There one must get not only finite but numerically appropriate results.[1]

The extension of our formalism to the quantum domain is in one sense immediate since the fundamental unconstrained Poisson brackets are known. However, such a correspondence quantization will encounter many possible difficulties (not found in linear theories) on the consistency level. A quantum principle that guarantees consistency (if it is possible to quantize at all) is the Schwinger Action Principle [9]. Investigation in this direction may show that some useful features, at least, of correspondence quantization are valid.

[1] See in this connection [8].

REFERENCES

[1] R. L. Arnowitt and S. Deser, *Phys. Rev.* **113**, 745 (1959).
[2] R. L. Arnowitt, S. Deser and C. W. Misner, *Phys. Rev.* **116**, 1322 (1959).
[3] R. L. Arnowitt, S. Deser and C. W. Misner, *Phys. Rev.* **117**, 1595 (1960).
[3a] R. L. Arnowitt, S. Deser and C. W. Misner, *J. Math. Phys.* **1**, 434 (1960).
[4] R. L. Arnowitt, S. Deser and C. W. Misner, *Phys. Rev.* **118**, 1100 (1960).
[4a] R. L. Arnowitt, S. Deser and C. W. Misner, *Nuovo Cim.* **19**, 668 (1961).
[4b] R. L. Arnowitt, S. Deser and C. W. Misner, *Phys. Rev.* **121**, 1556 (1961).
[4c] R. L. Arnowitt, S. Deser and C. W. Misner, *Phys. Rev.* **122**, 997 (1961).
[5] R. L. Arnowitt, S. Deser and C. W. Misner, *Phys. Rev.* **120**, 313 (1960).
[5a] R. L. Arnowitt, S. Deser and C. W. Misner, *Phys. Rev.* **120**, 321 (1960).
[5b] R. L. Arnowitt, S. Deser and C. W. Misner, *Ann. Phys.* (N. Y.) **11**, 116 (1960).
[6] R. L. Arnowitt, S. Deser and C. W. Misner, article in a forthcoming book edited by L. Witten, to be published by J. Wiley N. Y.
[7] A. Papapetrou, *Proc. R. Irish Acad.* **51**A, 191 (1947).
[8] L. D. Landau, *Niels Bohr and the Development of Modern Physics*, Pergamon Press, 1955, p. 60.
[9] J. Schwinger, *Phys. Rev.* **91**, 713 (1953).

THE EQUATIONS OF MOTION AND THE ACTION PRINCIPLE IN GENERAL RELATIVITY

S. Bażański

Institute of Physics, Polish Academy of Sciences, Warsaw

It is well known that in General Relativity (G. R.) as in any other classical field theory, we can obtain the equations of the field and of the motion of point particles interacting by means of this field by varying a functional[(1)] $W[g_{\alpha\beta}, g_{\alpha\beta|\sigma}, \overset{A}{\xi}{}^k, \overset{A}{\xi}{}^k{}_{|0}]$ with respect to the gravitational field $g_{\alpha\beta}$ and with respect to the coordinates of the particles. Independently of this, it is known that the equations of motion, expressed only in terms of the coordinates of the particles and their derivatives, in some cases (e.g. Lorentz equations in the case of a standing wave solution in electrodynamics, or EIH [1] equations of motion in G. R.) may be derived from a Fokker-type action principle with an action $W_F[\overset{A}{\xi}{}^k, \overset{A}{\xi}{}^k{}_{|0}]$. Such actions, which depend only on the positions and velocities of the particles, have been found (or rather guessed) from an explicit form of the equations of motion formulated by means of the concepts of the "action at a distance" theory. For instance, for the EIH equation of motion the Fokker-type action principle was found in [2] and in [4].

However, there is a simple mathematical criterion for the existence of a Fokker-type action $W_F[\overset{A}{\xi}{}^k \overset{A}{\xi}{}^k{}_{|0}]$ and a simple method of constructing such an action when only the field action $W[g_{\alpha\beta}, g_{\alpha\beta|\sigma}, \overset{A}{\xi}{}^k, \overset{A}{\xi}{}^k{}_{|0}]$ is known. Thus according to this method, we can construct the action $W_F[\overset{A}{\xi}{}^k, \overset{A}{\xi}{}^k{}_{|0}]$ without knowledge of the

(1) Latin indices = 1, 2, 3; Greek indices = 0, 1, 2, 3; $\overset{A}{\xi}{}^k$—spatial coordinates of the Ath particle; $A = 1, 2, \ldots, N$, where N is number of the particles.

equations of motion. More, the connection between the field and the Fokkerian action principle can be employed to formulate a method of deriving the equations of motion. This method as employed in G. R. is in some respects simpler than the classical methods [1], [3] or [4].

We shall formulate here by this method the Fokkerian action for the equations of motion in the post-Newtonian approximation of the EIH method in the case of G. R. combined with electrodynamics. [(1)]

1. Let us consider N charged point particles interacting by means of an electromagnetic and gravitational field. We shall describe these particles by singularities of the gravitational and electromagnetic fields, using the formalism of the δ function introduced by Infeld and Plebański in [6] and [7] (see the Appendix of [10]).

The gravitational field $g_{\alpha\beta}$ and the electromagnetic field $f_{\mu\nu}$ are defined by the combined system of Einstein–Maxwell equations

$$\boldsymbol{R}^{\alpha\beta}-\tfrac{1}{2}g^{\alpha\beta}\boldsymbol{R} = -8\pi(\boldsymbol{T}^{\alpha\beta}+\boldsymbol{E}^{\alpha\beta}), \tag{1.1}$$

$$(f^{\alpha\beta}\sqrt{-g}\,)_{|\beta} = 4\pi\boldsymbol{j}^{\alpha}, \tag{1.2}$$

$$f_{\alpha\beta} = A_{\alpha|\beta}-A_{\beta|\alpha}, \tag{1.3}$$

where $\boldsymbol{T}^{\alpha\beta}$, $\boldsymbol{E}^{\alpha\beta}$ and $\boldsymbol{j}^{\alpha}$ have the following form:

$$\boldsymbol{T}^{\alpha\beta} = \sum_{A=1}^{N}\overset{A}{m}\,\delta_3(x-\overset{A}{\xi})\,\overset{A}{\xi}{}^{\alpha}{}_{|0}\,\overset{A}{\xi}{}^{\beta}{}_{|0}, \tag{1.4}$$

$$\boldsymbol{E}^{\alpha\beta} = -\frac{\sqrt{-g}}{4\pi}\,(f^{\alpha\varrho}f_{\mu\varrho}g^{\mu\beta}-\tfrac{1}{4}g^{\alpha\beta}f^{\mu\nu}f_{\mu\nu}), \tag{1.5}$$

$$\boldsymbol{j}^{\alpha} = \sum_{A=1}^{N}\overset{A}{e}\,\delta_3(x-\overset{A}{\xi})\,\overset{A}{\xi}{}^{\alpha}{}_{|0}, \tag{1.6}$$

and $\overset{A}{\xi}{}^{\mu}(x^0)$ are the coordinates of the particles. We assume $\overset{A}{\xi}{}^{0}{}_{|0} = 1$. Employing Bianchi identities we deduce

$$\int\limits_{\overset{A}{\Omega}} d_3x\,(\boldsymbol{T}^{\alpha\beta}{}_{;\beta}+\boldsymbol{E}^{\alpha\beta}{}_{;\beta}) = 0. \tag{1.7}$$

---

(1) Another application and some generalizations of this idea are given in [5].

These equations define the motion of singularities. It can be shown (cf. [9]) that they are equivalent to the equations

$$(\overset{A}{m}\overset{A}{\overline{g_{\alpha k}}}\,\overset{A}{\xi}{}^{\alpha}{}_{|0})_{|0}-\tfrac{1}{2}\overset{A}{m}\overset{A}{\overline{g_{\mu\nu|k}}}\,\overset{A}{\xi}{}^{\mu}{}_{|0}\,\overset{A}{\xi}{}^{\nu}{}_{|0}+\overset{A}{e}\,\overset{A}{\overline{f_{k\mu}}}\,\overset{A}{\xi}{}^{\mu}{}_{|0}=0\,, \tag{1.8}$$

$$\overset{A}{m}=\overset{A}{m}_0\frac{dt}{\overset{A}{ds}}\,,\qquad \overset{A}{m}_0=\text{const}. \tag{1.9}$$

Assuming Eqs (1.3) we can derive Eqs (1.1), (1.2) and (1.8) from an action principle by varying[1]

$$W[g_{\alpha\beta},A_{\alpha},\overset{A}{\xi}{}^{k}]=\sum_{A=1}^{N}\overset{A}{m}_0\int_{t'}^{t''}(\overset{A}{\overline{g_{\alpha\beta}}}\,\overset{A}{\xi}{}^{\alpha}{}_{|0}\,\overset{A}{\xi}{}^{\beta}{}_{|0})^{1/2}dt+$$

$$+\sum_{A=1}^{N}\overset{A}{e}\int_{t'}^{t''}\overset{A}{\overline{A_{\alpha}}}\,\overset{A}{\xi}{}^{\alpha}{}_{|0}dt+\frac{1}{16\pi}\int_{\Omega}d_4x f^{\alpha\beta}f_{\alpha\beta}\sqrt{-g} \tag{1.10}$$

—where

$$G\sqrt{-g}=\sqrt{-g}\,g^{\alpha\beta}\left(\left\{{\lambda\atop \alpha\mu}\right\}\left\{{\mu\atop \lambda\beta}\right\}-\left\{{\lambda\atop \alpha\beta}\right\}\left\{{\mu\atop \lambda\mu}\right\}\right) \tag{1.11}$$

is Einstein's Lagrangian density—with respect to the independent variables $g^{\alpha\beta}$, A_{α}, $\overset{A}{\xi}{}^{k}$ and putting the variations of all these quantities equal to zero at the boundaries of corresponding regions of integration.

Let us suppose now that we have eliminated from (1.8) the fields $g_{\alpha\beta}(x^{\mu})$ and $A_{\alpha}(x^{\mu})$, replacing them by a solution[2] $g_{\alpha\beta}(x^{\mu},\overset{A}{\xi}{}^{k},\overset{A}{\xi}{}^{k}{}_{|0})$ and $A_{\alpha}(x^{\mu},\overset{A}{\xi}{}^{k},\overset{A}{\xi}{}^{k}{}_{|0})$ of the field equations. Thus we obtain the equations of motion in terms of the "interaction at a distance" concept. It is hard to decide *a priori* whether there exists an action principle leading to these equations in a direct way. However, it can easily be shown that when a solution $g_{\alpha\beta}(x^{\mu},\overset{A}{\xi}{}^{k},\overset{A}{\xi}{}^{k}{}_{|0})$, $A_{\alpha}(x^{\mu},\overset{A}{\xi}{}^{k},\overset{A}{\xi}{}^{k}{}_{|0})$ of the

(1) For brevity we use the notation: $W[g_{\alpha\beta},A_{\alpha},\overset{A}{\xi}{}^{k}]$ which suppresses the functional dependence of W on the derivatives $g_{\alpha\beta|\sigma}$, $A_{\alpha|\sigma}$, $\overset{A}{\xi}{}^{k}{}_{|0}$.

(2) For the moment we avoid all questions concerning the method of solving the field equations. Generally speaking, the solutions of the fields must be functionals of the world lines of the particles but we can assume that they are only functions of $\overset{A}{\xi}{}^{k}$ and $\overset{A}{\xi}{}^{k}{}_{|0}$ since we shall later use the EIH approximation method where this simpler assumption is fulfilled.

field equations[1] (1.1)–(1.3) behaves at spatial infinity in such a way that at any time[2]

$$\int\limits_{K_\infty}\left(\frac{\partial(G\sqrt{-g})}{\partial g^{\alpha\beta}{}_{|k}}\,\delta^* g^{\alpha\beta}+4f^{\alpha k}\sqrt{-g}\,\delta^* A_\alpha\right)n_k\,d_2\sigma=0,\qquad(1.12)$$

then

$$W[g_{\alpha\beta}(x^\mu,\overset{A}{\xi}{}^k,\overset{A}{\xi}{}^k{}_{|0}),A_\alpha(x^\mu,\overset{A}{\xi}{}^k,\overset{A}{\xi}{}^k{}_{|0}),\overset{A}{\xi}{}^k]=W_F[\overset{A}{\xi}{}^k,\overset{A}{\xi}{}^k{}_{|0}]\qquad(1.13)$$

is a (Fokker-type) action leading to the equations of motion formulated in the theory of "interaction at a distance", which can be derived by replacing the fields in the equations of motion of the field theory by the solution used in (1.12).

Let us calculate the variation δW_F with respect to $\overset{A}{\xi}{}^k$

$$\delta W_F=\sum_{A=1}^{N}\sum_{B=1}^{N}\overset{A}{m}_0\int\limits_{t'}^{t''}dt\left[\frac{\partial}{\partial\overset{B}{\xi}{}^k}\,\overline{(g_{\alpha\beta}\,\overset{A}{\xi}{}^\alpha{}_{|0}\,\overset{A}{\xi}{}^\beta{}_{|0})^{1/2}}^{A}\,\delta\overset{B}{\xi}{}^k+\frac{\partial}{\partial\overset{B}{\xi}{}^k{}_{,0}}\,\overline{(g_{\alpha\beta}\,\overset{A}{\xi}{}^\alpha{}_{|0}\,\overset{A}{\xi}{}^\beta{}_{|0})^{\frac12}}^{A}\times\right.$$

$$\left.\times\,\delta\overset{B}{\xi}{}^k{}_{|0}\right]+\frac{1}{16\pi}\int\limits_{\Omega}d_4x\left[\frac{\partial G\sqrt{-g}}{\partial g^{\alpha\beta}}\,\delta^* g^{\alpha\beta}+\frac{\partial G\sqrt{-g}}{\partial g^{\alpha\beta}{}_{|\sigma}}\,\delta^* g^{\alpha\beta}{}_{|\sigma}\right]+$$

$$+\sum_{A=1}^{N}\sum_{B=1}^{N}\overset{A}{e}\int\limits_{t'}^{t''}dt\left[\left(\frac{\partial\overset{A}{\overline{A}}_\alpha}{\partial\overset{B}{\xi}{}^k}\,\delta\overset{B}{\xi}{}^k+\frac{\partial\overset{A}{\overline{A}}_\alpha}{\partial\overset{B}{\xi}{}^k{}_{|0}}\,\delta\overset{B}{\xi}{}^k{}_{|0}\right)\overset{A}{\xi}{}^\alpha{}_{|0}+\delta_{AB}\,\overset{A}{\tilde{A}}_k\,\delta\overset{A}{\xi}{}^k{}_{|0}\right]-$$

$$-\frac12\int\limits_{\Omega}\boldsymbol{E}_{\alpha\beta}\,\delta^* g^{\alpha\beta}\,d_4x+\frac{1}{4\pi}\int\limits_{\Omega}f^{\mu\nu}\,\delta^* A_{\mu|\nu}\sqrt{-g}\,d_4x.\qquad(1.14)$$

---

[1] Hereafter we shall deal with the solution $g_{\alpha\beta}(x^\mu,\overset{A}{\xi}{}^k,\overset{A}{\xi}{}^k{}_{|0})$, $A_\alpha(x^\mu,\overset{A}{\xi}{}^k,\overset{A}{\xi}{}^k{}_{|0})$ and not with the field variables $g_{\alpha\beta}(x^\mu)$ and $A_\alpha(x^\mu)$; thus we shall denote this solution in brief by $g_{\alpha\beta}$ and A_α.

[2] K_∞ here denotes a sphere with infinite radius in the three-dimensional, space $x^0=\text{const}$; $\delta^* g^{\alpha\beta}$ and $\delta^* A_\alpha$ are the variations of the solution $g^{\alpha\beta}(x^\mu,\overset{A}{\xi}{}^k,\overset{A}{\xi}{}^k{}_{|0})$, $A_\alpha(x^\mu,\overset{A}{\xi}{}^k,\overset{A}{\xi}{}^k{}_{|0})$ caused by the variations of the world lines $\delta\overset{A}{\xi}{}^k$; for $\varphi=g^{\alpha\beta}(x^\mu,\overset{A}{\xi}{}^k,\overset{A}{\xi}{}^k{}_{|0})$, $A_\alpha(x^\mu,\overset{A}{\xi}{}^k,\overset{A}{\xi}{}^k{}_{|0})$ we have

$$\delta^*\varphi=\sum_{A=1}^{N}\left(\frac{\partial\varphi}{\partial\overset{A}{\xi}{}^k}\,\partial\overset{A}{\xi}{}^k+\frac{\partial\varphi}{\partial\overset{A}{\xi}{}^k{}_{|0}}\,\partial\overset{A}{\xi}{}^k{}_{|0}\right).$$

Taking into account (A.2) in [10], and that

$$\frac{\partial}{\partial \overset{B}{\xi}{}^k}\big(\overline{g_{\alpha\beta}}^{A}\,\overset{A}{\xi}{}^{\alpha}{}_{|0}\,\overset{A}{\xi}{}^{\beta}{}_{|0}\big)^{1/2} = \frac{1}{2}\frac{dt}{\overset{A}{\widetilde{ds}}}\,\overset{A}{\tilde g}_{\alpha\beta|\xi^k}\,\overset{A}{\xi}{}^{\alpha}_{|0}\,\overset{A}{\xi}{}^{\beta}{}_{|0}$$

$$= \frac{1}{2}\frac{dt}{\overset{A}{\widetilde{ds}}}\int d_3x\,\frac{\partial g_{\alpha\beta}}{\partial \overset{B}{\xi}{}^k}\,\delta_3(x-\overset{A}{\xi})\,\overset{A}{\xi}{}^{\alpha}{}_{|0}\,\overset{A}{\xi}{}^{\beta}{}_{|0} + \frac{1}{2}\frac{dt}{\overset{A}{\widetilde{ds}}}\,\overline{g_{\alpha\beta|k}}^{A}\,\overset{A}{\xi}{}^{\alpha}{}_{|0}\,\overset{A}{\xi}{}^{\beta}{}_{|0}\,\delta_{AB}, \qquad (1.15)$$

$$\frac{\partial}{\partial \overset{B}{\xi}{}^k{}_{|0}}\big(\overline{g_{\alpha\beta}}^{A}\,\overset{A}{\xi}{}^{\alpha}{}_{|0}\,\overset{A}{\xi}{}^{\beta}{}_{|0}\big)^{1/2} = \frac{dt}{\overset{A}{\widetilde{ds}}}\,\delta_{AB}\,\overline{g_{\alpha k}}^{A}\,\overset{A}{\xi}{}^{\alpha}{}_{|0} +$$

$$+ \frac{1}{2}\frac{dt}{\overset{A}{\widetilde{ds}}}\int d_3x\,\frac{\partial g_{\alpha\beta}}{\partial \overset{B}{\xi}{}^k{}_{|0}}\,\delta_3(x-\overset{A}{\xi})\,\overset{A}{\xi}{}^{\alpha}{}_{|0}\,\overset{A}{\xi}{}^{\beta}{}_{|0}, \qquad (1.16)$$

and repeatly using the formulae for $\delta^* g_{\alpha\beta}$ and $\delta^* A_\alpha$ (cf. footnote (2) p. 140), we have

$$\delta W_F = \sum_{A=1}^{N}\overset{A}{m}_0\int_{t'}^{t''} dt\,\frac{dt}{\overset{A}{\widetilde{ds}}}\big(\tfrac{1}{2}\overline{g_{\alpha\beta|k}}^{A}\,\overset{A}{\xi}{}^{\alpha}{}_{|0}\,\overset{A}{\xi}{}^{\beta}{}_{|0}\,\delta\overset{A}{\xi}{}^k + \overline{g_{\alpha k}}^{A}\,\overset{A}{\xi}{}^{\alpha}{}_{|0}\,\delta\overset{A}{\xi}{}^k{}_{|0}\big) +$$

$$+\frac{1}{2}\int_\Omega d_4x\,\boldsymbol{T}^{\alpha\beta}\delta^* g_{\alpha\beta} + \frac{1}{16\pi}\int_\Omega d_4x\left(\frac{\partial G\sqrt{-g}}{\partial g^{\alpha\beta}}\,\delta^* g^{\alpha\beta} + \frac{\partial G\sqrt{-g}}{\partial g^{\alpha\beta}{}_{|\sigma}}\,\delta^* g^{\alpha\beta}{}_{|\sigma}\right) +$$

$$+\int_\Omega d_4x\,\boldsymbol{j}^{\alpha}\delta^* A_\alpha + \sum_{A=1}^{N}\overset{A}{e}\int_{t'}^{t''}\big(\overline{A_k}^{A}\,\delta\overset{A}{\xi}{}^k{}_{|0} + \overline{A_{\alpha|k}}^{A}\,\delta\overset{A}{\xi}{}^k{}_{|0}\big)\,dt -$$

$$-\frac{1}{2}\int_\Omega d_4x\,\boldsymbol{E}_{\alpha\beta}\delta^* g^{\alpha\beta} + \frac{1}{4\pi}\int_\Omega f^{\mu\nu}\,\delta^* A_{\mu|\nu}\sqrt{-g}\,d_4x; \qquad (1.17)$$

here $T^{\alpha\beta}$ is given by Eqs (1.4) and (1.9). Integrating by parts (1)

(1) The four-dimensional region of integration Ω is bounded by a hypersurface $\sum$ which consists of two hyperplanes $x^0 = x^{0\prime} = \text{const}$, $x^0 = x^{0\prime\prime} = \text{const}$, and of a timelike hypersurface τ.

and making use of (A.3) in [10] we obtain

$$dW_F = \sum_{A=1}^{N} \int_{t'}^{t''} dt \Bigg[\frac{1}{2} \overset{A}{m}_0 \frac{dt}{d\overset{A}{s}} \overset{A}{g}_{\alpha\beta|k} \overset{A}{\xi}{}^{\alpha}{}_{|0} \overset{A}{\xi}{}^{\beta}{}_{|0} -$$

$$- \overset{A}{m}_0 \Big(\frac{dt}{d\overset{A}{s}} \overset{A}{g}_{\alpha k} \overset{A}{\xi}{}^{\alpha}{}_{|0} \Big)_{|0} + \overset{A}{e} \overset{A}{\tilde{f}}_{\alpha k} \overset{A}{\xi}{}^{\alpha}{}_{|0} \Bigg] \delta \overset{A}{\xi}{}^{k} -$$

$$- \frac{1}{2} \int_{\Omega} d_4 x \Big[\frac{1}{8\pi} \Big(R_{\alpha\beta} - \frac{1}{2} g_{\alpha\beta} R \Big) \sqrt{-g} + \boldsymbol{T}_{\alpha\beta} + \boldsymbol{E}_{\alpha\beta} \Big] \delta^* g^{\alpha\beta} -$$

$$- \frac{1}{4\pi} \int_{\Omega} d_4 x [(\sqrt{-g}\, f^{\mu\nu})_{|\nu} - 4\pi \boldsymbol{j}^{\mu}] \delta^* A_{\mu} +$$

$$+ \sum_{A=1}^{N} \Big(\overset{A}{m}_0 \overset{A}{g}_{\alpha k} \overset{A}{\xi}{}^{\alpha}{}_{|0} \frac{dt}{d\overset{A}{s}} + \overset{A}{e} \overset{A}{A}_k \Big) \delta \overset{A}{\xi}{}^{k} \Big|_{t'}^{t''} +$$

$$+ \frac{1}{16\pi} \int_{\Sigma} d_3 \sigma n_{\sigma} \Big(\frac{\partial G \sqrt{-g}}{\partial g^{\alpha\beta}{}_{|\sigma}} \delta^* g^{\alpha\beta} + 4 f^{\mu\sigma} \sqrt{-g}\, \delta^* A_{\mu} \Big). \qquad (1.18)$$

The second and the third integral vanish because $g_{\alpha\beta}(x^{\mu}, \overset{A}{\xi}{}^{k}, \overset{A}{\xi}{}^{k}{}_{|0})$ and the $A_{\alpha}(x^{\mu}, \overset{A}{\xi}{}^{k}, \overset{A}{\xi}{}^{k}{}_{|0})$ satisfy the field equations (1.1) and (1.2). The last integration can be found in the following way:

$$\int_{\Sigma} d_3 \sigma n_{\sigma} (\ldots) = \int d_3 x \Big(\frac{\partial G \sqrt{-g}}{\partial g^{\alpha\beta}{}_{|0}} \delta^* g^{\alpha\beta} + 4 f^{\mu 0} \sqrt{-g}\, \delta^* A_{\mu} \Big) \Big|_{t'}^{t''} +$$

$$+ \int_{t'}^{t''} dt \int_{K} d_2 \sigma n_k \Big(\frac{\partial G \sqrt{-g}}{\partial g^{\alpha\beta}{}_{|k}} \delta^* g^{\alpha\beta} + 4 f^{\mu k} \sqrt{-g}\, \delta^* A_{\mu} \Big), \qquad (1.19)$$

where K is a two-dimensional closed surface, being a section of the hypersurface τ by a hyperplane $x^0 = \text{const}$ $(x^{0\prime} \leqslant x^0 \leqslant x^{0\prime\prime})$. Thus we see that the action principle $\delta W_F = 0$ for any variations $\delta \overset{A}{\xi}{}^{k}(t)$, which together with their first time derivatives vanish at the boundaries of the interval (t', t''), leads to the equations of motion (1.8) (in which the mass $\overset{A}{m}$ must be replaced by (1.9)) from which the fields are eliminated, if and only if the fields $g_{\alpha\beta}$, A_α used for this elimination, fulfil condition (1.12). We observe that $\delta^* g^{\alpha\beta}$ and $\delta^* A_\mu$ vanish automatically on the part of the boundary defined by $x^0 = x^{0\prime}, x^0 = x^{0\prime\prime}$, since $\delta \overset{A}{\xi}{}^k$ and $\delta \overset{A}{\xi}{}^k{}_{|0}$ vanish at t' and t''; while at τ the arbitrary variations of the world lines cannot cause the vanishing of $\delta^* g^{\alpha\beta}$ and $\delta^* A_\beta$.

2. We shall use this relation between the field action and the Fokker-type action to find the post-Newtonian Lagrangian for the equations of motion. Thus we must combine the foregoing considerations with the EIH approximation procedure. According to the EIH approximation method we expand $h_{\alpha\beta} = g_{\alpha\beta} - \eta_{\alpha\beta}$ ($\eta_{00} = 1$, $\eta_{kl} = -\delta_{kl}$, $\eta_{0m} = 0$) into a series with respect to powers of c^{-1} (these powers will be suppressed in the terms of the expansion)

$$h_{\alpha\beta} = \sum_{i=1}^{\infty} \underset{i}{h_{\alpha\beta}}.$$

After a suitable change of the coordinate system we can reduce this expansion to the form

$$h_{00} = \underset{2}{h_{00}} + \underset{4}{h_{00}} + \underset{6}{h_{00}} + O\left(\frac{1}{c^7}\right),$$

$$h_{0m} = \underset{3}{h_{0m}} + \underset{5}{h_{0m}} + O\left(\frac{1}{c^6}\right),$$

$$h_{mn} = \underset{2}{h_{mn}} + \underset{4}{h_{mn}} + O\left(\frac{1}{c^5}\right).$$

We also expand the electromagnetic potential A_α in powers of c^{-1}. However, here we shall adopt only the standing wave potential of the form

$$A_0 = \sum_{i=1}^{\infty} \underset{2i}{A_0}, \qquad A_k = \sum_{i=1}^{\infty} \underset{2i+1}{A_k},$$

since for the whole expansion $\sum_{i=1}^{\infty} \underset{i}{A}$ condition (1.12) would not be fulfilled.

In the lowest order of the approximation method we can solve the field equations for an arbitrary motion of the singularities. Thus we have $\underset{2}{h_{00}}$, $\underset{2}{h_{mn}}$, $\underset{2}{A_0}$, and $\underset{3}{A_k}$ as functions depending on x^μ and on arbitrary $\overset{A}{\xi}{}^k$. Writing $\underset{\to 4}{W} = \underset{2}{W}+\underset{4}{W}$ ($\underset{2}{W}$ is usually a constant) we obtain

$$\underset{\to 4}{W_F}[\overset{A}{\xi}{}^k] = \underset{\to 4}{W}[\underset{2}{h_{\alpha\beta}}(x^\mu, \overset{A}{\xi}{}^k), \underset{2}{A_0}(x^\mu, \overset{A}{\xi}{}^k), \overset{A}{\xi}{}^k].$$

This functional will be a proper Fokker-type action in the Newtonian approximation if condition (1.12) is fulfilled. Of course, such an action leads to the Newtonian equations of motion which define the Newtonian motion $\underset{0}{\overset{A}{\xi}}{}^k$. In the next approximation step the field equations allow us to find $\underset{3}{h_{0m}}$ as a function of the $\overset{A}{\xi}{}^k$ which differs from the Newtonian $\underset{0}{\overset{A}{\xi}}{}^k$ by an arbitrary quantity $\underset{2\to}{\overset{A}{\xi}}{}^k = \underset{2}{\overset{A}{\xi}}{}^k + \underset{4}{\overset{A}{\xi}}{}^k + \ldots$ of higher (in comparison with Newtonian) order (cf. [4]). Thus, after checking condition (1.12) we obtain

$$\underset{\to 6}{W_F} = \underset{\to 4}{W_F}[\overset{A}{\xi}{}^k] + \underset{6}{W_F}[\underset{0}{\overset{A}{\xi}}{}^k + \underset{2\to}{\overset{A}{\xi}}{}^k].$$

The argument of $\underset{\to 4}{W_F}$ is quite arbitrary, while that of $\underset{6}{W_F}$ consists of two parts: the Newtonian $\underset{0}{\overset{A}{\xi}}{}^k$ and an arbitrary post-Newtonian deviation $\underset{2\to}{\overset{A}{\xi}}{}^k$. If in $\underset{\to 4}{W_F}$ we put $\overset{A}{\xi}{}^k = \underset{0}{\overset{A}{\xi}}{}^k + \underset{2\to}{\overset{A}{\xi}}{}^k$, we obtain the whole $\underset{\to 6}{W_F}$ as a functional of the thus restricted $\overset{A}{\xi}{}^k$. Thus we can obtain the post-Newtonian action which allows us to deduce the post-Newtonian equations of motion. By performing the explicit calculations it can be assumed that the whole $\overset{A}{\xi}{}^k$ varies arbitrarily because we are looking for equations of motion which define the world lines $\underset{\to 2}{\overset{A}{\xi}}{}^k = \underset{0}{\overset{A}{\xi}}{}^k + \underset{2}{\overset{A}{\xi}}{}^k$ up to the post-Newtonian approximation (and not for any approximation step separately).

In order to find the Lagrangian by the EIH approximation method we have to know the solution of the field equations in the lowest order of this method

$$\underset{2}{h_{00|rr}} = 8\pi \sum_{A=1}^{N} \overset{A}{m}_0 \delta_3(x - \overset{A}{\xi}), \qquad \underset{3}{h_{0m|rr}} = -16\pi \sum_{A=1}^{N} \overset{A}{m}_0 \delta_3(x - \overset{A}{\xi}) \overset{A}{\xi}{}^m_{|0}, \quad (2.1)$$

$$\underset{2}{A}_{0|rr} = -4\pi \sum_{A=1}^{N} \overset{A}{e}\delta_3(x-\overset{A}{\xi}), \qquad \underset{3}{A}_{l|kk} = 4\pi \sum_{A=1}^{N} \overset{A}{m}_0\delta_3(x-\overset{A}{\xi})\overset{A}{\xi}{}^{l}{}_{|0}, \tag{2.2}$$

$$\underset{2}{A}_{0|0} - \underset{3}{A}_{k|k} = 0. \tag{2.3}$$

We have (cf. [1] and [3])

$$\underset{2}{h}_{00} = -\sum_{A=1}^{N} \frac{2\overset{A}{m}_0}{\overset{A}{r}}, \qquad \underset{2}{h}_{mn} = \delta_{mn}\underset{2}{h}_{00}, \qquad \underset{3}{h}_{0m} = \sum_{A=1}^{N} \frac{4\overset{A}{m}_0}{\overset{A}{r}}\overset{A}{\xi}{}^{m}{}_{|0}, \tag{2.4}$$

$$\underset{2}{A}_0 = \sum_{A} \frac{\overset{A}{e}}{\overset{A}{r}}, \qquad \underset{3}{A}_m = -\sum \frac{\overset{A}{e}}{\overset{A}{r}}\overset{A}{\xi}{}^{m}{}_{|0} \tag{2.5}$$

where $\overset{A}{r}{}^2 = (x^s - \overset{A}{\xi}{}^s)(x^s - \overset{A}{\xi}{}^s)$. We can easily evaluate the asymptotic behaviour of these quantities and their derivatives at spatial infinity. We then have

$$\underset{2}{h}_{00} \sim \underset{3}{h}_{0m} \sim \underset{2}{A}_0 \sim \underset{3}{A}_k \sim \frac{1}{r}, \qquad \underset{2}{h}_{00|m} \sim \underset{3}{h}_{0m|l} \sim \underset{2}{h}_{00|0} \sim \underset{2}{A}_{0|m} \sim$$

$$\sim \underset{2}{A}_{0|0} \sim \frac{1}{r^2} \tag{2.6}$$

where $r^2 = x^k x^k$. Knowing $\underset{2}{h}_{00}$, $\underset{2}{h}_{mn}$, and $\underset{2}{A}_0$ we can find $(G+f^{\mu\nu}f_{\mu\nu})\sqrt{-g}$ in the Newtonian approximation order, verify condition (1.12) in this order, and get the Newtonian Lagrangian. From this Lagrangian we obtain the Newtonian equations of motion

$$\overset{A}{m}_0\overset{A}{\xi}{}^{s}{}_{|00} = \frac{1}{2}\sum_{\substack{B=1\\B\neq A}}^{N} \frac{\partial}{\partial \overset{A}{\xi}{}^{s}} \frac{\overset{A}{m}_0\overset{B}{m}_0 - \overset{A}{e}\overset{B}{e}}{\overset{AB}{r}} \tag{2.7}$$

where $\overset{AB}{r}{}^2 = (\overset{A}{\xi}{}^k - \overset{B}{\xi}{}^k)(\overset{A}{\xi}{}^k - \overset{B}{\xi}{}^k)$. To evaluate the asymptotic behaviour of $\underset{3}{h}_{0m|0}$ and of $\underset{3}{A}_{m|0}$ we have to make use of Eqs (2.7). We have

$$\underset{3}{h}_{0m|0} = 4\sum_{A=1}^{N} \frac{\overset{A}{m}_0\overset{A}{\xi}{}^{m}{}_{|00}}{\overset{A}{r}} - 4\sum_{A=1}^{N} \overset{A}{m}_0\overset{A}{\xi}{}^{m}{}_{|0}\overset{A}{\xi}{}^{s}{}_{|0}\left(\frac{1}{\overset{A}{r}}\right)_{|s}. \tag{2.8}$$

The second term above behaves at infinity like r^{-2}. Taking into account (2.7) and the formula: $\overset{A}{r}{}^{-1} = r^{-1} + O(r^{-2})$, we can find the first term in (2.8):

$$4\sum_{A=1}^{N} \frac{\overset{A}{m}_0}{\overset{A}{r}} \overset{A}{\xi}{}^m{}_{|00} = \frac{2}{r}\sum_{A=1}^{N}\sum_{\substack{B=1\\B\neq A}}^{N} (\overset{A}{m}_0\overset{B}{m}_0 - \overset{A}{e}\overset{B}{e})\frac{\partial}{\partial \overset{A}{\xi}{}^m}\frac{1}{\overset{AB}{r}} + O(r^{-2}).$$

The first expression vanishes here because of the symmetry properties; thus we conclude that the whole quantity (2.8) behaves like r^{-2}. The discussion of $\underset{3}{A}_{k|0}$ is quite analogous. Thus

$$\underset{3}{h}_{0m|0} \sim \underset{3}{A}_{m|0} \sim \frac{1}{r^2}. \tag{2.9}$$

In order to obtain the post-Newtonian Lagrangian it is not necessary to know $\underset{4}{h}_{00}$ and $\underset{4}{A}_0$ (as it was in previous methods); however we must know the asymptotic behaviour of these quantities. They are defined by the equations

$$\underset{4}{R}_{00} = -8\pi\underset{4}{\Theta}_{00}, \qquad \underset{4}{\underbrace{A_{0;\beta}^{\;\;\beta}}} = 4\pi\underset{4}{j}_0 - \underset{2}{A}_0\underset{2}{R}_{00}, \tag{2.10}$$

where $\sqrt{-g}\,\Theta_{00} = g_{\alpha 0}g_{\beta 0}(\boldsymbol{T}^{\alpha\beta} - \frac{1}{2}g^{\alpha\beta}\boldsymbol{T})$. From (2.10) we obtain

$$\underset{4}{h}_{00|ss} = \underset{2}{h}_{00|00} + 2\underset{}{\Lambda}_{00} + 16\pi\underset{4}{\Theta}_{00},$$

$$\underset{4}{A}_{0|ss} = \underset{2}{A}_{0|00} + \underset{4}{\mathscr{A}}_0 - 4\pi j_0 + \underset{2}{A}_0\underset{2}{R}_{00}$$

where $\underset{4}{\Lambda}_{00}$ and $\underset{4}{\mathscr{A}}_0$ are nonlinear expressions containing products of derivatives of both fields in the Newtonian approximation order (these expressions do not contain time derivatives). Only the contributions to $\underset{4}{h}_{00}$ and $\underset{4}{A}_0$ (denoted by $\underset{4}{\bar{h}}_{00}$ and $\underset{4}{\bar{A}}_0$) coming from $\underset{2}{h}_{00|00}$ and $\underset{2}{A}_{0|00}$ might tend to zero at infinity more slowly then r^{-1} (the other contributions tend to zero more rapidly than r^{-1} because they are solutions of the Poisson equations with the righthand side tending to zero at infinity). However, because of (2.7) the contributions of $\underset{4}{\bar{h}}_{00}$ and $\underset{4}{\bar{A}}_0$ also behave like r^{-1}. We have

$$\underset{4}{\bar{h}}_{00} = -\frac{1}{4\pi}\int d_3x'\frac{\underset{2}{h}_{00|00}}{r} = \frac{1}{2}\sum_{A}\overset{A}{m}_0\overset{A}{r}_{|00}.$$

For large r, $\overset{A}{r} = r - \overset{A}{\xi}{}^k x^k r^{-1} + O(r^{-1})$, thus

$$\underset{4}{\bar{h}_{00}} = -\frac{1}{2}\frac{x^s}{r}\sum_{A=1}^{N} \overset{A}{m}_0 \overset{A}{\xi}{}^s{}_{|0} + O(r^{-1}) = O(r^{-1}),$$

since the sum vanishes by (2.7) and by its symmetric properties. Repeating this treatment for $\underset{4}{\bar{A}_0}$ we finally obtain

$$\underset{4}{h_{00}} \sim \underset{4}{A_0} \sim \frac{1}{r}, \qquad \underset{4}{h_{00|mm}} \sim \underset{4}{A_{0|m}} \sim \frac{1}{r^2}. \tag{2.11}$$

Now we can check condition (1.12) in the post-Newtonian approximation. After some calculations we obtain

$$\underbrace{\sqrt{-g}\, G}_{\to 6} = \tfrac{1}{2}\underset{2}{h_{00|m}}\underset{2}{h_{00|m}} - \underset{2}{h_{00}}\underset{2}{h_{00|m}}\underset{2}{h_{00|m}} + \tfrac{3}{2}\underset{2}{h_{00|0}}\underset{2}{h_{00|0}} -$$

$$- 2\underset{2}{h_{00|m}}\underset{3}{h_{0m|0}} + \tfrac{1}{2}\underset{3}{h_{0l|m}}\underset{3}{h_{0m|l}} - \tfrac{1}{2}\underset{3}{h_{0m|l}}\underset{3}{h_{0m|l}} + \underset{2}{h_{00|m}}\underset{4}{h_{00|m}}, \tag{2.12}$$

$$\underbrace{f^{\mu\nu} f_{\mu\nu}\sqrt{-g}}_{\to 6} = -2\underset{2}{A_{0|m}}\underset{2}{A_{0|n}} - 4\underset{2}{A_{0|n}}\underset{4}{A_{0|n}} + 2\underset{2}{A_{0|n}}\underset{2}{A_{0|n}}\underset{2}{h_{00}} +$$

$$+ 4\underset{2}{A_{0|n}}\underset{3}{A_{n|0}} + 2\underset{3}{A_{l|k}}\underset{3}{A_{l|k}} - 2\underset{3}{A_{l|k}}\underset{3}{A_{k|l}}. \tag{2.13}$$

We see that according to (2.6), (2.9) and (2.11) the quantities (2.12) and (2.13) behave at least like r^{-4}. Thus the expression

$$\frac{\partial(G\sqrt{-g})}{\partial g^{\alpha\beta}{}_{|k}}\,\delta^* g^{\alpha\beta} + \frac{\partial(f^{\mu\nu} f_{\mu\nu}\sqrt{-g})}{\partial A_{\alpha|k}}\,\delta^* A_\alpha,$$

being the integrand in (1.12), behaves like r^{-3} (of course $\delta^*\varphi$ behaves like φ) and condition (1.12) is fulfilled. Thus we conclude that

$$L = \sum_{A=1}^{N} \overset{A}{m}_0 (\overset{A}{\overline{g_{\alpha\beta}}}\, \overset{A}{\xi}{}^{\alpha}{}_{|0}\, \overset{A}{\xi}{}^{\beta}{}_{|0})^{1/2} + \frac{1}{16\pi}\int d_3x\, G\sqrt{-g} + \sum_{A=1}^{N} \overset{A}{e}\, \overset{A}{\overline{A_\alpha}}\, \overset{A}{\xi}{}^{\alpha}{}_{|0} +$$

$$+ \frac{1}{16\pi}\int d_3x\, f^{\mu\nu} f_{\mu\nu}\sqrt{-g} \tag{2.14}$$

is the Lagrangian leading to the post-Newtonian equations of motion. To evaluate it we find expressions (2.12) and (2.13) using condition (2.3) and the relation: $2\underset{2}{h_{00|0}} + \underset{3}{h_{0m|m}} = 0$ which follows immediately from (2.4). We then have

$$\underbrace{G\sqrt{-g}}_{\to 6} = -\tfrac{1}{2}\underset{2}{h}_{00|mm}\underset{2}{h}_{00} - \underset{2}{h}_{00|mm}\underset{4}{h}_{00} + \tfrac{1}{2}\underset{3}{h}_{0m|ll}\underset{3}{h}_{0m} + \tfrac{1}{2}\underset{2}{h}_{00|mm}\underset{2}{h}_{00}\underset{2}{h}_{00} - \tfrac{1}{8}\underset{3}{h}_{0l|l}\underset{3}{h}_{0m|m} + \underset{\to 6}{W}_{m|m} + \underset{\to 5}{W}_{0|0}, \qquad (2.15)$$

$$\underbrace{\sqrt{-g}\,f^{\mu\nu}f_{\mu\nu}}_{\to 6} = 2\underset{2}{A}_{0|mm}\underset{2}{A}_{0} + 4\underset{2}{A}_{0|mm}\underset{4}{A}_{0} + 2\underset{2}{h}_{00}\underset{2}{A}_{0|mm}\underset{2}{A}_{0} + \underset{2}{h}_{00|mm}\underset{2}{A}_{0}\underset{2}{A}_{0} - 2\underset{3}{A}_{l|kk}\underset{3}{A}_{l} + 2\underset{3}{A}_{l|l}\underset{3}{A}_{k|k} + \underset{\to 6}{V}_{m|m} + \underset{\to 5}{V}_{0|0} \qquad (2.16)$$

where $\underset{\to 6}{W}_m$, $\underset{5}{W}_0$, $\underset{\to 6}{V}_m$, and $\underset{5}{V}_0$ are constructed by means of the fields h and A and its derivatives, so that $\underset{\to 5}{W}_m \sim \underset{\to 6}{V}_m \sim r^{-3}$. Therefore the contribution of these terms will vanish after integration. We also omit the time derivatives which give no contribution to the Lagrangian. Integrating (2.15), and (2.16), using the field equations (2.1) and (2.2) and taking into account that

$$\frac{1}{8\pi}\int d_3x \sum_{A=1}^{N}\sum_{B=1}^{N}\left(\frac{1}{\overset{A}{r}}\right)_{|l}\left(\frac{1}{\overset{B}{r}}\right)_{|m}\overset{A}{\xi}{}^{l}{}_{|0}\,\overset{B}{\xi}{}^{m}{}_{|0} = -\frac{1}{4}\sum_{A=1}^{N}\sum_{\substack{B=1\\ B\neq A}}^{N}\overset{AB}{r}{}_{|\overset{A}{\xi}{}^{l}\overset{B}{\xi}{}^{m}}\,\overset{A}{\xi}{}^{l}{}_{|0}\,\overset{A}{\xi}{}^{m}{}_{|0},$$

we have

$$\underbrace{\frac{1}{16\pi}\int d_3x\,(G+f^{\mu\nu}f_{\mu\nu})\sqrt{-g}}_{\to 6} = -\sum_{A=1}^{N}\Bigg\{\tfrac{1}{4}\overset{A}{m}_0\overset{A}{\overline{\underset{2}{h}_{00}}} + \tfrac{1}{2}\overset{A}{m}_0\overset{A}{\overline{\underset{4}{h}_{00}}} + \tfrac{1}{2}\overset{A}{m}_0\overset{A}{\overline{\underset{3}{h}_{0m}}}\,\overset{A}{\xi}{}^{m}{}_{|0} - \tfrac{1}{4}\overset{A}{m}_0\overset{A}{\overline{\underset{2}{h}_{00}}}\,\overset{A}{\overline{\underset{2}{h}_{00}}} - \tfrac{1}{4}\sum_{\substack{B=1\\ B\neq A}}^{N}\overset{A}{m}_0\overset{B}{m}_0\overset{AB}{r}{}_{|\overset{A}{\xi}{}^{m}\overset{B}{\xi}{}^{l}}\,\overset{A}{\xi}{}^{l}{}_{|0}\,\overset{B}{\xi}{}^{m}{}_{|0} + \tfrac{1}{2}\overset{A}{e}\,\overset{A}{\overline{\underset{2}{A}_{0}}} + \overset{A}{e}\,\overset{A}{\overline{\underset{4}{A}_{0}}} + \tfrac{1}{2}\overset{A}{e}\,\overset{A}{\overline{\underset{3}{A}_{k}}}\,\overset{A}{\xi}{}^{k}{}_{|0} + \tfrac{1}{4}\sum_{\substack{B=1\\ B\neq A}}^{N}\overset{AB}{e\,e}\,\overset{AB}{r}{}_{|\overset{A}{\xi}{}^{m}\overset{A}{\xi}{}^{l}}\,\overset{A}{\xi}{}^{l}{}_{|0}\,\overset{B}{\xi}{}^{m}{}_{|0} + \tfrac{1}{2}\overset{A}{e}\,\overset{A}{\overline{\underset{2}{h}_{00}}}\,\overset{A}{\overline{\underset{2}{A}_{0}}} - \tfrac{1}{2}\overset{A}{m}_0\overset{A}{\overline{\underset{2}{A}_{0}}}\,\overset{A}{\overline{\underset{2}{A}_{0}}}\Bigg\}. \qquad (2.17)$$

Expanding the remaining part of the Lagrangian (2.14) we get

$$\underbrace{\sum_{A=1}^{N}\overset{A}{m}_0(\tilde{g}_{\alpha\beta}\overset{A}{\xi}{}^{\alpha}{}_{|0}\overset{A}{\xi}{}^{\beta}{}_{|0})^{1/2}}_{\to 6} + \sum_{A=1}^{N}\underbrace{\overset{A}{e}\,\overset{A}{\overline{A}}_{\alpha}\,\overset{A}{\xi}{}^{\alpha}{}_{|0}}_{\to 6} = \sum_{A}\Bigg\{\overset{A}{m}_0\Big(1-\tfrac{1}{2}\overset{A}{\xi}{}^{k}{}_{|0}\overset{A}{\xi}{}^{k}{}_{|0} + \tfrac{1}{2}\overset{A}{\overline{\underset{2}{h}_{00}}} + \tfrac{1}{2}\overset{A}{\overline{\underset{4}{h}_{00}}} - \tfrac{1}{2}\overset{A}{\overline{\underset{2}{h}_{00}}}\,\overset{A}{\overline{\underset{2}{h}_{00}}} - \tfrac{1}{8}(\overset{A}{\xi}{}^{k}{}_{|0}\overset{A}{\xi}{}^{k}{}_{|0})^2 + \tfrac{3}{4}\overset{A}{\overline{\underset{2}{h}_{00}}}\,\overset{A}{\xi}{}^{k}{}_{|0}\overset{A}{\xi}{}^{k}{}_{|0} + \overset{A}{\overline{\underset{3}{h}_{0m}}}\,\overset{A}{\xi}{}^{m}{}_{|0}\Big) + \overset{A}{e}\,\overset{A}{\overline{\underset{2}{A}_{0}}} - \overset{A}{e}\,\overset{A}{\overline{\underset{4}{A}_{0}}} - \overset{A}{e}\,\overset{A}{\overline{\underset{3}{A}_{k}}}\,\overset{A}{\xi}{}^{k}{}_{|0} + \overset{A}{e}\,\overset{A}{\overline{\underset{2}{h}_{00}}}\,\overset{A}{\overline{\underset{2}{A}_{0}}}\Bigg\}. \qquad (2.18)$$

We see that the Lagrangian (2.14), being the sum of (2.17) and (2.18) does not depend on the fields $\underset{4}{h}_{00}$ and $\underset{4}{A}_0$. Thus to construct the equations of motion by this method we need only the fields $\underset{2}{h}_{00}$, $\underset{3}{h}_{0m}$, $\underset{2}{A}_0$, $\underset{3}{A}_k$. Taking into account (2.4) and (2.5) we obtain

$$\underset{\to 6}{L} = \sum_{A} \overset{A}{m}_0 - \tfrac{1}{2}\sum_{A=1}^{N} \overset{A}{m}_0 \overset{A}{\xi}{}^{k}{}_{|0} \overset{A}{\xi}{}^{k}{}_{|0} - \tfrac{1}{8}\sum_{A=1}^{N} \overset{A}{m}_0 (\overset{A}{\xi}{}^{k}{}_{|0} \overset{A}{\xi}{}^{k}{}_{|0})^2 - \tfrac{1}{2}\sum_{A=1}^{N}\sum_{B=1}^{N}{}' \frac{\overset{A}{m}_0\overset{B}{m}_0}{\overset{AB}{r}} +$$

$$+\tfrac{1}{6}\sum_{A=1}^{N}\sum_{B=1}^{N}{}'\sum_{C=1}^{N}{}'' \overset{A}{m}_0\overset{B}{m}_0\overset{C}{m}_0 \left(\frac{1}{\overset{AB}{r}\,\overset{BC}{r}} + \frac{1}{\overset{AC}{r}\,\overset{BC}{r}} + \frac{1}{\overset{AB}{r}\,\overset{AC}{r}}\right) +$$

$$+\tfrac{1}{4}\sum_{A=1}^{N}\sum_{B=1}^{N}{}' (\overset{A}{m}{}_0^2\overset{B}{m}_0 + \overset{B}{m}{}_0^2\overset{A}{m}_0)\left(\frac{1}{\overset{AB}{r}}\right)^2 +$$

$$+2\sum_{A=1}^{N}\sum_{B=1}^{N}{}' \frac{\overset{A}{m}_0\overset{B}{m}_0}{\overset{AB}{r}} \overset{A}{\xi}{}^{m}{}_{|0} \overset{B}{\xi}{}^{m}{}_{|0} - \frac{3}{4}\sum_{A=1}^{N}\sum_{B=1}^{N}{}' \frac{\overset{A}{m}_0\overset{B}{m}_0}{\overset{AB}{r}} (\overset{A}{\xi}{}^{s}{}_{|0}\overset{A}{\xi}{}^{s}{}_{|0} + \overset{B}{\xi}{}^{s}{}_{|0}\overset{B}{\xi}{}^{s}{}_{|0}) +$$

$$+\frac{1}{4}\sum_{A=1}^{N}\sum_{B=1}^{N}{}' \overset{A}{m}_0\overset{B}{m}_0 \overset{AB}{r}{}_{|\overset{A}{\xi}{}^{l}\overset{B}{\xi}{}^{m}} \overset{A}{\xi}{}^{l}{}_{|0}\overset{B}{\xi}{}^{m}{}_{|0} + \frac{1}{2}\sum_{A=1}^{N}\sum_{B=1}^{N}{}' \frac{\overset{A}{e}\overset{B}{e}}{\overset{AB}{r}} -$$

$$-\frac{1}{2}\sum_{A=1}^{N}\sum_{B=1}^{N}{}' \frac{\overset{A}{e}\overset{B}{e}}{\overset{AB}{r}} \overset{A}{\xi}{}^{k}{}_{|0}\overset{A}{\xi}{}^{k}{}_{|0} - \frac{1}{4}\sum_{A=1}^{N}\sum_{B=1}^{N}{}' \overset{AB}{ee}\; \overset{AB}{r}{}_{|\overset{A}{\xi}{}^{l}\overset{B}{\xi}{}^{m}} \overset{A}{\xi}{}^{l}{}_{|0}\overset{B}{\xi}{}^{m}{}_{|0} -$$

$$-\frac{1}{2}\sum_{A=1}^{N}\sum_{B=1}^{N}{}' \frac{\overset{AB}{ee}(\overset{A}{m}_0 + \overset{B}{m}_0)}{\overset{AB}{r}{}^2} + \frac{1}{4}\sum_{A=1}^{N}\sum_{B=1}^{N}{}' \frac{\overset{A}{m}_0\overset{B}{e}{}^2 + \overset{B}{m}_0\overset{A}{e}{}^2}{\overset{AB}{r}{}^2} -$$

$$-\frac{1}{2}\sum_{A=1}^{N}\sum_{B=1}^{N}{}'\sum_{C=1}^{N}{}'' \overset{ABC}{eme}\left(\frac{1}{\overset{AB}{r}\,\overset{AC}{r}} - \frac{1}{\overset{AB}{r}\,\overset{BC}{r}} + \frac{1}{\overset{AC}{r}\,\overset{BC}{r}}\right)$$

where $\sum\limits_{B=1}^{N}{}' = \sum\limits_{B=1, B\neq A}^{N}$; $\sum\limits_{C=1}^{N}{}'' = \sum\limits_{C=1, C\neq B, C\neq A}^{N}$. This is the final form of the post-Newtonian Lagrangian for the equations of motion in electrodynamics in G. R. It consists of the Lagrangian for uncharged bodies given in [2] and [4] (the first nine terms), of Breit's terms known from special relativity (the terms: tenth, eleventh and twelfth) and of terms responsible for the gravitational interaction between the electromagnetic fields of the particles. For two bodies it reduces to the Lagrangian given by another method in [9].

REFERENCES

[1] A. EINSTEIN, L. INFELD, and B. HOFFMANN, *Ann. Math.* **39**, 65 (1938).
[2] I. G. FICHTENHOLZ, *J. Eksp. Teor. Phys.* **20**, 233 (1950).
[3] L. INFELD, *Acta Phys. Polon.* **13**, 187 (1954).
[4] L. INFELD, *Rev. Mod. Phys.* **29**, 398 (1957).
[5] J. PLEBAŃSKI and S. BAŻAŃSKI, *Acta Phys. Polon.* **18**, 307 (1959).
[6] L. INFELD and J. PLEBAŃSKI, *Bull. Acad. Polon. Sci.* Cl. III, **4**, 687 (1956).
[7] L. INFELD and J. PLEBAŃSKI, *Bull. Acad. Polon. Sci.* Cl. III. **5**, 51 (1957).
[8] S. BAŻAŃSKI, *Acta Phys. Polon.* **15**, 363 (1956).
[9] S. BAŻAŃSKI, *Acta Phys. Polon.* **16**, 423 (1957).
[10] S. BAŻAŃSKI, The Problem of Motion p, 13. (This work).

TWO KINDS OF SCHRÖDINGER EQUATIONS IN GENERAL RELATIVITY THEORY

F. J. BELINFANTE

Department of Physics, Purdue University, Lafayette, Indiana, U. S. A.

QUANTIZATION of general-relativistic equations so far has usually been attempted in the Heisenberg picture. One may wonder whether also the Schrödinger picture and the interaction picture exist in general relativity theory.

The state vector Ψ and the q-number field components F in one of these pictures will be related to the corresponding quantities Ψ_{h} and ${}^{\mathrm{h}}F$ of the Heisenberg picture by a unitary transformation,

$$\Psi = U\Psi_{\mathrm{h}}, \quad F = U\,{}^{\mathrm{h}}FU^{-1}, \quad U^{-1} = U^{\dagger}. \tag{1}$$

While Ψ_{h} supposedly is a constant scalar, Ψ and therefore U will depend on the spacelike surface σ on which it describes the physical state.

When we call Ψ_{h} a constant scalar, we mean that it once and for all gives an invariant description of the state in which the physicist using it imagines nature to be. (By "nature" we mean the universe, or that part of the universe in which the physicist at the time is interested.) The time dependence of observable quantities which this physicist would want to predict is to be described by the time dependence of the quantized field variables ${}^{\mathrm{h}}F$. It is, however, well known that later experiments may inform the physicist more specifically about what actually has in the meantime happened around him, than the probability laws of quantum theory are able to predict. When this kind of an increase of his factual knowledge occurs, the physicist will want to change his description of the state of nature correspondingly. This procedure is well known in elementary wave mechanics as the "reduction of the wave packet". In quantum field theory, it means that Ψ_{h} is a constant merely as long as no such additional knowledge of nature is obtained and taken into account.

In as far as two physicists starting with the same knowledge of nature Ψ_h may acquire and take into account additional information on nature at different times (because of differences in their attention to the outcome of experiments), obviously the Heisenberg state vectors Ψ_h with which the two operate will not at all times be the same. This simply means that there is a subjective element in the state vector used by a particular person at a given time.

While quantum theory is deterministic in having definite equations of motion for the q-number quantities ${}^hF$, the actual happenings in nature are *not* bound by deterministic laws, in so far as we are fundamentally unable to tell in advance what in one individual case an elementary particle is going to do. Consequently, also the way in which Ψ_h by reductions of wave packets is going to depend on time is fundamentally unpredictable, even for the ideal physicist who plans to take into account *all* evidence that he will encounter.

In the following, therefore, we shall simply *ignore* the time dependence of Ψ_h. This amounts to considering a situation in nature where no new experimental evidence enters the picture, and where one merely tries to predict future probabilities on the basis of a definite amount of old information, irrespective of whether it has become obsolete by incompleteness or ignorance.

Not only the "constant" character of the Heisenberg state vector Ψ_h needs qualification. For a good understanding, also; its "scalar" character requires some discussion.

Consider first the nonrelativistic case of a single electron which at the time t_1 is near the point P_1 with coordinates $\boldsymbol{x}_1$ with respect to a certain spatial frame of reference Σ. This state is at t_1 described by a wave packet $\Psi(\boldsymbol{x}) = \varphi(\boldsymbol{x}-\boldsymbol{x}_1)$. We may take this wave function as the value of the Schrödinger wave function $\Psi(\boldsymbol{x}, t)$ at $t = t_1$; we may also use that particular representation in the Heisenberg picture in which $\varphi(\boldsymbol{x}-\boldsymbol{x}_1)$ describes Ψ_h.

When we apply a transformation $\boldsymbol{x}' = \boldsymbol{x}-\boldsymbol{a}$ from Σ to a new spatial coordinate system Σ' with the origin shifted over a distance $\boldsymbol{a}$, the center of the wave packet at t_1 is at $\boldsymbol{x}_1' = \boldsymbol{x}_1-\boldsymbol{a}$, and the wave function in Σ' may be given in the form $\Psi'(\boldsymbol{x}') = \varphi(\boldsymbol{x}'-\boldsymbol{x}_1')$ $= \varphi(\boldsymbol{x}-\boldsymbol{x}_1) = \Psi(\boldsymbol{x})$. In that case it is simple to see that $\Psi(\boldsymbol{x})$ behaves like a scalar field, and not as an invariant function of the coordinates.

Consider now the case that not the location but the momentum of the electron is pretty well known. Let the wave function in Σ be given by $\Psi(\boldsymbol{x}) = \int A(\boldsymbol{k})(\exp i\boldsymbol{kx})\, d^3\boldsymbol{k}$ or $\Psi(\boldsymbol{k}) = (2\pi)^{3/2} A(\boldsymbol{k})$.

If $\Psi(\boldsymbol{x})$ is to be scalar, then in Σ' (with $\boldsymbol{x}=\boldsymbol{x}'+\boldsymbol{a}$) we should use $\Psi'(\boldsymbol{x}') = \int A(\boldsymbol{k})(\exp i\boldsymbol{k}\boldsymbol{a})(\exp i\boldsymbol{k}\boldsymbol{x}')\,d^3\boldsymbol{k}$, so $\Psi'(\boldsymbol{k}) = \Psi(\boldsymbol{k})\exp i\boldsymbol{k}\boldsymbol{a}$.

An observer in Σ', however, finds the same momentum distribution for the electron as an observer in Σ, and therefore may want to use the wave function $\Psi''(\boldsymbol{k}) = \Psi(\boldsymbol{k})$, which would give $\Psi''(\boldsymbol{x}') = \int A(\boldsymbol{k})(\exp i\boldsymbol{k}\boldsymbol{x}')\,d^3\boldsymbol{k}$. (We use here the double prime merely for a distinction from the first choice for the wave function in Σ'.) In that case, the wave function would appear not to be a scalar field, but rather an invariant function of the coordinates.

In other words, whether the state vector is a scalar under coordinate transformations or not, depends on which representations of the state vector we use before and after the coordinate transformation. This means that the Heisenberg state vector Ψ_{h} is a scalar under coordinate transformations only if we properly choose the representations. Correspondingly, the q-numbers in the Heisenberg picture which represent the components of an observable tensor will transform as tensor components only with this proper choice of representations. The fact that Ψ_{h} is *not* invariant under a change of representation need not cause us much concern, because the alteration of the state vector is always coupled with a corresponding alteration of the q-numbers in the way of Eqs (1), so that the predictions of the theory, which are of the form $\big(\Psi^\dagger f(F)\Psi\big)$, are not affected by such a change.

Let $\mathfrak{L}$ be the scalar density serving as our Lagrangian. We take $\mathfrak{L}$ to be the sum of a matter Lagrangian $\mathfrak{L}_m$ and of Palatini's first-order Lagrangian density[1]

$$\mathfrak{L}_g = C\mathfrak{g}^{\varrho\sigma}[\Gamma^{\alpha}{}_{\varrho\sigma,\alpha} - \Gamma^{\alpha}{}_{\varrho\alpha,\sigma} - \Gamma^{\beta}{}_{\alpha\varrho}\Gamma^{\alpha}{}_{\beta\sigma} + \Gamma^{\beta}{}_{\alpha\beta}\Gamma^{\alpha}{}_{\varrho\sigma}] \tag{2}$$

for the gravitational field. In $\mathfrak{L}_m$, the Christoffel symbols $\begin{Bmatrix} \alpha \\ \varrho\sigma \end{Bmatrix}$ occurring in the covariant derivatives of tensors are considered functions of the metric $g_{\mu\nu}$, and so are the Vierbeine (by making a special choice for them) and the $\mathfrak{g}^{\varrho\sigma} = g^{\varrho\sigma}\sqrt{-g}$ occurring in $\mathfrak{L}_g$; the $\Gamma^{\alpha}{}_{\varrho\sigma}$, however, in the Lagrangian are treated as independent variables. Variation of these variables then yields the relations $\Gamma^{\alpha}{}_{\varrho\sigma} = \begin{Bmatrix} \alpha \\ \varrho\sigma \end{Bmatrix}$ as field equations. Variation of the metric yields the gravitational equations

$$C\mathfrak{G}^{\mu\nu} + \tfrac{1}{2}\mathfrak{T}^{\mu\nu} = 0 \tag{3}$$

(1) $C = c^4/16\pi G$.

where $\mathfrak{T}^{\mu\nu}$ is the matter tensor and where $\mathfrak{G}^{\mu\nu} = (R^{\mu\nu} - \frac{1}{2}g^{\mu\nu}R)\sqrt{-g}$. ($\mathfrak{L}_g = -CR\sqrt{-g}$.) If we want to use canonical quantization of the fields, we have to consider these field equations (3) to be weak equations. The commutators of the Lorentz tensor

$$\mathfrak{H}_\mu^{\ \nu} = \mathfrak{T}_\mu^{\ \nu} + 2C\mathfrak{G}_\mu^{\ \nu} \tag{4}$$

with other q-numbers then in general will not vanish.

Lorentz has suggested to use this tensor as the energy density tensor. It is related to the canonical energy density tensor

$$\mathfrak{P}_\mu^{\ \nu} = \delta_\mu^{\ \nu}\mathfrak{L} - \frac{\partial\mathfrak{L}}{\partial y_{A,\nu}} y_{A,\mu} \tag{5}$$

(where y_A comprises both the gravitational variables $g_{\mu\nu}$ and $\Gamma^\alpha_{\ \varrho\sigma}$, *and* the matter variables q_m) by

$$\mathfrak{H}_\mu^{\ \nu} = \mathfrak{P}_\mu^{\ \nu} + [\mathfrak{f}^{\alpha\cdot\nu}_{\cdot\mu\cdot} - \tfrac{1}{2}\mathfrak{B}_\mu^{\cdot\nu\alpha}]_{,\alpha} \tag{6}$$

where

$$\mathfrak{B}_\mu^{\cdot\nu\alpha} = 2C\sqrt{-g}\cdot(g^{\nu\beta}\Gamma^\alpha_{\ \beta\mu} - g^{\alpha\beta}\Gamma^\nu_{\ \beta\mu}) = -\mathfrak{B}_\mu^{\cdot\alpha\nu}, \tag{7}$$

and where

$$\mathfrak{f}^{\alpha\beta\nu} = \tfrac{1}{2}(\mathfrak{f}^{\nu\beta\alpha} + \mathfrak{f}^{\beta\alpha\nu} + \mathfrak{f}^{\nu\alpha\beta}) = -\mathfrak{f}^{\nu\beta\alpha}. \tag{8}$$

Here, $\mathfrak{f}^{\beta\alpha\nu}$ is the "spin integrand tensor density" of matter, defined by

$$\mathfrak{f}^{\beta\alpha\nu} = \frac{\partial\mathfrak{L}}{\partial q_{m,\nu}}(\hat{S}^{\alpha\beta} - \hat{S}^{\beta\alpha})q_m \tag{9}$$

where we sum over all matter variables q_m. The $\hat{S}^{\alpha\beta}$ in Eq. (9) are operators acting on the q_m, which give the effect of an infinitesimal coordinate transformation $x'^\mu = x^\mu + \varepsilon^\mu$ coupled with the corresponding transformation of the Vierbeine as functions of the metric, by means of

$$\delta q_m = q'_m - q_m = \varepsilon^\mu_{\ ,\beta}\hat{S}_\mu^{\cdot\beta} q_m = \varepsilon^\mu_{\ ,\beta} g_{\mu\alpha}\hat{S}^{\alpha\beta} q_m. \tag{10}$$

Now consider a spacelike surface σ with a field of (possibly timelike) infinitesimal four-vectors $d\xi^\mu$ defined on it. That is, from each point P of σ, an infinitesimal four-vector PP' originates. We shall assume that the points P' form a new spacelike surface σ'. The combination of the surface and the four-vectors we may call a "rug", the four-vectors forming the hairs of the rug.

On this rug, we now define the infinitesimal scalar

$$dS = -\int \mathfrak{H}_\mu^{\ \nu}\, d\xi^\mu\, d\sigma_\nu \tag{11}$$

where the surface elements $d\sigma_\nu$ are defined in the conventional way, in terms of parameters u^k in the surface, by

$$d\sigma_\nu = \varepsilon_{\nu\alpha\beta\gamma} \frac{\partial x^\alpha}{\partial u^1} \frac{\partial x^\beta}{\partial u^2} \frac{\partial x^\gamma}{\partial u^3} du^1 du^2 du^3. \tag{12}$$

Because of the scalar character of dS, we may use some special coordinate system for calculating it. By a "skin frame" on our rug we shall denote *any* coordinate system in which the skin σ of the rug (but not necessarily its top σ') is a surface $x^0 = \text{const}\ (= t)$; in such a skin frame, we shall always use the spatial coordinates x^k as the parameters u^k, so that, with $\varepsilon_{0123} = 1$, we have

$$d\sigma_\nu = \delta^0_\nu dx^1 dx^2 dx^3 \equiv \delta^0_\nu d^3\boldsymbol{x}. \tag{13}$$

Among the skin frames on a rug, there is a special kind which we shall call "Schrödinger frames". They are singled out by the following two additional properties: (first) also the top of the rug (σ') will be a surface $x^0 = \text{const}\ (= t + dt)$; and (second) the difference between the spatial coordinates of the ends P and P' of each of the hairs of the rug will be the same for all hairs:

$$x^k(P') - x^k(P) = b^k dt = \text{constant on the rug.} \tag{14}$$

Consequently, in a Schrödinger frame, $d\xi^\mu$ has the constant components $(dt, b^1 dt, b^2 dt, b^3 dt)$ all over the rug, and dS in a Schrödinger frame takes the simple form

$$dS = -(d\xi^\mu) \int \mathfrak{H}_\mu{}^0 d^3\boldsymbol{x} \mathrel{\hat{=}} -(d\xi^\mu) \int \mathfrak{P}_\mu{}^0 d^3\boldsymbol{x}, \tag{15}$$

on account of

$$\int [\mathfrak{t}^{\alpha\cdot 0}_{\cdot\mu} - \tfrac{1}{2}\mathfrak{B}^{\cdot 0\alpha}_{\mu}]_{,\alpha} d^3\boldsymbol{x} = \int [\mathfrak{t}^{k\cdot 0}_{\cdot\mu} - \tfrac{1}{2}\mathfrak{B}^{\cdot 0k}_{\mu}]_{,k} d^3\boldsymbol{x} \mathrel{\hat{=}} 0. \tag{16}$$

Here, the symbol $\mathrel{\hat{=}}$ means equality but for a non-vanishing boundary term which we assume to be a c-number commuting with all q-numbers to be considered.

In terms of the canonical variables y_A and $p^A = \dfrac{\partial \mathfrak{L}}{\partial y_{A,0}}$, we have $\mathfrak{P}_\mu{}^0 = \delta^0_\mu \mathfrak{L} - p^A \mathring{y}_{A,\mu}$. By Dirac's method we may express these quantities, modulo some constraints, in terms of the canonical variables and their spatial derivatives only, with time derivatives appearing only in terms with a constraint function as a factor. If also F is some function of the canonical variables and their spatial derivatives, and does not depend explicitly on the space-time coordinates x^μ in the Schrödinger frame of the rug considered, then the canonical quantization on the surface σ by

$$[y_A(\boldsymbol{x}); p^B(\boldsymbol{x}')] = i\hbar c \delta_A^B \delta(\boldsymbol{x}-\boldsymbol{x}'), \quad \text{etc.,} \tag{17}$$

by Eq. (15) will yield

$$[{}^{\mathrm{h}}F; {}^{\mathrm{h}}dS] = i\hbar c({}^{\mathrm{h}}F)_{,\mu} d\xi^\mu = i\hbar c d_\xi({}^{\mathrm{h}}F) \tag{18}$$

where the superscript prefixes ^{h} remind us of the fact that so far all our equations were in the Heisenberg picture, and where d_ξ denotes a difference in the direction $d\xi^\mu$ between values at P' and at P.

The equations (18) are a way of writing the Heisenberg equations of motion. Although we defined dS and d_ξ in a covariant way, we should not make the error of applying Eq. (18) now also to the transformed components F' in a different frame of reference. When expressed in terms of quantities in the original Schrödinger frame, the components F' depend not only on the canonical variables of the original frame, but also on the tensor transformation coefficients, which in general are explicit functions of the coordinates, of which the increment d_ξ from P to P' cannot be expressed as a commutator. From the point of view of the new coordinate system, the breakdown of Eq. (18) would be due to the fact that the hairs of our rug in this new frame no longer would have constant components, so that the $d\xi^\mu$ no longer can be factored out. Then, in the various integrations by part that are used in deriving (18) from (17) in the presence of spatial gradients of canonical variables, derivatives of $d\xi^\mu$ will enter the picture. These are, of course, related to the transformation coefficients which entered the problem from the other point of view.

In order to define a Schrödinger picture, we start by considering space-time filled up by rugs piled on top of each other. That is, there will be a spacelike surface through each point of space-time, and a world line which gives the direction of $d\xi^\mu$. If σ and σ' are two of these surfaces at an infinitesimal distance from each other, then the length of $d\xi^\mu$ is given by the distance one has to travel along the world line in order to reach σ' from σ. Thus, each pair of surfaces closely following each other, together with the pieces of the world lines that lie in between them, forms a rug, for which we can define the scalar ${}^{\mathrm{h}}dS$ in the Heisenberg picture. Now suppose that the Schrödinger equation

$$i\hbar c dU = U({}^{\mathrm{h}}dS) \tag{19}$$

has a solution $U[\sigma]$ for this particular pile of rugs. (By dU, we mean here $U[\sigma']-U[\sigma]$.) Then, let us define state vectors Ψ and q-numbers F in the Schrödinger picture by means of Eqs (1), so that

$$i\hbar c dU = (dS)U \quad \text{and} \quad i\hbar c d\Psi = (dS)\Psi \tag{20}$$

with (dS) now in the Schrödinger picture. Let us also consider a world coordinate system which is a Schrödinger frame for all of the rugs of our compilation. That is, the world lines that determine the directions of the hairs $d\xi^\mu$ on the surfaces $\sigma(x^0 = t)$ shall be given by equations

$$x^k = f^k(u^1, u^2, u^3) + g^k(t), \tag{21}$$

so that the hairs between the rugs at t and at $t+dt$ shall be given by $d\xi^0 = dt$ and $d\xi^k = \dfrac{dg^k}{dt}dt =$ independent of u^1, u^2, u^3. In this Schrödinger world frame, let F around some point P be a function of the canonical variables and their spatial derivatives, not depending explicitly on the world coordinates. Then, we may apply Eq. (18) to F in the Heisenberg picture. Consequently, in the Schrödinger picture we will find for the dependence of F on t in the space-time direction of $d\xi^\mu$:

$$\begin{aligned} d_\xi F &= (dU)U^{-1}F - F(dU)U^{-1} + U(d_\xi{}^{\mathrm{h}}F)U^{-1} \\ &= (i\hbar c)^{-1}\{[(dS)F - F(dS)] + U[{}^{\mathrm{h}}F; {}^{\mathrm{h}}dS]U^{-1}\} = 0. \end{aligned} \tag{22}$$

In other words, in the Schrödinger picture defined for a given set of spacelike surfaces σ and of space-time directions $d\xi^\mu$ in each point, the q-numbers which describe dynamical quantities in a Schrödinger world frame for this pile of rugs will be constant along the given world lines.

Since Eq. (19) gives $U+dU$ on σ' in terms of U on σ, we may perhaps believe that for a given pile of rugs this equation in principle can be integrated, if we (arbitrarily) give some (unitary) U on some initial surface σ_0. However, this fact alone does not allow us to talk about "the Schrödinger picture" on some later surface σ_1, because its definition would seem to depend not merely on an initial condition on σ_0 and the choice of the final surface and the choice of spatial coordinates on these two surfaces, but also on the entire pile of surfaces and their spatial coordinates in between.

Therefore, we shall call the Schrödinger equation integrable (in a generalized sense) only when the result of integration between σ_0 and σ_1 turns out to be independent of the shape of the pile of rugs in between. What condition should $\mathfrak{H}_\mu{}^\nu$ in the definition (11) of dS satisfy in order that this integrability may exist?

In order to find this condition, we integrate Eq. (19), accurately up to second-order terms, in two infinitesimal steps, from an initial surface σ to a final surface σ_1 lying close to it, once using σ' as an intermediary surface, and once using a different intermediary σ'' instead. Because of the second-order precision needed, one has to take the finite factors $\mathfrak{H}_\mu{}^\nu$ and the surface elements $d\sigma_\nu$ in Eq. (19) for each step halfway between the initial and the final surface for that particular step, and the integrals should be performed up to the second term in a Taylor expansion. That is, $dU = UK\,dt$ would be integrated as $U = U_0\left\{1 + \left[K_0 + \frac{1}{2}\left(\frac{dK}{dt}\right)_0 dt\right]dt + \frac{1}{2}K_0{}^2dt^2\right\}$. We perform the entire calculation in a skin frame on the initial surface σ. (Since σ' and σ'' differ, we cannot use a Schrödinger frame.) Surface elements on later surfaces are expressed in terms of surface elements on σ by using the hairs $d\xi^\mu$ for defining a correspondence between these surface elements. On the later surfaces, of course, Eq. (13) is not valid, but we can refer all components of $d\sigma_\nu$ to $d^3\boldsymbol{x}$ on the initial surface on which our world frame was a skin frame.

Obviously it cannot be hoped that the integral would be independent of the spatial coordinates on the final surface. As seen from Eq. (15), even in a given Schrödinger frame a change of the constant hairs $d\xi^\mu$ by, say, a constant change of the b^k of Eq. (14) would alter the amount of $U\int {}^{\rm h}\mathfrak{P}_k{}^0 d^3\boldsymbol{x}$ added to U in the first infinitesimal step of integration. Therefore, all we can hope is that the integral from σ to σ_1, once via σ' and once via σ'', will lead to the same results if the hairs from σ to σ_1 in both cases end up in the same points of σ_1. That is, if we arbitrarily choose hairs PP' and $P'P_1$ from σ via σ' to σ_1, and hairs PP'' from σ to σ'', then the hairs from σ'' to σ_1 shall be given by $P''P_1$.

For equality of the outcome of integration with this condition imposed on the hairs, we find that the tensor density $\mathfrak{H}_\mu{}^\nu$ which through (11) appears in Eq. (19) should satisfy on σ, in the Heisenberg picture and in a skin frame on σ, the requirement

$$i\hbar c\int_\sigma d^3\boldsymbol{x}\{(s^\mu t^0{}_{,r} - t^\mu s^0{}_{,r})^{\rm h}\mathfrak{H}_\mu{}^r - (s^\mu t^r{}_{,r} - t^\mu s^r{}_{,r})^{\rm h}\mathfrak{H}_\mu{}^0 + (s^\lambda t^\mu - t^\lambda s^\mu)({}^{\rm h}\mathfrak{H}_\mu{}^0)_{,\lambda}\}$$

$$= \int_\sigma d^3\boldsymbol{x}\int_\sigma d^3\boldsymbol{x}'\, s^\lambda(\boldsymbol{x})t^\mu(\boldsymbol{x}')[{}^{\rm h}\mathfrak{H}_\lambda{}^0(\boldsymbol{x});\ {}^{\rm h}\mathfrak{H}_\mu{}^0(\boldsymbol{x}')], \qquad (23)$$

for two arbitrary four-vector fields s^λ and t^μ defined on σ. Because the commutator in the right-hand member may be expected to contain some spatial derivatives of delta-functions, the right-hand member does not vanish. The time derivative appearing for $\lambda = 0$ in the last term of the left-hand member may be eliminated by using the conservation law $({}^{\mathrm{h}}\mathfrak{H}_\mu^{\ \lambda})_{,\lambda} = 0$.

The integrability condition (23) for the Schrödinger equation that defines the Schrödinger picture is by no means trivial. So far, we have not attempted at proving its general validity. All we have done so far is to consider a special case in the non-gravitational flat-space approximation in which $\mathfrak{H}_\mu^{\ \lambda}$ is replaced by the matter tensor $\mathfrak{T}_\mu^{\ \lambda}$. Also, we restricted ourselves so far to a vector field t^μ on σ describing an infinitesimal Lorentz transformation $\boldsymbol{x}' = \boldsymbol{x} - \boldsymbol{x}\boldsymbol{b}^0$, $x^{0\prime} = x^0 - \boldsymbol{b}\boldsymbol{x}$ by $t^\mu(\boldsymbol{x}) = \delta_0^\mu \boldsymbol{b}\boldsymbol{x}$, and a vector field s^λ describing a mere translation of σ in the time direction by $s^\lambda(\boldsymbol{x}) = \delta_0^\lambda \varepsilon$. Here, $\boldsymbol{b}$ and ε were infinitesimal constants. The condition (23) then, after division by ε, reduces to

$$i\hbar c \int d^3\boldsymbol{x}\, b_r \mathfrak{T}_0^{\ r}(\boldsymbol{x}) = \int d^3\boldsymbol{x} \int d^3\boldsymbol{x}'\, (\boldsymbol{b}\boldsymbol{x}')[\mathfrak{T}_0^{\ 0}(\boldsymbol{x});\, \mathfrak{T}_0^{\ 0}(\boldsymbol{x}')]\,. \tag{24}$$

The special case for which we have investigated in this restricted way the integrability of the Schrödinger equation is the case of gauge-independent quantum electrodynamics [1]. In this case, we have, in the non-gravitational approximation considered [2],

$$\left.\begin{aligned} -\mathfrak{T}_0^{\ 0} &= \mathfrak{T}^{00} = (8\pi)^{-1}\{\boldsymbol{E}^2 + \mathfrak{B}^2\} - \mathfrak{A}\boldsymbol{j} + \mathrm{Re}\{\psi^\dagger H^0_{\ \mathrm{op}}\psi\},\\ -\mathfrak{T}_0^{\ k} &= \mathfrak{T}^{0k} = (8\pi)^{-1}\{\boldsymbol{E}\times\mathfrak{B} - \mathfrak{B}\times\boldsymbol{E}\} - \mathfrak{A}\varrho -\\ &\qquad - \mathrm{Re}\{\psi^\dagger i\hbar c\nabla\psi\} - \tfrac{1}{4}\hbar c\,\mathrm{curl}\,(\psi^\dagger\boldsymbol{\sigma}\psi), \end{aligned}\right\} \tag{25}$$

where

$$\left.\begin{aligned} H^0_{\ \mathrm{op}} &= m_0 c^2 \beta - i\hbar c\boldsymbol{\alpha}\nabla,\\ \boldsymbol{j} &= e\psi^\dagger\boldsymbol{\alpha}\psi, \qquad \varrho = e\psi^\dagger\psi,\\ \mathfrak{A}(\boldsymbol{x}, t) &= \mathrm{curl} \int d^3\boldsymbol{x}'\mathfrak{B}(\boldsymbol{x}', t)/4\pi r,\\ \boldsymbol{E} &= \mathfrak{E}_\perp + \boldsymbol{E}_\parallel, \qquad \mathbf{E}_\parallel = -\nabla V,\\ V(\boldsymbol{x}, t) &= \int d^3\boldsymbol{x}'\, \varrho(\boldsymbol{x}', t)/r, \end{aligned}\right\} \tag{26}$$

so that

$$\left.\begin{aligned} \mathrm{curl}\,\mathfrak{A} &= \mathfrak{B}, \qquad \mathrm{div}\,\mathfrak{A} = 0,\\ \mathrm{div}\,\mathfrak{E}_\perp &= 0, \qquad \mathrm{div}\,\boldsymbol{E} = \mathrm{div}\boldsymbol{E}_\parallel = 4\pi\varrho\,. \end{aligned}\right\} \tag{27}$$

In the Heisenberg picture, $\mathfrak{B}$ forms an antisymmetric tensor with $\boldsymbol{E}$; the transformation properties of ψ, $\psi^\dagger$, $\mathfrak{A}$, V, $\boldsymbol{E}_\|$, and $\mathfrak{E}_\perp$ in the Heisenberg picture are rather complicated, but they are known [1], and they make $\mathfrak{T}_0{}^0$ and $\mathfrak{T}_0{}^k$ in the Heisenberg picture components of one and the same tensor under Lorentz transformations.

The commutation relations between the various variables are also known [1]. Using them, the validity at least of the special condition (24) has been proved. This shows that, at least if one restricts oneself to Lorentz transformations in the flat-space non-gravitational theory, the Schrödinger equation for the Schrödinger picture of gauge-independent quantum electrodynamics is integrable.

For this same case of gauge-independent quantum electrodynamics in flat-space Lorentz-covariant (though not manifestly covariant) approximation, we have also proved the existence of an interaction picture [1], which is defined by a transformation (1) from the Heisenberg picture, with U satisfying a Schrödinger equation in which the energy density $-\mathfrak{T}_0{}^0$ is replaced by the interaction energy density

$$-W_0{}^0 = W^{00} = (8\pi)^{-1}\{\boldsymbol{E}_\|^2 + 2\boldsymbol{E}_\|\mathfrak{E}_\perp\} - \mathfrak{A}\boldsymbol{j}. \tag{28}$$

Under infinitesimal Lorentz transformations in the Heisenberg picture, W^{00} transforms as the 00 component of a symmetric tensor for which, with $r^k = x^k - x'^k$,

$$\begin{aligned}-W_0{}^k(\boldsymbol{x}) &= W^{0k}(\boldsymbol{x})\\ &= (\boldsymbol{E}_\| \times \mathfrak{B})_k/8\pi - \tfrac{1}{2}\mathfrak{A}_k\varrho + \\ &+ \int d^3\boldsymbol{x}'\, r^k\{j^m(\boldsymbol{x}')\mathfrak{E}_\perp{}^n(\boldsymbol{x}) + j^m(\boldsymbol{x})E^n(\boldsymbol{x}')\}\nabla_m\nabla_n\left(\frac{1}{8\pi r}\right),\end{aligned} \tag{29}$$

so that (cf. [1])

$$\begin{aligned}\int d^3\boldsymbol{x} W_0{}^k(\boldsymbol{x}) &= \int d^3\boldsymbol{x}' \int d^3\boldsymbol{x}'\,(x^k - x'^k) j^m(\boldsymbol{x}')E_\|{}^n(\boldsymbol{x})\nabla_m\nabla_n\left(\frac{1}{8\pi r}\right)\\ &= \tfrac{1}{2}\int d^3\boldsymbol{x}\, x^k j_\|^n(\boldsymbol{x})\nabla_n V(\boldsymbol{x}) - \tfrac{1}{2}\int d^3\boldsymbol{x}'\, x'^k j^m(\boldsymbol{x}')\nabla'_m V(\boldsymbol{x}')\\ &= -\tfrac{1}{2}\int d^3\boldsymbol{x}\, x^k \boldsymbol{j}_\perp \nabla V = \tfrac{1}{2}\int d^3\boldsymbol{x}\, V j_\perp{}^k.\end{aligned} \tag{30}$$

On the other hand (cf. [1]),

$$\int d^3\boldsymbol{x} \int d^3\boldsymbol{x}'\, x'^k [W_0{}^0(\boldsymbol{x});\, W_0{}^0(\boldsymbol{x}')] = i\hbar c \int d^3\boldsymbol{x}\, V j_\perp{}^k. \tag{31}$$

Thus we see that $W_0^{\ 0}$ and $W_0^{\ k}$ in this case do *not* satisfy an integrability condition of the type of Eq. (24), but that, instead, they satisfy the relation

$$2i\hbar c \int d^3x\, b_r W_0^{\ r}(x) = \int d^3x \int d^3x'\,(bx')[W_0^{\ 0}(x);\, W_0^{\ 0}(x')]\,, \qquad (32)$$

with a factor 2 in front.

As we have pointed out in the past [3], also Eq. (32) is an integrability condition in Lorentz-covariant flat-space approximation for a Schrödinger equation. This Schrödinger equation and its integrability, however, are to be understood in a way different from what we did for the Schrödinger equation of the Schrödinger picture.

The general-relativistic formulation of this new type of a Schrödinger equation is as follows. We start by writing the Schrödinger equation for the interaction picture in a form similar to Eqs (19)–(20) with (11):

$$i\hbar c\, dU = U({}^{\rm h}dI) = (dI)\,U\,, \qquad i\hbar c\, d\Psi = (dI)\,\Psi\,, \qquad (33)$$

$$dI = -\int \mathfrak{W}_\mu^{\ \nu}\, d\eta^\mu\, d\sigma_\nu\,. \qquad (34)$$

Again, $dU = U[\sigma'] - U[\sigma]$, and the infinitesimal four-vectors $d\eta^\mu$ lead from points P on σ to points P' on σ'. The main difference is that the $d\eta^\mu$ do not form an arbitrary field on σ, like the $d\xi^\mu$ did, but they are normal[(1)] to σ. In other words, dI is fully determined by σ and σ' alone; we do not need a complete rug, but merely two consecutive skins for determining dI. Consequently, dU does *not* depend on a correspondence between spatial coordinates on σ and on σ' of the kind that was put to use in the definition of Schrödinger frames on rugs. Correspondingly, the interaction state vector $\Psi[\sigma]$ is as "independent" of the spatial coordinate system as "is" the Heisenberg state vector $\Psi_{\rm h}$. As we have discussed in the beginning, such an independence is realized only by "proper" choice of representations.

The surface element four-vector $d\sigma_\nu$ is related to the scalar surface element $d\sigma$ and to the normal four-vector n^μ by

$$d\sigma_\nu \sqrt{-g} = -n_\nu\, d\sigma\,. \qquad (35)$$

---

(1) P.S. (1961). Preferably use Fock's harmonic coordinate systems, which allow the Lorentz group only. Then use a Minkowski metric $\gamma_{\mu\nu}$ instead of $g_{\mu\nu}$ in Eqs (35) – (39), (41), (49) – (51), and in defining normality of $d\eta^\mu = \gamma^{\mu\nu} d\eta_\nu = \gamma^{\mu\nu} n_\nu d\eta$ to σ and in relating $W^{\mu\nu}$ to $W_\mu^{\ \nu}$.

The normal four-vector is usually normalized by

$$g^{\mu\nu} n_\mu n_\nu = -1, \quad n^0 > 0, \quad n_0 < 0. \tag{36}$$

Then, in a skin frame,

$$n_\nu = -\delta^0_\nu / \sqrt{-g^{00}}, \quad d\sigma = d^3x \sqrt{g^{00} g}. \tag{37}$$

We define the scalar distance $d\eta$ between σ and σ' by

$$d\eta^\mu = n^\mu d\eta. \tag{38}$$

With $W_\mu^{\ \nu} = \mathfrak{W}_\mu^{\ \nu} / \sqrt{-g}$, the interaction operator dI may then be written as

$$dI = \int_\sigma W^{\mu\nu} n_\mu n_\nu d\eta \, d\sigma. \tag{39}$$

This is a scalar, if the $W^{\mu\nu}$ form a symmetric tensor. (The antisymmetric part of $W^{\mu\nu}$ may be omitted, because it would not contribute to dI anyhow.)

By "integrability" of the interaction Schrödinger equation (33) we mean again that the result of integration from σ_0 to σ_1 shall be independent of the intermediary spacelike surfaces σ' chosen. The derivation of the integrability condition for this purpose to be imposed upon $W^{\mu\nu}$ is rather similar to the derivation of the condition (23) for the Schrödinger case. However, this time the condition imposed on the $d\eta^\mu$ vectors from σ to σ_1 via σ' and via σ'' is a different one. With second-order precision needed, we must put the vectors from σ to σ' normal to the "average" of σ and of σ', and so on. We may use the $d\eta^\mu$ vectors again for providing a correspondence between surface elements on later surfaces and surface elements on the original surface σ, on which we use a skin frame. But the surface elements on σ_1 in this way corresponding to a certain element on σ, once via σ' and once via σ'', are now two different ones, because the vectors starting from a single point on σ will no longer meet on σ_1 this time, but will end up in points which lie at a distance from each other that is small of the second order but cannot be neglected. However, it can be shown that the sums of the scalar distances from σ to the intermediary, and from the intermediary surface to σ_1, once via σ' and once via σ'', differ by an amount that may be neglected, so that equality of these sums for both paths of integration may now be used as the criterion that the $d\eta^\mu$ vectors from σ' and from σ'' both will end up on σ_1.

The result of the calculation is then that $W^{\mu\nu}$, on a skin frame on σ, should for integrability of (33) satisfy the following requirement for arbitrary scalar fields $s(\boldsymbol{x})$ and $t(\boldsymbol{x})$ defined on σ:

$$i\hbar c \int d^3\boldsymbol{x}(st_{,r} - ts_{,r})T^r = \int d^3\boldsymbol{x} \int d^3\boldsymbol{x}' s(\boldsymbol{x})t(\boldsymbol{x}')[W(\boldsymbol{x}); W(\boldsymbol{x}')], \quad (40)$$

where we have put

$$\left.\begin{aligned} W &= \mathfrak{W}^{00}/\sqrt{-g^{00}} = W^{00}/\sqrt{g^{00}g}, \\ T^r &= 2\mathfrak{W}^{00}g^{r0}/g^{00} - \mathfrak{W}^{0r} - \mathfrak{W}^{r0}. \end{aligned}\right\} \quad (41)$$

In non-gravitational approximation with the Minkowski metric of Lorentz-covariant theory, then, $W = W^{00} = -W_0{}^0$ and $T^r = 2W_0{}^r$, and the integrability condition (40) for $s(\boldsymbol{x}) = 1$, $t(\boldsymbol{x}) = (b\boldsymbol{x})$ takes the form of the relation (32) which is satisfied for gauge-independent quantum electrodynamics, and which is also satisfied in a number of other cases, such as vector meson theory [3], the linear theory of gravitation [4], and so on.

Therefore, one would expect (33) with (39) to be the general form of the Schrödinger equation for the interaction picture in general relativity theory.

In Lorentz-covariant field theory there always exists a set of field variables (*not* in general the transformed by Eq. (1) of the Lagrangian variables of the Heisenberg picture [4], [5]) which in the interaction picture satisfy field equations without interaction and without nonlinearity, and which in the interaction picture have simple transformation properties, if one sticks to skin frames, and therefore uses the Schrödinger equation (33) for finding the change of U in Eq. (1) that will be required by any change of the surfaces $x^0 = \text{const}$ by coordinate transformations. The problem we want to discuss now is to what extent something similar might be possible in general relativity theory.

Let z_A be the variables which in the interaction picture satisfy field equations without interaction. By expressing the original Lagrangian variables ${}^{\mathrm{h}}y_A$ in the Heisenberg picture in terms of the ${}^{\mathrm{h}}z_A$, we express the Lagrangian in terms of the ${}^{\mathrm{h}}z_A$ and the ${}^{\mathrm{h}}z_{A,\mu}$, and we define the new canonical conjugates by ${}^{\mathrm{h}}\pi^A = \partial\, {}^{\mathrm{h}}\mathfrak{L}/\partial\, {}^{\mathrm{h}}z_{A,0}$, thus achieving a canonical transformation from the y_A and the p^A to the z_A and the π^A. The z_A should have been chosen in such a way as to eliminate interactions from all field equations which do not contain time derivatives, and, especially in the presence of fermion fields, the choice of the z_A should take care of "canonization" [5], as to avoid the unusual quantization that is necessary when second-class constraints force us to introduce modified Poisson brackets.

We assume that the introduction of the new canonical variables on the surface σ ($x^0 = t$) does not introduce an explicit dependence of these variables on the time. Then, Heisenberg equations of motion are valid for them and may be written in the form

$$i\hbar c({}^{\mathrm{h}}F)_{,0} = [{}^{\mathrm{h}}F; -\int {}^{\mathrm{h}}\mathfrak{H}_0{}^0 d^3\boldsymbol{x}], \tag{42}$$

where F stands for z_A or π^A. Expressing also ${}^{\mathrm{h}}\mathfrak{H}_0{}^0$ in terms of the new canonical variables, we find the field equations of motion completely in terms of the new canonical variables, and we can now separate the interaction and nonlinearity terms in these equations from what we may call the "free field" terms. This is achieved by correspondingly splitting up the Hamiltonian appearing in Eq. [42]:

$$\int {}^{\mathrm{h}}\mathfrak{H}_0{}^0 d^3\boldsymbol{x} = \int {}^{\mathrm{h}}\mathfrak{H}^{(0)}{}_0{}^0 d^3\boldsymbol{x} + \int {}^{\mathrm{h}}\mathfrak{W}_0{}^0 d^3\boldsymbol{x}. \tag{43}$$

Eq. (43) obviously leaves undetermined in the interaction (and nonlinearity) density ${}^{\mathrm{h}}\mathfrak{W}_0{}^0$ an additive term of which the space integral vanishes. That term is to be chosen in such a way that the integrability condition (40)–(41) for the interaction Schrödinger equation (33)–(34) will be satisfied. Notice that ${}^{\mathrm{h}}\mathfrak{H}^{(0)}{}_0{}^0$ is free from interaction terms only when expressed in terms of the new canonical variables. In terms of the old y_A and p^A, it may contain some apparent interaction terms.

Now, let $d\xi^\mu$ be a four-vector PP' from σ to σ' along the x^0 axis, so that $d\xi^k = 0$. Using a world skin frame, in which all the surfaces are of the form $x^0 = t$, we then may write

$$d\xi^\mu = \delta_0^\mu dt. \tag{44}$$

In the interaction picture, we now find

$$\begin{aligned} dF &\equiv F(P') - F(P) = d(U\,{}^{\mathrm{h}}F\,U^{-1}) \\ &= [(dU)\,U^{-1}; F] + U({}^{\mathrm{h}}F)_{,0}\,dt\,U^{-1} \\ &= (i\hbar c)^{-1}\Big\{[(dI); F] + [F; -\int \mathfrak{H}_0{}^0 d^3\boldsymbol{x}]\,dt\Big\}. \end{aligned} \tag{45}$$

If this is to be equal to

$$F_{,0}\,dt = [F; -\int \mathfrak{H}^{(0)}{}_0{}^0 d^3\boldsymbol{x}]\,dt, \tag{46}$$

as we really want it, then we should have

$$[(dI); F] = [F; \int \mathfrak{W}_0{}^0 d^3\boldsymbol{x}]\,dt, \tag{47}$$

or, by (34),

$$[F; \int \mathfrak{W}_0{}^0 d^3x]\, dt = [F; \int \mathfrak{W}_\mu{}^\nu d\eta^\mu d\sigma_\nu]$$

$$= [F; \int \mathfrak{W}_\mu{}^0 d\eta^\mu d^3x] \tag{48}$$

in our skin frame. Therefore, for ensuring the validity of the Eqs (46), it is not sufficient that our coordinate system is a skin frame. We also must require that the normal four-vectors reaching from σ ($x^0 = t$) to σ' ($x^0 = t + dt$) shall be c-numbers given by

$$d\eta^\mu = \delta_0^\mu dt \quad (= d\xi^\mu), \tag{49}$$

if the equations of motion are to be free from interaction terms. That is, the skin frame should be a *normal* skin frame, by which we mean a coordinate system in which the time axis everywhere has the direction of the normal to the surface σ ($x^0 = t$), where the normal, in a skin frame given by

$$n^\mu = -g^{0\mu}/\sqrt{-g^{00}}, \tag{50}$$

apparently is to be defined using the metric in the interaction picture. Therefore, the conditions (49) apparently require(1)

$$g^{0k} = 0 \qquad (k = 1, 2, 3). \tag{51}$$

For $\mu = 0$, the condition (49) in a world skin frame is automatically satisfied, by $d\eta^0 = x^0(\sigma') - x^0(\sigma) = dt$.

In integrating the Schrödinger equation (33)–(34), of course, one need not require the condition (49) or (51). In regions where this condition is not satisfied, the field equations in the interaction picture simply will not be free from interaction terms. On reaching other regions in which the coordinate system has been chosen to be a normal skin frame all over some spacelike surfaces σ, however, one will find the interaction terms in the field equations to vanish on these surfaces.

The necessity of requiring normality of the world skin frame for ensuring simple field equations is not surprising, if one thinks of the fact that also in Lorentz-covariant field theory one restricts oneself to normal skin frames for ensuring simple field equations without interaction terms in the interaction picture [3], [1], [4].

The foregoing provides a program for further investigations. The variables z_A are to be found, and the additive term in $\mathfrak{W}_0{}^0$ is

(1) P.S. (1961). Automatically satisfied with $\gamma^{\mu\nu}$ here replacing $g^{\mu\nu}$!

to be determined. The actual validity of the two integrability conditions, (24) and (40), remains to be proved. Also, the questions of the c-number character of $d\eta^0$ and of the meaning of normality of skin frames in a theory with a quantized metric may need further investigation[1]. The latter problem would seem to be related to the problem of formulating a "true" theory, in which the quantization of the metric is not at all canonical. In it, only the "true" components of the field would be quantized in the conventional way, while the other components, such as g^{00}, would not appear as dynamical variables describing the gravitational field, but would be replaced by different quantities describing the gravitational action-at-a-distance of matter, like gauge-independent quantum electrodynamics in its Hamiltonian features the Coulomb field rather than a time component of a potential four-vector.

REFERENCES

[1] F. J. Belinfante and J. S. Lomont, *Phys. Rev.* **84**, 541 (1951).
[2] F. J. Belinfante, *Phys. Rev.* **84**, 648 (1951).
[3] F. J. Belinfante, *Phys. Rev.* **76**, 66 (1949).
[4] J. C. Swihart, Ph. D. Thesis, Purdue University, 1954.
[5] F. J. Belinfante, D. I. Caplan and W. L. Kennedy, *Rev. Mod. Phys.* **29**, 518 (1957), in particular pp. 529–30.

(1) P.S. (1961). The problem is solved for harmonic coordinate systems by using $\gamma_{\mu\nu}$ as indicated.

ON BIRKHOFF'S THEOREM

W. B. Bonnor

Queen Elizabeth College, London

Birkhoff's theorem is as follows: *Every spherically symmetric solution of the field equations of general relativity*

$$R_{ik} = 0 \tag{1}$$

may be reduced, by a coordinate transformation, to the Schwarzschild solution

$$ds^2 = -\left(1-\frac{2m}{r}\right)^{-1} dr^2 - r^2(d\theta^2 + \sin^2\theta\, d\varphi^2) + \left(1-\frac{2m}{r}\right) dt^2.$$

The theorem therefore states that there are no spherically symmetric solutions of (1) which are genuinely time-dependent. This is obviously an important negative result for the theory of gravitational radiation.

The original proof of Birkhoff [1] contained the implicit assumption that a function is uniquely determined if the value of the function and all its derivatives are given at a single point. Actually, however, if $f(x_0)$ and $f^{(n)}(x_0)$ are given for all n, $f(x)$ is undetermined to the extent of an additive function $g(x)$ such that $g(x_0) = g^{(n)}(x_0) = 0$ for all n. An example of such a function $g(x)$ is $\exp\{-(x-x_0)^{-2}\}$. Birkhoff's proof cannot therefore be considered completely satisfactory.

Different proofs of the theorem have been given by Tolman [3] and Eiesland [2]. Tolman's proof does not consider all the cases which may arise, and Eiesland's proof, though satisfactory, is long and difficult, so it seems worthwhile to offer a proof which is at once rigorous and fairly simple.

The theorem will be proved in the following slightly more general form: *Every physically significant spherically symmetric solution of the field equations*

$$R_{ik} = \Lambda g_{ik} \tag{2}$$

may be reduced, by a coordinate transformation, to the static solution

$$ds^2 = -\left(1-\frac{2m}{r}-\frac{\Lambda r^2}{3}\right)^{-1} dr^2 - r^2(d\theta^2+\sin^2\theta\, d\varphi^2) + \\ + \left(1-\frac{2m}{r}-\frac{\Lambda r^2}{3}\right) dt^2. \tag{3}$$

The starting-point for the proof is that a space-time with spherical symmetry about a given origin may always be reduced to the form

$$ds^2 = -A\, dx_1^2 - B(d\theta^2+\sin^2\theta\, d\varphi^2) + C\, dx_4{}^2 + 2\alpha\, dx_1\, dx_4, \tag{4}$$

where A, B, C, α are functions of x_1 and x_4 (Eiesland [2]; actually Eiesland showed that one may also take $\alpha = 0$, but it is convenient to use the form (4)).

We first suppose that B is not a constant. If this supposition is granted, then we can always arrange that $\partial B/\partial x_1 \neq 0$; for if in the coordinates of (4) B is a function of x_4 only, then on introducing a new coordinate x_4^* by $x_4 = \psi(x_1, x_4^*)$ we can arrange, without destroying the form of (4), that the new B has $\partial B/\partial x_1 \neq 0$.

Now define a new coordinate r by putting

$$r = B^{1/2};$$

this brings the metric (4) to the form

$$ds^2 = -\frac{4AB}{B'^2}\, dr^2 - r^2(d\theta^2+\sin^2\theta\, d\varphi^2) + dx_4^2\left(C - \frac{A\dot{B}^2}{B'^2} - \frac{2\alpha\dot{B}}{B'}\right) \\ + 4dr\, dx_4\left(\frac{AB^{1/2}\dot{B}}{B'^2} + \frac{\alpha B^{1/2}}{B'}\right), \tag{5}$$

where $'$ means $\partial/\partial x_1$ and $\cdot$ means $\partial/\partial x_4$.

The next step is to introduce a new time coordinate t by

$$dt = \eta\left\{2\left(\frac{A\dot{B}B^{1/2}}{B'^2} + \frac{\alpha B^{1/2}}{B'}\right)dr + \left(C - \frac{2\alpha\dot{B}}{B'} - \frac{A\dot{B}^2}{B'^2}\right)dx_4\right\}, \tag{6}$$

where η is an integrating factor which exists unless

$$C - \frac{2\alpha\dot{B}}{B'} - \frac{A\dot{B}^2}{B'^2} = 0. \tag{7}$$

Assuming for the moment that (7) *does not hold,* it follows, if we substitute for dx_4 from (6) into (5), that the metric (5) becomes

$$ds^2 = -e^{\lambda} dr^2 - r^2(d\theta^2 + \sin^2\theta\, d\varphi^2) + e^{\nu} dt^2, \tag{8}$$

where e^{λ}, e^{ν} are certain functions of r and t.

For the metric (8), Tolman's proof of Birkhoff's theorem holds. One of the field equations (2) is

$$R_{14} \equiv -\frac{1}{r}\frac{\partial\lambda}{\partial t} = 0,$$

so that $\lambda = \lambda(r)$. An examination of the remaining field equations shows that the only solution is (3).

We now turn to the two exceptional cases, given by $B = \text{const}$ in (4), and by (7).

$B = k^2 (= \text{const})$. In this case we can introduce coordinates r and t such that (4) becomes

$$ds^2 = -e^{\mu}(dr^2 - dt^2) + k^2(d\theta^2 + \sin^2\theta\, d\varphi^2). \tag{9}$$

By direct computation the field equations give two equations

$$\Lambda = k^{-2}, \qquad \frac{\partial^2\mu}{\partial r^2} - \frac{\partial^2\mu}{\partial t^2} + 2\Lambda e^{\mu} = 0.$$

If we do not use a cosmological constant, this solution does not exist at all; if $\Lambda > 0$, the solution exists and is time-dependent and distinct from (3). However, the surface of a sphere $r = r_0$ ($= \text{const}$) is for the metric (9) $4\pi k^2$, which is independent of r_0. We therefore conclude that the solution has no physical significance, at any rate for a spherically symmetrical field.

$C - \dfrac{A\dot{B}^2}{B'^2} - \dfrac{2a\dot{B}}{B'} = 0$. In this case we have the metric (5) with $g_{44} = 0$. Let us write it as

$$ds^2 = -e^{\omega} dr^2 - r^2(d\theta^2 + \sin^2\theta\, d\varphi^2) + 2\beta\, dr\, dx_4.$$

By direct calculation, one finds (taking $x_2 = \theta$)

$$R_{22} \equiv -1$$

and the field equation $R_{22} = \Lambda g_{22}$ cannot be satisfied. Thus this case leads to no solution.

This establishes the generalized form of Birkhoff's theorem.

REFERENCES

[1] G. D. Birkhoff, *Relativity and Modern Physics,* 1927, p. 253.

[2] J. Eiesland, *Trans. Amer. Math. Soc.* **27**, 213 (1925).

[3] R. C. Tolman, *Relativity, Thermodynamics and Cosmology,* 1934, p. 252.

UNE EXPÉRIENCE MACROSCOPIQUE POUR TESTER L'ASYMÉTRIE DU TENSEUR INERTIAL DES MILIEUX DOUÉS DE SPIN

O. Costa de Beauregard

Institut Henri Poincaré, Paris

Il est bien connu (et ceci dès le mémoire fondamental de H. Tetrode [2]) que le tenseur inertial T^{ij} dont la définition est la plus naturelle en théorie des ondes matérielles à spin est asymétrique, et qu'il satisfait à la relation $(i, j, k, l = 1, 2, 3, 4;\ x^4 = ict)$

$$2T^{\underset{\vee}{ij}} \equiv T^{ij} - T^{ji} = \partial_k \sigma^{\underset{\vee}{ij}k}; \tag{1}$$

$\sigma^{\underset{\vee}{ij}k}$ désigne la densité de spin, essentiellement antisymétrique en i, j. Si, alors, les deux divergences de T^{ij} sont égales,

$$2\partial_j T^{\underset{\vee}{ij}} \equiv \partial_j T^{ij} - \partial_j T^{ji} = 0, \tag{2}$$

le tenseur σ^{ijk} est complètement antisymétrique, et il est commode d'introduire son quadrivecteur dual

$$ic\,\varepsilon^{ijkl}\sigma_l = \sigma^{ijk}; \tag{3}$$

(2) se récrit alors

$$4T^{\underset{\vee}{ij}} = ic\,\varepsilon^{ijkl}(\partial_k \sigma_l - \partial_l \sigma_k). \tag{4}$$

Toutes ces formules sont classiques en théorie des ondes matérielles à spin.

Ceci étant, l'auteur de ces lignes [4] et J. Weyssenhoff [3] ont indépendamment discuté *a priori* la dynamique relativiste d'un milieu continu doué de spin; ils ont montré que le tenseur inertial T^{ij} d'un tel milieu *doit* être asymétrique, et satisfaire à la formule (1) ou (4) (ou peut-être à une formule un peu plus générale [5] que nous ne discuterons pas ici).

Il est bien connu, et par la théorie des ondes matérielles à spin, et par la théorie dynamique *a priori*, que les deux indices du T^{ij}

(qui ne jouent évidemment pas le même rôle) sont attachés l'un à l'impulsion-énergie P^i, l'autre à la quadrivitesse cinématique V^i; ceci est lié à la non-colinéarité des deux quadrivecteurs P^i et V^i pour une gouttelette matérielle douée de spin [1]. Si alors $\mathcal{E}$ désigne une hypersurface arbitraire du genre espace, δu_i son quadrivecteur élément de volume,[1] nous sommes amenés à définir et à distinguer:

— l'impulsion-énergie physique

$$P^i = \iiint_{\mathcal{E}} T^{ij}\,\delta u_j, \tag{5}$$

— l'impulsion-énergie "longitudinale"

$$L^i = \iiint_{\mathcal{E}} T^{ji}\,\delta u_j, \tag{6}$$

— l'impulsion-énergie "transversale"

$$T^i = 2\iiint_{\mathcal{E}} T^{\underset{\smile}{ij}}\,\delta u_j, \tag{7}$$

manifestement orthogonale à δu_i.

Il est aujourd'hui admis que l'ensemble des précédentes formules est bien vérifié en dynamique des particules à spin, et notamment en dynamique de l'électron. Toutefois, étant donné le grand intérêt physique de l'ensemble du problème, il semblerait souhaitable de rechercher une expérience impliquant la matière macroscopique, et susceptible de vérifier l'ensemble de cette théorie. C'est le projet d'une telle expérience que nous nous proposons à présent de discuter.

Existe-t-il, tout d'abord, des substances manifestant *macroscopiquement* l'existence d'une densité de spin σ^i? *Oui*: les expériences gyromagnétiques de Barnett et d'Einstein–Haas ont montré sans équivoque que le ferromagnétisme est dû au spin de l'électron et, par voie de corollaire, qu'il y a intégration des spins individuels de telle manière qu'une densité de spin puisse être définie *macroscopiquement*. Si donc nous prenons un morceau de matière ferro- ou ferrimagnétique, qui soit initialement dans un état non-aimanté et finalement dans un état aimanté, nous avons en principe le moyen de faire apparaître, entre l'état initial et l'état final, l'impulsion-énergie transversale T^i. Si, de plus, nous faisons en sorte d'aimanter ce morceau de matière sans lui appliquer directement une force

[1] Grandeurs que Schwinger appelle σ et $d\sigma_i$ dans ses mémoires classiques sur l'électrodynamique quantique. Nous conservons ici à dessein les notations de nos anciens travaux pour éviter toute confusion avec σ_i, densité de spin.

pondéromotrice, alors l'apparition de T^i devrait avoir pour corollaire un effet observable de recul [5].

Il ne nous reste plus qu'à rechercher une forme adéquate pour le morceau de matière et pour le champ de polarisations à faire apparaître en son intérieur.

D'après (7) et (4), l'expression de l'impulsion-énergie transversale se récrit

$$T^i = - \iiint_{\mathcal{E}} \partial_k \sigma^{ijk} \delta u_j = - \iint \sigma_j [dx^i dx^j], \tag{8}$$

où $[dx^i dx^j]$ désigne l'élément d'aire d'espace-temps à 6 composantes; en langage prérelativiste, (8) se récrit

$$\boldsymbol{T} = \iiint \operatorname{rot} \boldsymbol{\sigma}\, dv = - \iint \boldsymbol{\sigma} \wedge \boldsymbol{ds}, \qquad T_4 = 0. \tag{9}$$

La forme à choisir pour le morceau de matière et pour le champ de polarisations devient dès lors évidente. Prenons par exemple un de ces petits anneaux de ferrite utilisés dans les calculatrices électroniques, et aimantons le au moyen d'un courant rectiligne axial (Fig. 1). L'intégrale (8) ou (9) se décompose en quatre intégrales: deux intégrales "latérales" qui se détruisent mutuellement, une intégrale de cylindre extérieur et une intégrale de cylindre intérieur dont la différence donnera une impulsion transversale $\boldsymbol{T}$, dirigée suivant l'axe de l'anneau et valant en module

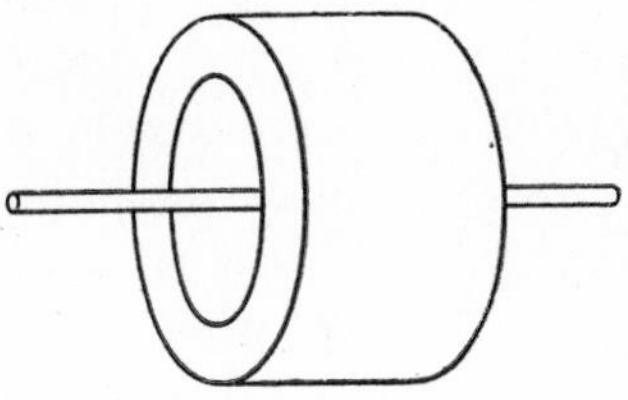

Fig. 1

$$T = 2\pi ab\sigma \tag{10}$$

(a, hauteur des cylindres, b, différence des reyons). Si ϱ désigne la densité massique de la matière considérée, et r le rayon moyen de l'anneau, la masse de cet anneau sera $2\pi abr\varrho$; la vitesse liée à l'impnlsion $\boldsymbol{T}$ vaudra donc en module

$$v = \frac{\sigma}{\varrho r}, \tag{11}$$

et elle aura pour direction l'axe du tore.

L'on voit que, σ et ϱ étant donnés, v sera d'autant plus grande que r sera plus petit: ceci vient de ce que l'effet pondéromoteur escompté est un effet de surface (équ. 8 ou 9).

L'idée naturelle est évidemment de suspendre élastiquement le petit anneau, et de provoquer des oscillations résonnantes au moyen d'un courant excitateur alternatif.

De préférence à une translation, l'on peut chercher à provoquer une rotation; le dispositif serait alors celui figuré ci-contre (Fig. 2): le circuit excitateur, formé de deux courants rectilignes antiparallèles, est fixe dans le laboratoire; l'équipage mobile est formé de deux petits anneaux ferro–ou ferrimagnétiques accolés en figure ∞, et suspendus à un fil de torsion. Rappelons que les lignes de champ de deux courants rectilignes antiparallèles sont (dans un plan normal aux fils) les cercles du faisceau admettant les traces des fils comme cercles-points: les anneaux devraient être centrés sur deux cercles du faisceau.

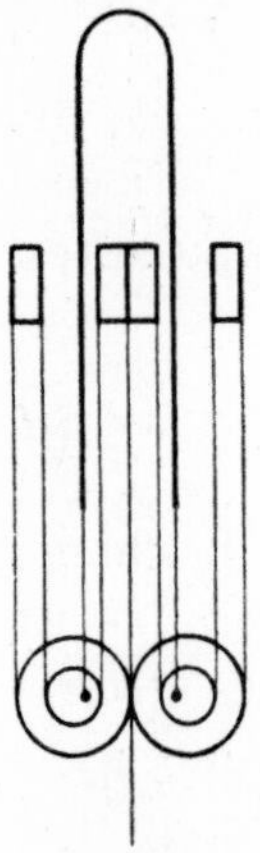

FIG. 2

En l'absence de couples de rappel et d'amortissement, la vitesse angulaire acquise par le dispositif passant d'un état non-aimanté à un état aimanté sera

$$\omega = \left(1+\frac{\Delta r}{r}\right)\frac{\sigma}{\varrho r_0^2}; \qquad (12)$$

σ, ϱ, r, comme précédemment; $2(r+\Delta r)$, distance des axes des anneaux; r_0, rayon de giration de l'équipage mobile. Cette formule est à rapprocher de celle de l'effet Einstein–Haas, $\omega = \sigma/\varrho r_0^2$: l'effet devrait donc être observable, à condition d'avoir un rayon de giration du même ordre que dans les expériences d'Einstein–Haas, ce qui en fait est possible.

BIBLIOGRAPHIE

[1] A. PROCA, *Ann. Phys., Paris* **20**, 347 (1933),

[2] H. TETRODE, *Z. Phy.* **49**, 858 (1928).

[3] J. WEYSSENHOFF et A. RAABE, *Acta Phys. Polon.* **9**, 7 (1947); J. WEYSSENHOFF, *ibid.* p. 26.

[4] O. COSTA DE BEAUREGARD, *C. R. Acad. Sci., Paris* **214**, 904 (1942); *J. Math. Pures Appl.* **22**, (118) 1943.

[5] O. COSTA de BEAUREGARD, *Cahier. Phys.* **99**, 407 (1958). **105**, 200 (1959).

INVARIANT COMMUTATORS FOR THE QUANTIZED GRAVITATIONAL FIELD

B. S. DeWitt

Department of Physics, University of North Carolina
*Chapel Hill, North Carolina**

The difficulties which have thus far beset all attempts to apply quantum mechanics to Einstein's theory of gravitation are twofold: (1) the nonlinearity of the theory, and (2) its coordinate invariance, which leads to constraints on the Cauchy data for the dynamical equations. It is the purpose of this communication to suggest that these difficulties are not as severe as has previously been imagined, and to display the basic commutators of the theory in covariant form.

We begin by pointing out that, apart from problems of factor ordering, the nonlinearity of the dynamical equations offers no complications for the commutators, contrary to a widespread impression. As Peierls [1] has shown, the commutator of two dynamical variables is determined by the variation in one of the variables due to an *infinitesimal* change in the action proportional to the other. But infinitesimal variations are propagated by means of *linear* equations, and standard techniques are available for handling the associated propagation functions.

Secondly, we note that the form of the Lagrange function appearing in the action is quite immaterial, provided it is understood that total divergences are to be discarded as necessary in order to render the action non-vanishing.(1) Since the commutators are completely

* This work was supported by the Air Force Office of Scientific Research under Contract No. AF-49(638)-563.

(1) In this respect our point of view differs from that of S. Deser and R. Arnowitt ([2] and subsequent papers appearing in collaboration with C.W. Misner) who have claimed a preferred status for Lagrangians which are linear in the first derivatives of the field variables.

determined by the form of the dynamical equations and the invariance groups of the theory, any Lagrange function which leads to the dynamical equations will do. Only the variations in the action are important, since these, by being chosen invariant, carry the group theoretical information.

In the general theory of relativity commutators can be obtained only between absolute invariants. The infinitesimal coordinate transformation law

$$\delta g_{\mu\nu} = \xi_{\mu\cdot\nu} + \xi_{\nu\cdot\mu} \qquad (\xi_\mu \text{ infinitesimal}) \tag{1}$$

leads to the characterization

$$(\delta A/\delta g_{\mu\nu})_{\cdot\nu} = 0, \qquad (\delta B/\delta g_{\mu\nu})_{\cdot\nu} = 0, \tag{2}$$

of any two absolute invariants, A and B, which are constructed solely out of the metric field $g_{\mu\nu}$.(1) Equations (2) may hold either as identities or in virtue of the field equations. Examples in the former category are provided by (a) the action, and (b) the space-time integral of any scalar density constructed out of the Riemann tensor and its covariant derivatives. Examples in the latter category are provided by (c) the energy-momentum 4-vector constructed from the canonical pseudo-tensor in an asymptotically Minkowskian coordinate system, and (d) any geometrical entity taken at a definite set of coordinate values in an "intrinsic" coordinate system built, for example, out of the invariants of the Riemann tensor in a "Ricci-flat" space-time.

In order to emphasize the applicability of the results obtained here to classical and quantum theory alike, our approach to the commutators will be through the canonical theory of Poisson brackets. Instead of following the arguments of Peierls we shall, for the sake of greater generality and increased insight, base our derivations on the recognition of the action as the generator of a finite canonical transformation and on the use of the fundamental theorem of classical transformation theory:

The variation in the functional form of the generator of a finite canonical transformation, due to independent infinitesimal canonical transformations of its arguments, is equal to the difference of the associated independent infinitesimal generators.(2)

(1) Covariant differentiation is here indicated by the dot followed by an index. The covariant divergences in Eq. (2) are to be computed with the understanding that the variational derivatives $\delta A/\delta g_{\mu\nu}$ and $\delta B/\delta g_{\mu\nu}$ are contravariant tensor densities of unit weight.

(2) A general proof of this theorem will be found in a previous paper by the author [3].

Nearly every important theorem in classical mechanics is a corollary of this one. In order to apply it to general relativity we consider the following change in the action:

$$S \to S + \varepsilon B \tag{3}$$

where ε is an infinitesimal constant. In Eq. (3) S is to be understood as the over-all space-time action which connects dynamical variables in the remote past with those in the remote future. We shall assume — and this will be the *only* assumption made in the course of our derivation — that the concepts "remote past" and "remote future" have an absolute invariant significance. For space-times in which this is not the case, alterations will be required in our results.

To determine the dynamical behavior of the space-time geometry in any finite domain it is necessary to break the action into two (or more) parts:

$$S = S(g_\infty | g_\Sigma) + S(g_\Sigma | g_{-\infty}). \tag{4}$$

Here the symbols g_∞ and $g_{-\infty}$ designate any set of invariant metric quantities associated with the remote future and past respectively which suffice (without redundancy) to determine the "history" of the gravitational field, and g_Σ designates the corresponding quantities associated with an arbitrary space-like hypersurface Σ as determined by the stationary action principle. These quantities must be invariants since only for such quantities can a canonical transformation theory be built up. Although neither the hypersurface Σ, which must itself be chosen in an "intrinsic" fashion, nor these invariants can therefore be regarded as having a *simple* structure in terms of the ordinary metric tensor $g_{\mu\nu}$, we shall see that it is unnecessary to have explicit knowledge of them to determine the Poisson brackets.

The change in the action (3), which may be regarded as a comparison between two slightly different physical systems, will induce a change in the dynamical variables, the precise nature of which depends upon the *boundary conditions* selected. For example, we may adopt *advanced* boundary conditions in which the dynamical states of the two systems are taken to coincide in the remote future. Since both the original and modified actions, when broken up as in Eq. (4), generate canonical transformations describing the unfolding-in-time of their respective "histories", it is evident that the dynamical variables of the two systems on any intrinsic space-like hypersurface Σ are themselves connected by an infinitesimal canonical transformation. Denoting the generator of this transformation by $s^+(\Sigma)$

and the corresponding variation in any invariant field quantity f_Σ by $\delta^+ f_\Sigma$, we have

$$\delta^+ f_\Sigma = -\big(f_\Sigma, s^+(\Sigma)\big), \tag{5}$$

the parentheses denoting Poisson brackets. From the fundamental theorem, on the other hand, we have

$$\bar{\delta} S(g_\infty | g_\Sigma) = s^+(\infty) - s^+(\Sigma) \tag{6}$$

where the symbol $\bar{\delta}$ is used to denote the change in the functional form. Since the advanced boundary conditions assure us that $s^+(\infty) = 0$, it therefore follows that

$$\delta^+ f_\Sigma = \big(f_\Sigma, \bar{\delta} S(g_\infty | g_\Sigma)\big). \tag{7}$$

For *retarded* boundary conditions, in which the dynamical states of the two systems are taken to coincide in the remote past, the corresponding equation is

$$\delta^- f_\Sigma = -\big(f_\Sigma, \bar{\delta} S(g_\Sigma | g_{-\infty})\big). \tag{8}$$

Under the variations $\delta^\pm$ associated with advanced or retarded boundary conditions, the segments $S(g_\infty | g_\Sigma)$ and $S(g_\Sigma | g_{-\infty})$ of the over-all action suffer two independent changes: (a) a change δ in *value* due to the changing values of their arguments, and (b) the change $\bar{\delta}$ in functional form. The change δ is determined simply by inserting the new field $g_{\mu\nu} + \delta^\pm g_{\mu\nu}$ into the old Lagrange function. The fact that the new field does not satisfy the field equations of the original system is unimportant. Because of the stationary action principle only the variations in the arguments at the end-points contribute. The change $\bar{\delta}$, on the other hand, is determined by the replacement (3):

$$\varepsilon B = \bar{\delta} S = \bar{\delta} S(g_\infty | g_\Sigma) + \bar{\delta} S(g_\Sigma | g_{-\infty}). \tag{9}$$

In evaluating this infinitesimal change (which is the only one we are really interested in) it suffices to use the old field $g_{\mu\nu}$ in B.

Equations (7), (8) and (9) together yield

$$\delta^+ f_\Sigma - \delta^- f_\Sigma = \varepsilon (f_\Sigma, B), \tag{10}$$

in which the generator is now independent of the hypersurface Σ. Since any absolute invariant A may be constructed out of hypersurface-associated invariants f_Σ, Eq. (10) may immediately be generalized to

$$\delta^+ A - \delta^- A = \varepsilon (A, B), \tag{11}$$

which is Peierls' result in the context of general relativity. It is important to note that reference to intrinsic space-like hypersurfaces Σ has completely disappeared from this equation.

The definition of Poisson brackets now rests on the possibility of an independent evaluation of the left side of Eq. (11). We begin by writing

$$\delta^{\pm} A = \int (\delta A / \delta g_{\mu\nu}) \delta^{\pm} g_{\mu\nu} d^4 x . \tag{12}$$

Since $g_{\mu\nu}$ is not an invariant its variations $\delta^{\pm} g_{\mu\nu}$ are determined only up to a coordinate transformation (1). In virtue of Eq. (2), however, the variations $\delta^{\pm} A$ remain well defined. The differential equations satisfied by the $\delta^{\pm} g_{\mu\nu}$ are obtained by varying the original field equations

$$0 = \delta S / \delta g_{\mu\nu} = (ck)^{-1} \mathfrak{G}^{\mu\nu} \equiv (ck)^{-1} g^{\frac{1}{2}} (R^{\mu\nu} - \tfrac{1}{2} g^{\mu\nu} R) . \tag{13}$$

Here g is the negative of the determinant of $g_{\mu\nu}$, $R^{\mu\nu}$ is the Ricci tensor, $R \equiv R_{\mu}{}^{\mu}$, and $k = 16\pi G / c^4$, G being the gravitation constant and c the velocity of light.

Under the alteration (3) the new field equations lead to

$$\delta^{\pm} \mathfrak{G}^{\mu\nu} = - \varepsilon c k \delta B / \delta g_{\mu\nu} . \tag{14}$$

By using the expressions

$$\delta^{\pm} \Gamma_{\mu\nu}{}^{\sigma} = \tfrac{1}{2} g^{\sigma\tau} (\delta^{\pm} g_{\mu\tau \cdot \nu} + \delta^{\pm} g_{\nu\tau \cdot \mu} - \delta^{\pm} g_{\mu\nu \cdot \tau}) , \tag{15}$$

$$\delta^{\pm} R_{\mu\nu\sigma}{}^{\tau} = \delta^{\pm} \Gamma_{\sigma\nu}{}^{\tau}{}_{\cdot \mu} - \delta^{\pm} \Gamma_{\sigma\mu}{}^{\tau}{}_{\cdot \nu} , \tag{16}$$

for the variations in the affinity and Riemann tensor respectively,[1] it is not hard to show that when the field equations (13) are satisfied the left side of (14) becomes

$$\delta^{\pm} \mathfrak{G}^{\mu\nu} = \tfrac{1}{2} g^{\frac{1}{2}} (g^{\mu\sigma} g^{\nu\tau} - \tfrac{1}{2} g^{\mu\nu} g^{\sigma\tau}) g^{\varrho\lambda} (\delta^{\pm} g_{\sigma\tau \cdot \varrho\lambda} + \delta^{\pm} g_{\varrho\lambda \cdot \sigma\tau} - \delta^{\pm} g_{\sigma\varrho \cdot \tau\lambda} - \delta^{\pm} g_{\tau\lambda \cdot \sigma\varrho}) . \tag{17}$$

One may then easily verify that the variation (1), if substituted into (17), gives zero when (13) is satisfied.[2] The general solutions of Eqs (14) are therefore obtained by adding (1) to particular solutions determined by appropriate boundary and supplementary conditions.

---

[1] Here the covariant derivatives are taken with respect to the original metric. The relation between the Riemann and Ricci tensors is $R_{\mu\nu} \equiv R_{\mu\sigma\nu}{}^{\sigma}$.

[2] $\mathfrak{G}^{\mu\nu}$ has the coordinate transformation law $\delta \mathfrak{G}^{\mu\nu} = (\mathfrak{G}^{\mu\nu} \xi^{\sigma})_{\cdot\sigma} - \xi^{\mu}{}_{\cdot\sigma} \mathfrak{G}^{\sigma\nu} - \xi^{\nu}{}_{\cdot\sigma} \mathfrak{G}^{\mu\sigma}$.

As supplementary conditions it is convenient to choose

$$(g^{\mu\sigma}g^{\nu\tau}-\tfrac{1}{2}g^{\mu\nu}g^{\sigma\tau})\,\delta^{\pm}g_{\sigma\tau\cdot\nu}=0\,. \tag{18}$$

Eqs (14) then take the form

$$g^{\frac{1}{2}}(g^{\mu\sigma}g^{\nu\tau}-\tfrac{1}{2}g^{\mu\nu}g^{\sigma\tau})g^{\varrho\lambda}\delta^{\pm}g_{\sigma\tau\cdot\varrho\lambda}-2g^{\frac{1}{2}}R^{\mu\sigma\nu\tau}\delta^{\pm}g_{\sigma\tau}=-2\varepsilon ck\,\delta B/\delta g_{\mu\nu}, \tag{19}$$

of which the solutions are

$$\delta^{\pm}g_{\mu\nu}=\varepsilon ck\int G^{\pm}{}_{\mu\nu\alpha\beta}(x,z)\,\delta B/\delta g_{\alpha\beta}\,d^4z\,, \tag{20}$$

where $G^{\pm}{}_{\mu\nu\alpha\beta}$ are the advanced and retarded Green's functions for Eq. (19), satisfying

$$g^{\sigma\tau}G^{\pm}{}_{\mu\nu\alpha\beta\cdot\sigma\tau}-2R_{\mu\ \nu}^{\ \sigma\ \tau}G^{\pm}{}_{\sigma\tau\alpha\beta}$$
$$=-(\bar g_{\mu\alpha}\bar g_{\nu\beta}+\bar g_{\mu\beta}\bar g_{\nu\alpha}-g_{\mu\nu}g_{\alpha\beta})g^{-\frac{1}{4}}(x)\delta^{(4)}(x,z)g^{-\frac{1}{4}}(z). \tag{21}$$

Green's functions of this type have been studied by DeWitt and Brehme [4], who have called them *bi-tensors* on account of their transformation properties at two different space-time points, x and z. The notation of these authors is followed here. Indices from the first part of the Greek alphabet refer to the point z and those from the latter part to the point x. The quantity $\bar g_{\mu\alpha}$ is the bi-vector which effects parallel displacements along the geodesic between x and z. The 4-dimensional delta function is regarded as a scalar density of weight $\frac{1}{2}$ at both x and z.

The general nature of the propagation characterized by the above Green's functions has been described by Hadamard [5]. Explicit forms for such Green's functions are given in [4]. In the present case these become

$$G^{-}{}_{\mu\nu\alpha\beta}(x,z)=2\theta[\Sigma(x),z]\bar G_{\mu\nu\alpha\beta}(x,z), \tag{22}$$

$$G^{+}{}_{\mu\nu\alpha\beta}(x,z)=2\theta[z,\Sigma(x)]\bar G_{\mu\nu\alpha\beta}(x,z), \tag{23}$$

$$\bar G_{\mu\nu\alpha\beta}=(8\pi)^{-1}[u_{\mu\nu\alpha\beta}\delta(\sigma)-v_{\mu\nu\alpha\beta}\theta(-\sigma)], \tag{24}$$

$$u_{\mu\nu\alpha\beta}=\Delta^{\frac{1}{2}}(\bar g_{\mu\alpha}\bar g_{\nu\beta}+\bar g_{\mu\beta}\bar g_{\nu\alpha}-g_{\mu\nu}g_{\alpha\beta})\,. \tag{25}$$

Here $\Sigma(x)$ is an arbitrary space-like hypersurface containing x, and $\theta[\Sigma(x),z]=1-\theta[z,\Sigma(x)]$ is equal to 1 when z lies to the past of $\Sigma(x)$ and vanishes when z lies to the future. Similarly $\theta(-\sigma)=0$ for $\sigma>0$ and $\theta(-\sigma)=1$ for $\sigma<0$, σ being one half the square of the geodetic interval between x and z (signature $-+++$). Furthermore,

$$\Delta=-g^{-\frac{1}{2}}(x)g^{-\frac{1}{2}}(z)\,|-\sigma_{\cdot\mu\alpha}|\,, \tag{26}$$

while $v_{\mu\nu\alpha\beta}$ is given by an infinite series

$$v_{\mu\nu\alpha\beta} = \sum_{n-0}^{\infty} v_{n\mu\nu\alpha\beta}\,\sigma^n, \tag{27}$$

whose coefficients satisfy the recurrence formulae [1]

$$v_{0\mu\nu\alpha\beta} + \Delta^{\frac{1}{2}}(\Delta^{-\frac{1}{2}} v_{0\mu\nu\alpha\beta})_{\cdot\tau}\sigma^{\cdot\tau} = -\tfrac{1}{2}(g^{\sigma\tau} u_{\mu\nu\alpha\beta\cdot\sigma\tau} - 2R_{\mu\ \nu}^{\ \sigma\ \tau} u_{\sigma\tau\alpha\beta}), \tag{28}$$

$$v_{n\mu\nu\alpha\beta} + (n+1)^{-1}\Delta^{\frac{1}{2}}(\Delta^{-\frac{1}{2}} v_{n\mu\nu\alpha\beta})_{\cdot\tau}\sigma^{\cdot\tau}$$
$$= -\tfrac{1}{2}n^{-1}(n+1)^{-1}(g^{\sigma\tau} v_{(n-1)\mu\nu\alpha\beta\cdot\sigma\tau} - 2R_{\mu\ \nu}^{\ \sigma\ \tau} v_{(n-1)\sigma\tau\alpha\beta}), \tag{29}$$

with $n = 1, 2, 3, \ldots$ The series (27) converges and the representation (24) holds in the region where σ is single valued. Beyond the caustic surfaces a continuation procedure must be employed. It will be noted that the Green's functions are singular on the light cone and vanish outside.

It is now important to check that the solutions (20) satisfy the supplementary conditions (18) which were invoked in order to get them in the first place. By using Eqs (13) and (21) together with the algebraic and differential identities satisfied by the Riemann tensor, one easily finds

$$g^{\varrho\lambda}[(g^{\mu\sigma}g^{\nu\tau} - \tfrac{1}{2}g^{\mu\nu}g^{\sigma\tau})G^{\pm}{}_{\sigma\tau\alpha\beta\cdot\nu}]_{\cdot\varrho\lambda}$$
$$= -[(\bar{g}^{\mu}{}_{\alpha}\bar{g}^{\nu}{}_{\beta} + \bar{g}^{\mu}{}_{\beta}\bar{g}^{\nu}{}_{\alpha})g^{-\frac{1}{4}}(x)\delta^{(4)}(x, z)g^{-\frac{1}{4}}(z)]_{\cdot\nu}$$
$$= [\bar{g}^{\mu}{}_{\alpha}g^{-\frac{1}{4}}(x)\,\delta^{(4)}(x, z)g^{-\frac{1}{4}}(z)]_{\cdot\beta} + [\bar{g}^{\mu}{}_{\beta}g^{-\frac{1}{4}}(x)\,\delta^{(4)}(x, z)g^{-\frac{1}{4}}(z)]_{\cdot\alpha}, \tag{30}$$

from which it may be inferred that

$$(g^{\mu\sigma}g^{\nu\tau} - \tfrac{1}{2}g^{\mu\nu}g^{\sigma\tau})G^{\pm}{}_{\sigma\tau\alpha\beta\cdot\nu} = -G^{\pm\mu}{}_{\alpha\cdot\beta} - G^{\pm\mu}{}_{\beta\cdot\alpha} \tag{31}$$

where $G^{\pm\mu}{}_{\alpha}$ are the advanced and retarded bi-vector Green's functions satisfying

$$g^{\nu\sigma}G^{\pm\mu}{}_{\alpha\cdot\nu\sigma} = -\bar{g}^{\mu}{}_{\alpha}g^{-\frac{1}{4}}(x)\,\delta^{(4)}(x, z)g^{-\frac{1}{4}}(z). \tag{32}$$

From Eqs (20) and (31) it then follows that

$$(g^{\mu\sigma}g^{\nu\tau} - \tfrac{1}{2}g^{\mu\nu}g^{\sigma\tau})\,\delta^{\pm}g_{\sigma\tau\cdot\nu} = -2\varepsilon k\int G^{\pm\mu}{}_{\alpha\cdot\beta}(x, z)\,\delta B/\delta g_{\alpha\beta}d^4z, \tag{33}$$

---

[1] With the techniques of [4] it can be shown that

$$\lim_{x\to z} v_{\mu\nu\alpha\beta} = R_{\mu\sigma\nu\tau}(\bar{g}^{\sigma}{}_{\alpha}\bar{g}^{\tau}{}_{\beta} + \bar{g}^{\sigma}{}_{\beta}\bar{g}^{\tau}{}_{\alpha}).$$

which, after an integration by parts and use of Eq. (2), leads back to (18), showing the complete self-consistency of these supplementary conditions.

We are now in a position to put all our results together to obtain the Poisson bracket. Substituting (20) into (12) and making use of (11), we find

$$(A, B) = ck \int d^4x \int d^4z \frac{\delta A}{\delta g_{\mu\nu}} G_{\mu\nu\alpha\beta}(x, z) \frac{\delta B}{\delta g_{\alpha\beta}}, \tag{34}$$

where

$$G_{\mu\nu\alpha\beta} \equiv G^+{}_{\mu\nu\alpha\beta} - G^-{}_{\mu\nu\alpha\beta}, \tag{35}$$

satisfying

$$g^{\sigma\tau} G_{\mu\nu\alpha\beta\cdot\sigma\tau} - 2R_{\mu\ \nu}^{\ \sigma\ \tau} G_{\sigma\tau\alpha\beta} = 0. \tag{36}$$

The simplicity of the manifestly invariant expression (34) is remarkable. While it is true that the "propagation function" $G_{\mu\nu\alpha\beta}$ itself has a rather complicated structure, the elucidation of this structure is a well defined analytical problem independent of canonical transformation theory. Moreover, the behavior of the covariant derivatives of $G_{\mu\nu\alpha\beta}$ and the nature of their singularities is quite simple when x and z are confined to the same space-like hypersurface, and the Poisson brackets of invariants associated with an "intrinsic" hypersurface can therefore generally be computed exactly.

The infinitesimal canonical transformations generated by absolute invariants have a special characteristic worth noting. Since

$$\delta^+ \mathfrak{G}^{\mu\nu} - \delta^- \mathfrak{G}^{\mu\nu} = 0, \tag{37}$$

it is evident that the metric $g_{\mu\nu} + \delta^+ g_{\mu\nu} - \delta^- g_{\mu\nu}$ satisfies the Einstein field equations if $g_{\mu\nu}$ does. Hence we see that absolute invariants transform solutions of the field equations into other solutions. This is the general relativistic version of the familiar theorem of classical mechanics that constants of the motion transform trajectories into trajectories.

The consequent role of absolute invariants as infinitesimal generators for the *group* of mappings of the set of all geometrically distinct solutions of the field equations into itself guarantees that the Poisson bracket (34) satisfies all of the identities usually associated with Poisson brackets, including the Poisson–Jacobi identity; for the Poisson brackets may be mapped into the commutators of the Lie ring associated with the group. These identities may also be verified directly, although the proof of the Poisson–Jacobi identity is extremely tedious. The antisymmetry of the Poisson bracket follows immediately from the reciprocity identity satisfied by the propagation function:[1]

$$G_{\mu\nu\alpha\beta}(x, z) \equiv -G_{\alpha\beta\mu\nu}(z, x). \tag{38}$$

The identity

$$(A, BC) \equiv (A, B)C + B(A, C) \tag{39}$$

is obvious.

In the case of the Poisson–Jacobi identity, instead of going through the process of deriving it directly one may turn the procedure around and use it to derive other identities which would otherwise be needed first. By straightforward application of (34) we get

$$\begin{aligned}
&\big(A, (B, C)\big) + \big(B, (C, A)\big) + \big(C, (A, B)\big) \\
&= (ck)^2 \int d^4x \int d^4x' \int d^4x'' \int d^4z \times \\
&\times \Bigg[\frac{\delta^2 A}{\delta g_{\alpha\beta}\,\delta g_{\mu\nu}} \frac{\delta B}{\delta g_{\mu'\nu'}} \frac{\delta C}{\delta g_{\mu''\nu''}} (G_{\mu''\nu''\alpha\beta} G_{\mu\nu\mu'\nu'} + G_{\mu'\nu'\alpha\beta} G_{\mu''\nu''\mu\nu}) + \\
&+ \frac{\delta A}{\delta g_{\mu\nu}} \frac{\delta^2 B}{\delta g_{\alpha\beta}\,\delta g_{\mu'\nu'}} \frac{\delta C}{\delta g_{\mu''\nu''}} (G_{\mu\nu\alpha\beta} G_{\mu'\nu'\mu''\nu''} + G_{\mu''\nu''\alpha\beta} G_{\mu\nu\mu'\nu'}) + \\
&+ \frac{\delta A}{\delta g_{\mu\nu}} \frac{\delta B}{\delta g_{\mu'\nu'}} \frac{\delta^2 C}{\delta g_{\alpha\beta}\,\delta g_{\mu''\nu''}} (G_{\mu'\nu'\alpha\beta} G_{\mu''\nu''\mu\nu} + G_{\mu\nu\alpha\beta} G_{\mu'\nu'\mu''\nu''}) + \\
&+ \frac{\delta A}{\delta g_{\mu\nu}} \frac{\delta B}{\delta g_{\mu'\nu'}} \frac{\delta C}{\delta g_{\mu''\nu''}} \left(G_{\mu\nu\alpha\beta} \frac{\delta G_{\mu'\nu'\mu''\nu''}}{\delta g_{\alpha\beta}} + G_{\mu'\nu'\alpha\beta} \frac{\delta G_{\mu''\nu''\mu\nu}}{\delta g_{\alpha\beta}} + G_{\mu''\nu''\alpha\beta} \frac{\delta G_{\mu\nu\mu'\nu'}}{\delta g_{\alpha\beta}} \right) \Bigg].
\end{aligned} \tag{40}$$

Here we have introduced additional point labels x', x'' and affixed corresponding primes to the associated indices. The first three terms in the square brackets vanish on account of the reciprocity relation (38) and the identities

$$\frac{\delta^2 A}{\delta g_{\alpha\beta}\,\delta g_{\mu\nu}} = \frac{\delta^2 A}{\delta g_{\mu\nu}\,\delta g_{\alpha\beta}}, \quad \text{etc.,} \tag{41}$$

satisfied by the second variational derivatives. Since the entire expression must vanish we therefore infer

$$\begin{aligned}
&\int d^4x \int d^4x' \int d^4x'' \int d^4z \frac{\delta A}{\delta g_{\mu\nu}} \frac{\delta B}{\delta g_{\mu'\nu'}} \frac{\delta C}{\delta g_{\mu''\nu''}} \times \\
&\times \left(G_{\mu\nu\alpha\beta} \frac{\delta G_{\mu'\nu'\mu''\nu''}}{\delta g_{\alpha\beta}} + G_{\mu'\nu'\alpha\beta} \frac{\delta G_{\mu''\nu''\mu\nu}}{\delta g_{\alpha\beta}} + G_{\mu''\nu''\alpha\beta} \frac{\delta G_{\mu\nu\mu'\nu'}}{\delta g_{\alpha\beta}} \right) = 0,
\end{aligned} \tag{42}$$

a result which has applications in the many-body problem.

---

(1) The reciprocity relations for the laws of propagation are proved in [5]. The corresponding identities for the explicit propagation functions are proved in [4].

It is of some interest to indicate, without actually going through the calculation, the procedure whereby one may evaluate the variational derivative of the propagation function. One begins by varying the equation

$$g^{\frac{1}{2}}(g^{\mu\sigma}g^{\nu\tau}-\tfrac{1}{2}g^{\mu\nu}g^{\sigma\tau})g^{\varrho\lambda}G^{\pm}{}_{\sigma\tau\mu'\nu'\cdot\varrho\lambda}-2g^{\frac{1}{2}}R^{\mu\sigma\nu\tau}G^{\pm}{}_{\sigma\tau\mu'\nu'}$$
$$=-(\bar{g}^{\mu}{}_{\mu'}\bar{g}^{\nu}{}_{\nu'}+\bar{g}^{\mu}{}_{\nu'}\bar{g}^{\nu}{}_{\mu'})g^{\frac{1}{4}}(x)\delta^{(4)}(x,x')g^{-\frac{1}{4}}(x'), \qquad (43)$$

which is an alternative form of (21). Observing that the right side of this equation is really independent of the metric (since $\bar{g}^{\mu}{}_{\mu'}\to\delta_{\mu'}{}^{\mu}$ as $x'\to x$) we obtain, on taking the variational derivative with respect to the metric at z, an equation of the form

$$g^{\frac{1}{2}}(g^{\mu\sigma}g^{\nu\tau}-\tfrac{1}{2}g^{\mu\nu}g^{\sigma\tau})g^{\varrho\lambda}\left(\frac{\delta G^{\pm}{}_{\sigma\tau\mu'\nu'}}{\delta g_{\alpha\beta}}\right)_{\cdot\varrho\lambda}-2g^{\frac{1}{2}}R^{\mu\sigma\nu\tau}\frac{\delta G^{\pm}{}_{\sigma\tau\mu'\nu'}}{\delta g_{\alpha\beta}}$$
$$=-T^{\pm\mu\nu}{}_{\mu'\nu'}{}^{\alpha\beta}, \qquad (44)$$

of which the solution, taking into account the kinematics of the Green's functions, is

$$\frac{\delta G^{\pm}{}_{\mu\nu\mu'\nu'}}{\delta g_{\alpha\beta}}=\tfrac{1}{2}\int G^{\pm}{}_{\mu\nu\mu''\nu''}T^{\pm\mu''\nu''}{}_{\mu'\nu'}{}^{\alpha\beta}d^4x''. \qquad (45)$$

In getting a preliminary expression for the quantity on the right of Eq. (44) it is necessary to make use of the variational identity

$$\delta(G^{\pm}{}_{\sigma\tau\mu'\nu'\cdot\varrho\lambda})=(\delta G^{\pm}{}_{\sigma\tau\mu'\nu'})_{\cdot\varrho\lambda}-G^{\pm}{}_{\varkappa\tau\mu'\nu'}\delta\Gamma_{\sigma\varrho}{}^{\varkappa}{}_{\cdot\lambda}-G^{\pm}{}_{\sigma\varkappa\mu'\nu'}\delta\Gamma_{\tau\varrho}{}^{\varkappa}{}_{\cdot\lambda}-$$
$$-2G^{\pm}{}_{\varkappa\tau\mu'\nu'\cdot\lambda}\delta\Gamma_{\sigma\varrho}{}^{\varkappa}-2G^{\pm}{}_{\sigma\varkappa\mu'\nu'\cdot\lambda}\delta\Gamma_{\tau\varrho}{}^{\varkappa}-G^{\pm}{}_{\sigma\tau\mu'\nu'}\delta\Gamma_{\varrho\lambda}{}^{\varkappa}. \qquad (46)$$

One then finds

$$T^{\pm\mu\nu}{}_{\mu'\nu'}{}^{\alpha\beta}\equiv G^{\pm}{}_{\sigma\tau\mu'\nu'\cdot\varrho\lambda}\delta[g^{\frac{1}{2}}(g^{\mu\sigma}g^{\nu\tau}-\tfrac{1}{2}g^{\mu\nu}g^{\sigma\tau})g^{\varrho\lambda}]/\delta g_{\alpha\beta}-$$
$$-2G^{\pm}{}_{\sigma\tau\mu'\nu'}\delta(g^{\frac{1}{2}}R^{\mu\sigma\nu\tau})/\delta g_{\alpha\beta}-$$
$$-g^{\frac{1}{2}}(g^{\mu\sigma}g^{\nu\tau}+g^{\mu\tau}g^{\nu\sigma}-g^{\mu\nu}g^{\sigma\tau})g^{\varrho\lambda}[(\delta\Gamma_{\sigma\varrho}{}^{\varkappa}/\delta g_{\alpha\beta})_{\cdot\lambda}G^{\pm}{}_{\varkappa\tau\mu'\nu'}+$$
$$+2(\delta\Gamma_{\sigma\varrho}{}^{\varkappa}/\delta g_{\alpha\beta})G^{\pm}{}_{\varkappa\tau\mu'\nu'\cdot\lambda}+\tfrac{1}{2}(\delta\Gamma_{\varrho\lambda}{}^{\varkappa}/\delta g_{\alpha\beta})G^{\pm}{}_{\sigma\tau\mu'\nu'\cdot\varkappa}]. \qquad (47)$$

The explicit form for use in (45) follows from this through use of the identities [cf. Eqs (15) and (16)]

$$\delta\Gamma_{\mu\nu}{}^{\sigma}/\delta g_{\alpha\beta}=\tfrac{1}{4}[(\bar{g}_{\mu}{}^{\alpha}\bar{g}^{\sigma\beta}+\bar{g}_{\mu}{}^{\beta}\bar{g}^{\sigma\alpha})g^{-\frac{1}{4}}(x)\delta^{(4)}(x,z)g^{-\frac{1}{4}}(z)]_{\cdot\nu}+$$
$$+\tfrac{1}{4}[(\bar{g}_{\nu}{}^{\alpha}\bar{g}^{\sigma\beta}+\bar{g}_{\nu}{}^{\beta}\bar{g}^{\sigma\alpha})g^{-\frac{1}{4}}(x)\delta^{(4)}(x,z)g^{-\frac{1}{4}}(z)]_{\cdot\mu}-$$
$$-\tfrac{1}{4}[(\bar{g}_{\mu}{}^{\alpha}\bar{g}_{\nu}{}^{\beta}+\bar{g}_{\mu}{}^{\beta}\bar{g}_{\nu}{}^{\alpha})g^{-\frac{1}{4}}(x)\delta^{(4)}(x,z)g^{-\frac{1}{4}}(z)]^{\cdot\sigma}, \qquad (48)$$

$$\delta R_{\mu\nu\sigma}{}^{\tau}/\delta g_{\alpha\beta} = (\delta\Gamma_{\sigma\nu}{}^{\tau}/\delta g_{\alpha\beta})_{\cdot\mu} - (\delta\Gamma_{\sigma\mu}{}^{\tau}/\delta g_{\alpha\beta})_{\cdot\nu}, \tag{49}$$

$$\delta g^{\frac{1}{2}}/\delta g_{\alpha\beta} = \tfrac{1}{2} g^{\alpha\beta} g^{\frac{1}{4}}(x)\delta^{(4)}(x, z) g^{-\frac{1}{4}}(z), \tag{50}$$

$$\delta g^{\mu\nu}/\delta g_{\alpha\beta} = -\tfrac{1}{2}(\bar{g}^{\mu\nu}\bar{g}^{\nu\beta} + \bar{g}^{\mu\beta}\bar{g}^{\nu\alpha}) g^{-\frac{1}{4}}(x)\,\delta^{(4)}(x, z) g^{-\frac{1}{4}}(z), \tag{51}$$

as well as the property

$$\lim_{x\to z} \bar{g}_{\mu\alpha\cdot\nu} = 0 \tag{52}$$

of the parallel displacement bi-vector. The resulting expression for $\delta G^{\pm}{}_{\mu\nu\mu'\nu'}/\delta g_{\alpha\beta}$ contains a large number of terms, most of which do not cancel but which group themselves in a symmetrical fashion. Typical terms, for example, are

$$\tfrac{1}{8} G^{\pm}{}_{\mu\nu\epsilon\zeta\cdot\gamma}\, g^{\frac{1}{2}}(z)(g^{\alpha\gamma}g^{\beta\delta} + g^{\alpha\delta}g^{\beta\gamma} - g^{\alpha\beta}g^{\gamma\delta})(g^{\epsilon\eta}g^{\zeta\theta} + g^{\epsilon\theta}g^{\zeta\eta} - g^{\epsilon\zeta}g^{\eta\theta}) G^{\pm}{}_{\eta\theta\mu'\nu'\cdot\delta} \tag{53}$$

and

$$\begin{aligned}
&\tfrac{1}{4}[G^{\pm}{}_{\mu\nu\sigma'\nu'}(\bar{g}^{\alpha\sigma'}\bar{g}^{\beta}{}_{\mu'} + \bar{g}^{\beta\sigma'}\bar{g}^{\alpha}{}_{\mu'}) + \\
&\qquad + G^{\pm}{}_{\mu\nu\sigma'\mu'}(\bar{g}^{\alpha\sigma'}\bar{g}^{\beta}{}_{\nu'} + \bar{g}^{\beta\sigma'}\bar{g}^{\alpha}{}_{\nu'})] g^{\frac{1}{4}}(z)\,\delta^{(4)}(z, x') g^{-\frac{1}{4}}(x') + \\
&+ \tfrac{1}{4} g^{-\frac{1}{4}}(x)\,\delta^{(4)}(x, z) g^{\frac{1}{4}}(z)[(\bar{g}_{\mu}{}^{\alpha}\bar{g}^{\sigma\beta} + \bar{g}_{\mu}{}^{\beta}\bar{g}^{\sigma\alpha}) G^{\pm}{}_{\sigma\nu\mu'\nu'} + \\
&\qquad + (\bar{g}_{\nu}{}^{\alpha}\bar{g}^{\sigma\beta} + \bar{g}_{\nu}{}^{\beta}\bar{g}^{\sigma\alpha}) G^{\pm}{}_{\sigma\mu\mu'\nu'}].
\end{aligned} \tag{54}$$

When these expressions are substituted into (42) one finds, after carrying out many integrations by parts and throwing covariant divergences over onto the factors $\delta A/\delta g_{\mu\nu}$, $\delta B/\delta g_{\mu'\nu'}$, $\delta C/\delta g_{\mu''\nu''}$ (which then vanish owing to Eq. (2)) that the terms of the resulting very long expression all cancel one another in an intricate but not particularly illuminating fashion. In this process it is necessary to use the identity (31) as well as the similar easily verified identities

$$G^{\pm\mu}{}_{\alpha\cdot\mu} = -G^{\pm}{}_{\cdot\alpha}, \tag{55}$$

$$G^{\pm}{}_{\mu}{}^{\mu}{}_{\alpha\beta} = -2 g_{\alpha\beta} G^{\pm}, \tag{56}$$

where $G^{\pm}(x, z)$ are the Green's functions for the scalar wave equation, satisfying

$$g^{\mu\nu} G^{\pm}{}_{\cdot\mu\nu} = -g^{-\frac{1}{4}}(x)\,\delta^{(4)}(x, z) g^{-\frac{1}{4}}(z). \tag{57}$$

It is also necessary to make use of the reciprocal relations

$$G^{\pm}{}_{\mu\nu\alpha\beta} = G^{\mp}{}_{\alpha\beta\mu\nu}, \quad G^{\pm}{}_{\mu\alpha} = G^{\mp}{}_{\alpha\mu}, \quad G^{\pm}(x, z) = G^{\mp}(z, x), \tag{58}$$

and to keep in mind the kinematical properties of these functions.

Having thus established the canonical formulation of the classical theory on a manifestly covariant foundation we may now have a brief look at the difficulty which remains on passing to the quantum theory, namely, the problem of choosing factor sequences. We begin by noting that because of the linearity of the coordinate transformation law (1), when expressed in the form

$$\delta g_{\mu\nu} = g_{\mu\nu,\sigma}\,\xi^{\sigma} + g_{\mu\sigma}\,\xi^{\sigma}{}_{,\nu} + g_{\nu\sigma}\,\xi^{\sigma}{}_{,\mu}\,, \tag{59}$$

the transformation law of any tensor constructed out of the metric tensor and its derivatives will possess a similar linearity (in terms of itself and its first derivatives) if the choice of factor sequences is itself coordinate invariant. The construction of quantum analogs of familiar tensors and invariants is therefore a simple although not unique process. The fact that the "factors" we have in mind here are the metric tensor and its derivatives, in the covariant form rather than some other form, is irrelevant provided we assume that the components of the metric tensor all commute with one another at the same point. The consistency of this assumption is revealed in Eq. (62) below. We should also note that we only consider coordinate transformations (59) in which the infinitesimal ξ^{μ} is a c-number.

We next point out that equations like (2) do not really hold as they stand in the quantum theory, and that their content must be re-expressed in the form of circumlocutions. Thus, for any absolute invariant A, Eq. (2) must be replaced by

$$\int \frac{\delta A}{\delta g_{\mu\nu}} \cdot (\xi_{\mu\cdot\nu} + \xi_{\nu\cdot\mu})\, d^4x = 0\,, \tag{60}$$

in which the dot is used to indicate that the factor in parentheses standing to the right is to be inserted as a replacement for $\delta g_{\mu\nu}$ in all the places in which it occurs in the variation δA. Special generalizations of this process are, of course, required if the components which go to make up A are not all expressible as simple factor sequences; for example, if there are occurrences of $g^{1/2}$ and $g^{\mu\nu}$. However, the important point is that the process is unique.

The dot multiplication process is similarly to be used in defining the commutator brackets by extension from Eq. (34):

$$[A\,, B] = i\hbar c k \int d^4x \int d^4z\, \frac{\delta A}{\delta g_{\mu\nu}} \cdot G_{\mu\nu\alpha\beta} \cdot \frac{\delta B}{\delta g_{\alpha\beta}}\,. \tag{61}$$

Here one may imagine that the propagation function $G_{\mu\nu\alpha\beta}$ is first inserted as a replacement for $\delta g_{\alpha\beta}$ in the variation δB and that the resulting "product" is then inserted as a replacement for $\delta g_{\mu\nu}$ in the variation δA, or, alternatively, that the process of insertion is first performed in δA and then in δB. That the two procedures are equivalent is evident from the familiar properties of commutator brackets when one takes note of the fact that in computing the commutator of two absolute invariants one may work directly with the factors themselves, proceeding as if the metric tensor had the simple commutation rule

$$[g_{\mu\nu}, g_{\alpha\beta}] = i\hbar ck G_{\mu\nu\alpha\beta}. \tag{62}$$

We therefore see that the question of the consistency of a quantum theory of gravitation falls squarely on the propagation function, which, contrary to the case of linear field theories, is here an *operator*. A possible choice of factor sequence which suggests itself for the definition of the propagation function is based on the expression for its variational derivative, of which the terms (53) and (54) above are representative. One may require that the variation in the propagation function shall be obtained by inserting the variation $\delta g_{\alpha\beta}$ between the factors $G^{\pm}{}_{\mu\nu\epsilon\zeta\cdot\tau}$ and $G^{\pm}{}_{\eta\vartheta\mu'\nu'\cdot\delta}$ in (53), placing it to the right in the first line of (54) and to the left in the second line, adopting a similar "time-ordering" procedure in all the other terms, integrating over all values of the space-time point z, and finally symmetrizing by taking one half the sum of the resulting expression and its Hermitian conjugate. The resulting nonlinear variational equation in the quantities $G^{\pm}{}_{\mu\nu\alpha\beta}$ may then be integrated by an iterative procedure which builds up the propagation function from its c-number value in a flat space-time.

It is not certain, however, that the Poisson–Jacobi identity will be satisfied with a propagation function constructed in this way. Even if the identities (31) and (55) should be satisfied, with the adoption of a suitable factor sequence in the definition of the covariant derivatives, so that integrations by parts could be performed which, through application of Eq. (60), eliminate many terms in the computation of the double commutators, the remaining terms will not necessarily cancel as they do in the classical theory, since these terms involve products of *three* Green's functions which will not stand in the same order in both members of a classically cancelling pair. It seems likely that a consistent quantum theory will have to be developed on a "build-as-you-go" plan. Since calculations of quantum gravitational processes will be based on procedures of successive approximation (for a long time to come at any rate) it will be appropriate to adjust things so that the consistency requirements are satisfied at the level of approximation in question. Difficulties will, in fact, not arise until the level of approximation is reached in which it is necessary to take into account effects involving at least *three* virtual "gravitons". In lower approximations it suffices to use the flat-space-time propagation function or, at most, a modification of it involving a term linear in the metric. In the higher approximations it is possible that "renormalization" questions will enter into the consistency adjustment. The renormalization problems are likely to prove especially severe in view of the strongly singular nature of the mutual graviton interactions, as exemplified, for instance, in the occurrence of *differentiated* Green's functions in (53).

In "practical" calculations we shall actually have to do not with the commutator function $G_{\mu\nu\alpha\beta}$ but with the "Feynman function" $G^F{}_{\mu\nu\alpha\beta}$ which propagates positive frequencies into an asymptotically flat remote future and negative frequencies into an asymptotically flat remote past.[1] The use of the time-ordering procedure outlined above seems particularly appropriate for the definition of the Feynman function, intimately associated with such procedures as it is. It satisfies a variational equation identical in form with that satisfied by the Green's functions $G^\pm{}_{\mu\nu\alpha\beta}$, and hence can be built up by iteration from its flat-space-time c-number value in precisely the same way. The time-ordering procedure guarantees that its Hermitian conjugate, which propagates negative frequencies into the future and positive frequencies into the past, is also built up in the same way. Only one remark should be added to indicate that the time-ordering process is slightly more complicated than was previously indicated. The insertion of the variation $\delta g_{\alpha\beta}$ between, for example, the two Green's functions in expression (53) is not completely unique since there are also the other factors $g^{\frac{1}{2}}$, $g^{\alpha\gamma}$, $g^{\epsilon\eta}$ etc., as well as the affinity at z involved in the covariant derivatives of the Green's functions, which do not necessarily commute with $\delta g_{\alpha\beta}$. The lack of commutativity of the ambiguously ordered factors

(1) The requirement that "remote future" and "remote past" shall have an absolute invariant significance and the requirement that the space-time regions so characterized shall be asymptotically flat are obviously related, although inequivalent. The self-consistency of the latter requirement is highly probable for all states in which the gravitational field can be said to contain a finite amount of "energy" (as represented, for example, by the "Bel–Robinson" tensor). It is clear that all results based on the use of the Feynman function are only approximate (however negligible the error) in a cosmology possessing a catastrophic remote past or future.

in the integrated result for the Feynman function, however, is of the divergent c-number type which occurs for quantities taken at the same space-time point, and can probably be dealt with by a straightforward symmetrization and subtraction procedure determined by other consistency requirements.

It is fitting to end these remarks by asking the question "Where do we go from here?" With the explicit exhibition of the Poisson bracket (34), it is important as soon as possible to get down to the serious business of calculating something. In order to do this, however, one must first ask "What?" In the realm of problems in which the gravitational field is regarded as externally imposed there are a number of calculations which should be performed, such as the production of particles by a gravitational field and the associated problem of stress renormalization. Interesting problems involving the quantized gravitational field, however, are not so obvious. (Scattering calculations are only amusing.) There are, to be sure, questions concerning self-mass, particularly the relation of gravitational self-mass to self-mass arising from other fields, which are of importance. But these lead at once to more basic questions involving further development of the formalism. Any notion of "self-mass" must of necessity be an invariant notion, expressible independently of any framework, such as a scattering calculation, which invokes special asymptotic conditions. Now that the theory has been formulated in an invariant fashion we must begin to learn how to ask invariant questions of it. Since this is certain to affect future developments strongly this should be the next order of business.

REFERENCES

[1] R. E. Peierls, *Proc. Roy. Soc.* A **214**, 143 (1952).

[2] R. L. Arnowitt and S. Deser, *Phys. Rev.* **113**, 745 (1959).

[3] B. S. DeWitt, *Rev. Mod. Phys.* **29**, 377 (1957).

[4] B. S. DeWitt and R. W. Brehme, *Ann. Phys.* **9**, 220 (1960).

[5] J. Hadamard, *Lectures on Cauchy's Problem in Linear Partial Differential Equations,* Yale University Press, New Haven 1923.

INTERACTING GRAVITATIONAL AND SPINOR FIELDS

P. A. M. DIRAC

St. John's College, Cambridge

Abstract–The theory of the interaction of the gravitational field with a spinor field is put into Hamiltonian form. The simplest Hamiltonian formalism for the gravitational field deals with the state at a certain value for x^0 and requires that the $g_{\mu 0}$ do not enter into the description of the state. To bring a spinor field into this formalism, the fourlegs to which the spinors are referred must be chosen so that one of the legs is normal to the hypersurface $x^0 =$ const. The Hamiltonian and the constraints are worked out for this scheme.

1. THE ACTION DENSITY

THE problem of putting the theory of the interaction of the gravitational field with a spinor field into Hamiltonian form has been treated by B. S. DeWitt and C. M. DeWitt [1]. Their work is incomplete in that they do not give all the constraints associated with their Hamiltonian.

A simplified Hamiltonian formalism for the gravitational field is provided by the author's method [2]. The present work uses this simplified formalism and gives the complete scheme.

For dealing with spinors in a Riemann space one must introduce a fourleg at each point, described by field functions $h_{\mu a}$ satisfying

$$h^{\mu}{}_{a} h_{\mu b} = \eta_{ab}, \qquad \eta^{ab} h_{\mu a} h_{\nu b} = g_{\mu\nu}, \tag{1}$$

where η_{ab} is the fundamental tensor of special relativity. The $h_{\mu a}$ become the fundamental field quantities of the gravitational field, instead of the $g_{\mu\nu}$. We shall suppose the signs chosen so that g_{00} and η_{00} are negative, this being more convenient for the Hamiltonian treatment.(1)

(1) The suffixes a, b, c are raised and lowered with η^{ab}, while Greek suffixes are raised and lowered with $g^{\mu\nu}$.

The field equations for the spinor field have been worked out by many people. We shall here take them in the form given by the author [3],

$$h^{\mu}{}_{a}\alpha^{a}(\psi_{\mu}-\tfrac{1}{4}h^{\nu}{}_{b}h_{\nu c,\mu}\beta\alpha^{b}\beta\alpha^{c}\psi)-im\beta\psi=0. \tag{2}$$

The notation is the same as in [3], except for the change in sign of all the $g_{\mu\nu}$, η_{ab}. Thus $\alpha^0 = 1$ and

$$\alpha^a\beta\alpha^b+\alpha^b\beta\alpha^a = -2\eta^{ab}\beta. \tag{3}$$

A suffix added with a comma denotes a covariant derivative and without a comma it denotes an ordinary derivative.

The field equations (2) follow from an action principle with the action density

$$\mathcal{L}_S = Jh^{\mu}{}_{a}\varphi\alpha^{a}\psi_{\mu}-\tfrac{1}{4}Jh^{\mu}{}_{a}h^{\nu}{}_{b}h_{\nu c,\mu}\varphi\alpha^{a}\beta\alpha^{b}\beta\alpha^{c}\psi-imJ\varphi\beta\psi. \tag{4}$$

Here

$$J = (-\det g_{\mu\nu})^{\frac{1}{2}} = |\det h_{\mu a}|,$$

and φ is another spinor field, satisfying field equations conjugate complex to those for ψ.

We must add $\mathcal{L}_S$ to the action density $\mathcal{L}_G$ for the gravitational field and vary the total action, to get the field equations that describe the interaction. In order that these equations may be physically meaningful, it is necessary that $\mathcal{L}_S$ should be real, or that it should differ from a real quantity by a perfect differential. There are two easy ways of satisfying this requirement. (i) We take $\varphi = i\psi^+$. It can now easily be checked that the imaginary part of $\mathcal{L}_S$ is a perfect differential. (ii) We use a representation of the matrices α^a, β for which the non-vanishing elements of α^a are all real and those of β are all pure imaginary. There then exist real solutions ψ of the field equations (2). We take ψ and φ to be real independent solutions, so that $\mathcal{L}_S$ is real. The following work is applicable with either way.

It is desirable to replace the covariant derivative in (4) by ordinary derivatives. We have from (3)

$$\begin{aligned}
h^{\mu}{}_{a}h^{\nu}{}_{b}h_{\nu c,\mu}\alpha^{a}\beta\alpha^{b}\beta\alpha^{c}
&= \tfrac{1}{2}h^{\mu}{}_{a}h^{\nu}{}_{b}(h_{\nu c,\mu}-h_{\mu c,\nu})\alpha^{a}\beta\alpha^{b}\beta\alpha^{c}-h^{\mu}{}_{a}h^{\nu}{}_{b}h_{\nu c,\mu}\eta^{ab}\alpha^{c}\\
&= \tfrac{1}{2}h^{\mu}{}_{a}h^{\nu}{}_{b}(h_{\nu c,\mu}-h_{\mu c,\nu})\alpha^{a}\beta\alpha^{b}\beta\alpha^{c}-h^{\mu}{}_{c,\mu}\alpha^{c}\\
&= \tfrac{1}{2}h^{\mu}{}_{a}h^{\nu}{}_{b}h_{\nu c\mu}(\alpha^{a}\beta\alpha^{b}-\alpha^{b}\beta\alpha^{a})\beta\alpha^{c}-J^{-1}(Jh^{\mu}{}_{a})_{\mu}\alpha^{a}.
\end{aligned} \tag{5}$$

To get a more symmetrical result, let $A(F^{abc})$ denote the quantity, antisymmetrical in the suffixes a, b, c, obtained from F^{abc} when one applies all permutations to the suffixes a, b, c, adds the results with a minus sign for the odd permutations, and divides by six. We find from (3)

$$A(\alpha^a\beta\alpha^b\beta\alpha^c) = \tfrac{1}{2}(\alpha^a\beta\alpha^b - \alpha^b\beta\alpha^a)\beta\alpha^c - \eta^{ac}\alpha^b + \eta^{bc}\alpha^a. \qquad (6)$$

Hence

$$\begin{aligned} h^\mu{}_a h^\nu{}_b h_{\nu c\mu} A(\alpha^a\beta\alpha^b\beta\alpha^c) - \tfrac{1}{2} h^\mu{}_a h^\nu{}_b h_{\nu c\mu}(\alpha^a\beta\alpha^b - \alpha^b\beta\alpha^a)\beta\alpha^c \\ = -h^\mu{}_a h^\nu{}_b h_\nu{}^a{}_\mu \alpha^b + h^\mu{}_a h^{\nu c} h_{\nu c\mu}\alpha^a \\ = h^\mu{}_{a\mu} h^\nu{}_b h_\nu{}^a \alpha^b + J^{-1} J_\mu h^\mu{}_a \alpha^a \\ = J^{-1}(J h^\mu{}_a)_\mu \alpha^a. \end{aligned}$$

Combining this result with (5) and substituting in (4), we get

$$\begin{aligned} \mathcal{L}_S = J h^\mu{}_a \varphi\alpha^a \psi_\mu + \tfrac{1}{2}(J h^\mu{}_a)_\mu \varphi\alpha^a\psi - \\ - \tfrac{1}{4} J h^\mu{}_a h^\nu{}_b h_{\nu c\mu} \varphi A(\alpha^a\beta\alpha^b\beta\alpha^c)\psi - imJ\varphi\beta\psi. \qquad (7) \end{aligned}$$

2. THE DYNAMICAL COORDINATES

The Hamiltonian form of dynamics is based on the concept of the state at a certain time, which becomes in relativistic theory the state on a three-dimensional space-like hypersurface in space-time. The Hamiltonian equations of motion show how the dynamical variables that describe the state vary as the hypersurface is varied.

To get the simplest Hamiltonian formalism, we deal only with states on the hypersurfaces $x^0 = \text{const}$, instead of on general space-like hypersurfaces, as was done by the DeWitts [1]. Thus we have a state described by the physical conditions for all values of x^1, x^2, x^3 for a fixed x^0. The symmetry between the four x's is now completely destroyed.

To describe the state on the hypersurface $x^0 = t$, where t is a constant, we need the $g_{rs} (r, s = 1, 2, 3)$ for all x^1, x^2, x^3, to fix the metric of the hypersurface. We do not need the $g_{\mu 0} (\mu = 0, 1, 2, 3)$. These serve only to fix a neighbouring hypersurface $x^0 = t + \varepsilon$.

We get the simplest Hamiltonian formalism if we describe the state on the hypersurface $x^0 = t$ entirely in terms of quantities that are independent of the $g_{\mu 0}$, that is, quantities that are invariant under a change of the hypersurface $x^0 = t + \varepsilon$ with no change of the hypersurface $x^0 = t$. Any fields that are present in addition to the gravitational field and any particles should therefore be described in terms of such quantities.

If the additional fields or particles involve a vector A^μ (either a vector field or a single vector for the description of a particle), the quantities independent of the $g_{\mu 0}$ are the three covariant components A_r and the normal component $A_L = A^\mu l_\mu$, l_μ being the unit normal to the hypersurface. If they involve a tensor, each tensor index must be handled in this way.

If there is a spinor field, we must choose the fourlegs to which the spinors are referred such that the leg 0 is normal to the hypersurface. We are left with an arbitrary choice of the threelegs 1, 2, 3 in the hypersurface. The spinor components are then independent of the $g_{\mu 0}$.

With such fourlegs, we have $h_{\mu 0} = l_\mu$ or

$$h_{00} = -(-g^{00})^{-\frac{1}{2}}, \qquad h_{r0} = 0. \tag{8}$$

Eqs (1) now give

$$h^0{}_0 = (-g^{00})^{\frac{1}{2}}, \qquad h^0{}_{a'} = 0, \tag{9}$$

$$h^r{}_{a'} h_{rb'} = \delta_{a'b'}, \qquad h_{ra'} h_{sa'} = g_{rs}, \tag{10}$$

$$h^0{}_0 h_{0a'} + h^r{}_0 h_{ra'} = 0, \qquad h_{ra'} h_{0a'} = g_{r0}, \tag{11}$$

where a', b' take on the values 1, 2, 3.

The threelegs in the hypersurface are described by the quantities $h^r{}_{a'}$, $h_{ra'}$ satisfying (10). The connection between $h^r{}_{a'}$ and $h_{ra'}$ is

$$h_{ra'} = g_{rs} h^s{}_{a'}, \qquad h^r{}_{a'} = e^{rs} h_{sa'},$$

where e^{rs} is the reciprocal matrix to g_{rs}. Thus

$$e^{rs} = h^r{}_{a'} h^s{}_{a'}.$$

Eqs (11) may be written

$$h^r{}_0 = -h^0{}_0 h_{0a'} h^r{}_{a'}, \qquad h_{0a'} = g_{r0} h^r{}_{a'}. \tag{12}$$

They show that all the $h^\mu{}_a$, $h_{\mu a}$ can be expressed in terms of the $h_{ra'}$ and $g_{\mu 0}$. They can be combined to give

$$h^r{}_0 = -h^0{}_0 g_{s0} e^{rs}. \tag{13}$$

We now take as our basic dynamical coordinates

$$g_{\mu 0}, \quad h_{ra'}, \quad \varphi, \quad \psi. \tag{14}$$

Apart from the $g_{\mu 0}$ occurring here explicitly, they are all independent of the $g_{\mu 0}$ in the sense described above and satisfy the requirement for giving the simplest description of the states on the hypersurfaces $x^0 = \text{const}$.

The action density can be expressed in terms of the quantities (14) and their first derivatives. Derivatives with respect to x^r are functions of the dynamical coordinates, those with respect to x^0 are velocities. In the expression (7) for $\mathcal{L}_S$ we can put c' for c in the third term, since if $c = 0$ we must take $\nu = 0$ from (8), and then we must take $b = 0$ from (9) and the term vanishes.

3. THE MOMENTA

The dynamical coordinates (14) have conjugate momenta, say $p^{\mu 0}$, $\pi^{r}{}_{a'}$, θ, χ respectively. One gets them by varying the velocities in the total action density and expressing the result as

$$\delta(\mathcal{L}_G + \mathcal{L}_S) = p^{\mu 0}\delta g_{\mu 00} + \pi^{r}{}_{a'}\,\delta h_{ra'0} + \theta\delta\varphi_0 + \chi\delta\psi_0. \tag{15}$$

We can arrange that the momenta $p^{\mu 0}$ are zero, by adding a suitable divergence term to $\mathcal{L}_G$, as was shown in [2]. The other momenta are independent of the $g_{\mu 0}$, since they have zero P.b. with the $p^{\mu 0}$, so all the effective Hamiltonian variables are then independent of the $g_{\mu 0}$ degrees of freedom.

The variation of the velocities in $\mathcal{L}_G$ has been carried out in [2] and the result is given by the equation preceding Eq. (21) there, namely, (allowing for the change in sign of all the $g_{\mu\nu}$)

$$\delta\mathcal{L}_G = J(e^{r\mu}e^{sv} - e^{rs}e^{uv})\Gamma_{uv}{}^{0}\,\delta g_{rs0} \tag{16}$$

$$= 2J(e^{ru}e^{sv} - e^{rs}e^{uv})\Gamma_{uv}{}^{0}\,h_{sa'}\,\delta h_{ra'0}. \tag{17}$$

From (7) we see that $\mathcal{L}_S$ is the sum of two parts,

$$\mathcal{L}_S = \mathcal{L}_S(0) + \mathcal{L}_S(1),$$

where $\mathcal{L}_S(0)$ is independent of the velocities and $\mathcal{L}_S(1)$ is linear homogeneous in the velocities. One gets $\mathcal{L}_S(0)$ by putting $\mu = r$ in (7), and $\mathcal{L}_S(1)$ by omitting the last term in (7) and putting $\mu = 0$ in the remainder.

Let

$$K = (\det g_{rs})^{\frac{1}{2}} = |\det h_{ra'}|,$$

so that, from the first of equations (9),

$$Jh^{0}{}_{0} = J(-g^{00})^{\frac{1}{2}} = K. \tag{18}$$

Then $\mathcal{L}_S(1)$ reduces to

$$\mathcal{L}_S(1) = K\varphi\psi_0 + \tfrac{1}{2}K_0\varphi\psi + \tfrac{1}{8}Kh^{r}{}_{b'}h_{rc'0}\varphi(a_{b'}a_{c'} - a_{c'}a_{b'})\psi, \tag{19}$$

so that

$$\delta \mathcal{L}_S = K\varphi\delta\psi_0 + \tfrac{1}{2}Kh^r{}_{a'}\varphi\psi\delta h_{ra'0} - \tfrac{1}{8}Kh^r{}_{b'}\varphi(\alpha_{a'}\alpha_{b'} - \alpha_{b'}\alpha_{a'})\psi\delta h_{ra'0}. \quad (20)$$

Comparing (17) plus (20) with (15), we find

$$p^{\mu 0} = 0, \quad \theta = 0, \quad \chi = K\varphi, \quad (21)$$

$$\pi^r{}_{a'} = 2J(e^{ru}h^v{}_{a'} - e^{uv}h^r{}_{a'})\Gamma_{uv}{}^0 + $$
$$+ \tfrac{1}{2}Kh^r{}_{a'}\varphi\psi - \tfrac{1}{8}Kh^r{}_{b'}\varphi(\alpha_{a'}\alpha_{b'} - \alpha_{b'}\alpha_{a'})\psi. \quad (22)$$

These momenta satisfy P.b. relations of the standard type, for example

$$[h_{ra'}, \pi'^s{}_{b'}] = \delta^s_r\delta_{a'b'}\delta_3(x - x'), \quad (23)$$

where π' means π at the point x'^1, x'^2, x'^3.

4. THE PRIMARY CONSTRAINTS

The equations (21), (22) that give the momenta in terms of the velocities lead to some equations involving only dynamical coordinates and momenta (i.e. independent of the velocities). These are the primary constraints of the system.

The three equations (21) are evidently primary constraints. From (22) we can deduce

$$M_{a'b'} = 0 \quad (24)$$

where

$$M_{a'b'} = \pi^r{}_{a'}h_{rb'} - \pi^r{}_{b'}h_{ra'} + \tfrac{1}{4}\chi(\alpha_{a'}\alpha_{b'} - \alpha_{b'}\alpha_{a'})\psi, \quad (25)$$

which is another primary constraint. There is, of course, one of each of the constraints (21), (24) for each point x^1, x^2, x^3 of the hypersurface.

There are also some secondary constraints, which follow from the field equations. These will be obtained later.

All the constraints, primary and secondary, are divided into two classes, first-class and second-class. The first-class ones are those that have zero P.b. with all the constraints (when the constraints are all written with zero on their right-hand sides). Any first-class constraint or linear combination of them, say $X = 0$, has the property that we can use X as a Hamiltonian, which means making each dynamical variable ξ vary according to

$$\delta\xi = \varepsilon[\xi, X]$$

with ε small. The resulting change in all the dynamical variables does not affect the physical state, but corresponds merely to some change in the system of reference.

From this property we can infer that the $p^{\mu 0}$ and $M_{a'b'}$ must be first-class without going to the trouble of working out the secondary constraints and checking all the P.b.'s. If we use $\int k_\mu p^{\mu 0} d^3x$ as a Hamiltonian, with k_μ any function of x^1, x^2, x^3, we merely change the variables $g_{\mu 0}$, and we have arranged that such a change shall not affect the physical state. Similarly, if we use $\int k_{a'b'} M_{a'b'} d^3x$ as a Hamiltonian, we get from (23)

$$\begin{aligned} \delta h_{ra'} &= \varepsilon \int k'_{b'c'} (\delta_{a'b'} h'_{rc'} - \delta_{a'c'} h'_{rb'}) \delta_3(x-x') d^3x' \\ &= \varepsilon (k_{a'b'} - k_{b'a'}) h_{rb'}, \end{aligned} \tag{26}$$

which is just the change corresponding to a rotation of the threelegs in the hypersurface, and we know that such a change does not affect the physical state.

The constraints $\theta = 0$ and $\chi - K\varphi = 0$ are second-class, since their P.b. is not zero. We absorb these constraints into the formalism by counting $K\varphi = \chi$ as a strong equation, or as a definition of φ in terms of χ, and eliminating the degrees of freedom associated with φ, θ for all x^1, x^2, x^3, so that they no longer contribute to P.b.'s.

From (22) we can deduce

$$\pi^r{}_{a'} h^s{}_{a'} + \pi^s{}_{a'} h^r{}_{a'} = 4J(e^{ru} e^{sv} - e^{uv} e^{rs}) \Gamma_{uv}{}^0 + e^{rs} \chi \psi, \tag{27}$$

which we shall need later.

5. THE HAMILTONIAN

The Hamiltonian is the quantity

$$H = \int (\pi^r{}_{a'} h_{ra'0} + \chi \psi_0 - \mathcal{L}_G - \mathcal{L}_S) d^3x$$

expressed in terms of dynamical coordinates and momenta. From (22), it can be divided into two parts

$$H = H_G + H_S,$$

where

$$H_G = \int \{2J(e^{ru} h^v{}_{a'} - e^{uv} h^r{}_{a'}) \Gamma_{uv}{}^0 h_{ra'0} - \mathcal{L}_G\} d^3x, \tag{28}$$

$$\begin{aligned} H_S &= \int \{[\tfrac{1}{2} K h^r{}_{a'} \varphi \psi - \tfrac{1}{8} K h^r{}_{b'} \varphi (\alpha_{a'} \alpha_{b'} - \alpha_{b'} \alpha_{a'}) \psi] h_{ra'0} + \chi \psi_0 - \mathcal{L}_S\} d^3x \\ &= -\int \mathcal{L}_S(0) d^3x, \end{aligned} \tag{29}$$

with the help of (19).

The formula (28) for H_G is the same as in the absence of a spinor field. We may therefore take for H_G the expression worked out in [2], Eq. (31), namely

$$H_G = \int \{(-g^{00})^{-\frac{1}{2}} \mathcal{H}_{GL} + g_{s0} e^{rs} \mathcal{H}_{Gr}\} d^3x, \tag{30}$$

with $\mathcal{H}_{GL}$ and $\mathcal{H}_{Gr}$ certain functions of the variables g_{rs}, p^{rs}. The p^{rs} here are the coefficients of δg_{rs0} in (16), so from (27) they equal

$$p^{rs} = \tfrac{1}{4}(\pi^r{}_{a'} h^s{}_{a'} + \pi^s{}_{a'} h^r{}_{a'} - e^{rs} \chi\psi). \tag{31}$$

By substituting these values for p^{rs} into the expressions for $\mathcal{H}_{GL}$ and $\mathcal{H}_{Gr}$ given in [2], we get $\mathcal{H}_{GL}$ and $\mathcal{H}_{Gr}$ as functions of our Hamiltonian variables $h_{ra'}$, $\pi^r{}_{a'}$, ψ, χ.

From (29) and (7),

$$H_S = \int \{-Jh^r{}_a \varphi a^a \psi_r - \tfrac{1}{2}(Jh^r{}_a)_r \varphi a^a \psi + $$
$$+ \tfrac{1}{4} Jh^r{}_a h^v{}_b h_{vc'r} \varphi A (a^a \beta a^b \beta a^c) \psi + imJ\varphi\beta\psi\} d^3x. \tag{32}$$

We must get it into the form (30), namely

$$H_S = \int \{(-g^{00})^{-\frac{1}{2}} \mathcal{H}_{SL} + g_{s0} e^{rs} \mathcal{H}_{Sr}\} d^3x, \tag{33}$$

where $\mathcal{H}_{SL}$ and $\mathcal{H}_{Sr}$ are functions only of the variables $h_{ra'}$, $\pi^r{}_{a'}$, ψ, χ.

We have from (13) and (18)

$$Jh^r{}_0 = -Kg_{s0} e^{rs}. \tag{34}$$

So the first term of the integrand in (32) with $a = 0$ contributes $\chi\psi_r$ to $\mathcal{H}_{Sr}$. With $a = a'$ it contributes $-h^r{}_{a'} \chi \alpha_{a'} \psi_r$ to $\mathcal{H}_{SL}$.

The second term of the integrand in (32) can be replaced by $\frac{1}{2} Jh^r{}_a (\varphi a^a \psi)_r$. Then with $a = 0$ it contributes $-\frac{1}{2}K(K^{-1}\chi\psi)_r$ to $\mathcal{H}_{Sr}$, and with $a = a'$ it contributes $\frac{1}{2}Kh^r{}_{a'}(K^{-1}\chi\alpha_{a'}\psi)_r$ to $\mathcal{H}_{SL}$.

In the third term of the integrand in (32), if we put $a = a'$, $b = b'$ we get a contribution to $\mathcal{H}_{SL}$ of amount

$$-\tfrac{1}{24} \varepsilon_{a'b'c'} h^r{}_{a'} h^u{}_{b'} h_{uc'r} \chi \alpha_1 \alpha_2 \alpha_3 \psi,$$

where $\varepsilon_{a'b'c'}$ is antisymmetric in the three suffixes and has the value 1 for $a' = 1$, $b' = 2$, $c' = 3$. If we put $a = 0$, $b = b'$ we get a contribution to $\mathcal{H}_{Sr}$ of amount

$$\tfrac{1}{8} h^u{}_{b'} h_{uc'r} \chi (\alpha_{b'} \alpha_{c'} - \alpha_{c'} \alpha_{b'}) \psi.$$

If we put $a = a'$, $b = 0$, then by using

$$\frac{h^v{}_0}{h^0{}_0} h_{vc'r} = -\left(\frac{h^v{}_0}{h^0{}_0}\right)_r h_{vc'} = -\left(\frac{h^u{}_0}{h^0{}_0}\right)_r h_{uc'} = (g_{s0} e^{us})_r h_{uc'}$$

from (13), we get the term

$$\tfrac{1}{8} h^r{}_{a'} (g_{s0} e^{us})_r h_{uc'} \chi (\alpha_{a'} \alpha_{c'} - \alpha_{c'} \alpha_{a'}) \psi .$$

After a partial integration, this gives a contribution to $\mathcal{H}_{Sr}$ of amount

$$-\tfrac{1}{8} \{ h^u{}_{a'} h_{rc'} \chi (\alpha_{a'} \alpha_{c'} - \alpha_{c'} \alpha_{a'}) \psi \}_u .$$

Finally, the last term of the integrand in (32) contributes $im\chi\beta\psi$ to $\mathcal{H}_{SL}$. Collecting results, we find

$$\mathcal{H}_{SL} = -h^r{}_{a'} \chi \alpha_{a'} \psi_{r'} + \tfrac{1}{2} K h^r{}_{a'} (K^{-1} \chi \alpha_{a'} \psi)_r + im\chi\beta\psi - \\ - \tfrac{1}{24} \varepsilon_{a'b'c'} h^r{}_{a'} h^u{}_{b'} h_{uc'r} \chi \alpha_1 \alpha_2 \alpha_3 \psi \tag{35}$$

$$\mathcal{H}_{Sr} = \chi\psi_r - \tfrac{1}{2} K (K^{-1} \chi \psi)_r + \\ + \tfrac{1}{8} h^u{}_{a'} h_{ub'r} \chi (\alpha_{a'} \alpha_{b'} - \alpha_{b'} \alpha_{a'}) \psi \\ - \tfrac{1}{8} \{ h^u{}_{a'} h_{rb'} \chi (\alpha_{a'} \alpha_{b'} - \alpha_{b'} \alpha_{a'}) \psi \}_u . \tag{36}$$

The Hamiltonian is undetermined to the extent that we can add to it a quantity of the form

$$\int k_{a'b'} M_{a'b'} d^3x , \tag{37}$$

with $k_{a'b'}$ any function of x^1, x^2, x^3, since this quantity vanishes, by (24). The effect of this quantity on the equations of motion is to give an arbitrary rotation to the threelegs in the hypersurface as the hypersurface proceeds from $x^0 = t$ to $x^0 = t + \varepsilon$.

6. THE SECONDARY CONSTRAINTS

Since $p^{\mu 0} = 0$ we have $p^{\mu 0}{}_0 = 0$, so that $p^{\mu 0}$ has zero P.b. with H. Hence

$$\mathcal{H}_{GL} + \mathcal{H}_{SL} = 0, \qquad \mathcal{H}_{Gr} + \mathcal{H}_{Sr} = 0. \tag{38}$$

These equations involve only the dynamical coordinates and momenta, so they are constraints. They are consequences of the field equations, so they are secondary constraints.

They must be first-class, as otherwise the conditions that they remain valid for all x^0, which means that they must have zero P. b.

with H, would lead to restrictions on the variables $g_{\mu 0}$, and we know that these variables are quite arbitrary.

We now have a complete Hamiltonian scheme. An initial state of our dynamical system is specified by any values for the Hamiltonian variables $h_{ra'}$, $\pi^{r}{}_{a'}$, ψ, χ satisfying the constraints (24), (38). The whole motion is then given by the Hamiltonian equations that follow from the Hamiltonian (30) plus (33) plus (37).

REFERENCES

[1] B. S. DeWitt and C. M. DeWitt, *Phys. Rev.* **87**, 116 (1952).
[2] P. A. M. Dirac, *Proc. Roy. Soc.* A **246**, 333 (1958).
[3] P. A. M. Dirac, *Max-Planck-Festschrift*, 339 (1958).

RELATIVISTIC HYDRODYNAMICS AND ITS RELATION TO INTERIOR SOLUTIONS OF THE GRAVITATIONAL FIELD EQUATIONS

J. Ehlers

University of Hamburg, Hamburg

1. INTRODUCTION

If the general theory of relativity is considered as a macroscopic theory of gravitation the appropriate description of matter is hydrodynamic. In the simplest case of dust-like matter the energy-momentum tensor has the form

$$T_{kl} = \varrho u_k u_l . \tag{1}$$

Here u^k is a timelike unit vector tangent to the world lines of matter, and ϱ is the mean proper density.

The gravitational interaction of matter is described by Einstein's field equations (1)

$$R_{kl} - (\tfrac{1}{2}R + \Lambda) g_{kl} = -T_{kl} . \tag{2}$$

It is natural to develop hydrodynamics in three steps. In the first step one studies the kinematic properties of fluid motions, which means the geometry of the set of stream lines defined by the four-velocity field u^k. In the second step one derives the consequences of the conservation law for the energy-momentum tensor, namely the continuity equation and the relativistic Euler-equation. Finally in the third step one takes into account the field equations (2).

(1) We use the signature $+++-$ of the metric and put $c = 1$, $\varkappa = 1$, where c denotes the fundamental velocity and $\varkappa$ Einstein's constant of gravitation. The sign of the Ricci tensor is chosen as in Eisenhart [1].

Essentially the first two steps have been performed by Synge [2] and Lichnerowicz [3], and some work concerning the third group of problems has been done by Lichnerowicz [4], Gödel [5], Raychaudhuri [6], and those authors who have studied special solutions of equations (2) (see Sec. 3 below).

In this report I wish to give a simple geometrical presentation of the relativistic kinematics of continuous media and to outline the application of hydrodynamics to the classification, construction, and characterization of interior solutions of equations (2).

2. BASIC CONCEPTS AND FORMULAE OF KINEMATICS

We assume that we have a normal hyperbolic four-dimensional Riemannian space with fundamental tensor g_{kl} and in it a set of non-intersecting, timelike "stream lines". We write

$$x^j = x^j(\tau, a^\nu) \qquad (\nu = 1, 2, 3), \tag{3}$$

a^ν being Langrangian coordinates of the fluid-elements, and τ the eigentime along the streamlines. The tangent vector

$$u^j = \frac{\partial x^j}{\partial \tau} \tag{4}$$

of the streamlines is then a unit vector.

Let

$$\delta = \delta a^\nu \frac{\partial}{\partial a^\nu} \tag{5}$$

denote the variation transverse to the stream lines and $\frac{D}{d\tau}$ the covariant differentiation along the stream lines.

If we formulate the equality of the mixed second derivatives of functions (3) with respect to the independent variables τ and a^ν, use the definitions (4) and (5) and add Γ-symbol terms we obtain:

$$\frac{D\delta x^k}{d\tau} = \delta x^l u^k{}_{;l}. \tag{6}$$

We further introduce the acceleration vector

$$\dot{u}^k \equiv \frac{Du^k}{d\tau} \tag{7}$$

and the space-metric

$$h_{kl} = g_{kl} + u_k u_l \tag{8}$$

associated with our set of stream lines.

The projection $\overline{\delta x}^k \equiv h^k_l\, \delta x^l$ of δx^k into the local space of a particle (a^ν) is the position vector of the particle $(a^\nu + \delta a^\nu)$ with respect to the first particle. It is possible that its change $\dfrac{D\overline{\delta x}^k}{d\tau}$ does not lie in the local space of (a^ν), but its projection[1]

$$\overline{\delta v}^j \equiv h^j_k \frac{D\overline{\delta x}^k}{d\tau} = \overline{\delta x}^l u^j{}_{;l} \tag{9}$$

does and represents the relative velocity of $(a^\nu + \delta a^\nu)$ with respect to (a^ν). The preceding equations (6), (7), and (8) have been used in deriving the last expression. Eq. (9) describes the velocity field in the vicinity of one particle; it therefore contains the kinematic information we wish to obtain. In fact, if we put

$$\omega_{rs} \equiv u_{[s,r]} - \dot{u}_{[r} u_{s]}, \tag{10}$$

$$\theta = u^r{}_{;r}, \tag{11}$$

$$\sigma_{rs} \equiv u_{(r;s)} + \dot{u}_{(r} u_{s)} - \tfrac{1}{3}\theta h_{rs} \tag{12}$$

equation (9) may be rewritten as

$$\overline{\delta v}^j = \overline{\delta x}^e (\omega_{e.}{}^{j} + \sigma_{e.}{}^{j} + \tfrac{1}{3}\theta \delta^j_e), \tag{13}$$

and we may consider the velocity field as a superposition of three parts which describe the rotation, shear, and expansion of the fluid element under consideration. The justification of this interpretation can be given as follows. We calculate the change $\dfrac{D\delta s}{d\tau}$ of the distance $\delta s = (g_{kl}\overline{\delta x}^k \overline{\delta x}^l)^{1/2}$ with the help of formula (13) and obtain:

$$\frac{D\delta s}{\delta s\, d\tau} = \sigma_{ke} \frac{\overline{\delta x}^k}{\delta s} \frac{\overline{\delta x}^e}{\delta s} + \frac{1}{3}\theta \tag{14}$$

which shows (together with $\sigma^r{}_r = 0$) that θ describes the relative change of volume, σ_{kl} describes the change of the shape of the fluid

---

(1) $\overline{\delta v}^j = 0$ means that $\overline{\delta x}^j$ is Fermi-propagated; then $\dfrac{D\overline{\delta x}^j}{d\tau} = u^j \overline{\delta x}^k \dot{u}_k$.

element, whereas $\omega_{e.}^{\ j}$ does not affect the local distances and therefore is a rotation. The axis of rotation is given by the vector

$$\omega^j \equiv \tfrac{1}{2}\eta^{jkem} u_k u_{e,m} \tag{15}$$

because of $u_j \omega^j = 0$ and $\omega^j \omega_{kj} = 0$.[1]

It is convenient to introduce the scalars

$$\dot{u} \equiv (\dot{u}_k \dot{u}^k)^{\frac{1}{2}}, \qquad \omega \equiv (\tfrac{1}{2}\omega_{rs}\omega^{rs})^{\frac{1}{2}} = (\omega_r \omega^r)^{\frac{1}{2}}, \qquad \sigma \equiv (\tfrac{1}{2}\sigma_{rs}\sigma^{rs})^{\frac{1}{2}} \tag{16}$$

which vanish only if the corresponding tensors $\dot{u}_k$, ω_{rs} resp. ω_r, σ_{rs} vanish, as may be seen from definitions (7), (10) and (12).

We have described these elementary considerations in detail because the method used here, unlike the usual treatments, leads in a geometric way, without reference to special coordinate systems or to classical hydrodynamics, to fundamental concepts and formulae. The method may be regarded as carrying out ideas sketched by Weyl in [7] in the section on rotation (§ 36).

It should be noted that the preceding kinematic relations can be applied whenever a congruence of timelike curves in a normal hyperbolic space is given. This congruence may be the set of stream lines of a moving fluid, the set of trajectories of a group of isometries, the congruence defined by the timelike principal vector of the conformal curvature tensor or the like. With slight modifications these relations can also be used in order to study congruences of null-lines; this is important for the theory of those radiation fields which define "rays" (see [14]).

In applying kinematic formulae it is sometimes appropriate to use the fact that the kinematic quantities are almost conformally invariant; if we have

$$\bar{g}_{kl} = F^2 g_{kl}, \qquad \bar{u}^k = \frac{1}{F}u^k, \qquad F = F(x^k) \tag{17}$$

it follows that

$$\begin{aligned} \bar{\theta} &= \frac{1}{F}\theta + \frac{3}{F^2}\frac{DF}{d\tau}, \\ \bar{\omega}_j &= \omega_j, \\ \bar{\sigma}_{jk} &= F\sigma_{jk}. \end{aligned} \tag{18}$$

---

(1) It has not always been noticed that the quantities ω_{rs} and ω^j are equivalent for the description of rotation; by (10) and (15) the bivectors ω_{rs} and $2u^{[q}\omega^{p]}$ are dual.

These formulae make it possible, for example, to reduce the vorticity theory of isentropic motions of perfect fluids to the corresponding theory for dust-like matter. (1)

3. SOLUTIONS OF EQUATIONS (1, 2) AND THEIR HYDRODYNAMIC PROPERTIES

As we consider only dust-like matter we always have a geodesic motion, $\dot{u} = 0$.

The kinematically simplest solution of the field equations (1, 2) should be such that matter "moves" without rotation ($\omega = 0$), preserving volume ($\theta = 0$) and form ($\sigma = 0$), so that u^j is a constant vector field. (2) It is well known that the static Einstein cosmos is characterized by these properties.

The simplest model with rotation should be such that the motion is again rigid ($\theta = 0$ and $\sigma = 0$) (3) and the angular velocity ω^j constant; by these properties Gödel's rotating universe is characterized [9].

In the following we shall assume that $\Lambda = 0$; then the two preceding results give non-existence theorems. Therefore we shall require solutions without rotation and shear, but with an expansion. It has been shown by Raychaudhuri [6] that the only solutions of this type are the Friedmann models with an expanding space of constant curvature. This local characterization of Friedmann's models can be made more elegant by using the fact that the differential Doppler shift is related to shear by

$$\frac{\delta \nu}{\nu} = \frac{D\delta s}{d\tau} \tag{19}$$

which can be derived from ray-optics. Because of (14) the differential red-shift is isotropic if and only if we have an isotropic expansion ($\sigma = 0$). Further we can use a remark of Gödel [5]: If any observer (on a fluid particle) is to see an isotropic distribution of density in his immediate neighbourhood we must have $h^j_k \varrho_{,j} = 0$ or $\varrho_{,k} = -u^j \varrho_{,j} u_k$; therefore the stream lines form a normal congruence, and the motion is non-rotational by equation (15). Consequently the Friedmann models are characterized by the fact that each observer

(1) Compare [2] and [3].

(2) $u^j{}_{;l} = 0$.

(3) This definition of rigid motions is equivalent with the one given in [8] as follows from (11) and (12).

travelling with the substratum sees an isotropic red-shift and observes an isotropic density distribution in his neighbourhood.

A volume preserving non-rotational motion — the most important case in classical hydrodynamics — is impossible for dust-like matter as can be seen from Raychaudhuri's generalization of Friedmann's equation governing the expansion along a stream line ([6], compare [10]).

Besides these well-known solutions of equations (1, 2) with high symmetries I know only three new types of solutions.

Bondi obtained the general solution with spherical symmetry [11]; naturally then the motion is non-rotational.

Heckmann and Schücking constructed solutions which admit metrically homogeneous space sections [12]. In their solutions matter expands anisotropically but does not rotate.

The only solutions with rotating matter and $\Lambda = 0$ which are known to me are those in which matter moves without shear and expansion.(1) Their line element in co-moving coordinates ($u^j = \delta^j_0$) is given by

$$ds^2 = d\sigma^2 - (dt - u_\lambda dx^\lambda)^2 \tag{20}$$

where

$$ds^2 = e^{-2U} d\sigma^2 - e^{2U} dt^2 \tag{21}$$

is an arbitrary static vacuum-metric ($\bar{R}_{kl} = 0$), and where u_λ is determined by

$$u_{[\lambda,\mu]} = -\eta_{\lambda\mu\nu} U^{,\nu}. \tag{22}$$

Eq. (22) is to be considered with respect to $d\sigma^2$. The vorticity vector is $\omega_j = U_{,j}$, and the density is $\varrho = 4\omega^2$. The mass M of matter within a surface F in the x^λ-space is given by

$$M = 4 \int_F U \frac{\partial U}{\partial n} do, \tag{23}$$

do being the surface element with respect to $d\sigma^2$. The curvature tensor is determined by the formulae

$$\begin{aligned} {}^*R^*_{hijk} u^i u^k &= -\omega_h \omega_j - \omega^2 h_{hj}, \\ R_{hijk} u^i u^k &= \omega_h \omega_j - \omega^2 h_{hj}, \\ -{}^*R_{hijk} u^i u^k &= \omega_{h;j}; \end{aligned} \tag{24}$$

here the star indicates real dual-operation.

---

(1) See my lecture at the Royaumont Conference 1959. A special case was treated earlier by van Stockum [13].

Hydrodynamic concepts and relations are useful not only for the purpose of interpretation and characterization of given solutions but are helpful, too, in a priori specification of the line elements which are to describe definite kinematic situations.

The study of rigorous solutions performed at the Hamburg seminar on general relativity held by Prof. P. Jordan includes work on hydrodynamic solutions; we especially hope to find cases in which it is possible to replace intrinsic singularities of exterior fields by matter and to obtain information on the meaning of such singularities.

REFERENCES

[1] L. P. Eisenhart, *Riemannian Geometry,* Princeton 1949.
[2] J. L. Synge, *Proc. Lond. Math. Soc.* **43** (1937).
[3] A. Lichnerowicz, *Théories relativistes de la gravitation et de l'électromagnétisme,* Paris 1955.
[4] A. Lichnerowicz, *J. Math. Pures Appliques* **23**, 37 (1944).
[5] K. Gödel, *Proc. Internat. Congr. Math.* (Cambridge, Mass.) 30. VIII.–5. IX. 1950, 1 p. 175 (1952).
[6] A. Raychaudhuri, *Phys. Rev.* **98**, 1123 (1955).
[7] H. Weyl, *Raum, Zeit, Materie,* 5. Aufl. 1923.
[8] G. Salzmann and A. H. Taub, *Phys. Rev.* **95**, 1659 (1954).
[9] J. Ehlers, Dissertation, Hamburg 1957.
[10] O. Heckmann and E. Schücking, Newtonsche und Einsteinsche Kosmologie, *Handbuch der Physik,* Bd. LIII, 489 (1959).
[11] H. Bondi, *Mon. Not. R. Astr. Soc.* **107**, 410 (1947).
[12] E. Schücking and O. Heckmann, Report to the Solvay Conference, 1958.
[13] W. J. van Stockum, *Proc. Roy. Soc. Edinb.* **57**, 135 (1937).
[14] R. Sachs, Distance and the Asymptotic Behavior of Waves in General Relativity, p. 397 [in this work].

EINSTEINIAN STATICS IN CONFORMAL SPACE*

V. Fock

Physical Institute, University of Leningrad

A new definition is proposed for the three-dimensional spatial metric that corresponds to a given four-dimensional space-time metric. A space with a metric so defined is called a conformal space. It is shown that the equations of Einsteinian statics in conformal space are simple in form and lead to definite expressions for the energy density and for the gravitational tensions. It is pointed out that the notion of conformal space conserves its meaning and can be useful in the general non-static case as well.

INTRODUCTION

In the Einstein theory of gravitation the static case is defined by the condition that the metric tensor is time-independent and that its mixed components vanish. In this case the temporal coordinate is uniquely determined and is harmonic. There remains a transformation group for the spatial coordinates. It is thus natural to apply to this case the formalism of three-dimensional tensor analysis and to write the gravitational equations correspondingly. This was done in the work of Levi-Cività [1]. But in this work no attention was paid to the fact that the complete separation of space from time, possible in the static case, can be achieved in different ways. Usually the space metric is simply defined as the spatial part of ds^2. In other words, it is tacitly assumed that the square of the spatial line-element appears in the expression for the square of the four-dimensional line-element with the coefficient (-1). But another assumption is also possible. In the present paper it will be shown that the most natural way of separating space from time is to assume that the above-mentioned coefficient is not a constant, but a quantity in-

---

* This paper has also been published in Russian in *J. Eksp. Teor. Phys.* **38**, 1485 (1960).

versely proportional to the coefficient of the square of the time differential. The space metric so defined is conformal to the metric usually taken, and the space so defined may be called *conformal* space.

Conformal space has remarkable properties. It is very nearly Euclidean; it may be assumed to be Euclidean with much greater accuracy than the space introduced according to the usual definition (see § 7). The coordinates that are harmonic in the four-dimensional sense remain harmonic in the three-dimensional sense (which is not the case with the usual definition of space). The known solutions of Einstein's equations with spherical and axial symmetry (the solutions of Schwarzschild, Weyl and Levi-Cività) are most simply obtained if the gravitational equations are written in conformal space. But the most striking advantage of conformal space is that these gravitational equations lead in a natural way to definite expressions for the energy density and for the gravitational tensions.

1. THE TRANSFORMATION OF LEVI-CIVITA

Let us recall the formulation of Einsteinian statics given by Levi-Cività (see [1] and [4]).

In the static case we have[(1)]

$$\frac{\partial g_{\mu\nu}}{\partial t} = 0, \qquad g_{0i} = 0 \qquad (x_0 = t) \tag{1.01}$$

Putting[(2)]

$$g_{00} = c^2 V^2, \qquad g_{ik} = -a_{ik} \tag{1.02}$$

we can write ds^2 in the form

$$ds^2 = c^2 V^2 dt^2 - a_{ik} dx_i dx_k . \tag{1.03}$$

Levi-Cività suggested that all the four-dimensional quantities involved in the Einstein equations be expressed in terms of three-dimensional quantities corresponding to the space with the line-element

$$dl^2 = a_{ik} dx_i dx_k . \tag{1.04}$$

---

(1) The Greek indices μ, ν, etc. assume the values 0, 1, 2, 3 and the Latin indices i, k etc. the values 1, 2, 3.

(2) We have modified the notations used in the books [1] and [4] and we write the coefficient of dt^2 as c^2V^2, and not as V^2.

In particular, a relation can be obtained in this way between the four-dimensional curvature tensor $(R_{\mu\nu})_g$ constructed by means of the metric tensor $g_{\mu\nu}$ and the three-dimensional curvature tensor $(R_{ik})_a$ built with the metric tensor a_{ik}. For the spatial components we have

$$(R_{ik})_g = (R_{ik})_a + \frac{(V_{ik})_a}{V} \tag{1.05}$$

where $(V_{ik})_a$ is the second covariant derivative of V taken in the sense of the metric (1.04). The mixed components vanish and the time component is

$$R_{00} = -c^2 V (\Delta V)_a \tag{1.06}$$

where

$$(\Delta V)_a = a^{ik} (V_{ik})_a \tag{1.07}$$

is the Laplacian for the metric (1.04). By use of these expressions the Einstein equations can be transformed. The corresponding formulae are given in Levi-Cività's book [1] and also in our book [4].

2. TRANSITION TO CONFORMAL SPACE

Unlike Levi-Cività, we shall write the four-dimensional line-element in the form

$$ds^2 = c^2 V^2 dt^2 - \frac{1}{V^2} h_{ik} dx_i dx_k \tag{2.01}$$

and we shall ascribe to the space the metric

$$d\sigma^2 = h_{ik} dx_i dx_k \tag{2.02}$$

so that

$$ds^2 = c^2 V^2 dt^2 - \frac{1}{V^2} d\sigma^2. \tag{2.03}$$

Thus we have

$$g_{00} = c^2 V^2, \quad g_{0i} = 0, \quad g_{ik} = -\frac{h_{ik}}{V^2} \tag{2.04}$$

and

$$g^{00} = \frac{1}{c^2 V^2}, \quad g^{0i} = 0, \quad g^{ik} = -V^2 h^{ik} \tag{2.05}$$

and finally

$$\sqrt{-g} = \frac{c}{V^2}\sqrt{h} \tag{2.06}$$

where h denotes the determinant with the h_{ik} as elements. All three-dimensional quantities will be referred to the metric (2.02). Comparing (1.03) with (2.01) we have

$$dl^2 = \frac{1}{V^2}\, d\sigma^2 \tag{2.07}$$

and thus

$$a_{ik} = \frac{1}{V^2}\, h_{ik}; \qquad a^{ik} = V^2 h^{ik}. \tag{2.08}$$

The spaces with the two metrics (1.04) and (2.02) are conformal to one another. According to a general formula due to Finzi (see [1]), the covariant components of the fourth rank curvature tensor of two conformal spaces are connected by the equation

$$V^2 (R_{kj,li})_a = R_{kj,li} + h_{kl}\frac{V_{ij}}{V} - h_{ki}\frac{V_{lj}}{V} + \\ + h_{ij}\frac{V_{kl}}{V} - h_{li}\frac{V_{jk}}{V} + (h_{ki}h_{jl} - h_{kl}h_{ji})\frac{V_m V^m}{V^2}. \tag{2.09}$$

The right-hand side of this equation (and of the following ones) involves only tensor symbols corresponding to the metric (2.02). From (2.09) we have:

$$(R_{ik})_a = R_{ik} - \frac{V_{ik}}{V} + h_{ik}\left(-\frac{\Delta V}{V} + 2\frac{V_j V^j}{V^2}\right). \tag{2.10}$$

On the other hand, the second covariant derivatives of some quantity W are connected by the relation

$$(W_{ik})_a = W_{ik} + \frac{V_i}{V} W_k + \frac{V_k}{V} W_i - h_{ik}\frac{V^j W_j}{V} \tag{2.11}$$

and if $W = V$:

$$(V_{ik})_a = V_{ik} + \frac{2 V_i V_k}{V^2} - h_{ik}\frac{V^j V_j}{V}. \tag{2.12}$$

From this it follows that

$$(\Delta V)_a = V^2\left(\Delta V - \frac{V_j V^j}{V}\right). \tag{2.13}$$

Using (2.10) and (2.12), formula (1.05) leads to the following expression for the spatial components of the second rank curvature tensor

$$(R_{ik})_g = R_{ik} + \frac{2V_i V_k}{V^2} + h_{ik}\left(-\frac{\Delta V}{V} + \frac{V_j V^j}{V^2}\right). \tag{2.14}$$

According to (1.06), the time component equals

$$(R_{00})_g = c^2 V^2(-V \cdot \Delta V + V_j V^j). \tag{2.15}$$

The mixed components vanish, as stated before. The four-dimensional scalar $(R)_g$ is

$$(R)_g = 2V \cdot \Delta V - 4V_j V^j - V^2 R. \tag{2.16}$$

For the components of the Einstein tensor

$$G_{\mu\nu} = (R_{\mu\nu})_g - \tfrac{1}{2} g_{\mu\nu}(R)_g \tag{2.17}$$

these equations give the following expressions

$$G_{ik} = H_{ik} + 2\frac{V_i V_k}{V^2} - h_{ik}\frac{V_j V^j}{V^2}, \tag{2.18}$$

$$G_{00} = c^2 V^2\{-V^2 H - 2V\Delta V + 3V_j V^j\}. \tag{2.19}$$

Here H_{ik} stands for the three-dimensional conservative tensor of the conformal space and H for the invariant of this tensor

$$H_{ik} = R_{ik} - \tfrac{1}{2}h_{ik}R, \qquad H = -\tfrac{1}{2}R. \tag{2.20}$$

We also have

$$R_{ik} = H_{ik} - h_{ik}H. \tag{2.21}$$

We state the expression for the four-dimensional d'Alembertian

$$\Box\,\psi = \frac{1}{c^2 V^2}\frac{\partial^2 \psi}{\partial t^2} - V^2 \Delta\psi. \tag{2.22}$$

Here $\Delta\psi$ denotes, as before, the Laplacian of the conformal space

$$\Delta\psi = \frac{1}{\sqrt{h}}\frac{\partial}{\partial x_i}\left(\sqrt{h}\,h^{ik}\frac{\partial\psi}{\partial x_k}\right). \tag{2.23}$$

We see that the coordinates, harmonic in the four-dimensional sense, are also harmonic in three-dimensional conformal space.

Our expressions (2.18) for the spatial components of the Einstein tensor differ from the expressions which follow from Levi-Cività's formulae (1.05) and (1.06) in that the former do not involve second derivatives of the quantity V. This feature of the expressions written for conformal space is of major importance for their physical interpretation.

3. EINSTEIN'S EQUATIONS IN CONFORMAL SPACE

Inserting expressions (2.15) and (2.16) for the Einstein tensor in the gravitational equations

$$G_{\mu\nu} = -\varkappa T_{\mu\nu}, \qquad \varkappa = \frac{8\pi\gamma}{c^2} \tag{3.01}$$

we obtain

$$H_{ik} + 2\frac{V_i V_k}{V^2} - h_{ik}\frac{V_j V^j}{V^2} = -\varkappa T_{ik}, \tag{3.02}$$

$$H + 2\frac{\Delta V}{V} - 3\frac{V_j V^j}{V^2} = \frac{1}{c^2 V^4}\varkappa T_{00} = \varkappa c^2 T^{00}. \tag{3.03}$$

Eliminating the quantities H_{ik} between (3.03) and (3.02), we can write

$$2\left(\frac{\Delta V}{V} - \frac{V_j V^j}{V^2}\right) = \varkappa\mu \tag{3.04}$$

where

$$\mu = c^2 T^{00} + h^{ik} T_{ik} \tag{3.05}$$

or else

$$\mu = \frac{1}{V^2}(T^0_0 - T^1_1 - T^2_2 - T^3_3). \tag{3.06}$$

The quantities T^α_β in the last equation are to be understood in the four-dimensional sense. The quantity μ can be interpreted as the mass density in conformal space. (1) At this stage it is convenient to introduce the quantity Φ connected with V by the relation

$$V = e^{-\Phi}. \tag{3.07}$$

The connection of the metric of space-time with that of conformal space will then have the form

$$ds^2 = c^2 e^{-2\Phi} dt^2 - e^{2\Phi} d\sigma^2. \tag{3.08}$$

(1) This value of μ agrees with the well-known expression due to Tolman (see Møller's book [3], p. 341).

Since we have

$$\Phi_i = -\frac{V_i}{V}, \quad \Delta\Phi = -\frac{\Delta V}{V} + \frac{V_j V^j}{V^2}, \tag{3.09}$$

the gravitational equations assume the form

$$H_{ik} = -2\Phi_i \Phi_k + h_{ik}\Phi_j \Phi^j - \varkappa T_{ik}, \tag{3.10}$$

$$\Delta\Phi = -\tfrac{1}{2}\varkappa\mu. \tag{3.11}$$

Now, μ is the mass density, and since the Einstein constant of gravitation $\varkappa$ is connected with the Newtonian constant γ by the relation (3.01), the last equation is essentially the Poisson equation for the Newtonian potential U. Approximately, we have

$$\Phi = \frac{U}{c^2} \tag{3.12}$$

and thus

$$\Phi_i = \frac{g_i}{c^2} \tag{3.13}$$

where g_i is the component of the acceleration due to gravity.

Let us now discuss the physical meaning of Eq. (3.10). We put

$$Q_{ik} = \frac{1}{\varkappa}(2\Phi_i \Phi_k - h_{ik}\Phi_j \Phi^j) \tag{3.14}$$

and write Eq. (3.10) in the form

$$H_{ik} = -\varkappa(Q_{ik} + T_{ik}). \tag{3.15}$$

The divergence of the tensor Q_{ik} equals

$$\nabla^k Q_{ik} = \frac{2}{\varkappa}\Phi_i \Delta\Phi = -\mu\Phi_i, \tag{3.16}$$

using (3.11). On the other hand, since H_{ik} is the conservative tensor of the conformal space, its divergence vanishes. Consequently, Eq. (3.15) gives

$$\nabla^k T_{ik} = \mu\Phi_i. \tag{3.17}$$

It can easily be seen that this equation has the same physical meaning as the usual equations of statics of an elastic body subject to gravitational forces. The quantities Q_{ik} are then to be interpreted as the spatial part of the energy-momentum tensor, or, since we consider the static case, as the gravitational stress tensor. From this point of view, Eqs (3.15), written for conformal space are analogous to the Einstein equations (3.01) written for space-time. In either set of equations we have on the left the conservative tensor and on the right the energy-momentum or the stress tensor. The gravitational stresses appear explicitly only after space is separated from time and after the transition to conformal space.

According to the gravitational Eqs (3.10), conformal space will be nearly Euclidean. Indeed, the estimate (3.13) shows that the right-hand side of (3.10) will be of the order g_i^2/c^4; from this it follows that the h_{ik} 's differ from their Euclidean values by quantities of the order U^2/c^4, and not of the order U/c^2 as in the case of the space metric (1.04).

All formulae of this section (apart from the estimates (3.12) and (3.13)) are exact. Nothing has been neglected in these formulae other than the supposition that the field is static. Our formulae are covariant with respect to the choice of coordinates in conformal space.

In a vacuum ($T_{\alpha\beta} = 0$) we have $\mu = 0$, and Eqs (3.11) will be a consequence of (3.10).

4. THE SCHWARZSCHILD SOLUTION IN THE CONFORMAL SPACE

In the case of spherical symmetry we can put

$$d\sigma^2 = dr^2 + \varrho^2 (d\vartheta^2 + \sin^2\vartheta \, d\varphi^2). \tag{4.01}$$

There is no restriction in putting the coefficient of dr^2 equal to unity. The quantity ϱ depends on the variable r only. The Laplacian in the space with the line-element (4.01) is of the form

$$\Delta\psi = \frac{1}{\varrho^2}\left\{\frac{\partial}{\partial r}\left(\varrho^2 \frac{\partial\psi}{\partial r}\right) + \Delta^*\psi\right\} \tag{4.02}$$

where Δ^* is the Laplacian on a sphere. On calculating the quantities H_{ik}, we obtain

$$H_{rr} = \frac{1-\varrho'^2}{\varrho^2}, \qquad H_{\vartheta\vartheta} = -\varrho\varrho'', \qquad H_{\varphi\varphi} = -\varrho\varrho''\sin^2\vartheta, \tag{4.03}$$

the non-diagonal elements being zero. The field equations for a vacuum are of the form

$$H_{rr} = -\Phi_r^2, \qquad H_{\vartheta\vartheta} = \varrho^2 \Phi_r^2. \tag{4.04}$$

Since $\Delta\Phi = 0$, we have on integrating

$$\varrho^2 \Phi_r = -a \tag{4.05}$$

where a is a constant (the gravitational radius of the central mass). Using (4.03) and (4.05), the first of equations (4.04) gives

$$\varrho'^2 = 1 + \frac{a^2}{\varrho^2}, \qquad \varrho\varrho' = \sqrt{\varrho^2 + a^2}. \tag{4.06}$$

Since

$$\varrho\varrho'' + \varrho'^2 = 1, \tag{4.07}$$

the second equation is also satisfied. We thus have

$$r = \sqrt{\varrho^2 + a^2}, \qquad \varrho = \sqrt{r^2 - a^2}. \tag{4.08}$$

We have put the additive constant equal to zero. Inserting (4.08) in (4.01), we obtain

$$d\sigma^2 = dr^2 + (r^2 - a^2)(d\vartheta^2 + \sin^2\vartheta\, d\varphi^2). \tag{4.09}$$

It is easily verified, using (4.02), that the coordinates

$$x_1 = r \sin\vartheta \cos\varphi, \qquad x_2 = r \sin\vartheta \sin\varphi, \qquad x_3 = r\cos\vartheta \tag{4.10}$$

are harmonic. To obtain the solution, we calculate Φ. From (4.05) we have

$$\frac{d\Phi}{dr} = -\frac{a}{r^2 - a^2}, \qquad \Phi = \frac{1}{2}\ln\frac{r+a}{r-a}, \tag{4.11}$$

since Φ must vanish for $r \to \infty$. Finally

$$ds^2 = c^2 \frac{r-a}{r+a} dt^2 - \frac{r+a}{r-a} d\sigma^2 \tag{4.12}$$

where $d\sigma^2$ is of the form (4.09).

The aim of the above calculations is to show the simplicity of the solution of the Schwarzschild problem in conformal space.

5. THE WEYL SOLUTION IN CONFORMAL SPACE

On the supposition of axial symmetry the line-element can be written in the form

$$d\sigma^2 = f^2(dz^2 + dr^2) + \varrho^2 d\varphi^2 \tag{5.01}$$

where f and ϱ are functions of z and r, but not of φ. Calculation of the H_{ik}'s gives

$$\left.\begin{aligned} H_{rr} &= -\frac{1}{\varrho}\frac{\partial^2\varrho}{\partial z^2} - \frac{1}{f}\frac{\partial f}{\partial r}\cdot\frac{1}{\varrho}\frac{\partial\varrho}{\partial r} + \frac{1}{f}\frac{\partial f}{\partial z}\cdot\frac{1}{\varrho}\frac{\partial\varrho}{\partial z}, \\ H_{zz} &= -\frac{1}{\varrho}\frac{\partial^2\varrho}{\partial r^2} + \frac{1}{f}\frac{\partial f}{\partial r}\cdot\frac{1}{\varrho}\frac{\partial\varrho}{\partial r} - \frac{1}{f}\frac{\partial f}{\partial z}\cdot\frac{1}{\varrho}\frac{\partial\varrho}{\partial z}, \\ H_{rz} &= \frac{1}{\varrho}\frac{\partial^2\varrho}{\partial r\partial z} - \frac{1}{f}\frac{\partial f}{\partial r}\cdot\frac{1}{\varrho}\frac{\partial\varrho}{\partial z} - \frac{1}{f}\frac{\partial f}{\partial z}\cdot\frac{1}{\varrho}\frac{\partial\varrho}{\partial r}, \end{aligned}\right\} \tag{5.02}$$

$$H_{\varphi\varphi} = -\frac{\varrho^2}{f^2}\left\{\frac{\partial}{\partial r}\left(\frac{1}{f}\frac{\partial f}{\partial r}\right) + \frac{\partial}{\partial z}\left(\frac{1}{f}\frac{\partial f}{\partial z}\right)\right\}. \tag{5.03}$$

Hence, by (2.21)

$$R_{\varphi\varphi} = \frac{\varrho}{f^2}\left(\frac{\partial^2\varrho}{\partial r^2} + \frac{\partial^2\varrho}{\partial z^2}\right). \tag{5.04}$$

If $R_{\varphi\varphi} = 0$, we can introduce in place of the variable z a function $\zeta(z, \varrho)$ such that $\zeta + i\varrho$ is a function of the complex variable $z + ir$. The quantity $d\sigma^2$ then assumes the form

$$d\sigma^2 = F^2(d\zeta^2 + d\varrho^2) + \varrho^2 d\varphi^2. \tag{5.05}$$

The variables ζ and ϱ are Weyl's cylindrical coordinates (see § 35 of Weyl's book [2]). In these coordinates the expressions for the H_{ik}'s are considerably simplified and reduce to

$$H_{\zeta\zeta} = -H_{\varrho\varrho} = \frac{1}{\varrho F}\frac{\partial F}{\partial\varrho}, \qquad H_{\varrho\zeta} = -\frac{1}{\varrho F}\frac{\partial F}{\partial\zeta}, \tag{5.06}$$

$$H_{\varphi\varphi} = -\frac{\varrho^2}{F^2}\left\{\frac{\partial}{\partial\varrho}\left(\frac{1}{F}\frac{\partial F}{\partial\varrho}\right) + \frac{\partial}{\partial\zeta}\left(\frac{1}{F}\frac{\partial F}{\partial\zeta}\right)\right\}. \tag{5.07}$$

To the metric (5.05) corresponds the Laplacian

$$\Delta\psi = \frac{1}{F^2}\left\{\frac{\partial^2\psi}{\partial\varrho^2} + \frac{1}{\varrho}\frac{\partial\psi}{\partial\varrho} + \frac{\partial^2\psi}{\partial\zeta^2}\right\} + \frac{1}{\varrho^2}\frac{\partial^2\psi}{\partial\varphi^2}. \tag{5.08}$$

Thus for a function independent of φ the Laplace equation assumes the same form as in Euclidean space.

Our supposition that $R_{\varphi\varphi} = 0$ and that Φ in (3.10) is independent of φ entails some conditions for the stress tensor. These conditions are

$$T_\varrho^\varrho + T_\zeta^\zeta = T_r^r + T_z^z = 0, \qquad T_\varphi^\varphi = 0. \tag{5.09}$$

In addition, the stress tensor must of course satisfy the equation of statics (3.17).

For empty space, the gravitational equations (3.10) assume the form

$$\left.\begin{aligned} \frac{1}{F}\frac{\partial F}{\partial \varrho} &= \varrho(\Phi_\varrho^2 - \Phi_\zeta^2), \\ \frac{1}{F}\frac{\partial F}{\partial \zeta} &= 2\varrho\Phi_\varrho\Phi_\zeta \end{aligned}\right\} \tag{5.10}$$

where Φ is a solution of the equation

$$\frac{\partial^2\Phi}{\partial\varrho^2} + \frac{1}{\varrho}\frac{\partial\Phi}{\partial\varrho} + \frac{\partial^2\Phi}{\partial\zeta^2} = 0. \tag{5.11}$$

When Φ is given, the function F is obtained from (3.10) by integrating a complete differential (with the condition that $F = 1$ if $\varrho = 0$). This is Weyl's solution. We see that using conformal space this solution can be obtained in a very simple way.[1]

6. THE CONNECTION BETWEEN THE SOLUTIONS OF WEYL AND SCHWARZSCHILD

Let us express in Weyl's coordinates the spherically symmetric solution considered above. If r, ϑ, φ are spherical coordinates of § 4, and ζ, ϱ, φ are Weyl's coordinates, then φ is obviously the same in both coordinate systems. Now, according to (5.08), ζ is harmonic, and we can put $\zeta = r\cos\vartheta$. As to the quantity ϱ, it can be obtained by equating the coefficients of $d\varphi^2$ in (5.05) and (4.08).

We thus have the relations

$$\zeta = r\cos\vartheta, \qquad \varrho = \sqrt{r^2 - a^2}\sin\vartheta \tag{6.01}$$

from which, inversely,

$$\left.\begin{aligned} r &= \tfrac{1}{2}\left(\sqrt{\varrho^2 + (\zeta + a)^2} + \sqrt{\varrho^2 + (\zeta - a)^2}\right), \\ a\cos\vartheta &= \tfrac{1}{2}\left(\sqrt{\varrho^2 + (\zeta + a)^2} - \sqrt{\varrho^2 + (\zeta - a)^2}\right). \end{aligned}\right\} \tag{6.02}$$

---

(1) In Weyl's book [2] the formulae for the axially-symmetric solution are given with some misprints or slips of the pen; we thought it advisable to state this because no deduction of the formulae is given in the book and the slips are not evident.

Spheres in harmonic coordinates correspond, in Weyl's coordinates, to ellipsoids of revolution with foci at $\varrho = 0$, $\zeta = \alpha$ and at $\varrho = 0$, $\zeta = -\alpha$. If we put

$$r = \alpha \cosh u \tag{6.03}$$

then u, ϑ will coincide with the usual ellipsoidal coordinates. In these coordinates Eq. (5.11) assumes the form

$$\frac{\partial^2 \Phi}{\partial u^2} + \frac{\partial^2 \Phi}{\partial \vartheta^2} + \coth u \frac{\partial \Phi}{\partial u} + \cot \vartheta \frac{\partial \Phi}{\partial \vartheta} = 0 . \tag{6.04}$$

The relevant solution is a function of the variable u only, namely

$$\Phi = \frac{1}{2} \ln \frac{\cosh u + 1}{\cosh u - 1} . \tag{6.05}$$

This solution is the same as (4.11). Integrating the complete differential, we obtain

$$F^2 = \frac{\sinh^2 u}{\sinh^2 u + \sin^2 \vartheta} \tag{6.06}$$

and since

$$d\varrho^2 + d\zeta^2 = \alpha^2 (\sinh^2 u + \sin^2 \vartheta)(du^2 + d\vartheta^2) \tag{6.07}$$

we finally have

$$d\sigma^2 = \alpha^2 \sinh^2 u (du^2 + d\vartheta^2 + \sin^2 \vartheta d\varphi^2) . \tag{6.08}$$

We see that in Weyl's coordinates the spherical symmetry is lost and that axial symmetry appears instead. The solution in which Φ is spherically symmetric in Weyl's coordinates is of the form

$$\Phi = \frac{\alpha}{\sqrt{\varrho^2 + \zeta^2}}, \quad \ln F = - \frac{\alpha^2 \varrho^2}{2(\varrho^2 + \zeta^2)^2} . \tag{6.09}$$

In the plane $\zeta = 0$ for $\varrho \to 0$ this solution has a singularity which is difficult to interpret physically. It thus appears that in the case considered Weyl's coordinates are less appropriate to the nature of the problem than harmonic coordinates.

7. CONCLUDING REMARKS

We have considered several aspects of the formulation of Einsteinian statics in conformal space. The possibility of a simple physical interpretation of the gravitational equations stated in conformal space, their simplicity and the ease of their solution, are convincing arguments in favour of the usefulness of the concept of conformal space. Another argument is that this concept gives an immediate interpretation of the known fact that the deflection of a light ray passing near a massive body is twice as large as that to be expected from the principle of equivalence. This fact is simply due to the circumstance that, according to (2.22), the speed of light in conformal space is equal to cV^2 and not to cV as in the usual definition of the space metric.

Hitherto only the static case was considered. The question of the appropriate separation of space from time may, however, arise in the general case also. The transformation of the Einstein equations to the three-dimensional form (without transition to conformal space) has been carried out by Zelmanov [5] who introduced the important notion of chronometric invariants.

In the general case, conformal space can be introduced by writing ds^2 in the form

$$ds^2 = V^2(cdt + p_i dx_i)^2 - \frac{1}{V^2}\,d\sigma^2. \tag{7.01}$$

The line element

$$d\sigma^2 = h_{ik}\,dx_i\,dx_k \tag{7.02}$$

defines the metric in conformal space. We thus have

$$g_{00} = c^2V^2, \quad g_{0i} = cV^2p_i, \quad g_{ik} = V^2p_ip_k - \frac{1}{V^2}h_{ik}. \tag{7.03}$$

As in the static case

$$\sqrt{-g} = \frac{c}{V^2}\sqrt{h}\,. \tag{7.04}$$

From (7.03) it follows that

$$g^{00} = \frac{1}{c^2}\left(\frac{1}{V^2} - V^2p_jp^j\right), \quad g^{0i} = \frac{1}{c}V^2p^i, \quad g^{ik} = -V^2h^{ik}. \tag{7.05}$$

Multiplying these expressions by (7.04) we obtain the quantities $\mathfrak{g}^{\mu\nu}$. As in the static case, the metric tensor of conformal space can be directly expressed in terms of the $\mathfrak{g}^{ik}$'s with spatial superfixes. If (i, k, l) is a permutation of the numbers (1, 2, 3) we have

$$\left.\begin{aligned} c^2h_{kl} &= \mathfrak{g}^{ik}\mathfrak{g}^{il} - \mathfrak{g}^{ii}\mathfrak{g}^{kl}, \\ c^2h_{ll} &= \mathfrak{g}^{ii}\mathfrak{g}^{kk} - \mathfrak{g}^{ik}\mathfrak{g}^{ki} \end{aligned}\right\} \tag{7.06}$$

(with no summation, of course).

It follows from our investigations of the solutions of Einstein's equations for the general, non-static case (see [4]) that the relative error introduced when the $\mathfrak{g}^{ik}$'s are replaced by their Euclidean values is of the order U^2/c^4 where U is the Newtonian potential. Relations (7.06) then show that with the same relative error, conformal space can be considered Euclidean.

We now discuss the question of the possible use of the concept of conformal space in approximate theories. Papapetrou [6] has suggested a theory of a gravitational field with a single field function, analogous to our Φ above. Papapetrou's theory corresponds to the hypothesis that conformal space is Euclidean. In the static case this theory can be considered as a reasonable approximation to the Einstein theory. But in the general non-static case a single field function is clearly insufficient. A more exact approximation could possibly be obtained if four field functions were introduced — the scalar and the vector potentials of gravitation, say. This is suggested by the approximate solutions of the gravitational equations obtained in [4]. It is shown there that with a relative error of the order U^2/c^4 in the quantities g_{ik} and of the order U^3/c^6 in g_{00} the gravitational field can be expressed in terms of four functions U^* and U_i. These functions satisfy the equations

$$\Delta U^* - \frac{1}{c^2}\frac{\partial^2 U^*}{\partial t^2} = -4\pi\gamma(c^2 T^{00} + T^{kk}), \tag{7.07}$$

$$\Delta U_i = -4\pi\gamma\varrho v_i \tag{7.08}$$

where ϱv_i is the momentum density or the mass flux density (Eqs (68, 30) and (68, 19) of our book [4]). In the static case Eq. (7.07) corresponds to Eq. (3.11) of this paper, the righthand side there of being proportional to μ defined by (3.05). In the approximation considered, the conformal space is Euclidean, and we have

$$V^2 = \frac{c^2 - U^*}{c^2 + U^*}, \qquad p_i = \frac{4}{c^3}U_i. \tag{7.09}$$

A next step would be a theory with field equations linear in p_i and in the deviations of the quantities h_{ik} from their Euclidean values, but non-linear in V.

In spite of the fact that the separation of space from time destroys the four-dimensional symmetry of the equations, the concept of conformal space may also be useful in the exact (non-static and non-linear) theory. This concept may suggest the most appropriate choice of field variables to which the Hamiltonian formalism is to be applied, and it may also elucidate the question of the correct definition of the energy-momentum tensor of the gravitational field.

REFERENCES

[1] T. Levi-Civita, *The Absolute Differential Calculus*, London 1927.

[2] H. Weyl, *Raum, Zeit, Materie*, Berlin 1923.

[3] C. Møller, *The Theory of Relativity*, Oxford 1952.

[4] V. A. Fock, *Teoriya prostranstva, vryemenny i tyagoteniya*, Moskva 1955.

[4a] V. Fock, *The Theory of Space, Time and Gravitation*, Pergamon Press, London 1959.

[4b] V. Fock, *Theorie von Raum, Zeit und Gravitation*, Academie-Verlag, Berlin 1960.

[5] A. Zelmanov, *Dokl. Acad. Nauk SSSR* **107**,815 (1956).

[6] A. Papapetrou, Eine Theorie des Gravitationsfeldes mit einer Feldfunktion, *Z. Phys.* **139**, 518 (1954).

THE ARROW OF TIME*

T. Gold

Institut International de Physique Solvay, Bruxelles

Subjectively, we are very clear about the sense of the arrow of time. There is no doubt in our minds which way time runs, what is future and what is past. The fact that introspection gives us a clear answer to the question whether there is a sense in which time runs makes it all the harder to discuss the question objectively as a problem in fundamental physical theory.

At first one might think that there is no real problem there. Why should not the time coordinate be equipped, as it were, with an arrow at each point which singles out for any process the positive time direction? Why should the world not be quite unsymmetrical with respect to past and future?

We have no doubt that the world is, in fact, unsymmetrical in this way. But it is a remarkable fact that the laws of physics, one by one as they have been discovered, have been found to be quite symmetrical with respect to the sense of time. Newton's laws of gravitation and dynamics single out no sense of the time coordinate. If somebody recorded the motion of the planets and reversed the record of the time coordinate, this would leave it an example of a dynamical system that is as much in accord with Newton's laws as the actual. The change from Newton's laws to Einstein's did not affect this symmetry.

The laws of electrodynamics, the Maxwell–Lorentz theory, similarly are quite symmetrical, and so are those of quantum theory. Could we argue that all this is accidental and that we will discover some other physical law which clearly specifies the sense of time and which is responsible for giving us our ideas on the subject? This, I think, is not a plausible explanation, since systems we

* First published in the Reports from Solvay Conference.

understand in detail seem to show time's arrow. But yet there must be some influence that serves to determine the arrow of time.

Usually at this point in the argument statistical or thermodynamical ideas are presented and the case is made out that it is through the investigation of these fields that the elusive arrow is found. "The entropy of any isolated system will always increase and never decrease"; so, it is said, you must merely look at a system at two instants of time and determine at which the entropy is greater. That will then be the later instant.

As there is no doubt about the correctness of this, the argument is usually not pursued any further. We and everything around us are simply taken to be aware of the arrow of time by the operation of the statistical processes which, after all, we understand very clearly. Why should there be anything else to think about?

One has to pursue this reasoning a little further, though. Why does the arrow of time appear when we are dealing with the statistical superposition of effects, each of which is determined by laws which have no arrow? Surely the fact that we had to deal with the problem in statistical terms rather than compute in detail the behavior of all the constituent parts of our system, constituted merely a lack of precision; surely it is not by rejecting information about our system that we can make it reveal to us the sense of time which it would otherwise not show. So let us see whether we can find the arrow without the statistics.

To see whether the system that we examine does or does not reveal the arrow of time, let us suppose that we are given a number of snapshots of it only, and we are asked whether we can be sure to sort them into the correct temporal sequence. We are told that the system was interfered with before the first and after the last of the snapshots, but was left quite undisturbed in the intervening period. Now if, for example, the system were a box full of gas and we found on our snapshots that one contained all the gas in one half of the box, another one showed 70% in that half of the box and 30% in the other half, and a third showed just 50% in each half of the box, then we should surely order the snapshots in that way. We would say that somehow the gas must have been put into that half of the box where it was found, and the first snapshot must have been taken very shortly, after it was put there, because we know that when left to itself it will quickly expand through the rest of the box and fill it uniformly. Whatever the way the box is interfered with after the last snapshot was taken does not enter into our considerations; but the interference the system received before the first is of importance in deciding the arrow of time. Of course, this argument is not absolutely certain; we might have ordered the snapshots the wrong way round, for the gas might have been uniformly distributed in the box to start with, but all the motions of its molecules might have been so contrived that by the operation of the ordinary laws that apply to the collision of molecules they will all have migrated at one time into half the box. But this, we think, is highly improbable. We can thus take on a bet and offer very high odds that we will be able to order the snapshots in the right sequence, but we cannot actually prove it. If we did a similar experiment with fewer particles, the same would apply, but we could offer only lower odds. Essentially, looking at a system of many particles is not very different from having many systems of a few particles on the same snapshots. There we would order the snapshots according to the appearance of one of the systems on the successive pictures, and we would then decide that our probability of being right increased when we saw each one of the other systems agreed with the sequence we had decided on. The certainty about the sense of the arrow of time then arises just from having many checks, and for this reason complicated systems reveal the effect most clearly; but this does not explain why each of our simple systems displayed an arrow at all.

The interference from outside clearly had something to do with it. If we take any system and isolate it from external influence completely and for a very long time and then take a series of snapshots, there will no longer be any way of deciding on the sequence from a subsequent examination of the pictures. We might still be able to recognize clearly the operation of fundamental physical laws in the changes that had taken place from one snapshot to the next. If all the snapshots were taken in sufficiently rapid sequence, we might be able to arrange them in order l to n, but we would not know whether it was l or n that was taken first. The physical laws that determine the motions that we can see all being time-symmetrical, there might be plenty of clues to demonstrate the laws and to find the neighbors in the sequence to any picture, but no clue at all about the arrow of time.

When the system was not isolated, there was, as usual, no doubt about the sense of time. After it became isolated, the arrow of time evidently persisted for a while, not definable with certainty, but only with a probability that decreased from a high value initially to zero. The time scale of this decrease of probability depended upon the details of the system.

It is this rule that isolated systems initially, after their isolations, retain and then gradually lose the arrow of time that makes its appearance in the statistical and thermodynamical definitions. "Entropy of an isolated system always increases", is a way of saying that after the system was isolated, it still showed changes from which the sense of time could be deduced. In some systems the effect is best described in thermodynamic terms, and entropy is then the relevant quantity. But in other systems other statistical descriptions may be more convenient. It is inconsequential from this point of view whether the system is deterministic or not; that case can be argued equally well with a number of billiard balls assumed to behave accurately according to Newton's laws of motion, as with a system of photons and atoms in a box where we do not know of any way of specifying the laws of motion except through probabilities.

Some simple mechanical systems seem to give a more clear-cut answer than others, but on closer examination are really not different in principle. For example, a ratchet with a tooth may be known to be an isolated system during the time that it changed from one state to another. There would seem to be no question that it must initially have had momentum in the direction in which it does not jam. One might think that any system only has to be equipped with such a ratchet mechanism in order for the arrow of time to be defined there. But, of course, this only works through the dissipative mechanism of the claw, and one has to allow that the process could happen in reverse if all the thermal motions of all the atoms in the claw and in the ratchet were all just right, namely, just the reverse of those that would be set up by the ratchet moving in the allowed direction. The claw would then spontaneously bounce open and the bar would recede by one tooth. This would be in no conflict with the laws of motion, but, because of the great number of atoms whose motions would have to be just right, it is an effect whose chance of occurrence is negligibly small. But if we had such a ratchet in a system that had been isolated for a very long time, then the probability of it moving by Brownian motion by one tooth in one direction is exactly equal to that of moving by one tooth in the other; and then again no arrow of time would be in evidence.

So we can be confident that the same rule applies to all systems: interference from without enables them to show time's arrow, and this may persist for some time after the interference has ceased. All completely internal effects merely reflect the physical laws that apply, and all those are then strictly time-symmetrical. On whatever scale we choose our system, we have to go to a larger scale to understand how it contrived to know the arrow of time.

Up to what scale, can we pursue this argument? On which scale do we find a law whose operation in fact serves to determine time's arrow for all the smaller scales? Let us take, for example, a star, and suppose we could put it inside an insulating box. It would still be true, then, that when the star has been in the box for long enough (which in this case will perhaps be rather long), time's arrow will have vanished. There is no reason to expect anything to be different in principle from the laboratory scale. But now if we were to open for a moment a small window in our box, then what would happen? Time's arrow would again be defined inside the box for some time, until the statistical equilibrium had been reestablished. But what had happened when we opened the hole? Some radiation had, no doubt, escaped from the box and the amount of radiation that found its way into the box from the outside was incomparably smaller. Some influence from outside had got in — though the only physical effect was that photons from inside got out.

The escape of radiation away from the system is, in fact, characteristic of the type of "influence" which is exerted from outside. Any outside influence to a system that gives it time's arrow can be traced to be associated with that process. The thermodynamic approach would be to explain that free energy was required for the interference, and that free energy can only be generated from the heat sources in the world by means of heat engines working between a source and a sink. There may be a variety of sources, but the sink is always eventually the depth of space, although there may be a number of intermediate cold bodies.

It is this facility of the universe to soak up any amount of radiation that makes it different from any closed box, and it is just this that enables it to define the arrow of time in any system that is in contact with this sink. But why is it that the universe is a non-reflecting sink for radiation? Different explanations are offered for this in the various cosmological theories and in some schemes, indeed, this would only be a temporary property. In the steady state universe it is entirely attributed to the state of expansion. The red shift operates to diminish the contribution to the radiation field of distant matter; even though the density does not diminish at great distances, the sky is dark because in most directions the material on a line of sight is receding very fast, and its radiation, therefore, shifted very far to the red.

The large scale motion of the universe thus appears to be responsible for time's arrow. A picture of the world lines of galaxies would clearly reveal the sense of time, namely, the sense in which the world lines are diverging. As we go to a smaller scale, this type of divergence is, for most purposes, quite negligible, and it is thus clearly not the local effects of the universal expansion law that make themselves felt. But it is the electromagnetic radiation that brings the effects of expansion down to a small scale. Radiation in the world is almost everywhere almost all the time violently expanding. This expansion of the radiation is, however, only made possible by the expansion of the material between which the radiation makes its way, that is, the expansion of the universe.

If we examine the pattern of world lines of systems that are open to the universe there will be much branching apart and much less convergence when looked at in the sense in which we think of time. As an example, the average hydrogen atom in the universe will suffer a conversion to helium in a time of the order of 10^{11} years at the present rate. This corresponds to an emission into the universe of some 10^6 photons in the visible spectrum. This photon expansion going on around most material is the most striking type of asymmetry, and it appears to give rise to all other time assymetries that are in evidence. The preferential divergence, rather than convergence, of the world lines of a system ceases when that system has been isolated in a box which prevents the expansion of the photons out into space. Time's arrow is then lost; entropy remains constant.

The motion of the universe is thus most intimately connected with all processes down to the smallest scale. A more profound understanding of physics than we now have might, in fact, allow one to deduce the expansion of the universe from an observation of the small scale effects only.

We see the universe expanding and not contracting. Does this mean that of the two possible senses of motion, nature chose one? Surely not. This would be the case if the laws of physics were not time-symmetrical: then an expanding universe would be a system that is distinguishable from a contracting one. The laws could describe two types, and ours would be one of them. In such a case the laws of physics would be capable of defining more schemes of the world than we have to look at. The laws would be too wide to fit the case, and we would suppose this due to some misunderstanding we have made. But just this is avoided by the time-symmetry of the laws. In a universe where no arrow of time exists except that defined by the motion, there is only a single possibility. We would need an independent clock to say whether the universe is expanding or contracting, and we have none. All the clocks we do have are themselves run by the motion.

It follows that if all the laws of physics are time-symmetrical, they would not be able to describe a contracting universe. If, naively, we think that, after all, we might have seen blue shifts in the spectra of distant galaxies instead of the red shifts, we must be making an error in pursuing the detailed consequences of the motions of the galaxies. If, in calculating radiation effects, we took the particular solution (of the intrinsically time-symmetrical electrodynamic theory) given by the retarded potentials, then of course there would appear the second possibility. But that is rather like supposing that an independent clock exists and that the laws are not time-symmetrical. Wheeler and Feynman [2], and Hogarth [3] have considered the question of a time-symmetrical electromagnetic theory and the way in which the choice of retarded potentials appears appropriate depending upon the cosmological boundary conditions.

There is nothing new in the idea that the physical laws are more symmetrical than the universe to which they apply. For example, the principle of Galilean relativity states that the physical laws are the same in all inertial systems. But, on the other hand, one particular such frame can be singled out through the observation of the universe, namely, that particular frame where the observer would see the expansion of the universe occur symmetrically around him. A cosmological observation, therefore, specifies one out of an infinite set of frames that would all be equivalent from all other points of view. With the arrow of time, it is not really dissimilar. A cosmological observation, such as, for example, opening a window in a box and letting some radiation escape, is the means of distinguishing between the two otherwise quite equivalent senses of time.

At this point one should think, perhaps, why it is that we are subjectively so sure that time "really goes" in one sense and not the other. With symmetrical physical laws we can, after all, construct the present equally well from a sufficient knowledge of the future as from such a knowledge of the past. Why, then, do we give the past a status quite different from that given to the future? We do not generally think of predicting the past, of constructing it from the present and the knowledge of the physical laws, yet that is what we do with respect to the future. We think of some evidence about the past as entirely definite, and we think it a rule that the future can not be known with certainty. Why is this so in a system operating with time-symmetrical laws? Why do we believe in the cause and effect relationship between events when, after all, there is no strictly logical way with time-symmetrical laws of specifying which is the cause and which the effect? Today's position and momenta of the planets are the cause of their position and momenta tomorrow. But this could equally well be stated the other way around—that tomorrow's configuration causes today's. In more complicated systems, as we have seen, there is a general overwhelming tendency for branching of world lines in the forward direction of time. If a lot of information is lacking for precise prediction, as for example all the photons out in space that have escaped, then the configuration of the system at one instant will serve to define much better its configuration in the sense in which its world lines are generally converging than in the sense in which they are generally diverging. The past will be better known than the future. It is difficult to reconcile oneself to this explanation that the assymmetry between past and future which seems so profound to us should be no more than an asymmetry connected with the probability of "predicting" correctly into the two senses of time. The qualitative difference arises from a statistical quantitative one. But, of course, one must appreciate that we are systems of a high order of complexity, and that the statistics are concerned, therefore, with a very large number of possible states. In such systems there may be, in effect, complete certainty attached to the consequences of the laws of chance. And these consequences appear, then, as the laws of physics.

The symmetry of the laws with regard to the time axis is then just what was required to prevent them from being too wide, from being able to describe more than just our universe. What is the situation with respect to other symmetries of physical laws?

Symmetry with respect to the sign of the electric charge and with respect to mirror reflection was thought until recently to be separately obeyed by all the laws of physics. Now the discovery of the non-conservation of parity in weak interactions implies that the laws are not invariant to a mirror reflection alone. A certain "handedness" is shown to be resident in elementary particles. Since a right-handed screw becomes a left-handed screw when viewed in the mirror, such a particle will be transformed into something different by reflection. But this does not force us to believe that nature is not mirror-symmetrical, for there may be complete symmetry between matter and anti-matter. For every right-handed particle of matter there may be a left-handed one of anti-matter having all the same properties, but possessing the opposite sign of electric charge or magnetic dipole moment. The symmetry may be complete, but only for the combined operation of mirror reflection and a change in the sign of the charge. I suppose that most physicists now would regard this as the most likely situation. If symmetry is preserved only with respect to the combined operation, then this could really be understood best if charge had a geometrical representation, possessing a "handedness".

Should we now think that the universe is in actual construction, symmetrical between matter and anti-matter? Or have we here another case of a symmetry in the laws not represented by symmetry of construction?

It is, of course, possible that amongst the various galaxies there are as many made of matter as of anti-matter. Not enough meeting ground exists between them for the annihilation process to be plainly demonstrable. From observation we can not yet tell. If, in fact, all galaxies were constructed from one type of matter only and anti-matter appeared everywhere, as it does here, only as a rare freak, would this, then, imply that the laws of physics are too wide? One might think that, after all, if our type of matter is the right-handed sort, the same laws of physics would have allowed the construction of a universe entirely similar to ours except made of matter of the left-handed type. Two universes would be specified by the laws and only one of them arbitrarily selected as ours.

But, do these laws really specify two different universes? The difference between a right-handed system and a left-handed system can be defined only when they can be compared. There is no absolute definition of either. If two systems cannot be compared, either directly or via some intermediary systems, then there is no way of defining whether they are of the same or the opposite handedness. But this is just the situation with respect to the two universes that would seem to be defined. If they are different universes, they cannot be brought together to be compared, and unless they can be so compared, there is no sense to be attached to the statement that they are of different handedness. The two universes, if they cannot be compared, are thus identical. We have then, again, the situation that a precise symmetry in the physical laws, namely that between matter and anti-matter, is just what is required to assure that only one type of universe is specified. If any law of physics had not been accurately time-symmetrical, then an expanding and a contracting universe would be different possibilities.

If the symmetry between matter and anti-matter were not complete, then two different universes, one composed of matter and one composed of anti-matter, would be possibilities. These symmetries are, then, in each case, just what is required to allow the laws of physics to describe as the only possibility the type of universe we have.

REFERENCES

[1] A. Grünbaum, Das Zeitproblem, *Archiv für Philosophie* 7, 165 (1957).
[2] J. A. Wheeler and R. P. Feynmann, *Rev. Mod. Phys.* **21**, 425 (1949).
[3] J. Hogarth, Advanced and Retarded Potentials in an Expanding Universe (unpublished thesis).

ON THE QUANTUM THEORY OF GRAVITATION

I. Goldberg

Department of Physics, The University of Michigan

It is the purpose of this note to outline a program now in progress which should lead to the quantization of the general theory of relativity. However, before the procedure is outlined it is perhaps instructive to enquire as to what one means by a quantized theory of relativity. The "simplest" part of the problem is to treat the free gravitational field as a classical field to which one may apply any self-consistent quantization scheme. One should then arrive at a set of observables, their commutation relations, and equations of motion. The commutation relations and equations of motion should allow the determination of matrix elements which then predict the results of measurements. However, as is well known the gravitational field has the weakest interaction of any physical field. It is extremely difficult to make sensitive macroscopic tests of the general theory of relativity; can one then expect to determine quantum effects.

It is extremely unlikely that any relations deduced from a study of the pure gravitational field should lead to experimentally verifiable results. However, the presence of the gravitational field completely modifies the ordinary field theories. That is to say that every field theory must be written in a covariant manner, and this must modify the results of all calculations. Whether the modifications introduced are sufficient to remove divergencies, that is to introduce finite instead of infinite renormalization constants can not be determined. However, it might be instructive to examine a sort of semi-classical theory. That is to introduce the metric $g_{\mu\nu}$ as a classical quantity used to write all field equations covariantly. Then one might look (in the weak field approximation) at the change in very accurately measured quantities such as the Lamb shift, life times in beta decay etc.

This paper will deal with the pure gravitational field and will attempt to point out what may be a more simple approach to quantization of the gravitational field in the Hamiltonian formalism than some methods presently being used. The basic method is the Hamiltonian analogue of the approach now employed by Bergmann and Komar [1], originally labeled the Dirac bracket technique [2]. One sets up in the Hamiltonian formalism a transformation group which can be related to the infinitesimal unitary transformations in a Hilbert space.

It is perhaps worth while to give a brief review of the basic technique. The problems which arise in the quantization of non linear theories are primarily due to the existence of constraints. As is well known, these constraints introduce inconsistencies if the usual Hamiltonian quantization scheme is carried out. That is if one relates the infinitesimal unitary transformations to the infinitesimal canonical transformations. However, if one modifies the canonical transformations by considering only those transformations canonical on the hypersurface in phase space on which all the constraints are satisfied and which transform the hypersurface into itself, one is led to a transformation group which can appropriately be related to the unitary transformations in Hilbert space.

Let the constraints of the theory be denoted by Y^s there will be one hypersurface per space point upon which the constraints are satisfied. Then if one labels the points on the hypersurface by y^m the total number of parameters per space point will be the difference between the number of field variables plus canonical momenta minus the number of constraints.

For a particle theory one can easily see what happens, if one introduces the quantities ξ^ν where ν runs from 1 to $2n$ to denote both coordinates and momenta. Then the Hamiltonian equations are expressible by

$$\dot{\xi}^\nu = \varepsilon^{\mu\nu} \frac{\partial H}{\partial \xi^\mu} \tag{1}$$

where

$$\varepsilon^{\mu\nu} = \begin{pmatrix} 0 & I \\ -I & 0 \end{pmatrix},$$

and I is the unit matrix.

The infinitesimal canonical transformation may be written

$$\delta \xi^\mu = \varepsilon^{\mu\nu} \frac{\partial C}{\partial \xi^\nu} \tag{2}$$

where C is the so-called generator of the transformation. Then those transformations which are canonical on the hypersurface and which transform the hypersurface into itself are given in terms of the parameters on the hypersurface by

$$\eta_{mn}\,\delta y^n = \frac{\partial C}{\partial y^m} \tag{3}$$

where C is the generator of the transformation and the matrix

$$\eta_{mn} = \frac{\partial \xi^\mu}{\partial y^m}\,\varepsilon_{\mu\nu}\,\frac{\partial \xi^\nu}{\partial y^n}\,.$$

The matrix η_{mn} is in general singular and this restricts the generators C to what are generally called observables. These observables will be the analogue of $\boldsymbol{E}$ and $\boldsymbol{H}$ in electrodynamics. The observables determined in this way are in general not restricted to any particular surface. The difficult problem is the determination of the C's for general relativity and their relation to Hilbert operators.

The principal difficulty encountered in the application of the above technique is the fact that one must eliminate some of the field variables by means of the constraints, since in order to form the matrix η_{mn} the field variables must be expressed as functions of the y^m. The purpose of this section is to indicate a technique which will simplify the constraint equations to the point where it is possible to carry out the above procedures.

Consider a classical field with field variables φ_a. The simplest way to apply quantization procedures is to Fourier analyze the field thus converting the field theory to an infinite set of particle theories. One first sets

$$\varphi(x) = \frac{1}{(2\pi)^{3/2}} \int d^3k\,\varphi(k)\,\mathrm{e}^{ikx}.$$

The question of the existence of this transformation is not trivial; however, for reasonable functions such existence can be proven. The Lagrangian which was previously

$$\int L(\varphi, \varphi_{,\mu})\,d^4x$$

now becomes

$$\int L\big(\varphi(k), \dot{\varphi}(k)\big)\,d^3k\,dt. \tag{4}$$

The technique of Fourier analysis is generally not applied to non-linear theories because the non-linear terms are difficult to handle.

If this problem is ignored temporarily one can examine the transformed theory. The scheme for setting up hypersurfaces is carried out as for the particle theory and the parameters obey the following transformation law:

$$\int d^3 h'' \eta_{mn}(k, k', k'')\, \delta y^m(k'') = \frac{\partial C(h)}{\partial y^m(h')} . \tag{5}$$

That Eq. (5) is the appropriate generalization of (3) can be seen by examining the way in which Eq. (3) arises. For complete details see reference [1], but the equation arises from an expression of the form

$$\dot{\xi}^\mu \varepsilon_{\mu\nu}\, \delta\xi^\nu = \frac{\partial C}{\partial t} \tag{6}$$

or

$$\int d^3 h' d^3 h'' \frac{\partial \xi^\mu(k)}{\partial y^m(k')} \dot{y}^m(k') \varepsilon_{\mu\nu} \frac{\partial \xi^\nu}{\partial y^n(k'')} \delta y^n(k'') = \int d^3 h' \frac{\partial C}{\partial y^m(k')} \dot{y}^m(k'),$$

if (6) is expressed in terms of $y^m(h)$ and the non linear character of the equations allowed for.

Consider the Lagrangian for the free gravitational field

$$\int L d^4 x = \int g^{\mu\nu} R_{\mu\nu} d^4 x = \int g^{\mu\nu} \{\Gamma^\alpha_{\mu\nu,\alpha} - \Gamma^\alpha_{\mu\alpha,\nu} + \Gamma^\alpha_{\mu\nu}\Gamma^\beta_{\alpha\beta} - \Gamma^\alpha_{\mu\beta}\Gamma^\beta_{\nu\alpha}\}\, d^4 x . \tag{7}$$

This may be rewritten

$$\begin{aligned}&\int d^3 k\, d^3 k'\, d^4 x\, e^{i(\boldsymbol{k}+\boldsymbol{k}')x} g^{\mu\nu}(k')\{k_s \Gamma^s_{\mu\nu} + \Gamma^0_{\mu\nu,0} - \delta^s_\nu k_s \Gamma^\alpha_{\mu\alpha} - \delta^0_\nu \Gamma^\alpha_{\mu\nu,0}\} + \\ &+ \int d^4 x\, d^3 k\, d^3 k'\, d^3 k''\, e^{i(\boldsymbol{k}+\boldsymbol{k}'+\boldsymbol{k}'')\cdot x} g^{\mu\nu}(k')\{\Gamma^\alpha_{\mu\nu}(k)\Gamma^\beta_{\alpha\beta}(k'') - \Gamma^\alpha_{\mu\beta}(k)\Gamma^\beta_{\nu\alpha}(k'')\} .\end{aligned} \tag{8}$$

Suppose the Pallitini approach is employed then the $g^{\mu\nu}$ and the $\Gamma^\alpha_{\mu\nu}$ are varied independently and the following equations result:

$$\begin{aligned} &h_s \Gamma^s_{\mu\nu}(h) + \Gamma^0_{\mu\nu,0}(k) - \delta^s_\nu h_s \Gamma^\alpha_{\mu\alpha} - \delta^0_\nu \Gamma^\alpha_{\mu\alpha,0}(k) + \\ &+ \int d^3 k' \{\Gamma^\alpha_{\mu\alpha}(k')\Gamma^\beta_{\alpha\beta}(k-k') + \Gamma^\alpha_{\mu\beta}(k)\Gamma^\beta_{\alpha\nu}(k-k')\} = 0, \\ &h_s g_{lb}(k) = \int d^3 h' \{g_{\nu l}(k+k')\Gamma^\nu_{bs}(k') + g_{\mu b}(k+k')\Gamma^\mu_{l\beta}(k)\}, \\ &g_{pb,0} = \int d^3 h' \{g_{\nu l}(k+k')\Gamma^\nu_{l0}(k') + g_{\nu l}(k+k')\Gamma^\nu_{b0}(k')\} . \end{aligned} \tag{9}$$

The so-called algebraic constraint equations may now be obtained. From Eqs (9) form

$$\begin{aligned} &e^{nt}(k'')\{k_s g_{rt}(k) + k_r g_{ts}(k) - k_t g_{rs}(k)\} \\ &\qquad = 2 \int d^3 h'\, \delta(\boldsymbol{k}+\boldsymbol{k}'+\boldsymbol{k}'') \left\{\Gamma^m_{st}(k') - \frac{g^{n0}(k'')}{g^{00}(k'')} \Gamma^0_{st}(k')\right\} \end{aligned} \tag{10}$$

where

$$e^{nr} = g^{nr} - \frac{g^{n0} g^{r0}}{g^{00}},$$

$$e^{rs}(k)\, g_{s0}(k') = -\frac{g^{r0}(k)}{g^{00}(k)}\, \delta(\boldsymbol{k}+\boldsymbol{k}'), \tag{11}$$

$$e^{rs}(k)\, g_{st}(k') = \delta^r_t\, \delta(\boldsymbol{k}+\boldsymbol{k}').$$

Eqs (9) can be solved for the ten quantities Γ^n_{st}:

$$\Gamma^n_{st}(k-k') = e^{rn}(k')[rs,t] + \frac{g^{n0}(k')}{g^{00}(k')}\,\Gamma^0_{sr}(k-k') \tag{12}$$

where

$$[rs,t] = \tfrac{1}{2}[k_s g_{rt}(k) + k_r g_{ts}(k) - k_t g_{rs}(k)].$$

The other algebraic constraints may be obtained by forming

$$k_s g^{\mu r}(k'')\, g_{r0}(k) + \tfrac{1}{2} g^{\mu 0}(k'') k_s g_{00}(k)$$
$$= \int d^3k' \{\delta(\boldsymbol{k}+\boldsymbol{k}'+\boldsymbol{k}'')\Gamma^\mu_{s0}(k') + g^{\mu r}(k'')\, g_{0\nu}(k+k')\Gamma^\nu_{rs}(k')\}.$$

This may be written purely in terms of Γ^μ_{s0} and Γ^0_{rs} using (12) and noting that if $k=0$ is chosen for (12):

$$\Gamma^n_{st}(k'') = \frac{g^{n0}(-k'')}{g^{00}(-k'')}\,\Gamma^0_{st}(k'') \tag{13}$$

then

$$\Gamma^\mu_{s0}(k-k') = -k_s g^{\mu r}(k'') g_{r0}(-k) + \tfrac{1}{2} g^{\mu 0}(k'') k_s g_{00}(-k) +$$
$$+ g^{\mu r}(k'')\,\delta(k) \int \frac{d^3k'\,\Gamma^0_{rs}(k')}{g^{00}(k')}. \tag{14}$$

Eq. (15) may be also written

$$\Gamma^\mu_{s0}(k-k') = \frac{g^{\mu r}(k'')}{g^{00}(0)}\{g^{0t}(0)[ts,r] + \Gamma^0_{rs}(k)\} - k_s[g^{\mu r}(k')\, g_{r0}(k) +$$
$$+ \tfrac{1}{2} g^{\mu 0}(k')\, g_{00}(k)]. \tag{15}$$

With the aid of the above relations the secondary constraints may be attacked. The calculations are too lengthy to reproduce here and the above derivations are only intended to illustrate the approach. The quantities most simply eliminated with secondary constraints are Γ^μ_{00}. When this has been accomplished one can choose the parameters y^m to be the quantities $g_{\mu\nu}$ and Γ^0_{rs}. Then the observables of the theory will be functions soley of $g_{\mu\nu}$, Γ^0_{rs}. The particular functions must be obtained from the condition that the gradients of the observables be orthogonal to the null vectors of the matrix η_{mn}. The observables could be obtained by integrating linear combinations of the rows of η_{mn}.

REFERENCES

[1] P. G. Bergmann and A. Komar, Report to the Royaumont Conference, 1959.

[2] P. G. Bergmann and I. Goldberg, *Phys. Rev.* **89** (1955)

DYNAMICAL VARIABLES AND SURFACE INTEGRALS

J. N. Goldberg

Aeronautical Research Laboratory, Wright-Patterson Air Force Base, Ohio

Abstract — Gravitational radiation from interacting particles is discussed briefly. It is suggested that the equations of motion may be separated from the problem of radiation by introducing the dynamical variables explicitly. The dynamical variables constitute that part of the gravitational field whose time development is uniquely determined by the field equations. In the linearized theory the dynamical variables are simply the completely transverse part of the metric $g_{rs} = \eta_{rs}+h_{rs}$. Using the coordinate conditions $h_{rs,s} = h_{0s,s} = 0$ surface integral which lead to the equations of motion are constructed. Multipole parameters are defined in terms of surface integrals. Only those corresponding to energy, linear momentum, and angular momentum are limited by the field equations and they are constants of the motion. Therefore, although the surface integrals are a satisfactory approach to the equations of motion with approximation methods, they are incapable of fully describing the quadrupole moments which may give rise to radiative effects.

1. INTRODUCTION

Plane wave solutions of the gravitational field equations have been exhibited by Bondi, Pirani and Robinson [1]. Presumably, this solution represents the asymptotic gravitational field which is radiated by a system of interacting masses. However, as yet there is no satisfactory proof that particles which interact through their gravitational fields alone can radiate. In fact, there has been some evidence which tends to indicate the contrary [2]–[4]. This evidence, which argues from successive approximations in a suggestive fashion, indicates that when gravitational radiation is present, the field tends to build up indefinitely. The argument is not yet conclusive, however, and we shall not be concerned with this problem here. Rather, we shall be concerned with formulating a method of solving the gravitational field equations which will be suitable for a two particle problem with and without an approximation method. The existence or lack of gravitational radiation should play no role here. However, once we have a solution, the question of radiation can be investigated.

There are a number of different approaches which one can take to the problem of interacting particles and their equations of motion. Some of these are being applied to the approximate solution of fast moving particles in order to look for radiation damping [5]–[7]. These methods do not look for a significant simplification of the field equations and, therefore, it is not likely that they will be applicable without approximation. The method we propose to use is based on two-dimensional surface integrals enclosing the particles as in E I H [8]–[10]. Of course, the surface integrals are not the crucial element, but they are important for their heuristic value and because they lead to a classification of particles as begun by Sachs and Bergmann [11]. Furthermore, use of the surface integrals gives us confidence that our results are independent of any model of matter. In no way does our approach negate the validity of other methods, such as that developed by Infeld [12].

With the generator of each infinitesimal coordinate transformation there is associated a strong conservation law [13]. Each conservation law, with the field equations leads to surface integral relations similar to those of E I H. These integrals are essentially integrals over the field equations, the surface S being taken in a matter-free region

$$\oint \sqrt{-g}\, G_\mu{}^s \xi^\mu n_s dS = 0 \tag{1.1}$$

where ξ^μ is the descriptor of the infinitesimal coordinate transformation $\delta x^\mu = \varepsilon \xi^\mu$. The conservation laws may be constructed as follows: Take any anti-symmetric object $U^{\nu\sigma}_{\smile}$ which depends linearly on the descriptor ξ^μ and contains no more than first derivatives of the field variables or ξ^μ. Now define ([14], [15])

$$E^\nu \overset{\text{def}}{=} U^{\nu\sigma}_{\smile\,,\sigma} - 2\sqrt{-g}\, G_\mu{}^\nu \xi^\mu. \tag{1.2}$$

When the field equations are satisfied, $G_\mu{}^\nu = 0$, E^ν satisfies a weak conservation law

$$E^\nu{}_{,\nu} = 0; \tag{1.3}$$

E^4 is clearly independent of second time derivatives, and, therefore, it is the generating density for the infinitesimal coordinate transformation described by ξ^μ ([14], [16]). The strong conservation law associated with (1.3) is

$$T^\nu{}_{,\nu} \equiv 0 \tag{1.4}$$

where

$$T^{\nu} \stackrel{\text{def}}{=} U^{\nu\sigma}_{\vee\ ,\sigma}.$$

Substituting from (1.2), the surface integrals (1.1) become

$$\frac{d}{dt}\oint U^{s0}_{\vee}\, n_s\, dS - \oint E^{s} n_s\, dS = 0. \tag{1.5}$$

Certainly, once the field equations have been satisfied, the surface integrals are empty. If this approach is to be useful, the above relationship must be independent of the surface in order to describe the properties of matter. Furthermore, one must be able to evaluate these integrals before all of the field equations have been satisfied, otherwise the integrals are trivial. Trautman [17] has shown that whenever a Killing vector exists, then one can construct a constant of the motion. Under these conditions one can choose $E^{\nu} = 0$ and the constant of the motion can be evaluated as a surface integral having solved only (cf. [15])

$$\sqrt{-g}\, G_{\mu}^{\ 4} = 0 \tag{1.6}$$

and

$$\sqrt{-g}\, G_{\mu}^{\ \mu} = 0.$$

This result is very general and depends only on the covariance of the theory and not upon the specific structure of the gravitational field equations. The existence of a Killing vector is a severe restriction on the geometry and as a result we are able to deduce the existence of a constant of the motion. However, in general, a Killing vector does not exist. What kind of restrictions can we impose in order to make some predictions about the particle motion? At each instant of time the coordinate system has a great deal of arbitrariness. Certainly, one cannot expect the particle motion to be restricted in any way unless the coordinate system is restricted in some fashion. Therefore, it is worthwhile to examine what kind of coordinate conditions might be suitable.

It is generally accepted that specifying four functions on a space-like surface will determine a physical situation uniquely ([18], [19]). In a Lagrangian theory, as contrasted with Hamiltonian equations, we usually think of two functions and their time derivatives. We shall call such field variables, whose time development is uniquely determined by the field equations, dynamical variables. (1)

(1) It is not clear that the dynamical variables must necessarily be "true observables" in the sense of Bergmann and his co-workers. The notion used here is certainly very close to the developed by Arnowitt, Deser and Misner, except that they are working with Hamiltonian equations.

In the E I H approximation method the field equations are ordered so that one can solve certain of the field equations; that is, for certain of the field variables, without knowing the time development of these variables. The time development is contained in the equations of motion for the particles producing the field. These motions are then determined by the surface integrals, (1.5). The surface integrals are consistency conditions on the time dependence of the already known variables, so that the remaining gravitational field equations may be solved.

The explicit use of dynamical variables appears to fit into this scheme. Since the time development of only the dynamical variables is determined by the field equations, it should be possible to separate out the dynamical variables. To carry out this program, one must have a minimum set of observables or dynamical variables on a hypersurface. Unfortunately, we do not know how to construct this set as yet. The Komar–Bergmann observables are redundant and the other sets of available dynamical variables are suitable for the Hamiltonian approach ([19], [20]).

However, in the linearized theory, this program can be carried out [21]. In the remainder of this paper we shall consider only the linearized gravitational equations.

2. LINEARIZED GRAVITATIONAL FIELD EQUATIONS

The linearized gravitational field equations are [2]

$$S^{(\check{\mu}\varrho\check{\nu}\sigma)}{}_{,\varrho\sigma} = 0; \tag{2.1}$$

$$\begin{aligned}
S^{\check{0}r\check{0}s} &= \eta^{rs}h_{nn} + h_{rs},\\
S^{\check{0}r\check{n}s} &= \eta^{nr}h_{0s} - \eta^{rs}h_{0n},\\
S^{\check{m}r\check{n}s} &= \eta^{rs}h_{mn} + \eta^{mn}h_{rs} - \eta^{nr}h_{ms} - \eta^{ms}h_{nr} -\\
&\quad -(\eta^{rs}\eta^{mn} - \eta^{nr}\eta^{ms})(h_{00} - h_{kk}),\\
h_{\mu\nu} &= g_{\mu\nu} - \eta_{\mu\nu}.
\end{aligned}$$

The surface integrals (1.5) may be written

$$\frac{d}{dt}\oint S^{\check{\mu}\varrho\check{s}0}{}_{,\varrho}\,\xi_\mu n_s\,dS - \oint S^{\check{\mu}\varrho\check{s}\sigma}{}_{,\varrho}\,\xi_{\mu,\sigma} n_s\,dS = 0. \tag{2.2}$$

As previously noted, these integrals yield constants of the motion if ξ^μ is a Killing vector. In the linearized theory ξ^μ need only be a Killing vector for the Minkowski metric. Therefore, there are

10 Killing vectors. The constants of the motion associated with these vectors have already been described by Sachs and Bergmann [11]. However, we are interested in introducing the dynamical variables explicitly in order to see whether using more information will allow us to glean more information from the field equations and surface integrals. Also, although in principle one need only solve the four field equations

$$S^{\mu\varrho\, 0s}_{\vee\ \vee\ ,\varrho s} = 0 \tag{2.3}$$

in order to evaluate the constants of the motion [13], in practice these equations involve all of the field variables and cannot be solved uniquely without coordinate conditions.

Since the time dependence of the dynamical variables is uniquely determined by the field equations, they will depend on a choice of a set of spacelike surfaces. In terms of the Minkowski background metric, it seems reasonable to choose the surfaces $x^0 = \text{const}$ without questioning how to make this choice covariant. Having chosen a particular set of surfaces, the dynamical variables must be invariants, for they are uniquely determined everywhere by their values on one member of the set.

Consider the behavior of $h_{\mu\nu}$ with respect to infinitesimal coordinate transformations

$$\bar{h}_{\mu\nu} = h_{\mu\nu} - \varepsilon(\xi_{\mu,\nu} + \xi_{\nu,\mu}),$$

$$\xi_\mu = \eta_{\mu\varrho}\,\xi^\varrho. \tag{2.4}$$

We shall use the superscripts (t) and (l) to refer to latin (spatial) indices. The (t) superscript means that the 3-divergence with respect to the corresponding index vanishes; the (l) means that the 3-curl with respect to the corresponding index vanishes:

$$A^{(tl)}_{mn,m} = 0, \qquad \varepsilon^{jkn} A^{(tl)}_{mn,k} = 0. \tag{2.5}$$

Thus we may write

$$h_{0r} = h_{0r}{}^{(t)} + h_{0r}{}^{(l)}, \tag{2.6a}$$

$$h_{rs} = h_{rs}{}^{(tt)} + h_{rs}{}^{(tl)} + h_{sr}{}^{(tl)} + h_{rs}{}^{(ll)} \tag{2.6b}$$

and similarly

$$\varepsilon\xi_r = -\omega^{rn}_{\vee\ ,n} + \zeta_{,r} \tag{2.7}$$

where the curl-free and divergence-free parts of the descriptor have been made explicit. From (2.4), (2.6) and (2.7) we find the following:

$$\left.\begin{aligned}
\bar{h}_{00} &= h_{00} - 2\varepsilon\,\xi_{0,0}\,,\\
\bar{h}_{0r}{}^{(l)} &= h_{0r}{}^{(l)} - \varepsilon\,\xi_{0,r} - \zeta_{,r0}\,,\\
\bar{h}_{0r}{}^{(t)} &= h_{0r}{}^{(t)} + \check{\omega}^{rm}{}_{,m0}\,,\\
\bar{h}_{rs}{}^{(ll)} &= h_{rs}{}^{(ll)} - 2\zeta_{,rs}\,,\\
\bar{h}_{rs}{}^{(tl)} &= h_{rs}{}^{(tl)} + \check{\omega}^{rm}{}_{,ms}\,,\\
\bar{h}_{rs}{}^{(tt)} &= h_{rs}{}^{(tt)}\,.
\end{aligned}\right\} \tag{2.8}$$

From the last of the above equations, it is clear that the $h_{rs}{}^{(tt)}$, the completely divergence-free part of h_{rs}, are the dynamical variables we require. We do not have to consider the Lorentz transformations for they can alter the equations of our set of surfaces, but they cannot alter the variables on the surfaces $x^0 = \text{const}$. Although the transformations (2.4) arise out of the coordinate transformations, within the linearized theory, they have no geometrical effects. These transformations only change the field variables within the underlying geometrical structure.

Therefore, it is convenient to impose the three coordinate conditions

$$h_{rs,s} = 0\,. \tag{2.9}$$

We are still free to choose another coordinate condition. It must not involve the h_{rs} because, being completely transverse, they are determined by the field equations. There does not seem to be a strong argument for choosing the fourth coordinate condition. However, from the field equations it seems convenient to choose

$$h_{0r,r} = 0\,. \tag{2.10}$$

Thus we eliminate the longitudinal parts of the field. Of course, h_{0r} is not invariant under the infinitesimal transformations.

With these coordinate conditions the linearized field equations become

$$G^{00} \equiv -h_{rr,ss} = 0\,, \tag{2.11a}$$

$$G^{0n} \equiv h_{rr,n0} + h_{0n,ss} = 0\,, \tag{2.11b}$$

$$\begin{aligned}
G^{mn} \equiv\; & h_{mn,00} - h_{mn,ss} - h_{0m,n} - h_{0n,m} + \\
& + h_{00,mn} - h_{ss,mn} + \\
& + \eta^{mn}[h_{rr,00} - h_{rr,ss} + h_{00,ss}] = 0\,,
\end{aligned} \tag{2.11c}$$

$$G^{rr} = -2h_{00,ss} - 2h_{rr,00} + h_{rr,ss} = 0\,. \tag{2.11d}$$

In order to study the surface integrals we shall proceed as follows. Eq. (2.2) tells us that the time derivative over some quantity is equal to a surface integral. Suppose the surface integral on the left can be made independent of the surface of integration. Then it will describe some characteristic of the matter enclosed by the surface: the total mass, angular momentum, quadrupole moment, etc. Eq. (2.2) would then say that the changes in the characteristics of matter are determined by what the field carries away. This kind of statement is what we shall look for.

Consider the first integral in (2.2),

$$I = \oint S^{\check{\mu}\varrho\check{s}0}{}_{,\varrho}\, \xi_\mu n_s dS. \tag{2.12}$$

This integral will be independent of the surface integration and, hence, characterizes the matter within the surface, if and only if

$$(S^{\check{\mu}\varrho\check{s}0}{}_{,\varrho}\, \xi_\mu)_{,s} = 0. \tag{2.13}$$

In general, when $G^{\mu 0} = 0$, this condition will be satisfied only if ξ_μ is a constant. To generalize the integral, we expand (2.13) and find

$$\begin{aligned}(S^{\check{\mu}\varrho\check{s}0}{}_{,\varrho}\, \xi_\mu - S^{\mu s\sigma 0}\, \xi_{\mu,\sigma})_{,s}\\ = S^{\check{\mu}0\check{\sigma}0}\, \xi_{\mu,\sigma} - S^{\check{\mu}s\check{\tau}0}\, \xi_{\mu,\tau s}.\end{aligned} \tag{2.14}$$

Clearly the right hand side vanishes when ξ_μ is a Killing vector:

$$\xi_{\mu,\nu} + \xi_{\nu,\mu} = 0. \tag{2.15}$$

As mentioned earlier, in this case

$$II = \oint (S^{\check{\mu}\varrho\check{s}0}{}_{,\varrho}\, \xi_\mu - S^{\check{\mu}s\check{\sigma}0}\, \xi_{\mu,\sigma}) n_s dS \tag{2.16}$$

defines a constant of the motion. This result may be seen easily, for with the modification of the first integral given in (2.16), the second integral of (2.2) becomes

$$\oint \left\{(S^{\check{\mu}0\check{s}\sigma} + S^{\check{\sigma}0\check{s}\mu})_{,0}\, \xi_{\mu,\sigma} + (S^{\check{\mu}\tau\check{s}\sigma}\, \xi_{\mu,\sigma})_{,\tau}\right\} n_s dS = 0 \tag{2.17}$$

when (2.15) is satisfied.

To obtain a further generalization, it is necessary to use the specific form of $S^{\mu\nu\varrho\sigma}$ given in (2.1) and the coordinate conditions (2.9) and (2.10). The right hand side of (2.14) then becomes

$$\begin{aligned}S^{\check{m}0\check{n}0}\, \xi_{m,n} - S^{\check{0}s\check{r}0}\, \xi_{0,rs} - S^{\check{m}s\check{r}0}\, \xi_{m,rs}\\ = [\dot{a}^{\check{m}n\check{r}s}{}_{,n}\, \xi_{m,r} + a^{\check{r}m\check{s}n}{}_{,r}\, \xi_{0,mn} - b^{s\check{n}}\, \xi^r{}_{,rn}]_{,s} +\\ + b^{m\check{n}}{}_{,n}\, \xi_{m,ss} + \dot{h}_{nn}\, \xi^s{}_{,s} - h_{nn}\, \xi_{0,ss}\end{aligned} \tag{2.18}$$

with

$$h_{mn} = a^{\check{m}r\check{n}s}{}_{,rs}, \qquad h_{0m} = b^{ms}{}_{,s} \tag{2.19}$$

which is allowed by the coordinate conditions.

Clearly, when

$$\xi_{0,ss} = 0, \qquad \xi_{m,ss} = 0, \qquad \text{and} \qquad \xi^{s}{}_{,s} = 0, \tag{2.20}$$

the right hand side of (2.18) is a total divergence. Therefore, (2.16) may be modified to describe various properties of the matter enclosed by the surface of integration. These multipole moments are defined by chosing different descriptors ξ_μ consistent with (2.20):

$$M = \oint \Big\{ S^{\mu\varrho s0}{}_{,\varrho}\, \xi_\mu - S^{\mu s\sigma 0}\, \xi_{\mu,\sigma} - \dot{a}^{\check{m}n\check{r}s}{}_{,n}\, \xi_{m,r} - \\ - a^{\check{r}m\check{s}n}{}_{,r}\, \xi_{0,mn} \Big\}\, n_s\, dS. \tag{2.21}$$

This integral may be rewritten as

$$M = \oint \Big\{ h_{nn,s}\, \xi_0 - h_{nn}\, \xi_{0,s} - \dot{h}_{nn}\, \xi_s + \\ + S^{\check{m}r\check{s}0}{}_{,r}\, \xi_m - S^{\check{m}s\check{r}0}\, \xi_{m,r} \Big\}\, n_s\, dS \tag{2.22}$$

which no longer depends on h_{rs} except through the trace. Therefore M may be evaluated having solved only the four field equations $G^{\mu 0} = 0$. However, unless ξ_μ is a Killing vector, the surface integral representing the time derivative of M can not be evaluated unless all of the field equations have been satisfied. In that case one gets simply $\dot{M} - \dot{M} = 0$.

If we limit our attention to the ten descriptors which are Killing vectors, we note that the field equations are just ordered so that one can apply the surface integrals to study the equations of motion in a method of successive approximations of the complete field equations. However, only seven of these descriptors lead to restrictions on the motion, because use of the field equations makes three of the conditions trivial. Thus, the technique of EIH is no longer restricted to slow motion. However, it must be recognized that these surface integrals impose no limitation on the quadrupole moment of the matter distribution. The quadrupole moment may have an arbitrary time dependence, consistent with the coordinate conditions, and the field will adjust to it.

If one carries out the argument in electrodynamics analogous to that presented here, one finds that the electric multipoles are given by

$$M = \oint [A^0\, \xi_{,s} - A^0{}_{,s}\, \xi\,]\, n_s dS \tag{2.23}$$

in the radiation gauge

$$A^r{}_{,r} = 0 . \tag{2.24}$$

The infinitesimal gauge transformation is given by

$$\delta A^\varrho = \eta^{\varrho\sigma}\xi_{,\sigma} \tag{2.25a}$$

and

$$\nabla^2 \xi = 0 . \tag{2.25b}$$

Only the charge which is given by $\xi = \text{const}$ is a constant of the motion. All other multipoles may have an arbitrary time dependence which is revealed in the radiation of electromagnetic energy.

A simple example of this situation can be given in the linearized gravitational theory: a particle at rest at the origin and having a time dependent quadrupole moment. The solution is given by

$$\begin{aligned} h_{rr} &= -4m/r , \\ h_{0n} &= 0 , \\ h_{00} &= -2m/r , \\ h_{mn} &= -m(x^m x^n/r^3 + \delta_{mn}/r) + \\ &\quad + [Q^{\check{m}r\check{n}s}(t-r)/r]_{,rs} , \end{aligned} \tag{2.26}$$

with

$$Q^{\check{m}r\check{m}s} = 0 .$$

Solutions of this type have been discussed by Sachs and Bergmann [11]. The quadrupole radiation solution alone has been examined in considerable detail by Boardman and Bergmann [22]. They find that these solutions represent spherical waves carrying energy away from the origin.

CONCLUSIONS

We have shown that by separating out the dynamical variables of the linearized gravitational field, it is possible to discuss all the essentially static features of the field before coming to grips with the problem of radiation. To show this result we used the surface integrals, but clearly they are not necessary. The important feature is the particular choice of coordinate conditions (2.9) and (2.10) which allow the dynamical variables to appear explicitly as the field variables. It should be noted that the dynamical variables used here are closely related to the variables Dirac obtains by his fixation of coordinates [20]. The main difference is that he separates out h_{nn} before imposing (2.9). It is possible to do so if one does not consider matter, for then h_{nn} may be set equal to zero as is evident from (2.11a).

The dynamical variables are defined with respect to a set of surfaces. If this approach is to be meaningful without approximation, it should be possible to define the set of surfaces in a covariant manner. In that case, the geometry determined by the field equations would be instrumental in determining the set of space-like surfaces. One would not then be imposing a geometrical situation which might be incompatible with the physical situation described by the field equations.

The weakness of the surface integrals as an approach to the problem of motion has been revealed. We have seen that these integrals describe essentially unchanging features of the field. Situations, in which interactions and possibly radiation can occur, are not adequately described by the surface integrals, except by approximation methods. Fortunately, the utility of introducing the dynamical variables is not thereby limited. If one can separate out the time development of the field, the problem of finding solutions for interacting particles may be simplified.

REFERENCES

[1] H. Bondi, F. Pirani and I. Robinson, *Proc. Roy. Soc.* A**251**, 519 (1959).
[2] L. Infeld, *Ann. Phys.* **6**, 341 (1959).
[3] A. Peres and N. Rosen, *Colloque sur les Théories Relativistes de la Gravitation*, to be published.
[4] A. Papapetrou, *Ann. d. Phys.* **20**, 399 (1957).
[5] P. Havas and J. N. Goldberg, in preparation.
[6] J. Plebański and B. Bertotti, *preprint*.
[7] R. P. Kerr, *Nuovo Cim.* **13**, 469 (1959).
[8] A. Einstein, L. Infeld and B. Hoffmann, *Ann. Math.* **39**, 66 (1938).
[9] A. Einstein and L. Infeld, *Ann. Math.* **41**, 455 (1940).
[10] A. Einstein and L. Infeld, *Canad J. Math.* **1**, 209 (1949).
[11] R. Sachs and P. G. Bergmann, *Phys. Rev.* **112**, 674 (1958).
[12] L. Infeld, *Rev. Mod. Phys.* **29**, 398 (1957).
[13] P. G. Bergmann, *Phys. Rev.* **112**, 287 (1958).
[14] A. Komar, *Phys. Rev.* **113**, 934 (1959).
[15] J. N. Goldberg, *Colloque sur les Théories Relativistes de la Gravitation*, to be published.
[16] R. Schiller and P. G. Bergmann, *Phys. Rev.* **89**, 4 (1953).
[17] A. Trautman, *Bull. Acad. Polon. Sci.* Cl III, **4**, 679 (1956).
[18] P. G. Bergmann and I. Goldberg, *Phys. Rev.* **98**, 531 (1955).
[19] R. Arnowitt, S. Deser, and C. W. Misner, *preprint*.
[20] P. A. M. Dirac, *Phys. Rev.* **114**, 924 (1959).
[21] J. N. Goldberg, *Bull. Amer. Phys. Soc.* **4**, 16 (1959).
[22] J. Boardman and P. G. Bergmann, *Phys. Rev.* **115**, 1318 (1959).

QUANTUM THEORY OF GRAVITATION*

Suraj N. Gupta

Department of Physics, Wayne State University, Detroit, Michigan

At the beginning of this century there were two field theories, which were well known. One was Maxwell's theory of electromagnetism, and the other was Newton's theory of gravitation. Then in 1905 Einstein proposed his special theory of relativity, which expressed Maxwell's theory in a more elegant form but at the same time pointed out the inadequacy of Newton's theory. At first many attempts were made to find an alternative to Newton's theory, and various theories of gravitation were proposed. But in 1916 Einstein formulated his theory of general relativity in the final form, which was gradually widely accepted.

Let us, however, look upon the problem of formulating the theory of gravitation in a more modernistic way, and let us ask ourselves the question, "What are the requirements which an acceptable theory of gravitation must satisfy?" From a purely scientific point of view one could lay down three conditions: (1) It should be Lorentz covariant. (2) It should reduce to Newton's theory as a very good approximation. (3) It should also explain the three crucial tests.

I have recently discussed [1] the problem of constructing various theories of gravitation with the above requirements, and I shall first make a few remarks in this connection. We start from the well-known fact that every classical field on quantization must correspond to particles of integral spin. Therefore, the gravitational field can have spin 0, 1, 2 or something more. If we apply the usual principles of the field theory to a gravitational field of spin 0, we obtain a theory of gravitation, which is Lorentz covariant and

* Supported in part by the U. S. National Science Foundation.

Presented as an invited paper at the Annual Meeting of the American Physical Society in New York City on January 29, 1960.

reduces to Newton's theory as a very good approximation, but is unable to account for the observed amount of the advance of the perihelion of Mercury and the deflection of light-rays in the gravitational field of the sun. If we consider the case of spin 1, we can show that such a theory of gravitation is identical with Maxwell's theory of the electromagnetic field, and therefore cannot account for the fact that the gravitational force between all particles is attractive. When we consider fields of spin higher than 1, the theory becomes much more complicated, and I think it will be enough not to go beyond spin 2. In the case of spin 2, the simplest theory of gravitation corresponds to a linear gravitational field given by

$$\Box^2 U_{\mu\nu} = \varkappa T_{\mu\nu} \tag{1}$$

where $\varkappa$ is the gravitational coupling constant, and $T_{\mu\nu}$ is the energy-momentum tensor of the matter field, which includes everything except the gravitational field. However, such a linear theory contains the serious difficulty that the energy of the field is not positive definite. This means that on quantization it corresponds to gravitons of positive as well as negative energies. But, particles of negative energy are strictly forbidden in quantum field theory, because they would lead to the spontaneous creation of real particles of positive and negative energies even in vacuum.

The above difficulty in the case of spin 2 arises from the fact that in order to make the energy of the gravitational field positive definite, one must impose the supplementary condition

$$\partial U_{\mu\nu}/\partial x_\mu = 0, \tag{2}$$

which is compatible with (1) only if $\partial T_{\mu\nu}/\partial x_\mu = 0$. But $\partial T_{\mu\nu}/\partial x_\mu$ cannot be equal to zero, because only the divergence of the total energy-momentum tensor, which must include the gravitational field also, can vanish. If we want to remove this difficulty, we must replace (1) by

$$\Box^2 U_{\mu\nu} = \varkappa (T_{\mu\nu} + t_{\mu\nu}) \tag{3}$$

where $t_{\mu\nu}$ is the energy-momentum tensor of the gravitational field. The supplementary condition (2) is then compatible with (3), because the required relation

$$\frac{\partial}{\partial x_\mu}(T_{\mu\nu} + t_{\mu\nu}) = 0 \tag{4}$$

is in agreement with the law of conservation of momentum and energy of a closed system. Since $t_{\mu\nu}$ must be at least a quadratic function of the gravitational field variables, we can see that the field equation (3) has become non-linear. Moreover, I have shown [2] that if we derive an equation of the type (3) from the Lagrangian density, then the Lagrangian density must consist of an infinite series of the form

$$L = L_0 + \varkappa L_1 + \varkappa^2 L_2 + \varkappa^3 L_3 + \dots \quad (5)$$

It is easy to find one or two terms in (5) in a direct way, but it is so difficult to obtain L_n in general that this approach at first sight does not seem encouraging. We, however, note that if we want to remove the difficulty of negative energy in the case of the gravitational field of spin 2, the field equation has to be non-linear and the Lagrangian density has to contain an infinite number of terms in various powers of the gravitational coupling constant.

Let us now look at this situation from Einstein's point of view. First of all, Einstein's theory of gravitation has a beautiful mathematical structure. Secondly, from Einstein's theory one can obtain a reasonable explanation of the three crucial tests without fiddling with coupling constants or carrying out other manipulations. Thirdly, after attempts for half a century, no one has been able to find a reasonable alternative to Einstein's theory. Considering all these things, Einstein was firmly convinced that his theory of gravitation is certainly correct. But then he was faced with two problems: Firstly, due to the use of the curved space, Einstein's theory of gravitation is strikingly different from other field theories; and secondly, it does not seem possible to quantize the gravitational field in the curved space. In his later years Einstein was particularly preoccupied with these two problems. Because his theory is different from other field theories, he tried to construct unified field theories, and because he could not see how his theory in the curved space could possibly be quantized, he criticized quantum mechanics.

Many scientists have found it very curious that Einstein, who himself played a pioneering role in the development of quantum physics, should so persistently criticize quantum mechanics. There has been a great deal of controversy, and the majority of physicists do not agree with Einstein in his criticism of quantum mechanics. Because relativity and quantum mechanics provide the basic foundations of modern theoretical physics, it certainly seems very surprising that there should be a conflict between general relativity and quantum mechanics. In fact, it will not be an exaggeration to say that from an intellectual point of view this has been the most outstanding problem facing the theoretical physicists for half a century. I shall now show how this problem can be solved by following a new approach ([3], [4]) to Einstein's theory of gravitation, which I suggested in 1951.

The Lagrangian density for Einstein's gravitational field is usually expressed in the curved space as

$$L = -\varkappa^{-2}\mathfrak{g}^{\mu\nu}\left(\begin{Bmatrix} \alpha \\ \mu\beta \end{Bmatrix}\begin{Bmatrix} \beta \\ \nu\alpha \end{Bmatrix} - \begin{Bmatrix} \alpha \\ \mu\nu \end{Bmatrix}\begin{Bmatrix} \beta \\ \alpha\beta \end{Bmatrix}\right) \tag{6}$$

where the symbols have the usual meaning. We put

$$\mathfrak{g}^{\mu\nu} = \varepsilon^{\mu\nu} - \varkappa\gamma^{\mu\nu} \tag{7}$$

where $\varepsilon^{\mu\nu}$ is the flat-space metrical tensor, and then we express the Lagrangian density as an infinite series in powers of $\varkappa$. Using the usual flat-space notation, in which $x_\mu = (x_1, x_2, x_3, ict)$, we can express this series as

$$\begin{aligned} L = & -\frac{1}{4}\left(\frac{\partial\gamma_{\mu\nu}}{\partial x_\alpha}\frac{\partial\gamma_{\mu\nu}}{\partial x_\alpha} - \frac{1}{2}\frac{\partial\gamma_{\mu\mu}}{\partial x_\alpha}\frac{\partial\gamma_{\nu\nu}}{\partial x_\alpha} - 2\frac{\partial\gamma_{\mu\beta}}{\partial x_\alpha}\frac{\partial\gamma_{\mu\alpha}}{\partial x_\beta}\right) - \\ & -\frac{\varkappa}{4}\left(\gamma_{\mu\nu}\frac{\partial\gamma_{\alpha\beta}}{\partial x_\mu}\frac{\partial\gamma_{\beta\alpha}}{\partial x_\nu} - \frac{1}{2}\gamma_{\mu\nu}\frac{\partial\gamma_{\alpha\alpha}}{\partial x_\mu}\frac{\partial\gamma_{\beta\beta}}{\partial x_\nu} + 2\gamma_{\mu\nu}\frac{\partial\gamma_{\mu\alpha}}{\partial x_\beta}\frac{\partial\gamma_{\nu\beta}}{\partial x_\alpha} + \right. \\ & \left. +\gamma_{\mu\nu}\frac{\partial\gamma_{\beta\beta}}{\partial x_\alpha}\frac{\partial\gamma_{\mu\nu}}{\partial x_\alpha} - 2\gamma_{\mu\nu}\frac{\partial\gamma_{\mu\beta}}{\partial x_\alpha}\frac{\partial\gamma_{\nu\beta}}{\partial x_\alpha}\right) + O(\varkappa^2) \end{aligned} \tag{8}$$

where $O(\varkappa^2)$ denotes terms involving second and higher powers of $\varkappa$. We can, of course, expand L up to any desired order in powers of $\varkappa$.

The terms independent of $\varkappa$ in (8) can be simplified by using the supplementary condition

$$\frac{\partial\gamma_{\mu\nu}}{\partial x_\mu} = 0, \tag{9}$$

and dropping a four-dimensional divergence term. We thus obtain

$$\begin{aligned} L = & -\frac{1}{4}\left(\frac{\partial\gamma_{\mu\nu}}{\partial x_\alpha}\frac{\partial\gamma_{\mu\nu}}{\partial x_\alpha} - \frac{1}{2}\frac{\partial\gamma_{\mu\mu}}{\partial x_\alpha}\frac{\partial\gamma_{\nu\nu}}{\partial x_\alpha}\right) - \\ & -\frac{\varkappa}{4}\left(\gamma_{\mu\nu}\frac{\partial\gamma_{\alpha\beta}}{\partial x_\mu}\frac{\partial\gamma_{\alpha\beta}}{\partial x_\nu} - \frac{1}{2}\gamma_{\mu\nu}\frac{\partial\gamma_{\alpha\alpha}}{\partial x_\mu}\frac{\partial\gamma_{\beta\beta}}{\partial x_\nu} + 2\gamma_{\mu\nu}\frac{\partial\gamma_{\mu\alpha}}{\partial x_\beta}\frac{\partial\gamma_{\nu\beta}}{\partial x_\alpha} + \right. \\ & \left. +\gamma_{\mu\nu}\frac{\partial\gamma_{\beta\beta}}{\partial x_\alpha}\frac{\partial\gamma_{\mu\nu}}{\partial x_\alpha} - 2\gamma_{\mu\nu}\frac{\partial\gamma_{\mu\beta}}{\partial x_\alpha}\frac{\partial\gamma_{\nu\beta}}{\partial x_\alpha}\right) + O(\varkappa^2). \end{aligned} \tag{10}$$

We now make the fundamental assumption that the physical space is flat and not curved, and that the curved space formalism is necessary for the theory of the gravitational field merely to express the Lagrangian density in a closed form. We can then regard (10) with (9) as our starting point for a theory of gravitation in flat space. The field equation, obtained from (10) in the usual way, also contains an infinite number of terms, but it can be expressed as

$$\Box^2 \gamma_{\mu\nu} = \varkappa t_{\mu\nu} \tag{11}$$

where $t_{\mu\nu}$ is the symmetrical energy-momentum tensor for the gravitational field. Although the field equation (11) has a simple form, it is indeed quite complicated mathematically, because $t_{\mu\nu}$ consists of an infinite number of terms. It should be noted that (9), (10) and (11) are in agreement with (2), (5) and (3) respectively.

In order to pass over from the classical to the quantum theory of gravitation, we must use an independent field variable γ instead of $\gamma_{\mu\mu}$ and replace (10) by the corresponding expression in terms of ordered products [5]. Thus, we take the quantum mechanical Lagrangian density as

$$:L: = :\left[-\frac{1}{4}\left(\frac{\partial \gamma_{\mu\nu}}{\partial x_\alpha}\frac{\partial \gamma_{\mu\nu}}{\partial x_\alpha} - \frac{1}{2}\frac{\partial \gamma}{\partial x_\alpha}\frac{\partial \gamma}{\partial x_\alpha} \right) + O(\varkappa) \right]:, \tag{12}$$

while the equivalence of $\gamma_{\mu\mu}$ and γ and the vanishing of $\partial\gamma_{\mu\nu}/\partial x_\mu$ is ensured by means of the supplementary conditions

$$\langle \gamma_{\mu\mu} - \gamma \rangle = 0, \tag{13}$$

and

$$\langle \partial\gamma_{\mu\nu}/\partial x_\mu \rangle = 0. \tag{14}$$

We can regard the terms independent of $\varkappa$ in (12) as the Lagrangian density for the unperturbed gravitational field, while the remaining terms can be regarded as direct interaction terms between the gravitons. Thus, using the interaction representation, we can express the field equations and the Hamiltonian density for the unperturbed gravitational field as

$$\Box^2 \gamma_{\mu\nu} = 0, \qquad \Box^2 \gamma = 0, \tag{15}$$

and

$$:H: = :\left[\frac{1}{4}\left(\frac{\partial \gamma_{\mu\nu}}{\partial x_i}\frac{\partial \gamma_{\mu\nu}}{\partial x_i} - \frac{1}{2}\frac{\partial \gamma}{\partial x_i}\frac{\partial \gamma}{\partial x_i} \right) + \frac{1}{4}\left(\frac{\partial \gamma_{\mu\nu}}{\partial x_0}\frac{\partial \gamma_{\mu\nu}}{\partial x_0} - \frac{1}{2}\frac{\partial \gamma}{\partial x_0}\frac{\partial \gamma}{\partial x_0} \right) \right]:, \tag{16}$$

while the commutation relations are

$$\begin{aligned} [\gamma_{\mu\nu}(x), \gamma_{\lambda\varrho}(x')] &= ic\hbar(\delta_{\mu\lambda}\delta_{\nu\varrho} + \delta_{\mu\varrho}\delta_{\nu\lambda})D(x-x'), \\ [\gamma(x), \gamma(x')] &= -4ic\hbar D(x-x') \end{aligned} \tag{17}$$

where

$$D(x-x') = -\frac{i}{(2\pi)^3}\int dk\, e^{ik(x-x')}\delta(k^2)\varepsilon(k), \tag{18}$$

$\varepsilon(k)$ being $+1$ or -1 according as k_0 is positive or negative. Carrying out the Fourier decomposition of field variables and using an indefinite metric, we can show that the gravitational field corresponds to eleven types of gravitons. But, due to the supplementary conditions (13) and (14), nine types of gravitons can appear only in virtual states, and we are left with only two types of real gravitons. These gravitons can be shown to be particles of spin 2, and their spin axes are always parallel or antiparallel to their directions of motion.

The interaction of the gravitational field with any other field can be investigated by first writing the total Lagrangian density in the curved space, and then expanding it in the flat space in powers of $\varkappa$. After this, we have only to replace the classical expression by the corresponding quantum mechanical expression in terms of ordered products, pass over to the interaction representation, derive the collision operator, and obtain the required element for a given physical process by using the contractions

$$\begin{aligned} \gamma^{\bullet}_{\mu\nu}(x)\gamma^{\bullet}_{\lambda\varrho}(x') &= -ic\hbar(\delta_{\mu\lambda}\delta_{\nu\varrho}+\delta_{\mu\varrho}\delta_{\nu\lambda})D_F(x-x'),\\ \gamma^{\bullet}(x)\gamma^{\bullet}(x') &= 4ic\hbar\, D_F(x-x') \end{aligned} \tag{19}$$

where

$$D_F(x-x') = \lim_{\varepsilon\to+0}\frac{1}{(2\pi)^4}\int dk\, e^{ik(x-x')}\frac{1}{k^2-i\varepsilon}. \tag{20}$$

In applications it is actually more convenient to put

$$\gamma_{\mu\nu}-\tfrac{1}{2}\delta_{\mu\nu}\gamma = h_{\mu\nu}, \tag{21}$$

and use the relation

$$h^{\bullet}_{\mu\nu}(x)h^{\bullet}_{\lambda\varrho}(x') = -ic\hbar(\delta_{\mu\lambda}\delta_{\nu\varrho}+\delta_{\mu\varrho}\delta_{\nu\lambda}-\delta_{\mu\nu}\delta_{\lambda\varrho})D_F(x-x'). \tag{22}$$

We thus obtain a quantum theory of gravitation, which is not only Lorentz covariant but also readily applicable to any physical problem involving the gravitational field.

An interesting application of the quantum theory of gravitation, which I have investigated, is whether it is possible to remove the divergencies in the interaction of gravitons and other particles by renormalization. A calculation of the second-order self-energy diagrams shows that the gravitational self-energy of a photon vanishes unambiguously, while the gravitational self-energy of an

GENERAL RELATIVITY AND THE SPECIAL RELATIVISTIC EQUATIONS OF MOTION OF POINT PARTICLES*

P. Havas

Department of Physics, Lehigh University, Bethlehem, Pennsylvania, U. S. A.

The relation of the general theory of relativity and of the special relativistic equations of motion for multipole singularities of arbitrary fields is discussed. It is shown first that the differential identities of the linearized equations of the general theory imply the law of conservation of energy-momentum of the special theory for the system of particles and fields. From this law the general form of the translational and rotational equations of motion follows by special relativistic methods. These equations involve the gravitational monopole and dipole moments of the particles, but no higher moments. Their interpretation is discussed, and examples of their application to particular fields are given.

I. INTRODUCTION

The first attempt to establish a connection between the properties of a field and the equations of motion of the sources of the field is due to Lorentz [1], who realized that Newton's equations of motion had to be modified if conservation of energy was to be maintained for a system of radiating electrons together with the electromagnetic field. Lorentz's theory led to infinities in the limit of point electrons, but Dirac [2] succeeded in showing that these infinities could be avoided by a consistent application of the requirement that the law of conservation of energy-momentum, valid for the electromagnetic field alone, should be maintained even in the presence of singularities. Dirac's method was extended to other special relativistic fields [3]–[5] (1) and other conservation laws ([6] conservation of angular momentum, [7] general case) and the explicit form of the equations of motion of multipole singularities

* This work was supported in part by the National Science Foundation.

(1) For further references see [3].

of such fields has been established [8]–[11].(1) These singularities, apart from their intrinsic interest, can be considered as the classical analogue of particles with spin, and their study may be of value in elementary particle theory.

Within the framework of the special theory of relativity the exact form of the equations of motion of arbitrary point singularities has thus been determined. However, the generalized Dirac method used to derive these equations is not free from ambiguities. Firstly, it is based on the arbitrary imposition of the requirement of the persistence of certain conservation laws in the presence of singularities; this limitation of the method is particularly serious considering that it is not possible to require the persistence of *all* conservation laws obeyed by the fields alone [12]. Secondly, the material (as distinguished from the field-producing) properties of the singularities enter the equations only through the requirement that certain quantities should be equal to otherwise undetermined perfect differentials; thus these properties are to a considerable extent arbitrary and the arbitrary quantities introduced can not be interpreted fully and in a physically satisfactory manner within the framework of the method.(2)

The above ambiguities can be avoided in part by the use of an alternative special relativistic method originated by Mathisson [14], [15] and developed after his untimely death by Shanmugadhasan [16]. This method takes the special relativistic law of conservation of energy-momentum for the system of particles and field as its starting point. The explicit introduction of the energy-momentum tensor of the particles allows both a demonstration that it is not necessary to require separately the conservation of angular momentum, and a partial interpretation of the functions characteristic of the particles. However, within the framework of the special theory of relativity the special role of the energy-momentum conservation law remains an arbitrary feature, and both the choice and the interpretation of the particle properties can not be fully justified. Furthermore, Mathisson's method is in part somewhat cumbersome, and its application to general fields and multipole singularities has not been carried as far as that of the Dirac method.

The elements of arbitrariness and ambiguity in the special relativistic theory of the equations of motion are expressions of the fact that the special relativistic field equations usually considered do

(1) For a review of recent work on special relativistic equations of motion see [11].

(2) For a discussion of various aspects of this point see [13], [4], [8]–[10].

not determine the equations of motion of their sources.[1] In the general theory of relativity, on the other hand, it has been established by the work of Einstein, Infeld and Hoffmann [18] that the equations of motion of mass points are determined by the field equations. The methods developed in this work were used by Infeld and Wallace [19] to obtain the exact special relativistic Lorentz-Dirac equations of motion of point charges on the basis of the linearized equations of general relativity. A somewhat modified version of the Infeld–Wallace method was used later to establish the special relativistic equations of motion of simple poles of the neutral scalar and vector meson fields [20].

This paper describes a general method of establishing the equations of motion of special relativity for multipole singularities of arbitrary fields on the basis of the linearized equations of general relativity. Many separate features of the calculations have been known before; however, a concise connected account may contribute to the clarification of the relations between the concepts, as well as the results, of the special and the general theory of relativity for the case of the problem of motion.

It is shown first that the differential identities of the linearized equations of the general theory imply the overall law of conservation of energy-momentum of the special theory. From this law the general form of the equations of motion of multipole singularities of arbitrary fields is derived by use of a modified form of Mathisson's method. It is shown that these equations involve the gravitational monopole and dipole moments of the particles, but no higher multipole moments, and their interpretation is discussed. Examples of the application of the general equations to particular fields are given in the Appendix.

II. THE EQUATIONS OF MOTION

We consider a Riemannian four-space with coordinates x^ϱ and metric tensor $g_{\mu\nu}$; furthermore we introduce the Minkowski metric tensor $\eta_{\mu\nu}$ with signature -2. The velocity of light is taken as unity. Greek indices run from 0 to 3; summation over repeated indices is understood. Indices are raised and lowered by means of the Minkowski metric tensor only. We shall use the notation

$$\partial_\varrho \equiv \partial/\partial x^\varrho, \; \partial_{\varrho\sigma}\ldots \equiv \partial_\varrho \partial_\sigma\ldots . \qquad (1)$$

(1) For a discussion of some aspects of this question compare [17].

We shall be concerned with the motion of N singularities. The coordinates of the ith particle are denoted by z_i^{ϱ}. Its proper time is defined by

$$d\tau_i \equiv (dz_{i\alpha} dz_i^{\alpha})^{\frac{1}{2}}; \tag{2}$$

derivatives with respect to τ_i are occasionally denoted by a dot. The four-velocity is given by

$$v_i^{\varrho} \equiv dz_i^{\varrho}/d\tau_i \tag{3}$$

and thus we have

$$v_{i\alpha} v_i^{\alpha} = 1, \qquad v_{i\alpha} \dot{v}_i^{\alpha} = 0. \tag{4}$$

We shall also use the notation

$$s_i^{\varrho} \equiv x^{\varrho} - z_i^{\varrho}(\tau_i), \qquad s_i^{2} \equiv s_{i\alpha} s_i^{\alpha}. \tag{5}$$

Now we consider Einstein's field equations

$$R_{\mu\nu} - \tfrac{1}{2} g_{\mu\nu} R = -8\pi G T_{\mu\nu}, \tag{6}$$

with

$$T_{\mu\nu} = T^{m}_{\mu\nu} + T^{f}_{\mu\nu}, \tag{7}$$

where $T^{m}_{\mu\nu}$ and $T^{f}_{\mu\nu}$ are the energy-momentum tensors of matter and of the non-gravitational fields, respectively. In general $T^{f}_{\mu\nu}$ depends on the metric, and is a quadratic function of the variables of the fields under consideration.

We develop the metric $g_{\mu\nu}$ in a series with the Minkowski metric as the zero-order approximation

$$g_{\mu\nu} = \eta_{\mu\nu} + {}_1g_{\mu\nu} + \ldots \tag{8}$$

and introduce the corresponding developments of the energy-momentum tensors

$$T^{m}_{\mu\nu} = {}_1T^{m}_{\mu\nu} + \ldots \tag{9}$$

and

$$T^{f}_{\mu\nu} = {}_1T^{f}_{\mu\nu} + \ldots . \tag{10}$$

At present we assume that the expansions (9) and (10) indeed start with the first-order terms indicated. However, the order in which the first non-vanishing term will appear in these two series depends on the relative magnitudes of $T^{m}_{\mu\nu}$ and $T^{f}_{\mu\nu}$; we shall return to this question later.

Introducing the quantity

$${}_1\gamma_{\mu\nu} = {}_1g_{\mu\nu} - \tfrac{1}{2}\eta_{\mu\nu}\, {}_1g_{\varrho}^{\ \varrho} \tag{11}$$

and keeping only the first-order terms in Eq. (6), we obtain the well-known linear approximation [21]

$$\partial^{\varrho}_{\varrho}\, {}_1\gamma_{\mu\nu} - \partial_{\nu}{}^{\varrho}\, {}_1\gamma_{\mu\varrho} - \partial_{\mu}{}^{\varrho}\, {}_1\gamma_{\nu\varrho} + \eta_{\mu\nu}\partial^{\varrho\sigma}\, {}_1\gamma_{\varrho\sigma} = -16\pi G({}_1T^{m}_{\mu\nu} + {}_1T^{f}_{\mu\nu}). \quad (12)$$

We note that the left hand side of (12) vanishes identically on contraction with ∂^{μ}. Thus we must have

$$\partial^{\mu}({}_1T^{m}_{\mu\nu} + {}_1T^{f}_{\mu\nu}) = 0. \quad (13)$$

This equation must be satisfied for Eq. (12) to be integrable and thus all the results we shall obtain from Eq. (13) are simply integrability conditions for the fundamental equation (12) of the liniear approximation method; however, we do not have to integrate this equation to be able to deduce the integrability conditions, and therefore do not have to choose any coordinate condition.

Equations (12) and (13) are Lorentz-invariant, as is the entire development discussed in this work. Hovewer, the criterion for special relativity is not formal Lorentz-invariance alone, but rather that the equations should not contain any quantity other than the Minkowski tensor $\eta_{\mu\nu}$ which is to be interpreted as the metric. In this sense Eq. (12) clearly is not special relativistic; the character of Eq. (13), on the other hand, remains to be investigated.

As ${}_1T^{f}_{\mu\nu}$ is the term of lowest order in the expansion (10), it can depend on the metric only through the lowest order term $\eta_{\mu\nu}$ in the expansion (8). Thus the term $\partial^{\mu}\, {}_1T^{f}_{\mu\nu}$ in Eq. (13) (called "force term" hereafter) is indeed the divergence of the special relativistic energy-momentum tensor of the non-gravitational fields. As the explicit form of $\partial^{\mu}\, {}_1T^{m}_{\mu\nu}$ is to be determined from Eq. (13) without further reference to Eq. (12) (except for purposes of comparison) it can not depend on any other metric than $\eta_{\mu\nu}$. Thus Eq. (13) expresses the energy-momentum conservation law of the system of particles and non-gravitational fields of the special theory of relativity.

Without loss of generality we can assume the matter energy-momentum tensor to be of the form

$${}_1T^{m}_{\mu\nu} = \sum_{i=1}^{N} {}_1T^{m}_{i\mu\nu} = \sum_{i=1}^{N}\sum_{l=0}^{\infty} \partial^{\alpha\beta\ldots\lambda} M_{i\alpha\beta\ldots\lambda,\,\mu\nu}(x^{\varrho}) \quad (14)$$

where the tensor $M_{i\alpha\beta\ldots\lambda,\,\mu\nu}$ of rank $l+2$ is the 2^l-pole density of the ith particle. l is the number of differentiations; clearly $M_{i\alpha\beta\ldots\lambda,\,\mu\nu}$ can always be chosen to be symmetric in the first l indices in addition to being symmetric in the last two indices. We shall represent the 2^l-pole density of a point singularity by

$$M_{i\alpha\beta\ldots\lambda,\mu\nu}(x^\varrho) = \int\limits_{-\infty}^{\infty} m_{i\alpha\beta\ldots\lambda,\mu\nu}(\tau_i)\,\delta^4(s_i^\varrho)\,d\tau_i \tag{15}$$

where δ^4 is a four-fold product of Dirac δ-functions.(1) The 2^l-pole moment $m_{i\alpha\beta\ldots\lambda,\mu\nu}$ has the same symmetry properties as $M_{i\alpha\beta\ldots\lambda,\mu\nu}$; its exact form remains to be determined.

Now we multiply Eq. (13) by a vector function $\xi^\nu(x^\varrho)$ and integrate over all x to obtain

$$\int \partial^\mu({}_1T^m_{\mu\nu} + {}_1T^f_{\mu\nu})\,\xi^\nu(x^\varrho)\,d^4x = 0\,. \tag{16}$$

ξ^ν is assumed to be completely arbitrary except for vanishing at the limits of the τ_i and x integrations together with all its derivatives.

As $\partial^\mu{}_1T^f_{\mu\nu}$ must vanish outside the singularities, we can assume it without loss of generality to be of the form

$$\sum_{i=1}^{N}\sum_{k=0}^{\infty}\int\limits_{-\infty}^{\infty} X_{i\alpha\beta\ldots\varkappa\nu}(\tau_i, x^\varrho)\,\partial^{\alpha\beta\ldots\varkappa}\,\delta^4(s_i^\varrho)\,d\tau_i \tag{17}$$

where the $X_{i\alpha\beta\ldots\varkappa\nu}$ are tensors of rank $k+1$ which can be assumed to be symmetric in their first k indices. Now we insert (17) and (14) into (16) and remove all the derivatives from $\delta^4(s_i^\varrho)$ by successive integrations by parts. We get

$$\begin{aligned}\sum_{i,l}(-1)^{l+1}\int m_{i\alpha\beta\ldots\lambda,\mu\nu}\,\partial^{\alpha\beta\ldots\lambda\mu}\,\xi^\nu(x^\varrho)\,\delta^4(s_i^\varrho)\,d^4x\,d\tau_i + \\ +\sum_{i,k}(-1)^k\int[\partial^{\alpha\beta\ldots\varkappa}X_{i\alpha\beta\ldots\varkappa\nu}(\tau_i, x^\varrho)\,\xi^\nu(x^\varrho) + k\partial^{\alpha\beta\ldots\varkappa-1}X_{i\alpha\beta\ldots\varkappa\nu}\,\partial^\varkappa\xi^\nu + \ldots \\ + X_{i\alpha\beta\ldots\varkappa\nu}\,\partial^{\alpha\beta\ldots\varkappa}\xi^\nu]\,\delta^4(s_i^\varrho)\,d^4x\,d\tau_i = 0\,.\end{aligned} \tag{18}$$

Now we carry out the x integration; then ξ^ν, $X_{i\alpha\beta\ldots\varkappa\nu}$ and their

(1) The representation of singular quantities by integrals of the type (15) is well known from special relativity [2]. Mathisson [14] did not make use of this representation and thus his derivation of the equation corresponding to Eq. (19) below (Eq. 9.4 of [14]) is much more cumbersome. It is also less easily applicable because he did not make use of a multipole expansion (17) for the force term.

derivatives, being evaluated at the positions $z_i^\varrho(\tau_i)$, become functions of the τ_i's. Thus we get

$$\sum_{i,l}(-1)^{l+1}\int m_{i\alpha\beta\ldots\lambda,\mu\nu}\,\partial^{\alpha\beta\ldots\lambda\mu}\xi^\nu(\tau_i)\,d\tau_i+$$
$$+\sum_{i,k}(-1)^k\int[\partial^{\alpha\beta\ldots\varkappa}X_{i\alpha\beta\ldots\varkappa\nu}(\tau_i)+k\,\partial^{\alpha\beta\ldots\varkappa-1}X_{i\alpha\beta\ldots\varkappa\nu}\partial^\varkappa+\ldots$$
$$+X_{i\alpha\beta\ldots\varkappa\nu}\partial^{\alpha\beta\ldots\varkappa}]\,\xi^\nu(\tau_i)\,d\tau_i=0\,. \qquad (19)$$

The tensors $X_{i\alpha\beta\ldots\varkappa\nu}$, unlike the $m_{i\alpha\beta\ldots\lambda,\mu\nu}$, are not symmetric in the last two indices. However, in all the terms in Eq. (19) in which ξ^ν is differentiated at least twice, they can be replaced by tensors $\overline{X}_{i\alpha\beta\ldots\varkappa\nu}$ which do possess this symmetry. We have

$$X_{i\alpha\beta\ldots\varrho\varkappa\nu}\partial^{\varrho\varkappa}=(X_{i\alpha\beta\ldots\varrho\varkappa\nu}+X_{i\alpha\beta\ldots\varrho\nu\varkappa}-X_{i\alpha\beta\ldots\varkappa\nu\varrho})\,\partial^{\varrho\varkappa}, \qquad (20)$$

because the last two terms are antisymmetric in ϱ and $\varkappa$ and ∂_i^ϱ is symmetric in these indices, and thus the contracted tensor vanishes. But the expression in parentheses is symmetric in $\varkappa$ and ν. Thus we can replace $X_{i\alpha\beta\ldots\varrho\varkappa\nu}$ by

$$\overline{X}_{i\alpha\beta\ldots\varrho\varkappa\nu}\equiv X_{i\alpha\beta\ldots\varrho\varkappa\nu}+X_{i\alpha\beta\ldots\varrho\nu\varkappa}-X_{i\alpha\beta\ldots\varkappa\nu\varrho} \qquad (21)$$

in all the terms of Eq. (19) involving two or more differentiations of ξ^ν. But then (changing dummy indices) these terms are of the same form as those in the first integral; as the $m_{i\alpha\beta\ldots\lambda,\mu\nu}$ are as yet undetermined, we can absorb the new $\partial^{\alpha\ldots\iota}\,\overline{X}_{i\alpha\ldots\iota\sigma\ldots\varrho\varkappa\nu}$ in the $m_{i\sigma\ldots\varrho,\varkappa\nu}$ of the same rank. In the terms involving a single differentiation $\partial^\varkappa$ of ξ^ν, we can similarly consider that part of $\partial^{\alpha\beta\ldots\varkappa-1}X_{i\alpha\beta\ldots\varkappa\nu}$ which is symmetric in $\varkappa$ and ν to be included in $m_{i\varkappa\nu}$.[1] Thus Eq. (19) is equivalent to

$$\sum_{i,l}(-1)^{l+1}\int m_{i\alpha\beta\ldots\lambda,\mu\nu}\,\partial^{\alpha\beta\ldots\lambda\mu}\xi^\nu d\tau_i+$$
$$+\sum_{i,k}(-1)^k\Big[\int\partial^{\alpha\beta\ldots\varkappa}X_{i\alpha\beta\ldots\varkappa\nu}\,\xi^\nu d\tau_i+$$
$$+k\int\partial^{\alpha\beta\ldots\varkappa-1}X_{i\alpha\beta\ldots[\varkappa\nu]}\partial^\varkappa\,\xi^\nu d\tau_i\Big]=0 \qquad (22)$$

---

(1) The above proof is patterned after one given by Mathisson (cf. [14], Sec. 9). However, it should be noted that our $X_{i\alpha\beta\ldots\varkappa\nu}$'s are defined differently than Mathisson's, which are not well suited for the description of the force terms due to the non-gravitational multipole moments.

where

$$X_{i\alpha\beta\ldots[\varkappa\nu]} \equiv \tfrac{1}{2}(X_{i\alpha\beta\ldots\varkappa\nu} - X_{i\alpha\beta\ldots\nu\varkappa}). \tag{23}$$

Now we proceed to obtain the equations of motion from Eq. (22). We first note that because of the arbitrariness of ξ^ν Eq. (22) has to be valid for each i separately. Furthermore it has been shown by Shanmugadhasan [16] that the equations of motion obtained from the resulting one-particle expression by considering terms up to order l in the first series are of the same form as those following from the first two terms alone.[1] We shall not repeat his proof here, but immediately consider the expression

$$\int\Big\{m_{i\alpha,\mu\nu}\partial^{\alpha\mu} - m_{i\mu\nu}\partial^\mu + \sum_k (-1)^k [\partial^{\alpha\beta\ldots\varkappa} X_{i\alpha\beta\ldots\varkappa\nu} + k\partial^{\alpha\beta\ldots\varkappa-1} X_{i\alpha\beta\ldots[\varkappa\nu]}\partial^\varkappa]\Big\}\xi^\nu(\tau_i)\,d\tau_i = 0\,. \tag{24}$$

As all subsequent considerations refer to a single particle, we shall drop the subscript i in the following.

An expression essentially equivalent to Eq. (24) has been discussed in Mathisson's posthumous paper [15] and, with a generalization the significance of which will be discussed later, by Shanmugadhasan [16], and we shall follow their procedure from here on. The difference between Eq. (24) and the equation considered by Mathisson is that in Eq. (24) the force terms appropriate for the description of non-gravitational multipoles have been made explicit and have been transformed from the original form (17) to an expression from which the equations of motion can be obtained readily, in analogy to the form used by Harish-Chandra [8] for the case of the neutral meson field. Mathisson, on the other hand, did not specify the force term obtained from the energy-momentum tensor ${}_1T^f_{\mu\nu}$ in as much detail as our Eq. (17), and thus on casual inspection of his paper one gets the mistaken impression that this term enters the final equation unchanged. This is actually not the case, but the modification necessary requires a reworking of his derivation in each particular case, whereas the derivation presented here treats the problem in full generality.

---

(1) In a paper by B. Średniawa [22] equations of motion of particles with a dipole moment $s^{\alpha\beta}$ and a quadrupole moment $k^{\lambda\alpha\beta}$ were derived by Mathisson's method, and it was claimed that these equations differ from those obtained by Mathisson. However, in Średniawa's final equations of motion the quadrupole moment enters only in the combination $k^{\lambda\alpha\beta}v_\lambda$ and in the same manner as $s^{\alpha\beta}$; as both $k^{\lambda\alpha\beta}v_\lambda$ and $s^{\alpha\beta}$ are antisymmetric in α and β, $k^{\lambda\alpha\beta}v_\lambda$ can be included in $s^{\alpha\beta}$, thus reducing the equations to Mathisson's.

Following Mathisson and Shanmugadhasan (except for minor changes in notation) we break up the tensors $m_{\mu\nu}$ and $m_{\alpha,\mu\nu}$ in components parallel and perpendicular to the four-velocity:

$$m_{\mu\nu} = {}^*m_{\mu\nu} + \tfrac{1}{2}(\bar{A}_\mu v_\nu + \bar{A}_\nu v_\mu) + M v_\mu v_\nu,$$

$${}^*m_{\mu\nu} = {}^*m_{\nu\mu}, \quad {}^*m_{\mu\nu} v^\nu = 0, \quad \bar{A}_\mu v^\mu = 0, \tag{25}$$

$$m_{\alpha,\mu\nu} = {}^*m_{\alpha,\mu\nu} + \tfrac{1}{2}(B_{\mu\alpha} v_\nu + B_{\nu\alpha} v_\mu) + p_\alpha v_\mu v_\nu,$$

$${}^*m_{\alpha,\mu\nu} = {}^*m_{\alpha,\nu\mu}, \quad {}^*m_{\alpha,\mu\nu} v^\alpha = 0, \quad {}^*m_{\alpha,\mu\nu} v^\nu = 0,$$

$$B_{\mu\alpha} v^\mu = 0, \quad B_{\mu\alpha} v^\alpha = 0, \quad p_\alpha v^\alpha = 0. \tag{26}$$

It is not necessary to include a component containing a factor v_α in $m_{\alpha,\mu\nu}$; as $v_\alpha \partial^\alpha = d/d\tau$, the term in Eq. (24) corresponding to this component can be transformed by an integration by parts to a form which, having the same symmetry properties, can be included in the monopole term described by (25). Similarly we have (changing dummy indices)

$$\int p_\alpha v_\mu v_\nu \partial^{\alpha\mu} \xi^\nu d\tau = \frac{1}{2} \int \frac{d}{d\tau} (p_\nu v_\mu - p_\mu v_\nu) \partial^\mu \xi^\nu d\tau -$$

$$- \frac{1}{2} \int \frac{d}{d\tau} (p_\nu v_\mu + p_\mu v_\nu) \partial^\mu \xi^\nu d\tau \tag{27}$$

where the last term again has the same symmetry properties as the monopole term and thus can be included in it. Furthermore we can perform an integration by parts in the part of the integral containing $B_{\nu\alpha} v_\mu$. Using these results, introducing the abbreviation

$$D_{\mu\nu} \equiv p_\nu v_\mu - p_\mu v_\nu, \tag{28}$$

and changing dummy indices, we can write Eq. (24) as

$$\int \Big\{ ({}^*m_{\alpha,\mu\nu} + \tfrac{1}{2} B_{\mu\alpha} v_\nu) \partial^{\alpha\mu} \xi^\nu - \Big[{}^*m_{\mu\nu} + \tfrac{1}{2}(\bar{A}_\mu v_\nu + \bar{A}_\nu v_\mu +$$

$$+ \dot{B}_{\nu\mu} - \dot{D}_{\mu\nu}) + M v_\mu v_\nu - \sum_k (-1)^k k \partial^{\alpha\beta\ldots\varkappa-1} X_{\alpha\beta\ldots[\mu\nu]} \Big] \partial^\mu \xi^\nu +$$

$$+ \sum_k (-1)^k \partial^{\alpha\beta\ldots\varkappa} X_{\alpha\beta\ldots\varkappa\nu} \xi^\nu \Big\} d\tau = 0. \tag{29}$$

Because of the arbitrariness of ξ^ν the part of the integral involving $\partial^{\alpha\mu}\xi^\nu$ must vanish separately, which implies

$${}^*m_{\alpha,\mu\nu} + {}^*m_{\mu,\alpha\nu} + \tfrac{1}{2} v_\nu (B_{\mu\alpha} + B_{\alpha\mu}) = 0, \tag{30}$$

from which we obtain by contraction with v^ν

$$B_{\mu\alpha} = -B_{\alpha\mu}. \tag{31}$$

But then Eq. (30) requires that $^*m_{\alpha,\mu\nu}$ be antisymmetric in α and μ, which because of the symmetry in μ and ν implies that

$$^*m_{\alpha,\mu\nu} = 0. \tag{32}$$

By (23), (28) and (31) the tensor

$$Y_{\mu\nu} \equiv \tfrac{1}{2}(\dot{B}_{\mu\nu} + \dot{D}_{\mu\nu}) + \sum_k (-1)^k k\, \partial^{\alpha\beta\ldots\varkappa-1} X_{\alpha\beta\ldots[\mu\nu]} \tag{33}$$

is antisymmetric; we break it up as

$$Y_{\mu\nu} = {}^*Y_{\mu\nu} + Y_\mu v_\nu - Y_\nu v_\mu,$$

$$^*Y_{\mu\nu} = -{}^*Y_{\nu\mu}, \quad {}^*Y_{\mu\nu} v^\nu = 0, \quad Y_\mu v^\mu = 0. \tag{34}$$

Introducing this into Eq. (29), integrating all terms containing a factor v_μ by parts, and dropping the term involving $\partial^{\alpha\mu}\xi^\nu$ as discussed above, we obtain

$$\int \Big\{ -({}^*m_{\mu\nu} - {}^*Y_{\mu\nu} + \tfrac{1}{2}\bar{A}_\mu v_\nu - Y_\mu v_\nu)\partial^\mu \xi^\nu + \\ + \Big[\sum_k (-1)^k \partial^{\alpha\beta\ldots\varkappa} X_{\alpha\beta\ldots\varkappa\nu} + \frac{d}{d\tau}\Big(Mv_\nu + \tfrac{1}{2}\bar{A}_\nu + Y_\nu\Big)\Big]\xi^\nu \Big\} d\tau = 0. \tag{35}$$

Because of the arbitrariness of ξ^ν the two parts of this integral must vanish separately and thus

$$^*m_{\mu\nu} - {}^*Y_{\mu\nu} + \tfrac{1}{2}\bar{A}_\mu v_\nu - Y_\mu v_\nu = 0, \tag{36}$$

$$\sum_k (-1)^k \partial^{\alpha\beta\ldots\varkappa} X_{\alpha\beta\ldots\varkappa\nu} + \frac{d}{d\tau}\Big(Mv_\nu + \tfrac{1}{2}\bar{A}_\nu + Y_\nu\Big) = 0. \tag{37}$$

Contracting Eq. (36) with v^ν we obtain

$$\tfrac{1}{2}\bar{A}_\nu - Y_\nu = 0 \tag{38}$$

and thus Eq. (37) reduces to

$$\frac{d}{d\tau}(Mv_\nu + \bar{A}_\nu) = \sum_k (-1)^{k+1} \partial^{\alpha\beta\ldots\varkappa} X_{\alpha\beta\ldots\varkappa\nu}. \tag{39}$$

From Eqs (36) and (38) we conclude because of the different symmetry properties of $^*m_{\mu\nu}$ and $^*Y_{\mu\nu}$ that

$$^*m_{\mu\nu} = 0, \tag{40}$$

$$^*Y_{\mu\nu} = 0. \tag{41}$$

Inserting Eq. (34) with (38) and (41) into (33), we obtain

$$\dot{B}_{\mu\nu}+\dot{D}_{\mu\nu}=2\sum_{k}(-1)^{k+1}k\partial^{\alpha\beta\ldots\varkappa-1}X_{\alpha\beta\ldots[\mu\nu]}+\bar{A}_{\mu}v_{\nu}-\bar{A}_{\nu}v_{\mu}. \qquad (42)$$

Eqs (39) and (42) are our final equations of motion. The quantities $B_{\mu\nu}$ and $D_{\mu\nu}$ are antisymmetric by (28) and (31), and $B_{\mu\nu}$ and $\bar{A}_{\nu}$ are orthogonal to v^{ν} by (25) and (26); no further restrictions are imposed.

In the above calculations we have treated the tensors $X_{\alpha\beta\ldots\varkappa\nu}$ and their derivatives as if they were finite, although in general they contain infinite contributions. However, it has been shown by Mathisson [14] and by Bhabha and Harish-Chandra [7] that these infinite contributions can be removed by a suitable redefinition of the quantities characterizing the energy-momentum tensor ${}_1T^{m}_{\mu\nu}$ of the particles. Thus it is always possible to obtain a set of equations of motion (39) and (42) which is finite. The explicit form of the $X_{\alpha\beta\ldots\varkappa\nu}$ entering these equations depends on the particular equations satisfied by the non-gravitational fields; examples are discussed in the Appendix.

III. DISCUSSION

A tentative interpretation of the quantities M, $B_{\mu\nu}$ and p_{α} was given by Mathisson [15] on the basis of a comparison with the theory of an extended body. He suggested that M should be interpreted as the mass and $B_{\mu\nu}$ as the angular momentum of the particle, and that p_{α} should be taken as zero if the center of mass of the particle was to be on its world line; thus he omitted the terms with p_{α} from the outset and arrived at a result corresponding to Eq. (42) with $D_{\mu\nu}=0$. A similar interpretation had been given earlier by Lubański [23] in a paper establishing the equations of motion of the linearized general theory of relativity without non-gravitational fields by a slightly different method. On the other hand, Shanmugadhasan [16] carried through the calculation without setting p_{α} or $D_{\mu\nu}$ equal to zero; he did not discuss the significance of this assumption, however.

In the absence of non-gravitational fields the analysis and interpretation given by Lubański and Mathisson appears to be well founded and convincing. On putting $p_{\alpha}=0$, Eqs (39) and (42) can be easily reduced to Lubański's equations (1)

(1) Lubański's $n_{\mu\nu}$ corresponds to $2B_{\mu\nu}$.

$$\frac{d}{d\tau}(Mv_\nu + \dot{B}_{\nu\mu}v^\mu) = 0, \tag{43}$$

$$B_{\mu\nu} - B_{\nu\alpha}\dot{v}^\alpha v_\mu + B_{\mu\alpha}\dot{v}^\alpha v_\nu = 0. \tag{44}$$

These equations imply

$$\dot{M} = 0, \tag{45}$$

$$B^{\mu\nu}\dot{B}_{\mu\nu} = 0. \tag{46}$$

Eqs (43) and (44) impose well-defined restrictions on the motion of the particle, although they do not force it to move with constant velocity. On the other hand, if the term $\dot{D}_{\mu\nu}$ is not dropped from Eqs (39) and (42) (without the force terms) these equations do not imply any restrictions whatever on the motion. From Eq. (39) we get

$$Mv_\nu + \bar{A}_\nu = C_\nu, \tag{47}$$

where C_ν is an arbitrary constant vector; substituting this into Eq. (42) and integrating we obtain

$$B_{\mu\nu} + D_{\mu\nu} = C_\mu z_\nu - C_\nu z_\mu + K_{\mu\nu}, \tag{48}$$

where $K_{\mu\nu}$ is an arbitrary constant antisymmetric tensor. As no restriction has been imposed on the sum $B_{\mu\nu} + D_{\mu\nu}$ (as contrasted to $B_{\mu\nu}$ alone) in the derivation of the equations of motion, Eq. (48) is compatible with an arbitrary motion $z_\mu(\tau)$ of the particle. If the motion is not to be arbitrary, some condition on $B_{\mu\nu} + D_{\mu\nu}$ would have to be postulated.

Such a condition suggests itself naturally if one considers a description of a particle as a singularity only as an approximate representation of an extended body, as stressed by Møller [24] and Tulczyjew.(1) In particular it was noted by Møller that a classical system with a positive energy density, a given intrinsic angular momentum and a given rest mass must always have a finite extension(2) and that for such a body Eqs (43) and (44) would describe the motion of "false" centers of gravity rather than of the actual center. However, this does not preclude a consistent theory of point particles, which are supposed to be fully described by the quantities introduced above, and whose position is defined unambiguously from the fact that they are true singularities of both the

(1) I am indebted to Dr Tulczyjew for many pleasant and stimulating discussions on this question.

(2) Compare also A. Papapetrou [25]; an earlier paper [26], mentioned by Møller, was not accessible to me.

gravitational and the non-gravitational fields; for such particles Eqs (43) and (44) are legitimate equations of motion even though they allow solutions other than those expected from analogy with the theory of an extended body. Such an interpretation also implies that these equations are applicable to particles which are fully characterized by a *finite* number of multipole moments of the non-gravitational fields, whereas the exact description of an extended, necessarily non-rigid, body requires the full *infinite* series (17).

Møller's observation is closely related to the early objections raised against the concept of an electron with spin as requiring surface speeds exceeding that of light. Although an adequate description of such an electron—as of all elementary particles—can only be given by quantum theory, an approximate description adequate for many purposes is provided by the classical analogue, a point particle possessing both mass and intrinsic angular momentum. Much information can be obtained by comparatively simple methods from the investigation of such singularities of electromagnetic or meson fields [11]. It is this study of classical *analogues* (i.e. structures possessing dynamical variables analogous to those appearing in the quantum mechanical description) which I believe to be able to provide some insight into elementary particle physics rather than the study of classical *models*[1] (i.e. structures designed to correspond in detail to features such as "Zitterbewegung" of the quantum mechanical description).

Thus we consider the objects described by the equations of motion (39) and (42) as true singularities, fully characterized by a finite number of parameters. As already realized by Mathisson [15], no adequate interpretation of the dynamical variables appearing in these equations can be given on the basis of comparison with extended bodies, but rather the interpretation must take into account that these equations are "the only firm basis of our knowledge of what the dynamical quantities *are*".

In the spirit expressed by this quotation, Mathisson's original interpretation appears to require some modification in the presence of non-gravitational fields. Then the quantities appearing on the left hand side of the equations of motion no longer have an unambiguous meaning as "particle" properties (originating in the matter tensor $T^{m}_{\mu\nu}$) as opposed to the "force" terms (originating in the field tensor $T^{f}_{\mu\nu}$): the "particle" quantities have been redefined in the course of the derivation both to include field terms with the same

---

(1) For a review of such work see H. Hönl [27].

symmetry properties and to compensate for infinities in the original force terms. Thus only the equations of motion characteristic of the interacting system are unambiguous, but the interpretation of a part of the terms by analogy with quantities appearing in a theory involving a matter tensor only must contain an element of arbitrariness. A modification of Mathisson's interpretation of M as the mass suggests itself from the fact that in general M can not be shown to be constant; on the other hand, in all the cases investigated in which a consistent set of equations of motion was obtained for particular fields [8]–[10] it was found that M contains a constant part m (equal to the value of M in the absence of the non-gravitational fields). Thus it appears that it is this quantity which should properly be interpreted as the mass of the particle. But then Mathisson's argument for setting $D_{\mu\nu}$ equal to zero is no longer valid; all we can conclude from it is that $D_{\mu\nu}$ should vanish in the absence of non-gravitational fields. Therefore we consider $B_{\mu\nu}$ as the intrinsic angular momentum of the particle, and $D_{\mu\nu}$ as a field-dependent ("induced") angular momentum [10].

Regardless of the presence of such an induced angular momentum, Eq. (46) is no longer a necessary consequence of the equations of motion. If the theory presented here should give a classical analogue of elementary particles, it appears natural to require that the magnitude of the intrinsic angular momentum should be constant, however. Therefore it has been postulated in most recent studies [8]–[10] that Eq. (46) should be maintained even in the presence of non-gravitational fields.

It might be thought that the constancy of $B_{\mu\nu}$ should be a consequence of the conservation of angular momentum. However, angular momentum can be exchanged between the particles and the non-gravitational fields, and the overall conservation of this quantity is expressed by the rotational equation of motion (42). It has been shown by Shanmugadhasan [16] that this equation can indeed be derived directly from the angular momentum conservation law; however, it should be noted that Mathisson's method leads directly from the law of conservation of energy-momentum (13) to Eq. (42), without necessitating the explicit consideration of angular momentum.

This is due to the fact that conservation of angular momentum is implied by the existence of a conserved energy-momentum tensor if only this tensor is symmetric; but the symmetry of the total $T_{\mu\nu}$ is required by the fundamental equation (6) of the general theory of relativity. On the other hand, non-gravitational fields of zero rest mass satisfy further conservation laws [28] [29] which similarly correspond to special properties of the energy-momentum tensor (vanishing of its trace for all but a scalar field); nevertheless, these conservation laws are not maintained in the presence of particles (and do not affect the equations of motion) because these special properties are not imposed on the total $T_{\mu\nu}$ by the requirements of general relativity [12].

Although, as noted before, there is no clear-cut separation between "particle" and "force" terms in the equations of motion (39) and (42), no consistent set of equations could have been obtained by omitting the matter tensor from the conservation law (13). The divergence of the usual energy-momentum tensor of any non-gravitational field considered in the special theory of relativity is infinite at the position of the singularities of the field and some "particle" properties are needed to compensate for these; if this difficulty is circumvented by the use of some modified energy-momentum tensors with finite divergence [30] [31], one obtains some algebraic relations between the field components at the position of the particles, which cannot in general be satisfied, rather than a set of differential equations, if no particle properties are introduced. Thus the inclusion of the matter tensor ${}_1T^m_{\mu\nu}$ in (13) is essential to obtain the special relativistic equations of motion: the inertial properties of the particles in the special theory of relativity are a consequence of the gravitational properties ascribed to the particles by the general theory.[1]

Of these properties only the gravitational monopole and dipole moments (25) and (26) appear in the equations of motion explicitly. The higher multipole moments lead to equations of the same form; this follows from the work of Shanmugadhasan [16] mentioned before, although this author did not consider the gravitational significance of the moments.

As noted in Sec. II, we assumed that the first non-vanishing terms in the expansions (9) and (10) of $T^m_{\mu\nu}$ and $T^f_{\mu\nu}$ are both of first order. The equations of motion implied by this assumption are integrability conditions for the first-order linearized equation (12) for the metric. However, this metric does not appear in the equations of motion, which thus are special relativistic.[2] From the discussion

[1] For similar conclusions concerning mass only see C. Møller [32].

[2] A similar conclusion was reached by A. Papapetrou and H. Hönl [33]; however, the considerations of these authors were not independent of a coordinate condition, and they did not prove that the equations of motion are a consequence of the conservation law (13).

above it is clear that no consistent results can be obtained at all if it is assumed that the expansion for $T^m_{\mu\nu}$ starts with a term of higher order than that for $T^f_{\mu\nu}$. We may, on the other hand, assume that the expansion for $T^f_{\mu\nu}$ starts with a term of higher order than that for $T^m_{\mu\nu}$. Then the first-order linearized theory (12) leads to a set of equations of motion (43) and (44) without any interaction. Equations of motion containing interactions can only be obtained by going to higher orders of approximation; these equations necessarily contain gravitational interactions in addition to the non-gravitational ones, and thus, though Lorentz-invariant, they involve a metric tensor which is no longer Minkowskian.[1]

Thus the assumption used in Eqs (9) and (10) is the only possible one which allows a derivation of equations of motion containing non-gravitational interactions without leaving the framework of the first-order linearized theory; the equations of motion implied by the linearized theory of general relativity do not transcend the metric framework of the special theory.

Discussions on several points with Drs J. N. Goldberg and W. Tulczyjew and with Mr J. Stachel are gratefully acknowledged.

APPENDIX: EXAMPLES

We first consider the case of a neutral spin zero meson field described by a scalar or pseudoscalar potential U. Then [8]

$$\partial^\mu{}_1 T^f_{\mu\nu} = \sum_{i,k} \int \partial_\nu U(x^\varrho) S_{i\alpha\beta\ldots\varkappa}(\tau_i) \partial^{\alpha\beta\ldots\varkappa} \delta^4(s_i{}^\varrho) d\tau_i \tag{49}$$

where the symmetric tensor $S_{i\alpha\beta\ldots\varkappa}$ of rank k is the 2^k-pole moment of the ith singularity. By comparison with Eq. (17) we have

$$X_{i\alpha\beta\ldots\varkappa\nu} = S_{i\,\alpha\beta\ldots\varkappa} \partial_\nu U\,. \tag{50}$$

Therefore Eqs (39) and (42) become

$$\frac{d}{d\tau}(Mv_\nu + \bar{A}_\nu) = \sum_k (-1)^{k+1} S_{\alpha\beta\ldots\varkappa} \partial_\nu{}^{\alpha\beta\ldots\varkappa} U\,, \tag{51}$$

$$\begin{aligned}\dot{B}_{\mu\nu} + \dot{D}_{\mu\nu} = \sum_k k(-1)^{k+1} (S_{\alpha\beta\ldots\varkappa-1\mu} \partial_\nu{}^{\alpha\beta\ldots\varkappa-1} U - S_{\alpha\beta\ldots\varkappa-1\nu} \partial_\mu{}^{\alpha\beta\ldots\varkappa-1} U) + \\ + \bar{A}_\mu v_\nu - \bar{A}_\nu v_\mu\,,\end{aligned} \tag{52}$$

---

(1) See P. Havas [34]; a paper on the derivation of the equations of motion containing gravitational interactions only, prepared jointly with J. N. Goldberg, will be published shortly, and a detailed account of the work involving non-gravitational interactions is in preparation.

which (except for minor changes in notation) are the equations of motion obtained by Harish-Chandra [8]. For the reasons discussed in Sec. III we impose the condition (46) on the angular momentum tensor $B_{\mu\nu}$. As discussed in references [9] and [10], a well determined problem can then be obtained by demanding that no new dynamical variables, but only a set of coupling constants, should be introduced through the multipole moments $S_{\alpha\beta\ldots\varkappa}$; forms of $S_{\alpha\beta\ldots\varkappa}$ have been determined for all k which (separately or conjointly) are compatible with all the requirements imposed both in the absence [9] and in the presence [10] of an induced angular momentum $D_{\mu\nu}$.

Now we consider the case of a neutral meson field of non zero rest mass and spin, with the generalized interaction introduced recently [5]. For simplicity we immediately consider the case $q = 1$, to which all equivalent cases can be reduced. Then the field of spin s is described by a symmetric tensor $U_{\alpha\beta\ldots\sigma}$ of rank s and the 2^k-pole moment of the ith singularity of this field by a tensor $S_{i\alpha\ldots\varkappa,\ldots\sigma}$ of rank $k+s$ symmetric in the first k and in the last s indices; combining Eqs (31), (35) and (36) of reference [5] we have

$$\partial^{\mu}{}_1 T^f{}_{\mu\nu} = \sum_{i,k} \int \Big\{ (\partial_\sigma U_{\ldots\lambda\nu} - \partial_\nu U_{\ldots\lambda\sigma}) \times \\ \times \Big[S_i{}^{\alpha\beta\ldots\varkappa,\ldots\lambda\sigma} \partial_{\alpha\beta\ldots\varkappa} + \frac{s-1}{\chi^2} S_i{}^{\alpha\beta\ldots\varkappa,\ldots\varrho\sigma} \partial^\lambda_{\alpha\beta\ldots\varkappa\varrho} \Big] + \\ + U_{\ldots\lambda\nu} S_i{}^{\alpha\beta\ldots\varkappa,\ldots\lambda\sigma} \partial_{\alpha\beta\ldots\varkappa\sigma} \Big\} \, \delta^4(s_i{}^\varrho)\, d\tau_i \qquad (53)$$

where χ is a constant with the dimensions of reciprocal length. We note that a term with a given value of k in the general expression (17) corresponds to several terms with different values of k in (53). Furthermore $X_{i\alpha\beta\ldots\varkappa\nu}$ in (17) is defined to be symmetric in its first k indices, and thus we would have to symmetrize the second and third term in (53). However, the final equations of motion (39) and (42) depend on an explicit symmetrization only through the factor k in Eq. (42) originating in the integration by parts (18). In the present case it is simpler to trace through the effect of the non-symmetry in Eq. (53) than to rewrite it in symmetrized form. This is due to the fact that the derivatives of the field quantities in the equations of motion can be simplified by use of the field equations satisfied by $U_{\alpha\beta\ldots\sigma}$. The derivative $\partial^\alpha U_{\alpha\beta\ldots\sigma}$ vanishes everywhere outside the singularities; at the ith singularity there is a singular contribution due to $S_{i\alpha\beta\ldots\varkappa,\ldots\sigma}$, which however can be removed by redefinition of the particle quantities, as discussed at the end of Sec. II. Thus we can omit all the terms involving $\partial^\alpha U_{\alpha\beta\ldots\sigma}$ from the equations of motion. Therefore the term proportional to $s-1$ in Eq. (53) does not contribute to the translational equation of motion (39), which reduces to

$$\frac{d}{d\tau}(Mv_\nu + \bar{A}_\nu) = \sum_k (-1)^k S^{\alpha\beta\ldots\varkappa,\ldots\sigma}\partial_{\alpha\beta\ldots\varkappa\nu} U_{\ldots\sigma}. \tag{54}$$

In the rotational equation of motion (42) we note that the last term of Eq. (53) contributes an extra term due to the unsymmetrized index σ. The term proportional to $s-1$ contributes only a single term after integration by parts, as all the terms containing a $\partial^{\cdots\lambda} U_{\ldots\lambda}$ vanish as discussed above. Thus we get

$$\begin{aligned}\dot{B}_{\mu\nu} + \dot{D}_{\mu\nu} = \sum_k (-1)^k [k(S_{\mu\beta\ldots\varkappa,\ldots\sigma}\partial_\nu^{\beta\ldots\varkappa} U^{\ldots\sigma} - S_{\nu\beta\ldots\varkappa,\ldots\sigma}\partial_\mu^{\beta\ldots\varkappa} U^{\ldots\sigma}) + \\ + S_{\alpha\beta\ldots\varkappa,\ldots\mu}\partial^{\alpha\beta\ldots\varkappa} U_\nu^{\cdots} - S_{\alpha\beta\ldots\varkappa,\ldots\nu}\partial^{\alpha\beta\ldots\varkappa} U_\mu^{\cdots}] + \\ + \sum_k (-1)^{k+1}\frac{s-1}{\chi^2} S^{\alpha\beta\ldots\varkappa,\ldots\varrho}\partial_{\alpha\beta\ldots\varkappa\varrho}(\partial_\mu U_{\ldots\nu} - \partial_\nu U_{\ldots\mu}) + \\ + \bar{A}_\mu v_\nu - \bar{A}_\nu v_\mu .\end{aligned} \tag{55}$$

Except for minor changes in notation, these are the equations of motion (38) and (45) of [5]. The equations of motion obtained by using the interactions proposed by Harish-Chandra [8] (which are those required for fields of zero rest mass) are special cases of Eqs (54) and (55).

Forms of the multipole moments compatible with the same requirements as were imposed in the case $s = 0$ have been determined in the case $s = 1$ for all k [10]. For $s \geqslant 2$ it is impossible to satisfy all these requirements. (1)

The extension of the theory to linear charged and charge-symmetric meson fields given in [5], [8], and [10] will not be repeated here. If the interaction between the electromagnetic fields and the charged meson fields is taken into account, the field equations become non-linear. The explicit determination of the forms of the multipole moments of such fields from the general equations of motion (39) and (42) will be given elsewhere.

---

(1) See P. Havas [35]; a detailed account is in preparation.

REFERENCES

[1] H. A. LORENTZ, *Collected Papers* (M. Nijhoff, The Hague, 1936), Vol. II, pp. 281 and 343; *The Theory of Electrons* (B. G. Teubner, Leipzig 1909), pp. 49 and 253.

[2] P. A. M. DIRAC, *Proc. Roy. Soc.* A**167**, 148 (1938).

[3] H. J. BHABHA and HARISH-CHANDRA, *Proc. Roy. Soc.* A**185**, 250 (1946).

[4] K. J. LECOUTEUR, *Proc. Camb. Phil. Soc.* **45**, 429 (1949).

[5] P. HAVAS, *Phys. Rev.* **113**, 732 (1959).

[6] H. J. BHABHA, *Proc. Indian Acad. Sci.* A**10**, 324 (1939).

[7] H. J. BHABHA and HARISH-CHANDRA, *Proc. Roy. Soc.* A**183**, 134 (1944).

[8] HARISH-CHANDRA, *Proc. Roy. Soc.* A**185**, 269 (1946).

[9] P. HAVAS, *Phys. Rev.* **93**, 1400 (1954).

[10] P. HAVAS, *Phys. Rev.* **116**, (1959)

[11] P. HAVAS, Classical Relativistic Theory of Elementary Particles, *"Argonne National Laboratory Summer Lectures on Theoretical Physics, 1958"*, ANL-5982, p. 124.

[12] P. HAVAS, *Phys. Rev.* **87**, 898 (1952).

[13] H. J. BHABHA and H. C. CORBEN, *Proc. Roy. Soc.* A**178**, 273 (1941).

[14] M. MATHISSON, *Proc. Camb. Phil. Soc.* **36**, 331 (1940).

[15] M. MATHISSON, *Proc. Camb. Phil. Soc.* **38**, 40 (1942).

[16] S. SHANMUGADHASAN, *Proc. Camb. Phil. Soc.* **42**, 54 (1946).

[17] A. E. SCHEIDEGGER, *Helv. Phys. Acta* **23**, 740 (1950).

[18] A. EINSTEIN, L. INFELD and B. HOFFMANN, *Ann. Math.* **39**, 65 (1938).

[19] L. INFELD and P. R. WALLACE, *Phys. Rev.* **57**, 797 (1940).

[20] F. R. CROWNFIELD, JR. and P. HAVAS, *Phys. Rev.* **94**, 471 (1954).

[21] A. EINSTEIN, *S.B. Preuss. Akad. Wiss.* 688 (1916).

[22] B. ŚREDNIAWA, *Acta Phys. Polon.* **9**, 99 (1948).

[23] J. LUBAŃSKI, *Acta Phys. Polon.* **6**, 356 (1937).

[24] C. MØLLER, *Comm. Dublin Inst. f. Adv. Studies*, Series A, No. 5 (1949).

[25] A. PAPAPETROU, *Spezielle Relativitätstheorie* (VEB Deutscher Verlag der Wissenschaften, Berlin 1955), Ch. V.

[26] A. PAPAPETROU, *Prahliha de l'Acad. d'Athènes* **14**, 540 (1939).

[27] H. HÖNL, *Ergebn. Exakt. Naturw.* **26**, 291 (1952).

[28] J. A. MCLENNAN, JR. and P. HAVAS, *Phys. Rev.* **87**, 898 (1952).

[29] J. A. MCLENNAN, JR., *Nuovo Cim.* **3**, 1360 (1956).

[30] M. H. L. PRYCE, *Proc. Roy. Soc.* A**168**, 389 (1938).

[31] HARISH-CHANDRA, *Proc. Roy. Soc.* A**183**, 142 (1945).

[32] C. MØLLER, *K. Norske Vidensk. Selsk. Forh.* **31**, No. 14 (1958).

[33] A. PAPAPETROU and H. HÖNL, *Z. Phys.* **114**, 484 (1939).

[34] P. HAVAS, *Phys. Rev.* **108**, 1351 (1957).

[35] P. HAVAS, *Bull. Amer. Phys. Soc.* II, **2**, 189 (1957).

ON THE EXTENSION OF BIRKHOFF'S THEOREM TO THE CASE IN WHICH AN ELECTROMAGNETIC FIELD IS PRESENT

B. HOFFMANN

*Queen's College, Flushing, N. Y., (U. S. A)**

I

IN 1932 I showed [1], [2] that in the general theory of relativity the spherically symmetric field of gravitation and electromagnetism must be static, thus generalizing the well known theorem of G. D. Birkhoff [3], [4] according to which the spherically symmetric field of gravitation alone must be static.

I return to this matter now for two reasons: to correct a minor error in my former proof, and to add for completeness a special case that I had overlooked, the existence of which was brought to my attention by Ivor Robinson.

II

In [1], at the bottom of page 233, the following equation was obtained:

$$\frac{\partial L}{\partial \varphi} + F_{12} \cos \theta = 0 \tag{1}$$

where, as was previously established, L and F_{12} are independent of θ. On page 234 the conclusion was correctly drawn that F_{12} must therefore be zero. But the argument was then made that from the equation

$$F_{13} = L \sin \theta \tag{2}$$

* This work was done while the author was on leave at the University of London, King's College. It was assisted by Wright ADC., ARDC., USAF through the European Office.

(there numbered equation (15)) it followed that F_{13} was zero. However, if $F_{12} = 0$, (2) shows only that L is independent of φ; it could be a constant, therefore, and need not be zero.

To show that F_{13} is indeed zero, we go to the field equation $\Phi(123)$, namely

$$\frac{\partial F_{13}}{\partial \theta} - \frac{\partial F_{12}}{\partial \varphi} = 0 . \qquad \Phi(123)$$

For, with F_{12} equal to zero, this shows that F_{13} is independent of θ, which would contradict (2) unless L was zero, and thus F_{13} itself zero.

III

Ivor Robinson pointed out to me that there was an exceptional case that I did not discuss, namely the case in which the line element

$$ds^2 = A(r, t)\,dt^2 - B(r, t)\,dr^2 - C(r, t)(d\theta^2 + \sin^2\theta\, d\varphi^2) \qquad (3)$$

is such that C is a constant. For in this case one can not make the transformation (16) on page 234 of [1] that reduces the line element to the form (1)

$$ds^2 = A(r)\,dt^2 - B(r)\,dr^2 - r^2(d\theta^2 + \sin^2\theta\, d\varphi^2).$$

This special case does not lead to a non-static gravitational field, for the conditions for a static gravitational field found by Eiesland [4], and used in my proof, still apply to this case. However, the spherically symmetric field in this case is not included as a special case of the "most general" such field given on page 235 of [1] and, when a cosmological term is present, on page 182 of [2]. We may obtain the field for this special case as follows.

Since we know that the gravitational part of the field is static, we may, by a suitable transformation of r and t, reduce the line element (3), for the case in which C is independent of the coordinates, to the form (1)

$$ds^2 = A(r)\,dt^2 - B(r)\,dr^2 - h^2(d\theta^2 + \sin^2\theta\, d\varphi^2) \qquad (4)$$

where we have written h^2 for the constant C. By a further transformation of r alone we can reduce $B(r)$ to unity, thus obtaining the form (1)

$$ds^2 = A(r)\,dt^2 - dr^2 - h^2(d\theta^2 + \sin^2\theta\, d\varphi^2). \qquad (5)$$

---

(1) Here r, t, A, B are not the same quantities as before but their transformed counterparts.

For this line element the field equations denoted by $\Phi'(\mathrm{ab})$ in [2] yield

$$\frac{F_{14}^{2}}{A}+\frac{F_{23}^{2}}{h^{2}\sin^{2}\theta}=2\left(\frac{1}{h^{2}}-\lambda\right), \qquad \Phi'(11),\ \Phi'(44)$$

$$\frac{F_{14}^{2}}{A}+\frac{F_{23}^{2}}{h^{2}\sin^{2}\theta}=\frac{A''}{A}-\frac{1}{2}\frac{A'^{2}}{A^{2}}+2\lambda \qquad \Phi'(22),\ \Phi'(33)$$

where λ is the cosmological constant, and dashes denote derivatives with respect to r. Also the field equations there denoted by $\Phi(\mathrm{a})$, $\Phi(\mathrm{abc})$ yield respectively

$$\left.\begin{aligned}\frac{\partial}{\partial\theta}\left\{\frac{F_{23}}{h\sin\theta}\right\}=0, \quad \frac{\partial}{\partial r}\left\{\frac{F_{14}}{\sqrt{A}}\right\}=0,\\ \frac{\partial F_{23}}{\partial\varphi}=0, \quad \frac{\partial F_{14}}{\partial t}=0\end{aligned}\right| \qquad \Phi(\mathrm{a})$$

and

$$\frac{\partial F_{23}}{\partial t}=0, \quad \frac{\partial F_{23}}{\partial r}=0, \quad \frac{\partial F_{14}}{\partial\varphi}=0, \quad \frac{\partial F_{14}}{\partial\theta}=0. \qquad \Phi(\mathrm{abc})$$

From these we easily find that

$$\frac{F_{14}}{\sqrt{A}}=\alpha, \quad \frac{F_{23}}{h\sin\theta}=\beta \tag{6}$$

where α, β are independent of the coordinates and satisfy the relation

$$\alpha^{2}+\beta^{2}=2\left(\frac{1}{h^{2}}-\lambda\right). \tag{7}$$

The electromagnetic part of the field is thus also static. Further, from $\Phi'(11)$ and $\Phi'(22)$ we have

$$\frac{A''}{A}-\frac{1}{2}\frac{A'^{2}}{A^{2}}=\frac{2}{h^{2}}-4\lambda \quad \left(=\frac{k^{2}}{2},\ \text{say}\right), \tag{8}$$

and this leads to the result that

$$A=a^{2}\cosh^{2}\frac{kr+b}{2} \tag{9}$$

where a, b are constants of integration. Then (6) gives

$$F_{14}=\alpha a\cosh\frac{kr+b}{2}, \quad F_{23}=h\beta\sin\theta, \tag{10}$$

and the whole solution is given by (5), (7), (9) and (10), with k defined in (8).

Though F_{14} and F_{23} depend on the coordinates, they actually represent uniform electric and magnetic fields respectively. For the physically important quantities are not F_{14}, F_{23} but $(g^{11}g_{44}F_{14}F_{14})^{\frac{1}{2}}$ and $(g^{22}g^{33}F_{23}F_{23})^{\frac{1}{2}}$ which represent respectively the magnitudes of the corresponding electric and magnetic fields. These magnitudes are just the constants α and β, as is clear from (6).

A different form of the above field was obtained by Robinson [5] for the case in which the cosmological constant is zero. I learned at the Royaumont Conference that B. Bertotti had independently obtained the field for the cosmological case, but I do not know whether it has the same form as that given here.

I am happy to have this opportunity to salute Professor Leopold Infeld. It is a pleasure to thank Professor H. Bondi for inviting me to work with him and the stimulating group that he has gathered around him at the University of London, King's College, and I am particularly indebted here to Ivor Robinson for interesting discussions and suggestions. I am grateful, too, to the USAF for their financial support, which enabled me to be in London.

REFERENCES

[1] B. Hoffmann, On the Spherically Symmetric Field in Relativity, *Quart. J. Math.* **3**, 226–37 (1932).

[2] B. Hoffmann, On the Spherically Symmetric Field in Relativity, II, *Quart. J. Math.* **4**, 179–183 (1933).

[3] G. D. Birkhoff, *Relativity and Modern Physics,* Harvard, p. 253, § 7.

[4] J. Eiesland, The Group of Motions of an Einstein Space, *Trans. Amer. Math. Soc.* **27**, 213–245 (1925).

[5] I. Robinson, A Solution of the Maxwell–Einstein Equations, *Bull, Acad. Sci. Polon.* Cl. III, **7**, 351 (1959).

EMPIRICAL CONFIRMATION OF DIRAC'S HYPOTHESIS OF DIMINISHING GRAVITATION

P. JORDAN

University of Hamburg, Hamburg

A DISCUSSION of empirical facts concerning not only astronomy and astrophysics but also geophysics, geology and paleoclimatology may seem to be a little outside the frame of a book dealing chiefly with mathematical problems of relativity. But surely the question whether Dirac's hypothesis of diminishing gravitation is supported or is not supported empirically is of great importance for natural science on the whole and for general relativity in particular. This importance is — though indirectly — also acknowledged by those authors who are inclined to think that this hypothesis would be too improbable to deserve much attention. These authors accept the hypothesis alternative to Dirac's — that of the constancy of gravitation — as a fundamental law of nature.

According to Dirac's hypothesis the "constant" of gravitation $\varkappa$ in reality undergoes a slow change during the development of the universe — $\varkappa$ is assumed to be inversely proportional to the age of the universe. Recently the author discussed in [1] whether such a slow change could be measurable directly. Indeed there is some hope that in the course of the next two or three decades a direct test by an exceedingly exact measurement of the Earth's gravitational field may become possible. It seems plausible that the rotation of the earth could also give some indication, because a certain slow *expansion* must result from such a diminution of the constant of gravitation. But the rotational velocity of the Earth is influenced by several effects in an intricate manner, and the hope of finding a convincing test here does not seem to be justified. (1)

But although it seems that some classes of newly formed stars

(1) Satellite experiments could help in this problem.

do exist, the modern idea is that the Earth and most stars are of an age comparable to the age of the universe. Thus, if Dirac's hypothesis is correct, then it should be supported by a broad variety of empirical facts which could be detected by a study of these old celestial bodies which, according to Dirac, were formed when the constant of gravitation had a considerably greater value than it does now. Inevitably a discussion of this question requires study of many facts in the realm of sciences not ordinarily regarded as sources of information about the fundamental laws of physics. For about our own Earth we have opportunities to obtain information in such great detail as is available about no other object in the universe.

A survey of the problem (including the ideas and results of several other authors like Gamow, Teller and Binge) was given some years ago in a book by the author [2]. In the meantime R. H. Dicke [3] made new and valuable contributions to this discussion, and the author gave a new survey of the problem, mentioning various further facts which also seem to indicate strongly that Dirac's hypothesis must be acknowledged as a necessary basis for the understanding of many empirical facts, some of which have long been known and some of which result from modern research. The following indications may perhaps help a little in stimulating interest in these problems and discussion with specialists in different fields of research.

Jeans looked anxiously for an effect causing *double stars* slowly to increase the radii of their orbits. From the well known theory of the splitting of rotating celestial bodies — one of the most beautiful achievements of theoretical astronomy — we learn that a rotating star can split under certain conditions and form a double star, the radius of the orbit being not much greater than the radius of the original star. But empirically the orbits of most double stars have far greater radii, and Jeans did not succeed in finding an explanation for those widely separated pairs which have periods of much more than 55 days.(1) In the end he was forced to assume that they must be generated directly (in a manner which can scarcely be understood) and not by division of rotating stars.

But if the constant of gravitation is assumed to be variable over a long period, then we get inverse proportionality of the orbital radii of double stars with this "constant". One of the most striking difficulties in astronomy is now removed. At the same time we get

(1) Interaction with other stars may — according to Jeans — have caused narrow pairs of stars to increase their distances so much that at last a period of the order of 55 days results.

a tenable theory of the origin of the system of planets. Weizsäcker's well-known theory, which is so convincing qualitatively, fails to give quantitatively satisfying results. Ter Haar showed that this theory is wrong by a factor of the order 10^5 because the large rotating lens of gaseous matter assumed by Weizsäcker as the first stage of formation of this system would be scattered long before there could be condensation and formation of planets. Now we can use another result of the classical theory of rotating stars: Under certain conditions instead of a splitting of the star a loss of mass along the equator must occur, surrounding the star with matter which rotates near its surface. According to Weizsäcker's model this matter could partially condense to planets moving at first in orbits near the sun, and later slowly increasing their distances. These two points have been discussed with more detail in my book mentioned above.

The well-known astrophysical formula

$$L = M^{\frac{11}{2}} R^{-\frac{1}{2}} \varkappa^{\frac{15}{2}} \tag{1}$$

shows that the brightness of the sun is strongly dependent on the gravitational constant $\varkappa$. Taking this together with the other consequence of Dirac's hypothesis—the inverse proportionality of the diameter of the Earth's orbit to $\varkappa$—we see that according to Dirac's hypothesis the Earth must during its history have received radiation from the sun proportional to $\varkappa^{10}$. In reality this simple formula (1) gives only a rough approximation and according to Schwarzschild, Howard and Herm the dependence on $\varkappa$ should be less pronounced.

But, qualitatively, we must conclude (according to Ter Haar) that in the early periods of the Earth's history, it must have been covered by closed clouds as a result of the radiation of the sun, a state of affairs similar to that on Venus today. This theoretical conclusion is confirmed in an extremely convincing manner by the paleontology of the carboniferous period. During the carboniferous period a type of vegetation growing under conditions of extreme shadow developed over large portions of the Earth's surface. The development was so widespread, constant in time, and free of seasonal variations that only a total coverage by clouds would seem to explain it. This has already been discussed in my book, where I considered some objections to Dirac's hypothesis made by Teller and Gamow. But in my new paper, mentioned above, I also showed that further facts of paleoclimatology fit very well into this picture. Dicke [3] made valuable and highly interesting contributions about the consequences of Dirac's hypothesis for very early times in the history of our Earth; these too are discussed — and modified slightly—in my recent paper.

It seems to me that my collaborator H. J. Binge gave the first convincing explanation of the phenomena of volcanoes, intrusions and so on. (Discussed in detail in my book and in my last paper.) The decisive empirical fact may be stated as follows: There is a tendency for rocks in the deeper layers of the Earth's crust to explode. Descriptive geology gives very impressive classes of examples of this tendency for rocks to explode, giving rise to intrusions and volcanoes. The interesting phenomenon is this: the planet Mars and our Moon do not show any signs of similar processes—the craters of the Moon having (according to Baldwin) an entirely different structure, pointing to great meteorites as their cause. Indications of a very small volcanic activity on the Moon, detected by modern investigations, seem to show no real resemblance to volcanoes and intrusions on the Earth. Therefore volcanoes must be considered as a special feature of the Earth (and probably Venus, though that cannot be tested today), not to be found on smaller celestial bodies like Mars or the Moon. The same can be said about the formation of mountains by folding processes—these too are absent in the case of Mars or the Moon.

Binge proposed the idea that the explosions mentioned may be caused by the fact that a *phase shift* of rocks may lead from high pressure phases to other phases, which are stable under lower pressure and possess a greater volume. In order to make this explanation convincing we have to assume that some deeper rocks are always on the verge of phase shift when a diminution of pressure takes place. Indeed, these explosions are in many cases connected with folding processes. But, as Binge pointed out, only the hypothesis of a systematically diminishing pressure can make this explanation possible; and only Dirac's hypothesis makes it believable that such diminution of pressure would take place.

But the most important feature of the surface of our Earth is its division into two parts—deep sea and continents. Mars also shows an analoguous division of its surface into two different levels, though there the deeper is not covered by water. Concerning the Earth we know today not only about the two different levels of altitude but also about the chemical and physical differences of the sial and the sima; the continents swim in the denser, deeper material. Since these continents have a nearly constant thickness, we may ask why they do not cover the whole surface of the Earth, but only $\frac{2}{5}$, and why the "continents" of Mars don't cover its whole surface, but only $\frac{3}{4}$ of it. J. Fisher some years ago indicated an answer to this problem, which may be called one of the great problems of geophysics; and L. Egyed [4] independently came to the same conclusion, giving valuable and very impressing arguments in its favour. In former years similar ideas were proposed by F. Keindl [5]. We have to assume that during the formation of the continental layer the Earth was considerably smaller than today, so that this layer covered the whole sphere of the Earth to a practically constant thickness. A process of expansion caused the continental layer to split into parts; the newly formed rifts were filled out to the equilibrium altitude by the more dense but also more mobile sima material of the deeper layer. In the course of time part of these rifts between the parts of the continental layer developed into wide oceans.

Another type of rifts has found much attention in recent years—the well known narrow rifts at the bottom of the oceans. The recent work of Ewing and Heezen gave us valuable new information about these narrow deep rifts which by isostatic anomalies are shown to have only short lifetimes; they are now considered by several authors as direct indications of an expansion of our Earth.

Returning to the theory of continents as residues of a sial layer which once covered the whole (correspondingly smaller) Earth, it may be mentioned here without going into detail that a great variety of empirical facts give very convincing confirmation. Some of the chief points—previously discussed in part by Egyed—have been mentioned in my paper [1]. Especially the inference that the water of the oceans, which today fills the deeper areas almost exactly to the level of the continents (apart from mountains), must formerly have covered wide portions of the continents, most closely agrees with the geological facts. According to Egyed these facts give us an empirical proof of the expansion of the Earth. Concerning the cause of this expansion Egyed at first indicated a physical hypothesis which is scarcely convincing. But Professor Egyed kindly informed me that he now prefers to believe that Dirac's hypothesis is correct and gives the theoretical explanation of this expansion, which Egyed believes to be an empirically proven fact.

The amount of expansion, necessary in order to explain the continents, is rather great, and certain consequences regarding the interior of the Earth must be drawn. Only by acknowledging Ramsey's idea about the discontinuity spheres inside the Earth we can make a model of the Earth capable of this expansion. Several authors are inclined to interpret these discontinuity spheres as surfaces of chemical discontinuity. But Ramsey interprets them as surfaces of phase differences only; then these surfaces are no longer fixed relative to the matter in the interior of the Earth — they can contract, giving rise to a pronounced expansion.[(1)]

New observations and calculations about the age of systems of stars seem to show that the age of the universe must be essentially greater than 6 billion years; ages of even 25 billion years have been discussed. But these values are derived from theoretical calculations concerning the processes of star development. Now these calculations require new investigation if Dirac's hypothesis is taken into consideration. Though surely Eq. (1) can give only a rough approximation which must be made more precise by new calculations on the basis of exact models of the interior of stars, L certainly depends strongly on $\varkappa$. Therefore according to Dirac's hypothesis star development must have been going on much more rapidly billions of years ago; the validity of Dirac's hypothesis means that the present method of calculating ages of stars from the velocity of evolution (assuming $\varkappa$ to be constant) must give values which are much too high when applied to quite old stars.

The mathematical formulation of a generalized theory of gravitation, assuming the constant of gravitation to be a scalar field variable, has been studied by me and a number of other physicists. The details of this mathematical theory being closely related to the mathematical problems of general relativity in Einstein's original formulation, the endeavour of the Hamburg Relativity Seminar has been devoted during recent years chiefly to the problems of Einstein's theory, about which my young friends Ehlers, Kundt, Sachs and Schücking have made contributions to this book. I am indebted to them and to H. J. Binge for many fruitful discussions. The Academy of Sciences and Literature (Mainz) and a very generous gift of Dr Friedrich Flick made our collaboration possible.

REFERENCES

[1] P. JORDAN, *Z. Phys.* **157**, 112 (1959).

[2] P. JORDAN, *Schwerkraft und Weltall,* 2nd ed., Braunschweig 1955; *Akad. Wiss. u. Lit.* (Mainz) 1959, p. 771. *Die Naturwiss.* (In course of publication).

[3] R. H. DICKE, *Rev. Mod. Phys.* **29**, 355 (1957).

[4] L. EGYED, *Geol. Rdschau* **46**, 108 (1957); *Ann. Univ. Budapest. Sect. Geol.* **1** 37 (1957).

[5] S. KEINDL, *Z. f. Geomorphol.* **9**, 169 (1936).

(1) In the meantime discussion with E. Teller convinced me that Ramsay's hypothesis must be discarded.

REMARKS ABOUT AMBARZUMIAN'S CONCEPTION OF PRE-STELLAR MATTER

P. Jordan

University of Hamburg, Hamburg

Nearly all the many astronomers and physicists who have speculated about the processes of formation of stars and galaxies have tried to put forward the conventional idea of condensation of inter-stellar gas. Oort, Spitzer and some other authors have obtained results which seem to indicate that a certain type of condensation does indeed occur which leads to the formation of stars. But this need not mean that most stars originated in this manner.

Ambarzumian, who began his study of the problem from unconventional ideas, and from a penetrating and convincing analysis of empirical facts, reached different conclusions. According to him, the chief process is not the formation of stars from gas but the common formation of both kinds of stellar matter—gas and stars—from "proto stars" or "pre-stellar matter". This thesis, first established by the extensive study of "associations" of stars, has been extended by Ambarzumian to galaxies and systems of galaxies. In the case of associations we have groups of stars (in some cases relatively young ones) which show by their motion that they originated from one point. In the case of galaxies there are many examples showing that the centre of a galaxy may be a field where the process of formation of gas and stars from pre-stellar matter is still going on. This can lead to a division of the galaxy, or to other effects discussed by Ambarzumian [1].

According to this thesis, the physical meaning of pre-stellar matter must be determined by a further analysis of the empirical facts, which are rapidly increasing with the progress of astrophysical research. Certainly this pre-stellar matter must have the following properties:

(1) High density,

(2) Invisibility as a result of the absence of luminosity,

(3) A tendency to expansion or explosive outbursts leading to the formation of normal matter like gas and stars.

It seems to be quite difficult to understand these properties by the use of current physical theories. There must exist conditions which prevent the pre-stellar matter—before its transformation into normal matter—from emission of radiation; and there must be conditions allowing to maintain the high density of this pre-stellar matter before the beginning of the expansion which leads to (or is equivalent with) the transformation. But the possibility must also remain that these expansive or explosive processes occur.

The most convincing answer seems to me to be that pre-stellar matter—as long as it remains pre-stellar—is prevented from emission and from explosion by geometrical conditions; that space has "pockets" containing the pre-stellar matter. Obviously in the frame of Riemannian geometry qualitatively no difficulty arises in conceiving such pockets separating the pre-stellar matter they contain from us, but varying geometrically in the course of time so that at last the pre-stellar matter is poured into normal, approximately Euclidean space.

But a quantitative theory of such developments cannot be given within the frame of Einstein's theory of gravitation without some generalization of this theory. For in this theory there is the well-known Birkhoff theorem, according to which any spherically symmetric vacuum field is necessarily static. This is a very essential point: the law of the conservation of matter $T^{kl}{}_{\|k} = 0$ contains no bar to this "pocket theory of pre-stellar matter". Naturally, the conservation of matter now means the conservation of the sum of normal and pre-stellar matter.[1] But Birkhoff's theorem prevents us from developing such ideas inside the frame of Einstein's theory; for in a certain approximation each point in the astronomical space is surrounded by a spherically symmetric vacuum field.

But a theory which can, perhaps, lead to a quantitative description of the outpouring of pre-stellar matter from space pockets already exists; the author's theory of a variable "constant" of gravitation offers such possibilities [2].

Originally I interpreted my theory as a theory of the creation of matter. But this was a misunderstanding, as is clearly shown

[1] The fact that $T^{kl}{}_{\|k} = 0$ does not, without additional conditions, give conservation of matter will not be discussed here, for probably this is not a decisive point.

by the valuable criticism of my late friend Pauli (discussed in my book) and of Fierz [3]. In reality my theory is a theory of prestellar matter.

The starting point of this theory was given by the two well-known hypotheses proposed by Dirac which can be formulated thus:

(I) The "constant" $\varkappa$ of gravitation is decreasing inversely proportional to $t =$ the age of the universe.

(II) The average density of matter in the universe (if conceived as expanding with a radius proportional to t) is also inversely proportional to t.

Hypothesis (I) leads to the assumption that $\varkappa$, not being a constant, must be a scalar field variable. This is the fundamental assumption of my theory. Direct evidence in favour of a decreasing $\varkappa$ is given by the double stars. This point has been discussed in detail in my book. Strong support of the hypothesis that $\varkappa$ decreases is also given by a series of important facts of geophysics, geology and paleoclimatology. This has also been discussed in my book, but a new paper could present augmented evidence [4], using in addition the especially interesting contributions of Dicke [5].

By acknowledging $\varkappa$ to be a scalar field variable (and formulating appropriate field equations, as in my theory) we overcome the difficulty of the Birkhoff theorem. The new theory allows solutions of such a kind that the four-dimensional metric, if intersected by $t = t_0 =$ const, for certain values of t_0 gives one, and for other values two three-dimensional spaces.

Hypothesis (II) induced me to interpret my theory also as a theory of the creation of matter, as mentioned above. But this surely erroneous interpretation is by no means necessary to understand the real meaning of Dirac's hypothesis (II). The correct new interpretation [6] is obviously the following: The conservation law of matter which also holds in this theory as well as in Einstein's, means the sum of normal matter and all parts of pre-stellar matter. But hypothesis (II) refers only to that part of the matter of the universe which already exists as normal matter, i.e. as gas and stars.

In the following I should like to give some indication of how the mathematical contents of my theory are to be understood in this framework of physical interpretation.

In the vacuum case, the field equations may be given by a variational principle with the Lagrangian

$$L = \frac{G}{\varkappa} - \frac{\zeta}{\varkappa^3} \frac{\partial \varkappa}{\partial x^k} \frac{\partial \varkappa}{\partial x^l} g^{kl} \tag{1}$$

instead of G as in the conventional theory. Here ζ denotes a dimensionless constant. An example of a vacuum field which is spherically symmetrical but not static, is given in the case $\zeta = 1$ by

$$ds^2 = \frac{dt^2}{1 - at/r} - \frac{dr^2}{1 - at/r} - r^2(d\theta^2 + \sin^2\theta \cdot d\varphi^2)\,, \qquad \varkappa = \frac{\varkappa_0}{1 - at/r} \tag{2}$$

with $a = \text{const} > 0$. Any space $t = \text{const}$ with $t > 0$ gives a spatial metric as in the Schwarzschild solution, the values of r running from $r = \infty$ down to $r = at$ and again up to $r = \infty$. But for $t < 0$ we have all values from $r = 0$ to $r = \infty$, and this means that at $t = 0$ two spaces unite. Naturally much work will still be necessary in order to obtain qualitatively similar solutions containing matter and also showing rotation instead of spherical symmetry.(1)

In studying questions of cosmology we must take account of the fact that cosmological models tend to give only a rough orientation, considering matter as homogeneously distributed instead of being concentrated in stars. In such a consideration, the processes of uniting spaces and of conversion of prestellar matter to normal matter can only be treated in such a manner that we confine ourselves to a recognition of their integral effects in parts of space great enough that they already contain great numbers of galaxies. Formulated in this manner, the problem of cosmological models can probably be treated according to the discussion given in my book.

In a radical treatment, the primary "pockets" of pre-stellar matter may contain only single elementary particles, these being later united with the normal space – not directly but through several different stages of the unification of spaces. Only the later stages of this development may be described by a macrophysical theory without quanta.

REFERENCES

[1] Ambarzumian, Solvay Congr, Brussels, 1958.
[2] P. Jordan, Schwerkraft und Weltall, 2. Aufl., Braunschweig 1955.
[3] M. Fierz, *Helv. Phys. Acta* **29**, 128 (1956).
[4] P. Jordan, *Akad. Wiss. u. Lit.* (Mainz) 1959, p. 771. – *Die Naturwiss.* (In course of publication).
[5] R. H. Dicke, *Rev. Mod. Phys.* **29**, 355 (1957).
[6] P. Jordan, *Z. Phys.* **151**, 112 (1959).

(1) Further research showed that this example (2) is not convincing. I hope to give better ones.

MACH'S PRINCIPLE AND COSMOLOGY IN THEIR RELATION TO GENERAL RELATIVITY*

O. Klein

Institute for Theoretical Physics, University of Stockholm

As Einstein himself has mentioned at several occasions he drew inspiration in developing the general theory of relativity from a remark by Mach [1] in the famous book *Die Mechanik in ihrer Entwicklung* made in connection with a critical review of Newton's concepts of *absolute space* and *absolute time* namely that the so-called inertial forces, to which a system in accelerated motion with respect to the fixed stars is subject, may be regarded as non-Newtonian gravitational effects of the distant masses of the universe moving with respect to the system. Mach came to this view from the standpoint that only motion with respect to material bodies—the word taken in its daily-life sense—could have a physical meaning.

It is natural that Mach's remark should have impressed Einstein as an argument in favour of a generalized relativity theory. But we also know that his main foundation of general relativity theory had a different origin, namely the *equivalence principle* together with *the claim that the physical laws ought to be invariant under arbitrary transformations of the space-time coordinates.* His later attempt to take Mach's idea for more than a hint of such general invariance started, as is well known, that particular branch of general relativity theory which is nowadays called *relativistic cosmology.* Thus, from

---

* This is a somewhat elaborated version of a lecture given at the Weizmann Institute, Rehovoth on April 25, 1960 at a symposion in connection with a memorial service to the late Professor W. Pauli. It is presented with some hesitation because — although it contains little new — its conclusions differ from the opinion of many eminent physicis s.

See, however, a remark by M. Fierz [2], where he expresses a similar view with regard to Mach's principle as that taken here.

Mach's somewhat exaggerated although fruitful antimystical tendency stemmed indirectly this most speculative trend of thought.

At the time when Mach put forward the remark in question the situation of electromagnetism and optics seemed to make the literal existence of an ethereal medium through which bodies would move without any direct viscosity effects, a most legitimate hypothesis. Therefore, at that time and until the Michelson experiment the identification of Newton's absolute space with the ether seemed quite natural. It seems probable that Newton in the back of his mind had ideas similar to those behind the ether hypothesis of the 19th century.[(1)] In fact, such ideas were quite current at his time but rather discredited through Descarte's premature attempt towards a general foundation of physics. That Newton expressed himself differently in his *Principia* was probably due to his somewhat exaggerated aversion against speculation — natural in view of the physics of Descartes — and not to any wish to seek more mystery in Nature than forced upon us, his tendency being intensely rationalistic and thereby open to the limitations of reason. Therefore the words *absolute space* as used in the *Principia* should probably be regarded just as a short expression of the experience illustrated by means of Newton's experiment of the rotating bucket with water. Had he expressed himself in terms of an ether hypothesis the relevant remarks in *Principia* would have seemed less mysterious in the 19th century but hardly more acceptable to Mach.

As to the development of general relativity theory the *field concept* formed certainly a fundamental part of Einstein's background. It is well known how by means of his remarkable use of the old experience that all bodies receive equal accelerations in a given gravitational field he was able to obtain the simultaneous solution of two fundamental problems: the reconciliation of gravitational theory with special relativity, i.e. a formulation compatible with the propagation of weak gravitational disturbances with the vacuum velocity of light, and the generalization of relativity theory to include the invariance with respect to non-uniform motions of the coordinate frame.

Although this very far-reaching generalization of Newtonian gravitational theory does not in itself contradict Mach's explanation of inertial forces as due to gravitational effects of distant bodies it

---

(1) See the interesting paper by M. Fierz, [3]. Strangely enough Mach did not believe that any such conception was behind Newton's idea of absolute space ([1], p. 225).

does put the idea in a different light since according to Einstein's theory the distant bodies can only act through the gravitational field to which they give rise *at the place of the body under consideration.* Thus, this theory is essentially based on the postulate—called by Einstein the *equivalence principle*—that we may always introduce a local frame of reference—which is freely falling in the local gravitational field—in which all the effects of gravitation are removed to a first approximation. As is well known this postulate led Einstein to the introduction of a mathematical description using Riemann's concept of differential geometry which is the generalization of Minkowski's treatment of special relativity theory. Hereby the gravitational field is characterized by means of the corresponding *metric tensor*, which satisfies field equations covariant with respect to general coordinate transformations. And the locally gravitation-free coordinate frame is a so-called *geodesic* coordinate system for the space-time point under consideration, the degree of approximation, when gravitation is neglected, depending on the *curvature tensor* at the point. Also, the whole theory may be formulated by means of an action principle, *the action being an invariant of the group of general coordinate transformations*, when the different field quantities are transformed according to their respective ways.

As to the inertial forces these are particular solutions of the differential equations for the gravitational field as follows from the general covariance of these equations. It is clear that this feature has no analogue in the Newtonian theory, although the equations of motion may, of course, be translated to an accelerated frame of reference whereby the inertial forces appear as extra terms. But these forces do not in general satisfy the Newtonian theory of gravitation. This appears already from the fact that in general—e.g. the Coriolis force—they have no potential.

Let us look a little more closely at the way the outlined programme works out in practice and especially how it is related to the much discussed question of boundary conditions for the field equations. Thus, in short-time laboratory experiments we may either altogether neglect gravitation or take its influence into consideration in performing the transformation from our practical frame of reference—in which the laboratory is so fixed to the solid earth that it is as permanently as possible in a state of equilibrium under the influence of the earth's gravitation—to the locally gravitation-free frame which is momentarily at rest with respect to the laboratory but freely falling in the local gravitational field. In fact, by means of the ordinary equations of motion not including gravitation we may, as is well known, with good approximation describe the influence of the Earth's gravitational field on the motion of bodies with respect to the Earth by means of a transformation of these equations of motion which corresponds to the momentary motion of the Earth with respect to the mentioned geodesic coordinate system.

Proceeding to the problem of the solar system from the point of view of general relativity but in Newtonian approximation we have to remember that this problem is characterized by the enormous distances—compared to the dimensions of the system—even to the nearest fixed stars. The centre of gravity of the solar system will, therefore, be freely falling in a practically homogeneous gravitational field, which, moreover—due to the small average density of the galaxy—is weak compared with the gravitational forces from the bodies of the system. The natural frame of reference will, therefore, be one in which the centre of gravity of the system is at rest and in which there is practically no gravitational field at distances so large compared with the dimensions of the system that the gravitational effects due to the bodies of the system are negligible. This treatment is seen to correspond to the usual boundary condition for the Einstein field equations which leads to the famous Schwarzschild solution for the line element in the space surrounding a spherically symmetric distribution of matter. We see that here this boundary condition contains nothing "deep" but has a simple practical significance, just as the boundary conditions used in optics and electromagnetism. Further, the treatment is clearly in conformity with the Copernican viewpoint, which is, therefore, not only compatible with but justified by the deeper viewpoint of general relativity.

The treatment just outlined is, of course, only sufficient, when we are not aiming at the long-time motions of the bodies within the galaxy but are only interested in the motions within the solar system with the ordinary practical degree of approximation. But due to the relatively large distances between galaxies, similar considerations may be repeated for the galaxy itself or, when such a treatment — as in certain known cases—is not sufficiently accurate, for smaller or bigger groups of galaxies.

The question now arises whether we can proceed in the same way with the system of galaxies. Could not this so-called metagalactic system again be just a large stellar system embedded in a still larger region where gravitational effects from bodies outside the system have a practically negligible influence on the motions taking part inside the system? Cosmologists and believers in the

Mach principle will answer this question with no. But have we really sufficient reasons for believing that any of the cosmological solutions of Einstein's field equations, *which seem to be essentially separated from the solutions used to describe the ordinary gravitational interactions,* have any application to our physical world?

As is well known Einstein's starting point for his cosmological considerations was not only the Mach principle but also the old paradox that in an infinite world where the average density of stars is different from zero the gravitational field as well as the luminosity would everywhere be infinite. It has often been pointed out, however, that an average density equal to zero is by no means in contradiction with a matter distribution as presented by our experience where, as far as our knowledge goes, systems of higher and higher order with sufficiently increasing dimensions do exist.

In general relativity this argument goes in the following way. Let us assume that a system of a certain order has the mass M and the radius R and that these fulfil the claim that outside of the system the Schwarzschild solution gives an approximate description of the gravitational field up to distances large with respect to the dimensions of the system. Then we shall have the inequality

$$\frac{2\gamma M}{c^2 R} < 1$$

where γ is the ordinary gravitational constant and c the vacuum velocity of light. Then the gravitational acceleration due to the average distribution of matter within the system at a distance r from its centre is $\sim \frac{\gamma M}{R^3} r$, which according to the above inequality is smaller than $\frac{1}{2}\frac{c^2}{R}\frac{r}{R}$. Now for $R \sim 10^{18}$ cm, which is several powers of 10 smaller than the dimensions of the galaxy, the quantity c^2/R is equal to g, the gravitational acceleration here on Earth. Thus with R of the order of magnitude of the largest observed distancies of galaxies the gravitational field will certainly be very weak, if the inequality in question is fulfilled.

On the other hand the fulfilment of this condition would not seem to be contradicted by present experience. In fact, assuming the average density of the metagalactic system to be $\sim 10^{-29}$ g/cm^3 it follows from the inequality that $R \lesssim 10^{28}$ cm and $M \lesssim 10^{22} M_\odot$, where $M_\odot$ is the mass of the Sun.

Thus from a logical and, so far, also from an empirical point of view there is hardly any argument favouring any of the cosmological solutions in comparison with the simpler assumption that also the metagalactic system is just one system in the ordinary sense of the word and not the universe. If this latter alternative would prove correct in the future the situation with respect to boundary conditions for the gravitational field equations would again be of the same practical nature as in the examples discussed above.

Let us now return to the Mach principle and especially to Mach's own argument, the apparent absurdity of a body in an empty universe possessing inertia. This leads us to the question of what we mean to day by the words "empty universe". Here the development of quantum field theory, especially the particle-antiparticle theory of Dirac has changed our ideas about the *vacuum* very radically, our nearest approach towards giving a meaning to the words just mentioned being the ground state of an ideal quantum field theory comprising the different kinds of elementary particles and their interactions, matter in the most general meaning of the word corresponding to all possible excitations of this ground state. Hereby we must not forget, however, that we are still very far from possessing such a general quantum field theory and that even quantum electrodynamics, the best developed part of quantum field theory treating the interaction of electrons and their antiparticles with the electromagnetic field, still suffers from inconsistencies appearing in the well-known divergencies.

Still there are certain general features of present quantum field theory in a somewhat idealized form, i.e. disregarding the divergencies, in which we may have a certain confidence, namely

1. The existence of a ground state of zero energy and momentum, *a property seen to be Lorentz-invariant.*

2. That in this state the expectation value of the Riemann–Christoffel tensor vanishes everywhere, so that in a suitable coordinate frame also the expectation value of the gravitational field vanishes everywhere.

3. That matter is represented by excitations of this ground state, the simplest excitations corresponding to ordinary elementary particles such as photons, electrons and nucleons with their characteristic relative masses and interactions, which for weak excitation – i.e. low energy density – are governed with good approximation by the ordinary physical laws.

From these statements it follows that the equations of motion of bodies with respect to a coordinate system in non-uniform motion with respect to the Lorentz frame considered under 2 will exhibit inertial forces in the usual way. This is in conformity with what I would take as another postulate, although a number of eminent physicists seem to disagree on this point, namely

4. That basic quantum field theory fulfils the claim of invariance against general coordinate transformations. From this it would follow that a state obtained by means of a coordinate transformation from the ground state is also a possible state.

In a generally relativistic quantum field theory gravitation will in all probability play an important role in the very definition of the ground state. In fact if we tried to define the ground state first without regard to gravitation taking account of it afterwords, the infinite vacuum state energy would give rise to infinite gravitation. From this and other similar reasons there would seem to be some basis for the belief that a generally relativistic formulation of quantum field theory would lead to the removal of the different kinds of infinities and that in such a theory a vacuum state corresponding to zero energy and zero momentum could be properly defined.

According to this view, which is admittedly based on some unproved assumptions, the world, as far as we know it, would approximately correspond to the vacuum state, the density of matter being modest even within the densest stars, so that the direct effects of gravitational forces are important only in connection with problems of macroscopical physics. On the present view the indirect effects of such forces would, however, play an essential role for the existence and properties of the elementary particles themselves as well as for the vacuum state.

The state of momentum and energy equal to zero which requires an infinitely extended space for its rigorous definition may with some justification be regarded as representing what Newton called *absolute space*. Hereby it is interesting that the explanation of the result of the rotating bucket experiment—the very background for Newton's use of the expression *absolute*—appears as an example of general relativity. This is, of course, quite in line with Einstein's foundation of general relativity theory but has hardly any apparent connection with Mach's ideas. Be it that the role of the gravitational field equations in the definition of the vacuum state together with the potentialities of this state as to the creation of matter could be regarded as a very symbolic expression of such ideas.

As to the cosmological problem the above analysis would seem to favour the simpler view, where the system of galaxies is considered as a relatively weak modification of the ground state—i.e. as a system embedded in an approximately flat exterior—as opposed to the cosmological solutions, which are very far from weak excitations of the ground state.

In finishing these remarks a few words may be said about the so-called *cosmological constant*, which played so essential a role in Einstein's first attempt towards a relativistic cosmology, and still held to be important by some investigators although Einstein himself, after having been acquainted with Friedmann's solutions, considered it as an unnecessary complication of his original field equations. This later view of Einstein would seem to be well in line with the above discussion since the existence of a cosmological term of the usually assumed magnitude would be a hindrance for the formation of a system—in the ordinary sense of the word—of the probable size of the metagalactic system. Further, we have so far no background for such a magnitude of the cosmological term. Still the possibility that such a term may come out as a property of the ground state of a rational quantum field theory may perhaps not be excluded.

In connection with the cosmological term it ought to be remembered that Einstein's interpretation of Mach's principle depended just on this term. In fact, with this term the field equations without matter have no solution corresponding to the constant metric of special relativity theory. And this gave a certain justification to the view that in a world devoid of matter such concepts as motion and force would be meaningless. There is no analogue to this in the cosmological solutions of the field equations without the cosmological term.

We shall end this discussion with a remark on the famous solution given by Thirring of the gravitational field inside a rotating spherical shell of matter. As is well known this solution and its generalizations has played a prominent role as an argument in favour of the Mach principle. In Thirring's solution the boundary condition is the same as for the Schwarzschild solution, i.e. the deviations from the Lorentz metric vanishing asymptotically at infinity. This means that the matter of the shell is assumed to rotate with respect to an asymptotic Lorentz frame. And the result is that inside the shell there are gravitational forces which resemble the inertial forces in a rotating frame of reference, their strength being proportional to the mass of the shell and vanishingly small even for masses as large as the total mass of the galaxy.

Now from our point of view this is an interesting result but one that has hardly any connection with the Mach principle. To make this statement clearer we shall regard the following modification of Thirring's model. Let us assume that the shell is at rest with respect to the asymptotic Lorentz frame and let us regard the motion of a particle inside the shell with respect to a coordinate frame which rotates around an axis through the centre of the spherical shell. We use first a coordinate frame x, y, z, t in which the shell is at rest. Since we have then spherical symmetry with respect to the centre of the shell we may write for ds^2, ds being the line element

$$ds^2 = \alpha(dx^2 + dy^2 + dz^2) - \beta c^2 dt^2$$

where α and β are functions of $r = \sqrt{x^2 + y^2 + z^2}$ alone. There being no matter but in the shell itself we have outside the shell the Schwarzschild solution

$$\frac{1}{\alpha} = \beta = 1 - \frac{2\gamma M}{c^2 r}$$

where M is the mass of the shell, and inside the shell simply

$$\alpha = 1, \qquad \beta = \beta_0 = \text{const}.$$

Assuming that the shell is infinitely thin β will be the same inside and just outside the shell, so that

$$\beta_0 = 1 - \frac{2\gamma M}{c^2 R}$$

where R is the value of r at the shell.

Inside the shell there is no gravitational field—just as in the corresponding Newtonian case—and with the local time variable $\tau = \sqrt{\beta_0}\, t$ we get pure Lorentz metric there. This means that the transformation

$$\xi + i\eta = (x + iy)\, e^{-i\omega t}, \qquad \zeta = z$$

leads to the well known expressions for the inertial forces without any visible effect of the shell. This is a particularly simple example of the general approximate treatment by means of the introduction of a local Lorentz frame. However, it is interesting to look at the thing from outside where asymptotically t is the natural time variable. Since $\omega\tau = \omega\sqrt{\beta_0}\, t$ we see that the angular velocity of the rotation as judged from outside is $\omega_0 = \omega\sqrt{\beta_0} = \omega\sqrt{1 - \dfrac{2\gamma M}{c^2 R}}$.

This means that the Coriolis force, which has the ordinary expression in ω, will appear as increased by the factor $\left(1-\frac{2\gamma M}{c^2 R}\right)^{-\frac{1}{2}}$ when ω_0 is regarded as the angular velocity, which, if $\frac{2\gamma M}{c^2 R} \ll 1$ is equal to $1+\frac{\gamma M}{c^2 R}$. Here the latter term, which is of the same order of magnitude as the Thirring effect, may be regarded as the contribution of the shell to the Coriolis force.

The conclusion of the above discussion would be that there is hardly any argument for a direct meaning of the Mach principle in general relativity theory nor any *a priori* argument in favour of any of the cosmological solutions. On the contrary the practical situation of general relativity theory taken together with our present knowledge regarding matter and vacuum would rather point to the assumption that the world as we know it is to be regarded as a weak excitation of the vacuum state, which state, in spite of its relative character, may be compared to the absolute space of Newton. But since this state is a kind of potential reservoir of all forms of matter and since gravitation is probably essential for its proper definition we may perhaps still say that its role concerning inertial forces is in line with the Mach principle.

REFERENCES

[1] E. Mach, *Die Mechanik in ihrer Entwicklung*, 7th ed., Leipzig 1912.

[2] M. Fierz, *La structure et l'évolution de l'univers*, Bruxelles 1958. Reports from the 11th Solvay Conference, p. 48.

[3] M. Fierz, *Über den Ursprung und die Bedeutung der Lehre Isaac Newtons vom absoluten Raum*, Gesnerus 11, 1954, p. 62.

DETERMINATION OF GRAVITATIONAL STANDARD TIME

W. KUNDT

Syracuse, New York, on leave from Hamburg University *

and

B. HOFFMANN

Queens College, Flushing, New York **

IN the general theory of relativity, the metrical tensor can be patchwise determined by making measurements with rigid rods and standard clocks (see [1]). However, rigid rods and atomic clocks are devices obeying the laws of electrodynamics and quantum theory. The fact that the metrical tensor has a gravitational-inertial as well as a metrical significance means that standard length and standard time are also determined by the inertial motions of free particles of both non-zero and zero rest masses. To be more precise: the projective structure of space-time given by the (timelike) non-null geodesics, together with the conformal structure given by the null lines determine the metrical structure to within a scale factor that is independent of position (see e.g. [2]).

The question therefore arises whether gravitational standard time and non-gravitational standard time are the same, a question which can only be answered by experiment. Thus it seems desirable to suggest an experiment by means of which, at least in principle, gravitational time can be measured within any degree of accuracy (allowed by the uncertainty principle).

Such an experiment must not be based on the period of a (rotating) gravitational system. For, quite apart from tidal effects due to

* Flick exchange fellow.

** Part of this work was done while one of us (B. H.) was on leave at King's College, London, and was assisted by Wright ADC, ARDC, USAF through its European office.

lack of symmetry and dependence on "landmarks", there is the difficulty that incoming gravitational waves can produce unpredictable disturbances. We avoid this difficulty by considering the situation of an arbitrary observer in an arbitrary space-time region who sets up a continual monitoring system. This observer, as we shall show, can measure standard time along his world line by continuously emitting geodesic test particles, continuously emitting and receiving light signals, and observing the coordinate velocities and accelerations of the former and the coordinate velocities of the latter, all this in his infinitesimal neighbourhood.

Let Greek indices run from 1 to 3, Latin indices from 0 to 3; and choose the coordinate system such that the observer is described by $x^\iota = \text{const}$. We shall show later that the following 21 quantities can be obtained observationally as functions of x^0 along the observer's world line:

$$\tilde{g}_{\varkappa\lambda} \overset{\text{def}}{=} \frac{g_{\varkappa\lambda}}{g_{00}}, \qquad g_\varkappa \overset{\text{def}}{=} \frac{g_{\varkappa 0}}{g_{00}}, \tag{1}$$

$$\Gamma^\iota_{00}, \qquad \Delta^\iota_{\iota 0} \overset{\text{def}}{=} \Gamma^\iota_{\iota 0} - \tfrac{1}{2}\Gamma^0_{00} \text{ (not summed over } \iota), \qquad \Gamma^\iota_{\varkappa 0} \ (\iota \neq \varkappa). \tag{2}$$

For the present we suppose these quantities to be known. Write the line element as

$$ds^2 = e^{2v}\{\tilde{\gamma}_{\varkappa\lambda} dx^\varkappa dx^\lambda - (dx^0 + g_\iota dx^\iota)^2\}, \tag{3}$$

with

$$g_{00} \overset{\text{def}}{=} -e^{2v}, \qquad \tilde{\gamma}_{\varkappa\lambda} = -\tilde{g}_{\varkappa\lambda} + g_\varkappa g_\lambda, \tag{4}$$

$\tilde{\gamma}_{\varkappa\lambda}$ being conformal to Møller's space metric. Then the determination of gravitational standard time means obtaining v as a function of x^0.

Now the following 10 equations link $v_0 \overset{\text{def}}{=} \partial_0 v$ with the data of (1), (2):

$$\partial_0 g_{kl} = 2 g_{r(k} \Gamma^r_{l)0}. \tag{5}$$

Using the notations of (3), (4), we can rewrite these equations successively as

$$\Gamma^0_{00} - v_0 = -g_\varrho \Gamma^\varrho_{00}, \tag{6}$$

$$\Gamma^0_{\varkappa 0} - \tfrac{1}{2} g_\varkappa v_0 = \partial_0 g_\varkappa - g_\varkappa \Delta^\varkappa_{\varkappa 0} - g_{\varrho'} \Gamma^{\varrho'}_{\varkappa 0} + (\tilde{\gamma}_{\varkappa\varrho} + \tfrac{1}{2} g_\varkappa g_\varrho) \Gamma^\varrho_{00}, \tag{7}$$

$$\begin{aligned} \tilde{\gamma}_{\varkappa\lambda} v_0 = {} & -\partial_0 \tilde{\gamma}_{\varkappa\lambda} + \tilde{\gamma}_{\varkappa\lambda}(\Delta^\varkappa_{\varkappa 0} + \Delta^\lambda_{\lambda 0}) + 2\tilde{\gamma}_{\varrho'(\varkappa} \Gamma^{\varrho'}_{\lambda)0} - \\ & -(\tilde{\gamma}_{\varkappa\lambda} g_\varrho + 2 g_{(\varkappa} \tilde{\gamma}_{\lambda)\varrho}) \Gamma^\varrho_{00}, \end{aligned} \tag{8}$$

with no summation over $\varkappa$, λ, and with ϱ' running over all values different from the other index values in the same Γ-symbol. We can obtain v_0 from any one of the 6 equations (8). (The 4 equations (6), (7) contain the 4 unknowns Γ^0_{k0}; after v_0 is obtained from one of the equations (8), the Γ^0_{k0} could be calculated, if so desired). From v_0 we can calculate v by integration to within an additive constant, and thus g_{00} to within a constant multiplier.

We now come to the subtle question of how to measure the quantities (1), (2) without using rigid rods or standard clocks. We must first set up a space-time coordinate system in the infinitesimal neighbourhood of the observer. To do this we use three test particles equipped with coordinate clocks—they may be realized by satellites. These three satellites and the observer (who is taken to be at the spatial origin), together with their four coordinate clocks, form a local space-time 4-bein, relative to which the coordinates of other neighbouring events can be determined by linear interpolation with light rays.

In order to get the conformal space metric $\tilde{\gamma}_{\varkappa\lambda}$ defined in (4), we provide the observer and each satellite with radar equipment and measure continually, by the radar method, the six edges of the tetrahedron formed by the observer and the three satellites, using the formula

$$\sqrt{\tilde{\gamma}_{\varkappa\lambda}dx^{\varkappa}dx^{\lambda}} = \tfrac{1}{2}dx^0. \tag{9}$$

Here $dx^{\varkappa}$ is the coordinate distance, and dx^0 is the time between the emission and reception of a signal.

The remaining 3 quantities $g_{\varkappa}$ in (1) are connected, as was shown by Møller [1], with the one-way coordinate velocity of light via

$$g_{\iota}dx^{\iota} = \sqrt{\tilde{\gamma}_{\varkappa\lambda}dx^{\varkappa}dx^{\lambda}} - dx^0, \tag{10}$$

and hence can be obtained from the same experiment by noting the local coordinate times of reflection of the signals.

Finally, to measure the quantities (2), the observer emits geodesic test particles. (This will pose practical problems since the effects of spin motion and of the electromagnetic field must be made negligible.) The equations of geodesic motion, referred to an arbitrary parameter σ, are

$$\ddot{x}^i + \Gamma^i_{jk}\dot{x}^j\dot{x}^k + \frac{d^2\sigma}{ds^2}\left(\frac{d\sigma}{ds}\right)^{-2}\dot{x}^i = 0, \qquad \dot{x} \overset{\text{def}}{=} \frac{dx^i}{d\sigma}, \tag{11}$$

whence

$$\Gamma^{[i}_{jk}\dot{x}^{l]}\dot{x}^j\dot{x}^k = -\ddot{x}^{[i}\dot{x}^{l]} = \text{known quantities}. \tag{12}$$

For a geodesic observer, (12) implies (since $\dot{x}^i = \delta^i_0$)

$$\Gamma^{\iota}_{00} = 0, \tag{13}$$

20

which causes a considerable simplification of equations (6), (7), and (8). Further, by starting the test particles in the directions of the coordinate axes, we bring (12) into the form

$$[2\Gamma^{\lambda}_{\iota 0}\dot{x}^0+\Gamma^{\lambda}_{\iota\iota}\dot{x}^{\iota}](\dot{x}^{\iota})^2 = -\Gamma^{\lambda}_{00}(\dot{x}^0)^2\dot{x}^{\iota}+ \text{known quantities} \tag{14}$$

$$(\text{for } i = \iota, \quad l = \lambda \neq \iota),$$

$$[2\Delta^{\iota}_{\iota 0}(\dot{x}^0)^2-2\Delta^0_{0\iota}\dot{x}^0\dot{x}^{\iota}-\Gamma^0_{\iota\iota}(\dot{x}^{\iota})^2]\dot{x}^{\iota} = -\Gamma^{\iota}_{00}(\dot{x}^0)^3+ \text{known quantities}$$

$$(\text{for } i = \iota, \quad l = 0) \tag{15}$$

where $\Delta^0_{0\iota} \overset{\text{def}}{=} \Gamma^0_{0\iota}-\frac{1}{2}\Gamma^{\iota}_{\iota\iota}$, and no summation is assumed over repeated indices. For a geodesic observer (13) holds, and the 9 equations (14), (15) contain 21 unknowns of which we are interested in only 9. To solve for these 9 quantities we need three sets of equations (14), (15), (with 6 equations to spare) which can be obtained for instance by starting three particles with different velocities along each coordinate axis.

It should be remarked that our experiment as suggested so far was not elaborated on the basis of economy: if we restrict ourselves to but one of equations (8), say the equation with $\varkappa = 1 = \lambda$, and assume the observer to be geodesic, the only quantities needed are $\tilde{\gamma}_{1\varkappa}$, g_1, Δ^1_{10}, and Γ^{λ}_{10} for $\lambda \neq 1$. This means, roughly speaking, restricting the four-dimensional experiment to a two-dimensional one.

Thus all the necessary information is available for the experimental determination of gravitational standard time. There are, of course, serious difficulties in the practical aspects of the experiment, including the experimental checking of the validity of the linear interpolation in the coordinate system (which can be done by emitting further test particles) and the problem of the "continual" emission of geodesic test particles. But, in principle, the gravitational standard time can be measured to any desired non-quantum degree of accuracy.

Robert Marzke, in his Princeton A. B. Senior thesis (1959) suggests a different experimental determination of gravitational time, which in addition to our experimental tools (test particles, radar signals) needs the device of a neighbouring satellite at constant distance. A report will be submitted to the Reviews of Modern Physics.

REFERENCES

[1] C. Møller, *The Theory of Relativity*, Oxford 1952, § 89.

[2] T. Y. Thomas, *The Differential Invariants of Generalized Spaces*, Cambridge 1934, § 7.

NOTE ON THE EQUIVALENCE PROBLEM

W. Kundt *

Syracuse University, New York; on leave from Hamburg University

Abstract—A consideration of the symmetry classes of plane-fronted gravitational waves lead to two interesting results: (1) Dealing with the question of equivalence it is not, in general, admissible to restrict oneself to scalar invariants which are integer rational in g^{ab}, R_{abcd}, and $\nabla_{e_\varrho \ldots e_1} R_{abcd}$. (2) In special cases the scalar invariants of the second and third order of differentiation do not form a complete set (complete with respect to functional dependence on the coordinates).

The latest version of the theorem of equivalence reads as follows:

Theorem (of Equivalence): Given two Riemannian manifolds V_n, $\bar{V}_n$ of dimension n. They can be locally mapped onto each other (are locally equivalent) if and only if the set of equations

$$f\big(g_{ab,c_1\ldots c_\varrho}(x^i)\big) = f\big(\bar{g}_{ab,c_1\ldots c_\varrho}(\bar{x}^i)\big) \tag{1}$$

has a solution $\bar{x}^i = \bar{x}^i(x^k)$, where f runs through a basis of scalar invariants of order r, $r \leqslant N \leqslant n+3$.[(1)] Here $g_{ab,c_1\ldots c_\varrho}(x^i)$ stands symbolically for the functions $g_{ab}(x^i)$, $g_{ab,c}(x^i)$, $\ldots$, $g_{ab,c_1\ldots c_\varrho}(x^i)$, ϱ being the order of the invariant. If V_n is equivalent to $\bar{V}_n$, the equations (1) of order N are dependent on those of order $N-1$.

A complete proof of this theorem does not yet seem to exist in the literature. Essentially it can be based on the following two steps: (1) The "reduction theorem" proven in several textbooks,[(2)] reduces the analytic problem to the problem of algebraic equivalence of the two systems of tensors:

$$\{g_{ab}, R_{abcd}, \nabla_e R_{abcd}, \ldots, \nabla_{e_N} \ldots \nabla_{e_1} R_{abcd}\} \tag{2}$$

* Flick Exchange Fellow.

(1) The upper bound $n+3$ will be proved under the assumption that the Riemann tensor uniquely defines an n-bein (up to reflections) at each point. It is an open question whether or not this bound is valid in general; examples indicate an even smaller bound. A more detailed discussion of this theorem will be given in an article by P. Jordan, J. Ehlers and W. Kundt [1].

(2) See for instance [2] or [3].

in corresponding points of the two V'_ns, where $N \geqslant 1$ is some number which depends on V_n, and is determined by the fact that from an increase in the order of differentiation in (2) from $N-1$ to N there results no increase in the number of independent conditions on a possibly existing transformation (2). The second step is an algebraic theorem stating that two systems of affine tensors, being in a one-to-one correspondence, can simultaneously be transformed into each other if and only if they agree in all their simultaneous algebraic scalar invariants.[(1)] Taking these two steps for granted, the above theorem has been proven except for the upper bound of $n+3$ to the order N needed in (1). Now, according to steps (1) and (2), if the number of functionally independent scalar invariants does not increase when the order in (1) is increased by one, we have reached the order N. A (non-constant) scalar invariant is at least of order two.[(2)] Hence N will be maximal, if all invariants of order two are constant and if, further, there exists only one non-constant invariant of order three, only one functionally independent invariant of order four, and so on up to at most $n+2$, for there cannot exist more than n functionally independent scalar invariants with respect to the coordinates.

Remark: If V_n admits a group of motions, and q is the dimension of the group orbits, then the upper bound $n+3$ in the theorem can be replaced by $n-q+3$.

We shall now consider the plane-fronted gravitational waves[(3)] defined as solutions of $R_{ab} = 0$ which possess a covariantly constant vector field l^a, as a non-trivial example. Robinson showed that they can be described by the line element:[(4)]

$$ds^2 = 2\,du\,dv + dy^2 + dz^2 + 2H(u, y, z)\,du^2 \tag{3}$$

with $H_{yy} + H_{zz} = 0$, and we mention that in general they only admit the one-dimensional group generated by l^a.[(5)] The Riemann tensor for (3) reads

$$R_{abcd} = H_{,pq} \overset{p}{w}_{ab} \overset{q}{w}_{cd} \tag{4}$$

(1) A similar theorem for rational scalar invariants was proved by R. Weitzenböck [4].

(2) See for instance the book by T. Y. Thomas [2].

(3) Meanwhile their name has been changed into "plane-fronted waves with parallel rays".

(4) I am most grateful for a private communication.

(5) A detailed discussion of this class of empty space metrics will be contained in the article [1] and in [6].

where $\overset{p}{w}_{ab} = \delta^{1p}_{ab}$, $(u, y, z, v) \overset{\text{def}}{=} (x^i)$, $1 \leqslant i \leqslant 4$, and $l^a = \delta^a_4$. The bivectors $\overset{p}{w}_{ab}$, for $p = 2, 3$, are simple and lightlike, duals of each other, orthogonal on l^a, and covariantly constant. Hence the ϱth covariant derivative of the Riemann tensor reads

$$\nabla_{e_\varrho} \ldots \nabla_{e_1} R_{abcd} = \overset{p}{w}_{ab} \overset{q}{w}_{cd} \nabla_{e_\varrho} \ldots \nabla_{e_1} H_{,pq}, \tag{5}$$

and it can easily be seen that all tensors (5) are orthogonal on l^a (note: $H_{,4} = 0$) and contain l^a, and consequently have vanishing contractions with each other. This proves the first statement in the abstract.

Next we observe that there are no (non-constant) scalar invariants of order two: the Riemann tensor (4) is of Petrov type II with vanishing eigenvalues. (1)

We ask for a complete set of scalar invariants of the lowest possible order. Writing

$$P_{abcd} \overset{\text{def}}{=} R_{abcd} + i\overset{*}{R}_{abcd}, \qquad K \overset{\text{def}}{=} H_{,22} - iH_{,23} \tag{6}$$

where $\overset{*}{R}_{abcd} = \frac{1}{2}\eta_{ab}{}^{pq}R_{pqcd}$ is the (left handed) dual of R_{abcd}, we obtain

$$P_{abcd;e} = (\ln K)_{,e} P_{abcd}, \tag{7}$$

showing that $\partial_e \ln K$ is an invariant (complex) vector of order three. From its real and imaginary part we immediately get three invariant scalar products J_α. But the set of tensors $S \overset{\text{def}}{=} \{g^{ab}, R_{abcd}, R_{abcd;e}\}$ with (4) possesses at each point precisely four independent (rational) affine invariants:(2) P_{abcd} can be written as

$$P_{abcd} = v_{ab} v_{cd}, \tag{8}$$

v_{ab} being simple, lightlike, complex, and orthogonal on l^a. In a Minkowski frame adapted to the 2-spaces defined by v_{ab}, and

(1) A complete derivation of Petrov's type classification can be found in [5] The fact that a type II null Weyl tensor has no (rational) scalar invariants can also be gathered from the following considerations.

(2) This statement is made without regard to the field equations (or Bianchi identities) which imply $\partial_a \ln K = \lambda(\overset{2}{\xi}_a + i\overset{3}{\xi}_a) + \mu l_a$ (λ, μ complex). We ignore the case $\lambda = 0$ (plane waves), and find precisely two independent invariants of order 3. Thus there are even fewer lowest order invariants. See also [6].

such that $\partial_a \ln K$ is orthogonal on the time axis—such a frame is unique up to reflections—the only non-trivial components of S are the two real and two imaginary parts of the components of $\partial_a \ln K$ (note: $l^a \partial_a \ln K = 0$). They are the real and imaginary parts of $\overset{p}{J}$ defined by

$$l_{[a}\partial_{b]} \ln K = \overset{p}{J}\overset{p}{w}_{ab} \tag{9}$$

where $w_{ab} = l_{[a}\xi_{b]}, \; \xi^b \xi_b = 1$.

Generally the three scalar products J_a defined above are independent functions of the coordinates u, y, z; this means that they form a complete set. (The v-lines in (3) are the group orbits generated by the Killing vector l^a.) But there exist special cases in which they are not. For instance, take in (3):

$$H = F(u)G(y, z). \tag{10}$$

Now even the $\overset{p}{J}$ defined in (9) become independent of u, and we have to use invariants of order four to obtain a complete set. A u-dependent invariant J can, for instance, be obtained by expressing the vector $k_a \overset{\text{def}}{=} 2\,\mathrm{Re}(\partial^p \ln K)\,\mathrm{Re}(K^{-1}V_{ap}K)$ as a linear combination of the vectors $\mathrm{Re}\,\partial_a \ln K$, $\mathrm{Im}\,\partial_a \ln K$, l_a:

$$k_a = \lambda\,\mathrm{Re}\,\partial_a \ln K + \mu\,\mathrm{Im}\,\partial_a \ln K + \nu l_a \tag{11}$$

and multiplying the scalar ν by a suitable power of $|K|$ to make it independent of the constant gauge factor in l^a ($l^a{}_{;b} = 0$). In gauge independent form J can be defined by the equation:

$$\begin{aligned} &[(P_{bcde}{}^{;p}\overline{P}_{fghi} + P_{bcde}\overline{P}_{fghi}{}^{;p})(P_{jklm;pa}\overline{P}_{rstu} + P_{jklm}\overline{P}_{rstu;pa}) - \\ &- \{\lambda(P_{bcde;a}\overline{P}_{fghi} + P_{bcde}\overline{P}_{fghi;a}) + \mu(P_{bcde;a}\overline{P}_{fghi} - P_{bcde}\overline{P}_{fghi;a})\}P_{jklm}\overline{P}_{rstu}]^4 \\ &= 4\,[JP_{bcde}\overline{P}_{fghi}P_{jklm}\overline{P}_{rstu}]^4 P_{a_1 v a_2 w}\overline{P}_{a_3}{}^{v}{}_{a_4}{}^{w} \end{aligned} \tag{12}$$

where "$[\ldots]^4$" stands symbolically for the product of four factors, each given by the contents of the brackets, but with different indices. This proves the second statement in the abstract.

Acknowledgements—The author wishes to thank the members of Professor P. Jordan's seminar in Hamburg, especially Dr J. Ehlers and Dr R. Sachs, for much stimulating discussion. He also wishes to thank Professor P. Bergmann for his true hospitality in Syracuse. The author's stay in the United States is supported by the Flick foundation and by the N. S. F.

REFERENCES

[1] P. Jordan, J. Ehlers and W. Kundt, to be published in "Abhandl. Mainzer Akad. Wissu. Lit."

[2] T. Y. Thomas, *Differential Invariants of Generalized Spaces*, Princeton 1934, sections 85, 86.

[3] E. Cartan, *Leçons sur la Géométrie des Espaces de Riemann*, Paris 1946, No. 318.

[4] R. Weitzenböck, *Invariantenheorie*, Groningen 1923, VII, 10, p. 202.

[5] W. Kundt, Thesis, Hamburg 1958.

[6] J. Ehlers and W. Kundt, *The Theory of Gravitation*, New York, Chapt. 2.

SOME PROPERTIES OF THE RIEMANN-CHRISTOFFEL CURVATURE TENSOR

C. LANCZOS

Dublin Institute for Advanced Studies,
School of Theoretical Physics

THE great discovery of Einstein in the field of gravity called attention to the geometrical properties of a four-dimensional universe of Riemannian structure. The fundamental quantity of such a geometry is the Riemann–Christoffel curvature tensor R_{ijkm}. Under the impact of Einstein's gravitational theory the "contracted curvature tensor"

$$R_{ik} = R_{ijkm}g^{jm} \tag{1}$$

came in the focus of interest while the full curvature tensor receded in the background. On the other hand, we can hardly doubt that Riemannian geometry, even without any generalizations, may include a larger variety of phenomena than the mere gravitational fields, characterized by the vanishing of the "metrical matter tensor"

$$T_{ik} = R_{ik} - \tfrac{1}{2}Rg_{ik} = 0. \tag{2}$$

The present paper calls attention to some interesting properties of the full curvature tensor R_{ijkm} which may have some bearing on the behaviour of physical fields which are not of the gravitational variety.

SYMMETRIZATION OF THE CURVATURE TENSOR

The tensor R_{ijkm} can be written as the sum of two tensors:

$$S_{ikjm} = \tfrac{1}{2}(R_{ijkm} + R_{kjim}) \tag{3}$$

and

$$A_{ikjm} = \tfrac{1}{2}(R_{ijkm} - R_{kjim}). \tag{4}$$

The second tensor is of no particular interest because — in view of the cyclic identity — it is reducible to $-\frac{1}{2}R_{ikjm}$. The tensor (3), however, deserves special study. The symmetry properties of this tensor are given by the equations

$$S_{ijkm} = S_{jikm} = S_{ijmk} = S_{kmij}. \tag{5}$$

If we replace the first indexpair and the second indexpair by a single subscript which can assume $\nu = n(n+1)/2$ different values, we obtain a symmetric matrix of second order in a space of ν dimensions. Our tensor has thus, on account of the symmetry conditions $\varrho = \nu(\nu+1)/2$ algebraically independent components.

We can demonstrate, however, on the basis of the definition (3), that the tensor (3) satisfies also the cyclic identity

$$S_{ikjm} + S_{ijmk} + S_{imkj} = 0. \tag{6}$$

This proof demands only the customary symmetry properties of the Riemann tensor:

$$R_{ijkm} = -R_{jikm} = -R_{ijmk} = R_{kmij} \tag{7}$$

without making use of the cyclic identity.

The total number of independent conditions (7) is the number of "combinations with repetitions" of the order 4, formed out of n elements. This number is

$$\mu = \frac{n(n+1)(n+2)(n+3)}{24}. \tag{8}$$

Hence the total number of independent components that the tensor S_{ijkm} possesses, is

$$\varrho - \mu = \frac{n^2(n^2-1)}{12}. \tag{9}$$

The surprising fact that the tensor S_{ijkm} has just as many independent components as the original Riemann tensor, can be demonstrated by observing that in the case of the original tensor the number ν has to replaced by $\nu' = n(n-1)/2$ and the number μ by

$$\mu' = \frac{n(n-1)(n-2)(n-3)}{24} \tag{10}$$

because the combinations *without* repetitions have to be counted. Both numbers ϱ' and μ' follow from ϱ and μ by replacing n by $-n$. Since, however, the number of algebraically independent components of the Riemann tensor is an *even* function of n, the change from n to $-n$ leaves the number of components unchanged.

If the tensor of curvature would *not* satisfy the cyclic identity, then the relation (3) would not be reversible and the tensor R_{ijkm} could not be obtained from the tensor S_{ijkm}. In view of the cyclic identity, however, we obtain

$$R_{ijkm} = \tfrac{2}{3}(S_{ikjm} - S_{jkim}). \tag{11}$$

The tensor S_{ijkm} can thus be conceived as a full-fledged substitute for the original tensor R_{ijkm}.

CONSTRUCTION OF THE RIEMANN TENSOR

The advantage of the tensor S_{ijkm} is that it is more easily constructed than the original Riemann tensor. Let B_{ijkm} be a tensor of the symmetry properties (7), but not satisfying the cyclic identity. Then the tensor

$$S_{ikjm} = \tfrac{1}{2}(B_{ijkm} + B_{kjim}) \tag{12}$$

satisfies all the demanded algebraic conditions (symmetry properties (5), plus cyclic identity (6)), which are prescribed for this tensor. If we now construct the difference (11), we obtain

$$R_{ijkm} = \tfrac{1}{3}(2B_{ijkm} + B_{ikjm} + B_{imkj}). \tag{13}$$

This tensor satisfies all the algebraic conditions (symmetry properties plus cyclic identity) which are prescribed for the Riemann tensor.

A possible construction of the tensor B_{ijkm} can occur on the following general basis. Let us choose two tensors of second order A_{ik} and G_{ik} of no specified symmetry properties. If we now construct the tensor of fourth order

$$\begin{aligned} B_{ijkm} = {} & A_{ik}G_{jm} + A_{jm}G_{ik} - \\ & - A_{jk}G_{im} - A_{im}G_{jk} + \\ & + A_{ki}G_{mj} + A_{mj}G_{ki} - \\ & - A_{mi}G_{kj} - A_{kj}G_{mi} \end{aligned} \tag{14}$$

this tensor satisfies all the demanded symmetry conditions (7). Of particular interest is the case of choosing for the second tensor the metrical tensor g_{ik}:

$$G_{ik} = \tfrac{1}{2}g_{ik}. \tag{15}$$

In that case (14) can be replaced by the simpler expression:

$$B_{ijkm} = A_{ik}g_{jm} + A_{jm}g_{ik} - \\ - A_{jk}g_{im} - A_{im}g_{jk} \tag{16}$$

with the understanding that A_{ik} is *symmetric*; (the anti-symmetric part of A_{ik} drops out of the sum (14).)

If this expressions is substituted in (13), we obtain

$$R_{ijkm} = B_{ijkm} \tag{17}$$

that is, B_{ijkm} can be used as a Riemann tensor without any corrections.

The interesting feature of the expression (16) is that it yields the general Riemann tensor in two and three dimensions. In fact, in two dimensions the further simplification takes place that we can put

$$A_{ik} = \frac{R}{4} g_{ik} \tag{18}$$

while in three dimensions we obtain

$$A_{ik} = R_{ik} - \frac{R}{4} g_{ik}. \tag{19}$$

THE CASE OF FOUR DIMENSIONS

When we come to four dimensions, the representation (16) fails to yield the full Riemann tensor, because A_{ik} has only 10, the full Riemann tensor 20 independent algebraic components. Let us now return to the more general form (14) of the tensor B_{ijkm}. We will generalize the relation (15) by putting

$$G_{ik} = \tfrac{1}{2}(g_{ik} + \gamma_{ik}) \tag{20}$$

where γ_{ik} is anti-symmetric. This is reminiscent of Einstein's idea to introduce a non-symmetric line-element in the geometry of nature, in order to obtain an anti-symmetric tensor for the interpretation of electromagnetic phenomena. In our present discussion γ_{ik} plays only *formally* the role of the anti-symmetric portion of the line-element, but in fact we have not abandoned Riemannian geometry with its symmetric line-element.

Similarly we want to leave A_{ik} as a *general* tensor of second order, or we may equally say that we replace A_{ik} by $A_{ik} + a_{ik}$ where A_{ik} is symmetric and a_{ik} anti-symmetric. Once more we can conceive

a_{ik} as a formal analogy of the anti-symmetric part of R_{ik} with which Einstein operated in his later unified field theories.

We now obtain

$$\begin{aligned} B_{ijkm} = & A_{ik}g_{jm} + A_{jm}g_{ik} - \\ & - A_{jk}g_{im} - A_{im}g_{jk} + \\ & + a_{ik}\gamma_{jm} + a_{jm}\gamma_{ik} - \\ & - a_{jk}\gamma_{im} - a_{im}\gamma_{jk}. \end{aligned} \tag{21}$$

Substituting this B_{ijkm} in (13) yields

$$\begin{aligned} R_{ijkm} = & A_{ik}g_{jm} + A_{jm}g_{ik} - \\ & - A_{jk}g_{im} - A_{im}g_{jk} + \\ & + \tfrac{1}{3}[2a_{ij}\gamma_{km} - a_{ik}\gamma_{mj} - a_{im}\gamma_{jk} + \\ & + 2a_{km}\gamma_{ij} - a_{mj}\gamma_{ik} - a_{jk}\gamma_{im}]. \end{aligned} \tag{22}$$

We have obtained a representation of the full Riemann tensor in four dimensions which has a sufficient number of degrees of freedom: we have the 10 components of A_{ik}, the 6 components of a_{ik} and the 6 components of γ_{ik} at our disposal, altogether 22 quantities for the representation of 20 components. The form of the representation is such that a factor in either a_{ik} or γ_{ik} must remain undetermined and thus we can normalize this factor by putting

$$\gamma_{ik}\gamma^{ik} = 1. \tag{23}$$

This leaves only *one* surplus degree of freedom. It is this freedom which is the weakness of the representation (22) since in the purely algebraic realm we have no inherent principle at our disposal for the removal of this freedom. We will assume that the second invariant associated with the tensor γ_{ik} vanishes:

$$\gamma_{ik}\gamma^{*ik} = 0. \tag{24}$$

We will show that this is a possible, although by no means necessary hypothesis. (1)

Contraction over j, m yields

$$A_{ik} = \tfrac{1}{2}R_{ik} - \tfrac{1}{2}(a_i{}^{\mu}\gamma_{k\mu} + a_k{}^{\mu}\gamma_{i\mu}) - \left(\frac{R}{6} - \frac{a}{3}\right)g_{ik} \tag{25}$$

where

$$a = a_{ik}\gamma^{ik}. \tag{26}$$

(1) The unsatisfactory feature of these normalizations is that they do not permit the superposition of weak fields. If weak normalized fields are superposed, the resulting field is not normalized.

The symmetric tensor A_{ik} is thus reducible to the contracted tensor R_{ik} and the two anti-symmetric tensors a_{ik} and γ_{ik}.

The determination of the two tensors a_{ik} and γ_{ik} must involve all the four indices since in three dimensions this part of the Riemann tensor drops out. For the sake of algebraic simplicity we will assume that we have introduced a local reference system in which the g_{ik} assume their normal values δ_{ik}; (this still leaves an orthogonal transformation free.) We then find that in the following 10 combinations of curvature components the A_{ik} drop out and only the a_{ik} and γ_{ik} appear:

$$R_{1234}, \quad R_{1342}$$

$$\left.\begin{array}{lll} R_{1314}-R_{2324}, & R_{1214}-R_{3234}, & R_{1213}-R_{4243}, \\ R_{2124}-R_{3134}, & R_{2123}-R_{4143}, & R_{3132}-R_{4142}, \end{array}\right\} \tag{27}$$

$$\left.\begin{array}{l} R_{1212}+R_{3434}-R_{1313}-R_{2424}, \\ R_{1212}+R_{3434}-R_{1414}-R_{2323}. \end{array}\right\}$$

We will simplify our algebraic problem by assuming that by a local orthogonal transformation we bring one of the tensors, e.g. γ_{ik}, to a normal form. We can use up four parameters of the six-parameter rotation group to make

$$\gamma_{12}=\gamma_{13}=\gamma_{24}=\gamma_{34}=0 \tag{28}$$

retaining only the two components γ_{23} and γ_{14} as differing from zero. We can satisfy the two normalization conditions (23) and (24) by putting

$$\gamma_{23}=1, \quad \gamma_{14}=0. \tag{29}$$

The tensor γ_{ik} is now uniquely determined. This choice of the coordinates demands the following four relations (which are incidentally not influenced by the two normalization conditions (29) but hold equally without normalization):[1]

$$\left.\begin{array}{l} R_{2124}-R_{3134}=0, \\ R_{1213}-R_{4243}=0, \\ R_{2143}+R_{2413}=0, \\ R_{2121}-R_{2424}-R_{3131}+R_{3434}=0. \end{array}\right. \tag{30}$$

[1] That these conditions can always be satisfied by a *real* Lorentz transformation, is by no means self-evident and requires further investigation.

In this reference system only six conditions remain for the determination of the a_{ik}; (the others are satisfied by the choice of the reference system)

$$R_{2123}-R_{4143} = a_{21}$$

$$R_{2423}-R_{1413} = a_{24}$$

$$R_{3432}-R_{1412} = -a_{34}$$

$$R_{3132}-R_{4142} = -a_{31}$$

$$R_{1234} = -\tfrac{1}{3}a_{14}$$

$$R_{2323}+R_{4141}-R_{2121}-R_{4343} = 2a_{23}.$$

THE SCHWARZSCHILD FIELD

It seems of interest to apply the general relations to a known example. In the case of a pure gravitational field the contracted curvature tensor R_{ik} vanishes and the field becomes completely reducible to the two anti-symmetric fields a_{ik} and γ_{ik}. We choose the particular example of the Schwarzschild line-element which is static and spherically symmetric:

$$ds^2 = -A(r)dr^2 - r^2(d\theta^2+\sin^2\theta\, d\varphi^2)+A^{-1}(r)dt^2, \qquad A(r) = \frac{1}{1-\dfrac{2m}{r}}. \tag{32}$$

In this field all the curvature components which are not of the form R_{ijij}, vanish. Hence the first three conditions of the special coordinate system (30) are already fulfilled. Furthermore, let us put

$$\varrho_{ij} = \frac{R_{ijij}}{g_{ii}g_{jj}} \tag{33}$$

and

$$p = \frac{1}{2}\frac{A'}{rA^2}. \tag{34}$$

Then we obtain

$$\varrho_{12} = \varrho_{13} = \varrho_{24} = \varrho_{34} = p, \qquad \varrho_{14} = \varrho_{23} = -2p. \tag{35}$$

Hence the last of the conditions (30) is also fulfilled and we are confronted with the special reference system we have studied in (29) and (30). We now obtain

$$a_{12} = a_{13} = a_{14} = a_{24} = a_{34} = 0,$$

$$a_{23} = -3p = \frac{3m}{r^3}. \tag{36}$$

This shows that the tensors a_{ik} and γ_{ik} are *proportional to each other*. This holds at first for spherically symmetric fields only. Since, however, for weak fields the principle of superposition holds, we can extend the law of proportionality to more general gravitational fields of weak and quasi-stationary character, such as the gravitational field of the planetary system.[1]

If we represent the anti-symmetric tensor a_{ik} in the usual manner with the help of two vectors $\boldsymbol{E}$ and $\boldsymbol{H}$ (corresponding to the electric and magnetic field strengths of electromagnetism), we observe that the static and spherically symmetric gravitational field shows a certain analogy to a static and spherically symmetric electric field, with an $\boldsymbol{E}$ which is radially oriented and an $\boldsymbol{H}$ which is zero. The distribution law of the field strengths and their dynamical action is totally different, however, in the two cases.

ELECTROMAGNETISM

A special case of particular interest occurs if we assume that the tensor A_{ik} is proportional to g_{ik} and a_{ik} to γ_{ik}. Since a factor in γ_{ik} is free, we can in fact *equate* a_{ik} to γ_{ik}. In that case we have

$$A_{ik} = \frac{\lambda}{6} g_{ik}, \qquad a_{ik} = \gamma_{ik}. \tag{37}$$

The contraction of (22) over j, m now yields

$$R_{ik} = \lambda g_{ik} + 2a_i^{\mu} a_{k\mu} \tag{38}$$

and if we put

$$\lambda = \lambda_0 - \tfrac{1}{2} a_{ik} a^{ik} \tag{39}$$

we obtain a cosmological field, combined with a Maxwellian electromagnetic field. The assumptions (37) and (38) are not permissible,

---

[1] In the course of superposition the two normalization conditions (23) and (24) cannot be maintained.

of course, in view of the Bianchi conditions, but they are permissible if the proper corrections are made. The resulting matter tensor seems to indicate that the general decomposition (22) of Riemann's curvature tensor is in harmony with both the gravitational and electromagnetic aspects of nature.

CONCLUSIONS

We have started with a representation of the Riemann–Christoffel tensor in 2 and 3 dimensions. We have seen that this representation can be extended to four dimensions if we formally assume that the line-element and the contracted curvature tensor possess an anti-symmetric part. We thus obtain an explicit representation of the full curvature tensor with the help of 22 components which demand two normalization conditions in order to reduce them to the required 20 components. The appearance of the two fundamental phenomena of gravitation and electromagnetism may have something to do with the symmetric and the anti-symmetric part of the proposed decomposition. We have not investigated, however, the question of the field equations and have no right to claim that these formal results are of necessity of physical importance.

ON A GENERALLY COVARIANT QUANTUM THEORY*

B. E. LAURENT

Institute for Theoretical Physics, University of Stockholm

Summary—A theory, expressed *ab initio* in generally covariant form, and satisfying the usual quantum postulates, is outlined. The basis for the theory is the structure of the general coordinate transformation group and a way of representing it introduced by Klein [1]. Various representations of the general coordinate transformation group are discussed. As a particular example the mixed second rank tensor density (weight $\frac{1}{2}$) field is treated in some detail due to its possible connexion with gravitation.

I. INTRODUCTION

In the past, many methods have been tried for combining general relativity and quantum theory. In these attempts, one has, naturally, started from classical gravitation theory and applied various quantization procedures. It seems as if this kind of approach towards a general relativistically covariant quantum theory should not be too far from success, in spite of all the difficult problems in connexion with it.

Instead of starting with a definite classical theory, we will try in this paper to construct a covariant quantum theory based on the structure of the group of general coordinate transformations. This will be done using ideas developed by Klein [1].

In Section II, some general properties of the coordinate transformation group are summarized. In [1] the group considered differed in some respects from the coordinate transformation group;(1) we shall therefore express, in Sections III and IV, parts of [1] in terms

* Work supported by the National Science Foundation, Contract No. NSF-G-4356, Institute of Field Physics, University of North Carolina, Chapel Hill.

(1) Specifically, the Jacobian need not be unity and the coefficients $a^{\mu}{}_{,\nu}$ of the transformation (see formula (1)) are not all independent here.

of the latter group. In these sections, a particular method for the construction of unitary repesentations of the coordinate transformation group is given.

Sections V and VI, finally, are devoted to a discussion of gravitation-like representations.

II. GENERAL PROPERTIES OF THE COORDINATE TRANSFORMATION GROUP

Let us consider the group of general coordinate transformations[1]

$$x' = a(x) = x + \alpha(x), \qquad \left|\frac{\partial x'}{\partial x}\right| \neq 0, \tag{1}$$

and a unitary representation of it composed of matrices $D[a(x)]$, where D is a functional of the functions $a(x)$.

The tangent vectors, $Q_\mu(x)$, at the unit element of the group are defined by

$$Q_\mu(x) \equiv \left.\frac{\delta D}{\delta\alpha^\mu(x)}\right|_{\alpha=0}. \tag{2}$$

The right-hand side of (2) is a functional derivative with respect to the functions $\alpha^\mu(x)$.

The $Q_\mu(x)$ are antihermitian because D is unitary. They transform as components of a covariant vector density (see Appendix 1) and fulfill the following Lie integrability conditions

$$[Q_\mu(x'), Q_\nu(x'')] = -Q_\nu(x')\,\delta_{,\mu}(x'-x'') + Q_\mu(x'')\,\delta_{,\nu}(x''-x'). \tag{3}$$

This formula is derived in Appendix 1. A straightforward calculation shows that it is covariant.[2]

The reason why unitary representations of the group are interesting is well known from discussions of the Lorentz group (see for instance Bargmann and Wigner [2]). To each transformation (1), there must exist an active transformation of the quantum mechanical state vector

$$\Psi' = D[a(x)]\Psi. \tag{4}$$

The requirement that the inner product[3] $(\Psi, \Psi) > 0$ be invariant under the transformation shows that D is unitary apart from

---

[1] Here, and often in what follows, we omit the indices on the coordinates.

[2] The author wishes to thank Dr B. DeWitt for clearing up a mistake in this connexion.

[3] We exclude indefinite metric, though this case is a possibility when the physical vector space is a proper subspace of the space considered (see Sec. IV).

a similarity transformation.(1) Hence the set of matrices $D[a(x)]$ is a unitary representation of the group.

In the following section, a method will be given for the construction of such representations or, what is the same, sets of antihermitian operators $Q_\mu(x)$ satisfying (3).

III. THE BASIC FIELDS

Following [1] we introduce certain "basic fields" satisfying simple commutation relations and construct from these fields operators Q satisfying our requirements. The procedure is best shown by examples. Let us, as a first example, choose one closely connected with the example treated in [1].

As basic fields, we introduce one covariant vector field operator, $\varphi_\mu(x)$, and one contravariant vector density field operator, $\pi^\mu(x)$. They are both assumed to be hermitian and to fulfill the commutation relations

$$[\varphi_\mu(x'), \varphi_\nu(x'')] = 0, \tag{5}$$

$$[\pi^\mu(x'), \pi^\nu(x'')] = 0, \tag{6}$$

$$[\varphi_\mu(x'), \pi^\nu(x'')] = i\delta^\nu_\mu \delta(x' - x''). \tag{7}$$

In [1], π^μ was assumed to be an ordinary contravariant vector and (7) was not covariant under transformations with Jacobians different from unity. Due to the density property of π^μ, (5)–(7) are here covariant under arbitrary coordinate transformations. One can show by straightforward computations that the $Q_\mu(x)$ in the expression(2)

$$Q_\mu = -i(\varphi_\mu \pi^\nu)_{,\nu} + i\varphi_{\nu,\mu}\pi^\nu \tag{8}$$

are antihermitian and satisfy the commutation relations (3). In fact, by calculating

$$\delta\varphi_\mu(x) = \int [\varphi_\mu(x), Q_\nu(x')]\, a^\nu(x')\, dx' \tag{9}$$

and

$$\delta\pi^\mu(x) = \int [\pi^\mu(x), Q_\nu(x')]\, a^\nu(x')\, dx', \tag{10}$$

(1) In the following D is always taken to be unitary.

(2) When the same coordinate argument appears everywhere in an equation we do not as a rule write it down explicitly. Symmetrization of terms with noncommuting factors in (8) and in similar expressions in the following is understood.

and considering $a^{\nu}(x')$ as infinitesimal, one finds the active variations of φ_{μ} and π^{μ} corresponding to infinitesimal coordinate transformations. When put into (9), the first term in (8) gives the contribution from the vector transformation while the second one gives the translation term. The corresponding terms for other kinds of fields satisfying relations like (5)–(7) are easily found. Thus one can find a great number of antihermitian representations of (4). Two more examples will be given later.

By performing the differentiation in the first term of (8), one finds that

$$Q_{\mu} = -i\varphi_{\mu}\pi^{\nu}{}_{,\nu} + i(\varphi_{\nu,\mu} - \varphi_{\mu,\nu})\pi^{\nu}. \tag{11}$$

This shows explicitly the covariance of the equation.[1]

IV. THE PHYSICAL FIELDS

So far nothing has been explicitly said about the nature and dimensionality of the space in which we perform the coordinate transformation but the idea is of course to apply what we have done to the four-dimensional space-time continuum. One then immediately notices that all kinds of dynamical operator equations of the "basic fields" must contradict the commutation relations (5)–(7) which state that any field quantity at one space-time point commutes with all the field quantities at any other space-time point. Hence the basic fields (e.g. φ_{μ} and π^{μ}) cannot be physical fields (e.g. vector meson fields). Now, the physical fields are not directly observables in quantum field theories and no damage is done to the theory if they are replaced by other quantities which may be easier to handle; but still the following question remains to be answered: How does dynamics enter the theory? An answer was given in [1] by using subsidiary conditions to pick out from the state vector space a subspace containing the dynamically realizable state vectors (or physical state vectors). We will denote such a vector by Ψ_p.

It is clear that also the Ψ_p vectors must form a representation of the transformation group, i.e. the physical subspace must be an invariant subspace. The simplest way of obtaining this is to use a subsidiary condition of the form

$$A\Psi_p = 0, \tag{12}$$

[1] The expression in [1] corresponding to (8) differs from it due to the differences between the respective groups (see footnote [1] p. 323).

where A is a covariant set of quantities constructed from the basic fields.[(1)]

As to the question of what are here the observable quantities, it can be said that they must have, among other properties, the property that, when they operate on a physical vector, they transform it into another physical vector. For the interpretation of the theory, such operators must be constructed from the basic fields. We already know one example of such quantities. They are the Q_μ operators in (11). With A being a covariant, it is immediately clear that they transform the Ψ_p vectors of (12) into each other, due to their property of generating the coordinate transformations (9) and (10).

V. SECOND RANK TENSORS AS BASIC FIELDS

In order to come a little closer to gravitation, let us try to choose as basic fields one covariant symmetric tensor $h_{\mu\nu}$ and one contravariant symmetric tensor density $f^{\mu\nu}$. They are both assumed to be hermitian and to satisfy the following covariant commutation relations

$$[h_{\mu\nu}(x'), h_{\varkappa\lambda}(x'')] = 0, \tag{13}$$

$$[f^{\mu\nu}(x'), f^{\varkappa\lambda}(x'')] = 0, \tag{14}$$

$$[h_{\mu\nu}(x'), f^{\varkappa\lambda}(x'')] = i(\delta^\varkappa_\mu\delta^\lambda_\nu + \delta^\varkappa_\nu\delta^\lambda_\mu)\,\delta(x'-x''). \tag{15}$$

Using the general rules for constructing the Q_μ field given in connection with the vector field example, one obtains in this case

$$Q_\mu = -ih_{\mu\varkappa}f^{\varkappa\lambda}{}_{,\lambda} - \tfrac{1}{2}i(h_{\mu\varkappa,\lambda} + h_{\mu\lambda,\varkappa} - h_{\lambda\varkappa,\mu})f^{\varkappa\lambda}. \tag{16}$$

Using the $h_{\mu\nu}$ field like the metric to lower indices and to define covariant derivatives, (16) can be written

$$Q_\mu = -if^\sigma_{\mu;\sigma}, \tag{17}$$

which expression is explicity covariant. So far everything is easy but the formulation of the subsidiary conditions remains to be done. It is well known from linear quantum field theories that a subsidiary condition like (12) must contain only annihilation operators. Otherwise difficulties arise concerning the normalization of the state vectors.[(2)] There is no reason to believe that we are better off in a theory of the kind outlined here. Klein used only annihilation

(1) (12) was used in [1] in connexion with Maxwell and Dirac fields. A was there taken to be the annihilation part of the left side of the field equations.

(2) See e.g. [3] p. 100.

operators in his formulation of the subsidiary conditions in the Maxwell and Dirac cases (there he did not require general invariance and the conditions were linear).

It is, however, not possible in any simple fashion to combine our $h_{\mu\nu}$ and $f^{\mu\nu}$ fields to obtain a field and its hermitian conjugate field, which satisfy the usual commutation relations for annihilation and creation operators.[1] This is so because $h_{\mu\nu}$ and $f^{\mu\nu}$ transform differently.

As a matter of fact this difficulty does show up already in the Maxwell case, but in a milder form. It is responsible for the well-known and troublesome fact that, for the fourth component of the vector potential, annihilation and creation operators are interchanged.

The only simple way out of this seems to be to use as basic field not $h_{\mu\nu}$, but a field C^{ν}_{μ} transforming as a mixed tensor density of weight one half. We assume C^{ν}_{μ} to be hermitian and consider it as the sum of a non-hermitian field $\frac{1}{\sqrt{2}} B^{\nu}_{\mu}$ and its hermitian conjugate field

$$C^{\nu}_{\mu} = \frac{1}{\sqrt{2}} (B^{\nu}_{\mu} + B^{+\nu}_{\ \ \mu}). \tag{18}$$

Further we assume the commutation relations

$$[B^{\mu}_{\nu}(x'), B^{\varkappa}_{\lambda}(x'')] = 0, \tag{19}$$

$$[B^{+\mu}_{\ \ \nu}(x'), B^{+\varkappa}_{\ \ \lambda}(x'')] = 0, \tag{20}$$

$$[B^{\mu}_{\nu}(x'), B^{+\varkappa}_{\ \ \lambda}(x'')] = \delta^{\mu}_{\lambda}\delta^{\varkappa}_{\nu}\delta(x'-x''), \tag{21}$$

which are covariant if the B^{ν}_{μ} are assumed to transform like the C^{ν}_{μ}. (19)–(21) have exactly the required appearance of commutation relations for annihilation and creation operators.

The Q_{μ} for this case are

$$Q_{\mu} = (B^{+\sigma}_{\ \ \alpha} B^{\alpha}_{\mu})_{,\sigma} - (B^{+\alpha}_{\ \ \mu} B^{\sigma}_{\alpha})_{,\sigma} + \tfrac{1}{2} B^{+\alpha}_{\ \ \beta,\mu} B^{\beta}_{\alpha} - \tfrac{1}{2} B^{+\beta}_{\ \ \alpha} B^{\alpha}_{\beta,\mu}. \tag{22}$$

VI. DYNAMICAL EQUATIONS FOR THE MIXED TENSOR-CASE

The dynamics for the C^{ν}_{μ} field must be expressed through subsidiary conditions containing B^{ν}_{μ} and $B^{+\nu}_{\ \ \mu}$ (and no other fields; no metric for instance). We also know that these should have some connexion with Einstein's equations.

[1] Here we refer only to the formal property of these operators (see Eqs (19)–(21)) because no dynamics has been introduced so far.

It is natural then to look first for a set of classical, covariant equations for C_μ^ν related to Einstein's equations. How such a set may be found is shown in [4]. These equations consist of terms that are products of the C_μ^ν and their derivatives. Let us write them symbolically

$$E(C) = 0. \tag{23}$$

One way of translating equations of this type to quantum mechanics is the following: First we put

$$\Psi^+ NE(C)\Psi = 0 \tag{24}$$

where N stands for "normal order", i. e. all creation operators are to the left of all annihilation operators. The normal-ordering is an invariant operation (see Appendix 2). We then notice that the terms in $NE(C)$ always appear in pairs in which one of the terms is the hermitian conjugate of the other. Thus we can split $NE(C)$ into two terms

$$NE(C) = e(B, B^+) + e^+(B, B^+) \tag{25}$$

where $e(B, B^+)$ contains, among other terms, the one consisting of B-factors (1) only. One unambiguous and invariant, though somewhat arbitrary, manner of performing this splitting will be shown in an appendix.

As subsidiary condition we now take (2)

$$e(B, B^+)\Psi = 0, \tag{26}$$

from which equation the equation (24) follows according to (25).

VII. CONCLUSION

The intention of this paper has been to investigate the possibility of constructing a covariant quantum theory along the lines set out in the introduction; so far no definite obstacle has been encountered.

It is tempting to try to found the dynamics not, as above, on correspondence-like assumptions regarding the subsidiary conditions but on irreducible, unitary representations of the general coordinate

(1) For definition see Appendix 2.

(2) There is no reason to believe that the subsidiary condition must contain annihilation operators *only*, like in the linear case. What we demand is that the last operator on the right hand side in any term should not be a creation operator.

transformation group, i.e. a procedure similar to the one used for the Lorentz-transformation group (see e.g. [2]). It is probably true that very few of these representations will correspond to physical reality and some kind of selection principle must still be employed. It is possible, however, that this principle can be simply expressed.

The reason why we have not followed this path here is partly due to mathematical difficulties and partly due to the the intricate problem of the physical interpretation in a theory so far removed from the current ones.

Acknowledgements—The author wishes to thank, in particular, Professor Oskar Klein for his inspiration and valuable criticism. Professors Bryce and Cecile DeWitt for their hospitality and many discussions at the University of North Carolina, and Dr Stanley Deser for helpful criticism.

REFERENCES

[1] O. Klein, *Niels Bohr and the Development of Physics*, Pergamon Press, 1955, p. 96.
[2] V. Bargmann and E. P. Wigner, *Proc. Nat. Acad. Sci., Wash.* **34**, 211 (1948).
[3] J. M. Jauch and F. Rohrlich, *The Theory of Photons and Electrons*, Addison-Wesley, 1955.
[4] B. E. Laurent, *Ark. f. Phys.*, **16**, 247 (1959).

APPENDIX 1

Transformation properties and commutation relations for the Q-field

We write (1) and its inverse transformation

$$x' = a(x) = x + \alpha(x), \tag{A1}$$

$$x = a^{-1}(x') = x' + \alpha^{-1}(x'). \tag{A2}$$

Then

$$D^{-1}[\alpha(x)]D[\beta(x)]D[\alpha(x)] = D[\gamma(x)] \tag{A3}$$

is correct if

$$\gamma(x) = \alpha(x) + \beta[x + \alpha(x)] + \alpha^{-1}\{x + \alpha(x) + \beta[x + \alpha(x)]\}. \tag{A4}$$

Differentiating (A3) with respect to $\beta^{\mu}(x')$ and putting $\beta = 0$, we obtain, using (2), the transformation law for the Q-field

$$D^{-1}[\alpha]Q_{\mu}(x')D[\alpha] = \int Q_{\alpha}(x)\frac{\delta\gamma^{\alpha}(x)}{\delta\beta^{\mu}(x')}\bigg|_{\beta=0} dx. \tag{A5}$$

In the right-hand side, we have used the fact that $\gamma = 0$ if $\beta = 0$. This follows from (A4). Differentiating (A5) with respect to $\alpha^\nu(x'')$ and putting $\alpha = 0$, we obtain the commutation relations

$$[Q_\mu(x'), Q_\nu(x'')] = \int Q_\alpha(x) \left. \frac{\delta^2 \gamma^\alpha(x)}{\delta \alpha^\nu(x'') \, \delta \beta^\mu(x')} \right|_{\alpha=\beta=0} dx. \tag{A6}$$

What remains is only to calculate the right-hand sides of (A5) and (A6) with the help of (A4). We obtain

$$\frac{\delta \gamma^\alpha(x)}{\delta \beta^\mu(x')} = \delta^\alpha_\mu \delta[x + \alpha(x) - x'] +$$

$$+ \alpha^{-1^\alpha}{}_{,\varrho}\{x + \alpha(x) + \beta[x + \alpha(x)]\} \delta^\varrho_\mu (x + \alpha(x) - x'),$$

$$\left. \frac{\delta \gamma^\alpha(x)}{\delta \beta^\mu(x')} \right|_{\beta=0} = \delta(x + \alpha(x) - x') \left[\delta^\alpha_\mu + \alpha^{-1^\alpha}{}_{,\mu}(x + \alpha(x))\right] \tag{A7}$$

and

$$\left. \frac{\delta^2 \gamma^\alpha(x)}{\delta \alpha^\nu(x'') \, \delta \beta^\mu(x')} \right|_{\alpha=\beta=0}$$

$$= \delta^\alpha_\mu \delta_{,\sigma}(x - x') \delta^\sigma_\nu \delta(x - x'') + \left. \frac{\delta \alpha^{-1^\alpha}{}_{,\mu}(x)}{\delta \alpha^\nu(x'')} \right|_{\alpha=0} \delta(x - x')$$

$$= \delta^\alpha_\mu \delta_{,\nu}(x - x') \delta(x - x'') - \delta^\alpha_\nu \delta_{,\mu}(x - x'') \, \delta(x - x'). \tag{A8}$$

From (A7) and (A5) with the substitution

$$y = x + \alpha(x) \tag{A9}$$

one obtains

$$Q'_\mu(x') = D^{-1}[\alpha] Q_\mu(x') D[\alpha]$$

$$= \int Q_\alpha[y + \alpha^{-1}(y)] \, \delta(y - x') \, [\delta^\alpha_\mu + \alpha^{-1^\alpha}{}_{,\mu}(y)] \left| \frac{\partial x}{\partial y} \right| dy$$

$$= \left| \frac{\partial x}{\partial y} \right|_{y=x'} Q_\alpha[x' + \alpha^{-1}(x')] \, [\delta^\alpha_\mu + \alpha^{-1^\alpha}{}_{,\mu}(x')]$$

where $|\partial x / \partial y|$ stands for the inverse Jacobian of the transformation (A9). Hence if we define

$$x = x' + \alpha^{-1}(x'), \qquad x' = x + \alpha(x)$$

(previously x has been used only as an integration variable), we obtain

$$Q'_\mu(x') = \left| \frac{\partial x}{\partial x'} \right| \frac{\partial x^\alpha}{\partial x'^\mu} Q_\alpha(x). \tag{A10}$$

(A10) shows that the Q_a transform together as a covariant vector density. Finally, we use (A8) in (A6), which gives

$$[Q_\mu(x'), Q_\nu(x'')] = Q_\mu(x'')\,\delta_{,\nu}(x''-x') - Q_\nu(x')\,\delta_{,\mu}(x'-x''). \qquad \text{(A11)}$$

This is the formula (3).

APPENDIX 2

Splitting of a normal-ordered product

It will be shown here that the normal-ordered product $NE(C)$ in (24) can be split up in a sum like (25) consisting of two hermitian conjugate terms, each of which transforms like the covariant $E(C)$.

First we notice that the normal-ordering does not affect the transformation property of $E(C)$. This follows simply by applying the ordering to both members of the transformation formula for $E(C)$. We are going to use the term "B-factor" to mean a B or a derivative of B appearing in a product of B's, B^+'s and their derivatives. The corresponding definition applies to "B^+-factor". A product of the kind mentioned here gives, in general, several terms when transformed, but each of these terms must contain the same number of B-factors as the original product (and consequently also the same number of B^+-factors as the original product).

It is now obvious that the terms in $NE(C)$ which contain a certain number of B-factors must form a sum which transforms exactly like $E(C)$.

An example of the kind of splitting we want is the following: Let $e(B, B^+)$ in (25) be formed by all the terms in $NE(C)$ containing more B-factors than B^+-factors and one half times all the terms containing equally many B- and B^+-factors. The remaining terms form a sum which is the hermitian conjugate of $e(B, B^+)$. (This special splitting is of course to a large extent arbitrary and there might be reasons for using a different one.)

This accomplishes what we desired because apparently $e(B, B^+)$ transforms like $E(C)$.

LOCALLY ISOMETRIC SPACE-TIMES

L. Marder

Department of Mathematics, University of Exeter

Abstract—The local intrinsic geometry of a solution of Einstein's gravitational equations need not fully determine the nature of the field. This is shown by a consideration of the properties, for varying values of an arbitrary parameter, of a complete physically reasonable solution.

1. INTRODUCTION

Because of the essentially local character of the general theory of relativity, one might expect that the local metrical structure of a solution, together with appropriate boundary and continuity conditions, determines all the properties of the gravitational field. However, in a recent paper [1] the writer showed by means of simple examples that experimentally distinguishable fields can correspond to space-time regions whose differences are entirely topological. One example showed in particular that a solution may be singularity-free everywhere, and locally flat except in a finite non-empty region, although the empty space-time admits no universal Minkowskian coordinate system and possesses what would sensibly be regarded as a non-trivial gravitational field. A second example related to the effect of a cylindrical pulse wave on a background cylindrically symmetric static field. The local intrinsic geometry of the background field is unaffected by the passage of the wave, but there is a change in topology which would be detected by suitable experiments with light-rays or test particles.

However, neither of these examples refers to possible fields in nature. It was shown that in the first case the source of the field would need to consist at least partly of matter with negative density; in the second the source is infinite. A question which remained unanswered, therefore, was whether locally isometric exterior solutions exist for distinct physically realizable fields. In this paper we show that they *do* exist by giving the construction for a set of such solutions, a field being regarded here as physically realizable if its sources are finite with positive density and moderate stresses, and if the continuity conditions of Lichnerowicz [2] are satisfied everywhere. No discussion is given of internal equations of state.

It is convenient first to recall the solutions for locally isometric cylindrical space-times, upon which our construction is based.

2. CYLINDRICALLY SYMMETRIC FIELDS

The metric for the exterior field of a static infinite cylinder may be expressed in the canonical form [3]:

$$ds^2 = r^{2C}dt^2 - r^{2(1-C)}d\varphi^2 - A^2 r^{-2C(1-C)}(dr^2 + dz^2) \tag{1}$$

where r, φ and z are effectively cylindrical polar coordinates with φ ranging from 0 to 2π, t is the timelike coordinate, and C and A are constants depending on the source distribution. We choose $A > 0$, and on physical grounds shall assume $0 \leqslant C < 1$.

It was shown in [3] that the permanent effect of the emission by the source of a cylindrical pulse wave (of finite duration except for a residual "tail") is to reduce the value of A without affecting C. For any given value of C, the set of exterior solutions (1) generated as A varies represents a set of physically distinguishable fields, although each solution has the same local intrinsic geometry.

Given two solutions of the set their local isometry is easily seen, since we can transform one into the other by simple changes of coordinate scale. But the two solutions, which then have the same C and A, no longer have the same range for the angular coordinate φ. The situation is most clearly illustrated by the particular case $C = 0$, which corresponds to locally flat space-time (the Riemann tensor vanishing identically). On putting

$$r' = Ar, \qquad z' = Az, \qquad \varphi' = \varphi/A \tag{2}$$

in (1), we obtain

$$ds^2 = dt^2 - r'^2 d\varphi'^2 - dr'^2 - dz'^2. \tag{3}$$

If (2) is to be merely a coordinate transformation, then φ' will range from 0 to $2\pi/A$. It follows that although (3) is locally flat for all $A \neq 0$, there is no universal Minkowskian coordinate system for the exterior space-time unless $A = 1$. For every other value of A each 2-surface $t = \text{const}$, $z' = \text{const}$ has the geometry of a Euclidean cone.

Consider possible paths of light-rays in space-time (3). These include the lines

$$r'\cos(\varphi' - \alpha) = \text{const}, \qquad z' = \text{const}$$

where α is an arbitrary constant. Suppose two such rays to be emitted at the same time t, from a point $r' = r'_0$, $\varphi' = 0$, $z' = z'_0$, in directions symmetrically inclined to the 2-space $\varphi' = 0$. The equations of their paths will take the form

$$r'\cos(\varphi' \pm \beta) = r'_0 \cos\beta, \qquad z' = z'_0$$

where the constant β depends on the angle of inclination and may be chosen so that $0 \leqslant \beta < \frac{1}{2}\pi$. Because $\varphi' = -\pi/A$ is to be identified with $\varphi' = \pi/A$, we find that if $A > 1$ and $\beta > \pi(1/A - \frac{1}{2})$ the two paths intersect in a second point

$$r' = r'_0 \cos\beta \sec(\pi/A - \beta), \qquad \varphi' = \pi/A, \qquad z' = z'_0.$$

By symmetry the rays reach this point simultaneously. Hence it is natural to regard the source (for which a model with positive density is easily constructed) as having the effect of deflecting light-rays just as occurs, say, in Schwarzschild's space-time. The extent of this deflection clearly depends on the value of A, the source attracting or repelling the rays according as A is greater or less than 1.(1) The case $A > 1$ is illustrated in Fig. 1 which represents the 2-space $z' = z'_0$. Here the line OB is identified with OC as $\varphi' = \pi/A$, the point O being $r' = 0$. The rays are emitted from D and pass on opposite sides of the source (shaded), meeting again at $B \equiv C$.

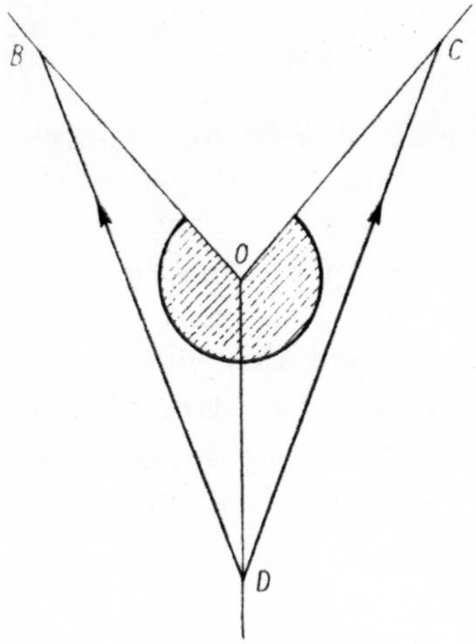

FIG. 1

A similar analysis is possible when $C \neq 0$, showing that the properties of the gravitational field corresponding to (1) depend on both the constants C and A, although the local metrical properties depend on C alone. When $C = 0$ and $A \neq 1$ the space-time

(1) Exactly the same behaviour occurs with the motion of test particles, whose paths coincide with those of light-rays and are independent of the speed of projection.

is locally flat but the gravitational field could hardly be considered trivial.

We next show that the exterior solution, can be extended to the interior of a particular source with positive density. For this purpose, it is convenient to work with a form slightly different from (1) for the general exterior metric. We write instead

$$ds^2 = (r/a)^{2C}dt^2 - (r/a)^{-2C}r^2d\varphi^2 - A^2(r/a)^{-2C(1-C)}(dr^2 + dz^2) \qquad (4)$$

where the constant of length a is introduced purely for dimensional reasons, which become more important at this stage, and where φ still ranges from 0 to 2π. For definiteness we shall choose $r = a$ to be the coordinate radius of the source. All the properties discussed so far for (1), as C and A vary, apply equally to (4) if a is kept fixed.

For the interior of the source we shall assume the form

$$ds^2 = e^{2\alpha}dt^2 - e^{-2\alpha}r^2d\varphi^2 - e^{2\beta-2\alpha}(dr^2 + dz^2) \qquad (5)$$

where α and β are functions of r, although in fact this is not entirely general [3]. We note that (4) is a particular case of (5) with

$$\alpha = C\ln(r/a), \qquad \beta = C^2\ln(r/a) + \ln A. \qquad (6)$$

To satisfy Lichnerowicz's conditions we may choose, for example, in $r \leqslant a$:

$$\alpha = -C(1-u^2)/2, \qquad \beta = (3\ln A - C^2)u^2 + (C^2 - 2\ln A)u^3 \qquad (7)$$

where $u = r/a$. For small positive C one finds that this solution has approximately uniform positive density and that the stress/density ratios are all of order C. With its aid we return now to the construction of solutions with finite sources.

3. FINITE SYSTEMS

We consider systems with axial symmetry. Let the metric take the form (5) everywhere, but with α and β now as functions of both r and z. (This is the well-known metric of Weyl [4] and Levi-Cività [5] which, in an empty region, is quite general.) Let a, b and d be positive constants with $a < b < d$, and write $R = (r^2 + z^2)^{\frac{1}{2}}$. In $R < b$ we take, provisionally,

$$\alpha = \alpha_0, \qquad \beta = \beta_0 \qquad (8)$$

where a_0, β_0 are expressions (6) (for $r \geqslant a$) and (7) (for $r \leqslant a$). Thus, this region is cylindrically symmetric and the properties discussed in Section 2 apply.

Let the region $R > d$ be empty, and take as metric Curzon's solution for one body [6], namely,

$$a = -m/R, \qquad \beta = -m^2r^2/2R^4 \tag{9}$$

where m is a positive constant.

If we are now able, for the remaining region $b \leqslant R \leqslant d$, to find values for a and β satisfying the continuity conditions at each boundary and leading to a physically acceptable stress-energy tensor, then the construction will be complete. Fig. 2 shows in rz-space the region to be occupied by matter.

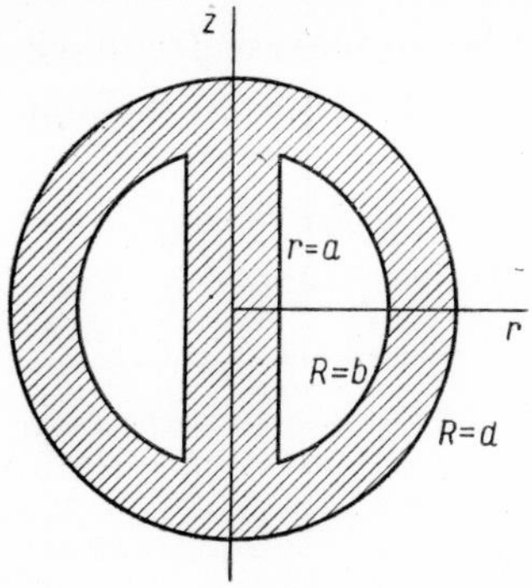

FIG. 2

The writer has, in fact, been able to complete the solution only by first amending (8), slightly, by the addition of a suitable constant to a. Nothing is lost by this; the isometry properties discussed earlier will still apply in $R < b$, to which (8) refers. With such an amendment it is possible to find a wide variety of solutions, of which a particular example is given below.

In $R < b$, let

$$a = a_0 - 3m(b+d)/2(b^2+bd+d^2), \qquad \beta = \beta_0, \tag{8a}$$

and in $b \leqslant R \leqslant d$, let

$$\left.\begin{aligned} a &= a_0 \cos^2 \frac{\pi(R-b)}{2(d-b)} + m(R^3 - 3d^2R + 2b^3)/2(d^3-b^3)R, \\ \beta &= \beta_0 \cos^2 \frac{\pi(R-b)}{2(d-b)} - \frac{m^2r^2}{2R^4} \cos^2 \frac{\pi(d-R)}{2(d-b)}. \end{aligned}\right\} \tag{10}$$

It is easy to show that Lichnerowicz's conditions are satisfied at $R = b$ and $R = d$, and that the stress-energy tensor corresponding to (10) is physically reasonable if certain restrictions are placed on the constant parameters involved. For example, if $0 < C \ll m/a \ll 1$ and $A = 1 + O(C^2)$, one finds that the density is positive everywhere and that no stress/density ratio exceeds $O(m/a)$. It is probable, however, that much weaker conditions, allowing greater freedom of A, would suffice to ensure a satisfactory stress-energy tensor.

In any case our task is fulfilled. The solutions generated as A varies are locally isometric in the empty region $R < b$, $r > a$, whereas suitable optical or other experiments would distinguish between the corresponding fields. Hence the local intrinsic geometry does not, in this example, provide a complete description of the gravitational field. It follows, therefore, that we should not regard general relativity as a *purely* local theory of gravitation, since the physical properties of a solution may well depend on its topology.

REFERENCES

[1] L. Marder, *Proc. Roy. Soc.* A (to be published shortly).
[2] A. Lichnerowicz, *Théories Relativistes de la Gravitation et del'Électro magnétisme,* Masson et Cie, Paris 1955.
[3] L. Marder, *Proc. Roy. Soc.* A **244**, 524 (1958).
[4] H. Weyl, *Ann. Phys., Lpz.* **54**, 117 (1917).
[5] T. Levi-Civita, *R. C. Acad. Lincei* **28**, 3 (1919).
[6] H. E. I. Curzon, *Proc. Lond. Math. Soc.* (2), **23**, 477 (1924).

AN ANTI-MACH METRIC

I. Ozsváth and E. Schücking

Hamburg University, Hamburg

Abstract—An exact solution is given for Einstein's vacuum field equations which is free of singularities, is complete, and has a nonvanishing Riemann tensor. The curvature tensor of this anti-Mach-metric is of the null-type in the Petrov-Pirani-Penrose classification. The singularities and the periodicity structure of the light cone of an arbitrary event in such a universal pure gravitational radiation field are discussed.

Among the many statements which are described as "Mach's principle" in Einstein's theory of gravitation there is one version of this postulate that has been defined unambiguously. It was designated as "Mach's principle 3" by F. Pirani at the Bern Conference in 1955 [1]. It runs: "In the absence of matter, space-time should necessarily be Minkowskian". If we interpret "the absence of matter" as the absence of singularities in the solutions of Einstein's vacuum field equations for gravitational fields then this "Mach-3" principle is, as we shall see, not valid.

During the investigation of all world-models which allow a transitive group of motions in space-time, we found a solution of the field equations with vanishing energy-momentum tensor and with the cosmological constant equal to zero. The line element for this metric is given by the following expression:

$$ds^2 = (dx^1)^2 - 4x^4 dx^1 dx^3 + 2\,dx^2 dx^3 + 2\,(x^4)^2 (dx^3)^2 + (dx^4)^2. \qquad (1)$$

This fundamental form can be written

$$ds^2 = -(\underset{1}{A}_\mu dx^\mu)^2 + (\underset{2}{A}_\mu dx^\mu)^2 + (\underset{3}{A}_\mu dx^\mu)^2 + (\underset{4}{A}_\mu dx^\mu)^2 \qquad (2)$$

(μ and all Greek indices run from 1 to 4).

The four covariant vectors $\underset{1}{A}_\mu, \underset{2}{A}_\mu, \underset{3}{A}_\mu, \underset{4}{A}_\mu$ are given by

$$\underset{1}{A}_\mu = \frac{1}{\sqrt{2+(x^4)^2}}\,(x^4,\,-1,\,1,\,0)$$

$$\underset{2}{A}_\mu = \frac{1}{\sqrt{2\left(2+(x^4)^2\right)}}\left(-x^4-\sqrt{2+(x^4)^2},\,1,\,1+(x^4)^2+x^4\sqrt{2+(x^4)^2},\,0\right) \tag{3}$$

$$\underset{3}{A}_\mu = \frac{1}{\sqrt{2\left(2+(x^4)^2\right)}}\left(-x^4+\sqrt{2+(x^4)^2},\,1,\,1+(x^4)^2-x^4\sqrt{2+(x^4)^2},\,0\right)$$

$$\underset{4}{A}_\mu = (0,\,0,\,0,\,1).$$

These vectors are regular and linearly independent in the whole range of coordinates $-\infty < x^\mu < +\infty$. This shows that the fundamental form given by (1) does not become singular anywhere and has the right signature $+2$ in the whole chart of coordinates.

The non-vanishing Christoffel symbols of the second kind are

$$\Gamma^4_{13} = 1, \quad \Gamma^2_{14} = -1, \quad \Gamma^4_{33} = -2x^4, \quad \Gamma^1_{34} = -1. \tag{4}$$

For (1), the curvature tensor

$$R^{\mu}_{\cdot\nu\lambda\varrho} = 2\Gamma^{\mu}_{\nu[\lambda|\varrho]} + 2\Gamma^{\alpha}_{\nu[\lambda}\Gamma^{\mu}_{\varrho]\alpha} \tag{5}$$

(the symbol "$_{|\varrho}$" denotes partial differentiation with respect to x^ϱ) takes the form:

$$R_{\mu\nu\lambda\varrho} = 4\{\delta^3_{[\mu}\delta^4_{\nu]}\delta^3_{[\lambda}\delta^4_{\varrho]} - \delta^3_{[\mu}\delta^1_{\nu]}\delta^3_{[\lambda}\delta^1_{\varrho]}\}. \tag{6}$$

Here δ^α_β is Kronecker's delta symbol and the brackets around the indices indicate the skew symmetric part of an expression.

If we construct a contracted product of (6) and

$$g^{\mu\nu} = \begin{Vmatrix} 1 & 2x^4 & 0 & 0 \\ 2x^4 & 2(x^4)^2 & 1 & 0 \\ 0 & 1 & 0 & 0 \\ 0 & 0 & 0 & 1 \end{Vmatrix}, \tag{7}$$

then for the Ricci tensor $R_{\nu\varrho}$ we obtain:

$$g^{\mu\lambda}R_{\mu\nu\lambda\varrho} = R_{\nu\varrho} = 0. \tag{8}$$

Thus we have established that (1) is a solution of Einstein's vacuum field equations with the curvature tensor (6) different from zero.

The covariant derivative of the Riemann tensor with respect to x^σ is given by

$$R_{\mu\nu\lambda\varrho\|\sigma} = 8(\delta^1_{[\mu}\delta^3_{\nu]}\delta^3_{[\lambda}\delta^4_{\varrho]} + \delta^3_{[\mu}\delta^4_{\nu]}\delta^1_{[\lambda}\delta^3_{\varrho]})\delta^3_\sigma.$$

The space-time with metric (1) is therefore not "symmetric" [2].

Now we want to show that the solution given above is complete. We call a space-time manifold complete if it does not become singular in points that may be reached from any other point on geodesic lines for finite values of a preferred (affine) parameter. By the term "singular at a point" we mean that the metric tensor $g_{\mu\nu}$ does not have differentiability structure C^2 in a whole neighbourhood of this point or does not have rank four with signature $+2$. By a preferred parameter we mean a parameter s along a geodesic line for which the equation of the geodesic $x^\mu(s)$ is

$$\frac{d^2x^\mu(s)}{ds^2}+\Gamma^\mu_{\nu\lambda}[x^\varrho(s)]\frac{dx^\nu(s)}{ds}\frac{dx^\lambda(s)}{ds}=0. \tag{9}$$

To prove that the metric (1) is complete we have to integrate equations (9) for an arbitrary initial point $x^\mu(s)|_{s=0}=x^\mu_0$ and arbitrary initial directions $dx^\mu(s)/ds|_{s=0}=\xi^\mu$. The solution of (9) for the fundamental form (1) fulfilling these general initial conditions is in the case $\xi^3\neq 0$

$$\begin{aligned}
x^1 &= x^1_0+(2x^4_0\xi^3-\xi^1)s+\frac{\xi^4}{\xi^3}(1-\cos\sqrt{2}\,\xi^3 s)+\frac{\sqrt{2}\,(\xi^1-x^4_0\xi^3)}{\xi^3}\sin\sqrt{2}\,\xi^3 s,\\
x^2 &= x^2_0+\left\{\xi^2+\frac{(\xi^4)^2+2(\xi^1)^2}{2\xi^3}+x^4_0(3x^4_0\xi^3-4\xi^1)\right\}s+\\
&\quad+\frac{\xi^4}{2(\xi^3)^2}\{2(\xi^1-2x^4_0\xi^3)\cos\sqrt{2}\,\xi^3 s-(\xi^1-x^4_0\xi^3)\cos2\sqrt{2}\,\xi^3 s-\\
&\quad-(\xi^1-3x^4_0\xi^3)\}-\frac{\sqrt{2}}{(\xi^3)^2}\{(\xi^1)^2-x^4_0\xi^3(3\xi^1-2x^4_0\xi^3)\}\sin\sqrt{2}\,\xi^3 s+\\
&\quad+\frac{1}{2\sqrt{2}\,(\xi^3)^2}\left\{(\xi^1)^2-\frac{(\xi^4)^2}{2}-x^4_0\xi^3(2\xi^1-x^4_0\xi^3)\right\}\sin 2\sqrt{2}\,\xi^3 s,\\
x^3 &= x^3_0+\xi^3 s,\\
x^4 &= x^4_0(2-\cos\sqrt{2}\,\xi^3 s)-\frac{\xi^1}{\xi^3}(1-\cos\sqrt{2}\,\xi^3 s)+\frac{\xi^4}{\sqrt{2}\,\xi^3}\sin\sqrt{2}\,\xi^3 s,
\end{aligned} \tag{10}$$

and in the case $\xi^3=0$:

$$\begin{aligned}
x^1 &= x^1_0+\xi^1 s,\\
x^2 &= x^2_0+\xi^2 s+\xi^1\xi^4 s^2,\\
x^3 &= x^3_0,\\
x^4 &= x^4_0+\xi^4 s.
\end{aligned} \tag{11}$$

These equations for the geodesics show that the coordinates x^μ remain finite for all finite values of a preferred parameter s. Since the metric (1) has all the required properties for finite coordinate values x^μ the completeness of this manifold has been proved. Therefore the "Mach-3" principle cannot be valid.

We shall now discuss some global properties of the manifold with metric (1). From Eqs (4) and (6) it follows that

$$l^\varrho = \delta_2^\varrho, \tag{12}$$

with

$$g_{\mu\varrho} l^\mu l^\varrho = g_{22} = 0, \qquad l^\varrho_{\|\sigma} = 0, \tag{13}$$

is a covariantly constant null vector obeying the equation

$$R_{\mu\nu\lambda\varrho} l^\varrho = 0. \tag{14}$$

These equations show that the curvature tensor of metric (1) is of the nulltype in the Petrov–Pirani–Penrose classification [3]. F. Pirani has demonstrated that such a metric represents a spacetime filled with pure gravitational radiation [4]. Therefore we shall gain some insight into the global behaviour of a special gravitational radiation field by discussing properties of metric (1) in the large.

The complete continuous group of motions permitted by the metric (1) has six parameters. The infinitesimal transformations of the group which leave the metric unchanged are given by

$$x'^\mu = x^\mu + \varepsilon \underset{A}{\xi}^\mu (x^\lambda), \qquad (\varepsilon \text{ infinitesimal}) \tag{15}$$

$$A = 1, 2, 3, 4, 5, 6,$$

with the six Killing vectors $\underset{A}{\xi}^\mu$:

$$\underset{1}{\xi}^\mu = \delta_1^\mu, \qquad \underset{2}{\xi}^\mu = \delta_2^\mu, \qquad \underset{3}{\xi}^\mu = \delta_3^\mu, \qquad \underset{4}{\xi}^\mu = x^3 \delta_1^\mu + x^1 \delta_2^\mu + \delta_4^\mu,$$

$$\underset{5}{\xi}^\mu = \cos\sqrt{2}\, x^3 \delta_1^\mu + x^4 \cos\sqrt{2}\, x^3 \delta_2^\mu - \frac{1}{\sqrt{2}} \sin\sqrt{2}\, x^3 \delta_4^\mu, \tag{16}$$

$$\underset{6}{\xi}^\mu = \sin\sqrt{2}\, x^3 \delta_1^\mu + x^4 \sin\sqrt{2}\, x^3 \delta_2^\mu + \frac{1}{\sqrt{2}} \cos\sqrt{2}\, x^3 \delta_4^\mu .$$

The first four Killing vectors generate a transitive subgroup of the whole group of motions. The finite transformations of this subgroup are expressed by means of four independent parameters u^a:

$$\begin{aligned} x'^1 &= x^1 + x^3u^4 + u^1, \\ x'^2 &= x^1u^4 + x^2 + \tfrac{1}{2}x^3(u^4)^2 + u^2, \\ x'^3 &= x^3 + u^3, \\ x'^4 &= x^4 + u^4. \end{aligned} \tag{17}$$

These transformations allow us to transform any point, given by coordinates x^μ, into any other point given by coordinates x'^μ without changing the metric. This group is transitive in the large.

For some investigations it might be useful to transform the metric (1) into another coordinate system. If we introduce new coordinates by the equations

$$\begin{aligned} x^1 &= y\sin u + z\cos u, \\ x^2 &= v + \tfrac{1}{2}(y^2 - z^2)\sin 2u + yz\cos 2u, \\ x^3 &= u, \\ x^4 &= y\cos u - z\sin u, \end{aligned} \tag{18}$$

the metric (1) takes the form

$$\begin{aligned} ds^2 &= dy^2 + dz^2 + 2\,du\,dv + 2H du^2, \\ H &= \tfrac{1}{2}(y^2 - z^2)\cos 2u - yz\sin 2u. \end{aligned} \tag{19}$$

This is a special case of a Robinson wave; it was studied independently of us by W. Kundt. The transformation (18) is a one-to-one correspondence between the coordinates x^μ and the coordinates y, z, u, v.

For a preliminary discussion of global properties we study the singularities on the light-cone of an event in the space-time with the metric (1). Because of the homogeneity of this manifold it is no restriction of generality to study only the light-cone with the vertex $x^\mu = 0$. From Eqs (10) and (11) we get for the null geodesics on this light-cone with $x_0^\mu = 0$, for $\xi^3 \neq 0$:

$$x^1 = -\xi^1 s + \frac{\xi^4}{\xi^3}(1-\cos\sqrt{2}\,\xi^3 s) + \frac{\sqrt{2}\,\xi^1}{\xi^3}\sin\sqrt{2}\,\xi^3 s,$$

$$x^2 = \frac{(\xi^1)^2}{2\xi^3}s + \frac{\xi^1\xi^4}{2(\xi^3)^2}(2\cos\sqrt{2}\,\xi^3 s - \cos 2\sqrt{2}\,\xi^3 s - 1) -$$

$$-\frac{\sqrt{2}\,(\xi^1)^2}{(\xi^3)^2}\sin\sqrt{2}\,\xi^3 s + \frac{2(\xi^1)^2-(\xi^4)^2}{4\sqrt{2}\,(\xi^3)^2}\sin 2\sqrt{2}\,\xi^3 s, \tag{20}$$

$$x^3 = \xi^3 s,$$

$$x^4 = -\frac{\xi^1}{\xi^3}(1-\cos\sqrt{2}\,\xi^3 s) + \frac{\xi^4}{\sqrt{2}\,\xi^3}\sin\sqrt{2}\,\xi^3 s;$$

and for $\xi^3 = 0$:

$$x^1 = 0, \quad x^2 = \xi^2 s, \quad x^3 = 0, \quad x^4 = 0. \tag{21}$$

In both cases we have the supplementary condition

$$g_{\mu\nu}(x^\lambda)|_{x^\lambda=0}\,\xi^\mu\xi^\nu = (\xi^1)^2 + 2\xi^2\xi^3 + (\xi^4)^2 = 0. \tag{22}$$

The "exceptional null geodesic" given by Eqs (21) is a ray in the direction $l^\varrho = \xi^\varrho$. This exceptional ray does not intersect the other null geodesics given by Eq. (20) outside the vertex. This can be seen by comparing the equations for x^3 in Eqs (20) and (21).

We shall now discuss some properties of the non-exceptional null geodesics. We take the timelike vector $t^\mu = \delta^\mu_2 - \delta^\mu_3$ at the origin as the definition of the arrow of time. Then we define the directions ξ^μ of that part of the null cone which is directed into the future by the equation

$$g_{\mu\nu}(x^\lambda)|_{x^\lambda=0}\,t^\mu\xi^\nu = \xi^3 - \xi^2 < 0. \tag{23}$$

In the following we deal only with this part of the null cone. We assume, therefore, that always $\xi^3 < \xi^2$. The ratios of the ξ^μ's restricted by (22) and (23) are the essential parameters for the initial directions of the null lines in the vertex. It is therefore no restriction of generality to normalize by assuming

$$\xi^2 - \xi^3 = \sqrt{2}. \tag{24}$$

We now introduce new directional parameters:

$$\gamma_1 = \xi^1, \quad \sqrt{2}\,\gamma_2 = \xi^2 + \xi^3, \quad \gamma_3 = \xi^4. \tag{25}$$

From (22) it then follows that

$$(\gamma_1)^2+(\gamma_2)^2+(\gamma_3)^2 = 1. \tag{26}$$

Each light-ray which contains the origin of the coordinate system intersects the surface of this celestial unit sphere with equation (26). Two coordinates on this sphere suffice to determine the direction of a light-ray. If for $\xi^3 \neq 0$ we introduce a new preferred parameter on the null lines by

$$w = \frac{1}{\sqrt{2}} \xi^3 s, \tag{27}$$

equations (20) and (21) take the following form, with the new directional parameters

$$\alpha = \frac{\gamma_1}{\gamma_2-1}, \quad \beta = \frac{\gamma_3}{\gamma_2-1}, \quad \gamma_2 < 1: \tag{28}$$

$$\begin{aligned}
x^1 &= -2\alpha w+\sqrt{2}\,\beta(1-\cos 2w)+2\alpha\sin 2w,\\
x^2 &= \sqrt{2}\,\alpha^2 w+\alpha\beta(2\cos 2w-\cos 4w-1)-\\
&\quad -2\sqrt{2}\,\alpha^2\sin 2w+\frac{1}{\sqrt{2}}(\alpha^2-\tfrac{1}{2}\beta^2)\sin 4w\\
&= -\frac{1}{4\sqrt{2}}\sin 4w(\sqrt{2}\,\beta-2\alpha\operatorname{tg} w)^2+\sqrt{2}\,\alpha^2(w-2\operatorname{tg} w),\\
x^3 &= \sqrt{2}\,w,\\
x^4 &= -\sqrt{2}\,\alpha(1-\cos 2w)+\beta\sin 2w.
\end{aligned} \tag{29}$$

For the exceptional ray we may write

$$x^\mu = s\delta_2^\mu \tag{30}$$

with a new preferred parameter s.

The light-cone directed into the future is a three-dimensional space described by coordinates α, β, w with $-\infty < \alpha < +\infty$, $-\infty < \beta < +\infty$, $w \geqslant 0$; it is imbedded in the four dimensional singularity-free manifold described by the coordinates x^μ. The light-cone given by equations (29) and (30) can become singular where the matrix of the derivatives

$$\left\| \frac{\partial x^\mu}{\partial \alpha}, \frac{\partial x^\mu}{\partial \beta}, \frac{\partial x^\mu}{\partial w} \right\|$$

has a rank < 3.

This could happen only where

$$\frac{\partial x^3}{\partial w}\left(\frac{\partial x^1}{\partial \alpha}\frac{\partial x^4}{\partial \beta}-\frac{\partial x^1}{\partial \beta}\frac{\partial x^4}{\partial \alpha}\right)$$

$$= 2\sqrt{2}\,[(\sin 2w - w)\sin 2w + (1-\cos 2w)^2] = 0 . \qquad (31)$$

From this equation it follows that

$$w = k\pi, \quad k = 0, 1, 2, \dots \qquad (32)$$

or

$$\tan w = \frac{w}{2} . \qquad (33)$$

In both cases we get an infinite number of w-values for which (31) vanishes. We call the values (32) "points of the first kind" and the positive solutions of Eq. (33) "points of the second kind". The point $w = 0$ is the only one which is a point of both kinds. Points of both kinds lie alternately on a geodesic null ray beginning at this point. For all these points the rank of the matrix

$$\left\| \frac{\partial x^\mu}{\partial \alpha}, \frac{\partial x^\mu}{\partial \beta}, \frac{\partial x^\mu}{\partial w} \right\|$$

is two for $w > 0$.

We shall now try to answer the question whether it is possible that the null rays originating in the zero point intersect again in another point. It would be so if the following equations admitted solutions besides $x^\mu = 0$ and $(\alpha, \beta) = (\bar{\alpha}, \bar{\beta})$:

$$\begin{aligned}
x^1 &= -2\alpha w + \sqrt{2}\,\beta(1-\cos 2w) + 2\alpha \sin 2w \\
&= -2\bar{\alpha}\bar{w} + \sqrt{2}\,\bar{\beta}(1-\cos 2\bar{w}) + 2\bar{\alpha}\sin 2\bar{w}, \\
x^2 &= -\frac{1}{4\sqrt{2}}\sin 4w(\sqrt{2}\,\beta - 2\alpha \tan w)^2 + \sqrt{2}\,\alpha^2(w - 2\tan w) \\
&= -\frac{1}{4\sqrt{2}}\sin 4\bar{w}(\sqrt{2}\,\bar{\beta} - 2\bar{\alpha}\tan\bar{w})^2 + \sqrt{2}\,\bar{\alpha}^2(\bar{w} - 2\tan\bar{w}) \\
x^3 &= \sqrt{2}\,w = \sqrt{2}\,\bar{w}, \\
x^4 &= -\sqrt{2}\,\alpha(1-\cos 2w) + \beta \sin 2w \\
&= -\sqrt{2}\,\bar{\alpha}(1-\cos 2\bar{w}) + \bar{\beta}\sin 2\bar{w} .
\end{aligned} \qquad (34)$$

These equations may be derived from (29). Here we have taken into account the fact that two different rays characterized by their direction parameters (α, β) and $(\bar{\alpha}, \bar{\beta})$ might reach their intersecting point x^μ for different values of their distinguished parameters w and $\bar{w}$.

Besides the trivial solutions $x^\mu = 0$ and $\alpha = \bar{\alpha}$, $\beta = \bar{\beta}$ Eqs (34) admit of other solutions. We use the third Eq. (34) and obtain from the first and last Eq. (34) with the abbreviations

$$A = \alpha - \bar{\alpha}, \qquad B = \beta - \bar{\beta}, \tag{35}$$

the following system

$$\begin{aligned} 2(\sin 2w - w)A + \sqrt{2}(1-\cos 2w)B &= 0, \\ -\sqrt{2}(1-\cos 2w)A + \sin 2w B &= 0. \end{aligned} \tag{36}$$

Non-trivial solutions for A and B are possible if

$$2(\sin 2w - w)\sin 2w + 2(1-\cos 2w)^2 = 0. \tag{37}$$

This is the same condition as (31). For points of the first kind we obtain:

$$w = k\pi, \qquad A = \alpha - \bar{\alpha} = 0, \qquad B = \beta - \bar{\beta} \text{ arbitrary}. \tag{38}$$

The second equation of (34) is also fulfilled for these solutions. We have the result that all rays with the same α but different β form a ray system that is focused periodically in an infinite series of world points. The coordinates of these points are:

$$x^1 = -2\alpha k\pi, \qquad x^2 = \sqrt{2}\alpha^2 k\pi, \qquad x^3 = \sqrt{2}k\pi, \qquad x^4 = 0. \tag{39}$$

For each integer value of $k > 0$, Eq. (39) gives the equation of a spacelike world line with parameter α.

The other non-trivial solutions of (36) are obtained for points of the second kind. In this case we have:

$$w = 2\tan w, \qquad \sqrt{2}\beta - \alpha w = \sqrt{2}\bar{\beta} - \bar{\alpha} w = \lambda(w) \text{ arbitrary}. \tag{40}$$

The second equation of (34) is also fulfilled for these solutions. From this it follows that for each solution of the equation $w = 2\tan w$ with $w > 0$ all rays with $\sqrt{2}\beta - \alpha w = \lambda(w)$ will intersect in one space-time point. The coordinates of these points of the second kind are

$$\begin{aligned} x^1 &= 2\lambda(w)\sin^2 w, & x^2 &= -\frac{1}{4\sqrt{2}}\lambda^2(w)\sin 4w, \\ x^3 &= \sqrt{2}w, & x^4 &= \frac{\lambda(w)}{\sqrt{2}}\sin 2w. \end{aligned} \tag{41}$$

For each solution of the equation $w = 2\tan w$ with $w > 0$ we get a spacelike world line $x^{\mu} = x^{\mu}(\lambda)$ for the points of the second kind. Lines of different kinds do not intersect for arbitrary values of both their parameters k and $w > 0$. This may be seen by comparing their x^3-coordinates. In order to form a picture of the intersecting rays we replace the directional parameters α and β by the parameters $\gamma_1, \gamma_2, \gamma_3$ at the celestial sphere of an observer at the zero point. The exceptional ray which does not intersect all other rays has on the sphere $(\gamma_1)^2 + (\gamma_2)^2 + (\gamma_3)^2 = 1$ the coordinates of the "north pole" $\gamma_1 = \gamma_3 = 0$, $\gamma_2 = 1$. All rays that intersect in points of the first kind are given by $\alpha = \text{const}$ or by means of (28) as an intersection of the plane

$$\gamma_1 - \alpha\gamma_2 + \alpha = 0 \tag{42}$$

with the unit sphere $(\gamma_1)^2 + (\gamma_2)^2 + (\gamma_3)^2 = 1$. For different values of α we get "circles of the first kind" on the sphere, which always go through the north pole. The circles cover the whole sphere if α runs from $-\infty$ to $+\infty$. The north pole must be excluded from all circles. Then through each point of the sphere with exception of the north pole runs one and only one open circle. All light-rays which are emitted in the directions of such an open circle on the sphere intersect periodically and infinitely often.

In the same manner we get for the rays which intersect in points of the second kind, taking into account Eqs (28) and (40), the intersection of the plane

$$\sqrt{2}\gamma_3 - \gamma_1 w - \lambda(w)\gamma_2 + \lambda(w) = 0 \tag{43}$$

with the sphere $(\gamma_1)^2 + (\gamma_2)^2 + (\gamma_3)^2 = 1$. For different values of λ we thus get "circles of the second kind" on the sphere which always go through the north pole. These circles cover the whole sphere as λ runs from $-\infty$ to $+\infty$. The north pole must be excluded from all circles. Through each point of the sphere with the exception of the north pole passes one and only one open circle. All light-rays which are emitted from the origin in the directions of such an open circle on the sphere intersect in a point of the second kind.

However there is a decisive difference between the circles of the second kind and those of the first kind. The system of circles of the second kind is still dependent on the parameter w which takes on the discrete set of values which are the solutions of the equation $w = 2\tan w$ with $w > 0$. There is indeed an infinite number of different circle systems of the second kind. If we travel on a null ray which is not the exceptional one we come first to a singularity on the light-cone where all those rays meet which intersect the unit sphere in the same circle of the first kind. Then we run into a second singularity on the light-cone where all those rays meet which intersect the unit sphere in the same circle of the second kind. At the next singularity we meet the same rays we met before at the first singularity. But at the following singularity we shall meet new rays which are in general different from the rays which intersected in the second singularity, and so on. This space-time which is filled with gravitational radiation represents, in spite of its simplicity, a complicated optical instrument with some startling properties.

The periodic and quasi-periodic singularity structure along each ray of the light-cone which is not the exceptional one leads to the assumption that there might be a periodic or quasi-periodic structure of the curvature properties along the null rays. For such a discussion it seems useful to study the covariant tensor

$$K_{\mu\varrho} = R_{\mu\nu\lambda\varrho}\dot{x}^{\nu}\dot{x}^{\lambda}, \qquad \dot{x}^{\nu} = \frac{dx^{\nu}}{dw}, \tag{44}$$

along a ray. For this tensor we have

$$K_{\mu\varrho}\dot{x}^{\varrho} = 0, \qquad K_{\mu\varrho}l^{\varrho} = 0, \qquad K^{\mu}_{\cdot\mu} = 0. \tag{45}$$

The second equation follows from Eq. (14) and is a consequence of the fact that we deal with a metric of the null type. The last Eq. (45) follows from the vacuum field equations. The ratios of the eigenvalues of (44) along the ray should mirror the periodic structure of curvature properties in an invariant way. But in our case we obtained the result (compare (45)) that two eigenvalues vanish and the other two have the ratio -1. R. Sachs suggested to us that perhaps the eigenvectors of $K_{\mu\varrho}$ might show a rotation and in this way exhibit a periodicity structure. Following this suggestion we obtained from Eqs (6), (29), (44) besides the null eigenvectors $\dot{x}^{\mu}$ and l^{μ}, the two spacelike eigenvectors

$$a^{\mu} = (1, -\sqrt{2}\,\alpha, 0, 0), \qquad b^{\mu} = (0, 2\alpha\sin 2w - \sqrt{2}\,\beta\cos 2w, 0, 1), \tag{46}$$

with

$$g_{\mu\nu}a^{\mu}a^{\nu} = 1, \qquad g_{\mu\nu}a^{\mu}b^{\nu} = 0, \qquad g_{\mu\nu}b^{\mu}b^{\nu} = 1, \tag{47}$$

$$g_{\mu\nu}a^{\mu}\dot{x}^{\nu} = 0, \qquad g_{\mu\nu}a^{\mu}l^{\nu} = 0, \qquad g_{\mu\nu}b^{\mu}\dot{x}^{\nu} = 0, \qquad g_{\mu\nu}b^{\mu}l^{\nu} = 0.$$

The four vectors define a tetrad along the whole ray. We have normalized $l^{\mu} = \delta^{\mu}_{2}$ so that $g_{\mu\nu}\dot{x}^{\mu}l^{\nu} = \sqrt{2}$. If we compare this tetrad with the tetrad in the origin by parallel propagation along the null ray we find the following result: $\dot{x}^\mu$ and l^μ are transferred into themselves but a^μ and b^μ are rotated in their plane with respect to the parallel transferred vectors $\bar{a}^\mu$ and $\bar{b}^\mu$. We have the result that

$$g_{\mu\nu} a^\mu \bar{a}^\nu = \cos\sqrt{2}w. \tag{48}$$

This shows that there is a periodic structure of curvature properties along those rays of the light-cone which do not coincide with the exceptional ray.

We wish to thank the "Deutsche Forschungsgemeinschaft" and the "Joachim Jungius Gesellschaft der Wissenschaften e. V." who supported this work. We should also like to express our gratitude especially to O. Heckmann who enabled us to work together in his institute on the questions discussed here. He gave us much encouragement and advice. We thank P. Jordan and the members of his Hamburg Relativity Seminar for stimulating comment and criticism. We wish especially to thank R. Sachs for a valuable suggestion. W. Kundt and J. Ehlers supplied us with an unpublished manuscript which gives an exposition of Robinson's method for the characterization of his waves. This helped us in computing Eq. (18).

REFERENCES

[1] *Helv. Phys. Acta* Suppl. IV, p. 199 (1956).
[2] E. Cartan, *Géométrie des espaces de Riemann,* Paris 1951, p. 260–2.
[3] A. Lichnerowicz, *C. R. Acad. Sci, Paris* **246**, 893 (1958).
[4] F. Pirani, *Phys. Rev.* **105**, 1089 (1957).

SHOCK WAVES IN GENERAL RELATIVITY

A. Papapetrou and H. Treder

Institut für reine Mathematik der Deutschen Akademie der Wissenschaften zu Berlin

1. The problem of gravitational radiation has undoubtedly become a topic of major importance in general relativity theory. Several partial results which have so far been obtained seem to prove definitely that the field equations of general relativity necessarily imply the existence of gravitational radiation. But detailed knowledge of the properties of this radiation is still lacking as it has not been possible yet to determine exact solutions of the Einstein's field equations which represent gravitational radiation and are at the same time physically interpretable without ambiguity. It must be added that the experimental verification of the existence of gravitational radiation constitutes an independent, extremely difficult problem, on which no progress whatever has been made until now.

A problem intimately connected with that of gravitational radiation is that of gravitational shock waves. This problem has been solved completely and, as shock waves are the boundaries of any radiation field of finite duration, it is reasonable to hope that a knowledge of the properties of shock waves may be helpful in the task of constructing gravitational radiation fields. It is the aim of the present article to give a brief survey of the different forms under which the problem of shock waves appears, as well as of the methods by which it has been solved and of the results to which the solution has led.

2. The first treatment of the problem of gravitational shock waves was given by Stellmacher [1]. In his paper Stellmacher completely solved the problem of a shock wave of the order $n = 2$. This is the case in which the derivatives of $g_{\mu\nu}$ of order $\geqslant 2$ have discontinuities on the hypersurface determined by the equation $z(x^a) = 0$, while

the first derivatives are continuous on the surface. Let us denote by $[A]$ the discontinuity of a quantity A on the surface $z = 0$:

$$[A] = (A)_{z=+0} - (A)_{z=-0}.$$

It follows from the assumption that the first derivatives of the $g_{\mu\nu}$ are continuous on the surface $z = 0$, that the discontinuities of the second derivatives have tensor character with regard to coordinate transformations which are continuously differentiable to the third order and that they have the following structure:

$$[g_{\mu\nu,\alpha\beta}] = \gamma_{\mu\nu} p_\alpha p_\beta .$$

In this formula $\gamma_{\mu\nu}$ is a discontinuity tensor (defined on the surface $z = 0$) characterizing the structure of the discontinuity, while p_α denotes the normal to the surface:

$$p_\alpha = \frac{\partial z}{\partial x^\alpha}. \tag{1}$$

A more intuitive way of looking at the tensor $\gamma_{\mu\nu}$ is the following [2]. Let us call V^- the region of space neighbouring on the surface $z = 0$, which corresponds to $z < 0$, and V^+ that corresponding to $z > 0$. We denote the components of $g_{\mu\nu}$ in V^- by $g^-_{\mu\nu}$, those in V^+ by $g^+_{\mu\nu}$. Both sets of functions are assumed to have, each in the corresponding region V^- or V^+, continuous derivatives up to the order $n = 3$. It is always possible to determine a continuation of $g^-_{\mu\nu}$ into V^+ having continuous derivatives up to the order $n = 3$ in both regions V^- and V^+ as well as on the surface $z = 0$. If $g^-_{\mu\nu+}$ is one such continuation, then we can write

$$g^+_{\mu\nu} = g^-_{\mu\delta+} + \frac{z^2}{2}\gamma_{\mu\nu}(x^\alpha) + \frac{z^3}{6}\varepsilon_{\mu\nu}(x^\alpha), \tag{2}$$

with functions $\gamma_{\mu\nu}(x^\alpha)$ and $\varepsilon_{\mu\nu}(x^\alpha)$ also having continuous derivatives up to the order $n = 3$. The discontinuity tensor $\gamma_{\mu\nu}$ will then be given by the values of $\gamma_{\mu\nu}(x^\alpha)$ on the surface $z = 0$:

$$\gamma_{\mu\nu} = \{\gamma_{\mu\nu}(x^\alpha)\}_{z=0}.$$

Detailed discussion has shown that the problem of shock waves splits into two partial problems. The first, which will be called the local problem, deals with the conditions which must be fulfilled by the discontinuity tensor $\gamma_{\mu\nu}$ in order to ensure that the field equations

$$R_{\mu\nu} = 0 \tag{3}$$

will be satisfied on both sides of the surface $z = 0$. These conditions follow from the relation

$$[R_{\mu\nu}] = 0 \tag{3a}$$

and they are found to be essentially different in the following two cases:

(i) p_μ is not a null-vector, $p^\mu p_\mu \neq 0$,
(ii) p_μ is a null-vector, $p^\mu p_\mu = 0$.

In case (i) equations (3a) lead to 6 algebraic conditions for the 10 components $\gamma_{\mu\nu}$, so that 4 of them remain arbitrary. In case (ii) there are only 4 conditions, so that 6 of the $\gamma_{\mu\nu}$ are arbitrary. Remembering now that because of the general covariance of the field equations the tensor $\gamma_{\mu\nu}$ in all cases contains 4 arbitrary quantities, we conclude that in case (i) the discontinuities will be trivial in the sense that they can be eliminated by means of a suitable coordinate transformation (with discontinuous third derivatives). Non-trivial discontinuities, i.e. physically meaningful shock waves, are therefore possible only on null-surfaces, i.e. on surfaces $z(x^a) = 0$, at every point of which the normal vector is a null-vector:

$$p^\mu p_\mu = 0. \tag{4}$$

When the trivial part has been eliminated, the discontinuity tensor of such a wave will depend on two arbitrary quantities.

From the subsequent discussion of the conditions on $\gamma_{\mu\nu}$ Stellmacher concluded that the most convenient choice of the two arbitrary quantities on which $\gamma_{\mu\nu}$ depends is an amplitude factor P and a polarization angle δ. We start by choosing two conjugate-complex vectors ω_μ and $\bar{\omega}_\mu$, which are orthogonal to p_μ and have vanishing length:

$$\omega_\mu p^\mu = \bar{\omega}_\mu p^\mu = \omega_\mu \omega^\mu = \bar{\omega}_\mu \bar{\omega}^\mu = 0. \tag{5}$$

We then construct two real vectors π_μ and $\tilde{\pi}_\mu$:

$$\pi_\mu = P(e^{i\delta}\omega_\mu + e^{-i\delta}\bar{\omega}_\mu), \qquad \tilde{\pi}_\mu = \frac{P}{i}(e^{i\delta}\omega_\mu - e^{-i\delta}\bar{\omega}_\mu) \tag{6}$$

which are orthogonal to p_μ as well as to each other:

$$\pi_\mu p^\mu = \tilde{\pi}_\mu p^\mu = \pi_\mu \tilde{\pi}^\mu = 0. \tag{7}$$

The discontinuity tensor $\gamma_{\mu\nu}$ has the simple form

$$\gamma_{\mu\nu} = \pi_\mu \tilde{\pi}_\nu + \tilde{\pi}_\mu \pi_\nu. \tag{8}$$

With the help of $\gamma_{\mu\nu}$ or, equivalently, of π_μ and $\tilde{\pi}_\nu$ we can determine the discontinuity of any other field quantity. For example we find for the curvature tensor

$$[R_{\sigma\mu\nu\lambda}] = \tfrac{1}{2}(\gamma_{\sigma\lambda}p_\mu p_\nu + \gamma_{\mu\nu}p_\sigma p_\lambda - \gamma_{\sigma\nu}p_\mu p_\lambda - \gamma_{\mu\lambda}p_\sigma p_\nu).$$

The second part of the problem of gravitational shock waves consists in discussing the propagation of the discontinuity tensor $\gamma_{\mu\nu}$ on the surface $z = 0$ along the null-geodesics, which are the bi-characteristics of the field equations. The propagation conditions for $\gamma_{\mu\nu}$ follow from the equations

$$\left[\frac{D}{Dz} R_{\mu\nu}\right] = 0, \tag{9}$$

which are an immediate consequence of the field equations (3). The operator D/Dz means differentiation across the discontinuity surface:

$$\frac{D}{Dz}(\ ) = (\ )_{;\mu} d^\mu,$$

the vector d^μ fulfilling the conditions

$$d^\mu d_\mu = 1 = d^\mu p_\mu.$$

A discussion of (9) is equivalent to a discussion of the discontinuities of the third derivatives of $g_{\mu\nu}$ and leads in the first instance to conditions containing, besides $\gamma_{\mu\nu}$, the quantities $\varepsilon_{\mu\nu}$ appearing in (2). From these conditions we can eliminate the $\varepsilon_{\mu\nu}$ and find two propagation equations for $\gamma_{\mu\nu}$. These two equations take a very simple form if (a) the vectors ω_μ, $\bar{\omega}_\mu$ are chosen in such a way, that they are parallel translated along the bi-characteristics:

$$\frac{D}{D\tau}\omega_\mu \equiv \omega_{\mu;\alpha}p^\alpha = 0, \quad \frac{D}{D\tau}\bar{\omega}_\mu = 0;$$

(b) they are normalized so that

$$\omega_\mu \bar{\omega}^\mu = -\tfrac{1}{2};$$

(c) the function $z(x^\alpha)$ entering into the equation $z(x^\alpha) = 0$ of the null-surface is chosen in such a way that the neighbouring surfaces $z(x^\alpha) = \text{const}$ are also null-surfaces. Conditions (a) (b) (c) do not introduce any restriction as they can always be satisfied. The first of the propagation equations is then a conservation law for the scalar $E = \gamma_{\mu\nu}\gamma^{\mu\nu} = 2P^4$:

$$(E\sqrt{-g}\,p^\alpha)_{,\alpha} = 0. \tag{10}$$

The second propagation relation is

$$\frac{d\delta}{d\tau} \equiv \delta_{,\alpha} p^{\alpha} = 0. \tag{11}$$

3. The results derived for the gravitational shock waves are completely analogous to those valid for electromagnetic shock waves (in Minkowski space or in any *given* Riemannian space). It will be useful to show this analogy in some detail by briefly summing up the discussion of the electromagnetic case.

The discontinuities of the second derivatives of the electromagnetic potential A_μ can be expressed by a relation analogous to (2):

$$A^{+}_{\mu} = A^{-}_{\mu+} + \frac{z^2}{2}\varphi_\mu + \frac{z^3}{6}\psi_\mu. \tag{12}$$

The local problem concerning the structure of the discontinuity vector φ_μ is here solved with the help of the discontinuity of Maxwell's equations:

$$[(F^{\mu\nu}\sqrt{-g})^{\xi}_{,\nu}] = 0. \tag{13}$$

In case (i)—$p^\mu p_\mu \neq 0$—Eq. (13) leads to 3 conditions for the 4 components φ_μ, while in case (ii) —$p^\mu p_\mu = 0$—there is only one condition. Now from the gauge invariance of the theory it follows that φ_μ will in all cases contain one arbitrary quantity. Therefore in case (i) the shock wave will be trivial, as it will always be possible to transform it away by a suitable gauge transformation (with discontinuous third derivatives). Physically meaningful shock waves can exist only on null-surfaces and the corresponding vector φ_μ depends essentially on two arbitrary quantities. Here, too, it is convenient to take these quantities in the form of an amplitude factor J and a polarization angle χ. The discontinuity vector is given by

$$\varphi_\mu = \sqrt{J}(e^{i\chi}\omega_\mu + e^{-i\chi}\bar{\omega}_\mu), \tag{14}$$

with vectors ω_μ, $\bar{\omega}_\mu$ again satisfying equations (5).

The solution of the propagation problem now follows from the equation

$$\left[\frac{D}{Dz}(F^{\mu\nu}\sqrt{-g})_{,\nu}\right] = 0.$$

The result is again given by two equations, one for the amplitude J:

$$(J\sqrt{-g}\,p^{\alpha})_{,\alpha} = 0, \tag{15}$$

and one for the angle χ:

$$\frac{d\chi}{d\tau} = 0. \tag{16}$$

It is remarkable that, in spite of the different tensor character of the gravitational and the electromagnetic field, the shock waves depend in both cases on two arbitrary quantities and satisfy practically identical propagation laws. Furthermore, in both cases the discontinuity tensor is orthogonal to p_μ:

$$\varphi_\mu p^\mu = 0, \qquad \gamma_{\mu\nu} p^\mu = 0,$$

i.e. the shock waves are transversal.

The next problem which suggests itself at this point is the problem of shock waves of the combined gravitational and electromagnetic field in the (non-unified) Einstein–Maxwell theory with the field equations

$$R_{\mu\nu} = -kT_{\mu\nu}, \qquad (F^{\mu\nu}\sqrt{-g})_{,\nu} = 0$$

($T_{\mu\nu}$ Maxwell's stress-tensor). The solution of this problem is straightforward, as has been shown by Stellmacher [1], and the results are the following. In the local problem the two fields are completely separated and we again have equations (8) for the gravitational and (14) for the electromagnetic field. The discussion of the propagation problem leads to 4 equations containing $\gamma_{\mu\nu}$ and φ_μ, i.e. the amplitudes and the polarization angles of both fields. We shall write down here only two remarkably simple equations, which are obtained by combination of the initial equations:

$$\{(E+4kJ)\sqrt{-g}\,p^\alpha\}_{,\alpha} = 0, \qquad \frac{d\delta}{d\tau} = 2k\frac{J}{E}\frac{d\chi}{d\tau}.$$

4. A more general form of a shock wave is the following. On the surface $z(x^\alpha) = 0$ the field variables have discontinuous derivatives of order $m \geqslant n\,(n \geqslant 2)$, while all derivatives of a lower order are continuous. The discussion of this form of the problem is essentially the same as before [1]. The discontinuities of the derivatives of the order n are now, e.g. in the case of the pure gravitational field, of the form:

$$[g_{\mu\nu,\alpha_1\alpha_2\ldots\alpha_n}] = \gamma_{\mu\nu}p_{\alpha_1}p_{\alpha_2}\cdots p_{\alpha_n}.$$

The solution of the local problem follows from the equation

$$\left[\frac{D^{n-2}}{Dz^{n-2}} R_{\mu\nu}\right] = 0$$

and that of the propagation problem from

$$\left[\frac{D^{n-1}}{Dz^{n-1}} R_{\mu\nu}\right] = 0 .$$

The final results are the same as for shock waves of order $n = 2$: Non-trivial shock waves can exist on null-surfaces only and the discontinuity tensor $\gamma_{\mu\nu}$ satisfies exactly the same local and propagation conditions as in the case $n = 2$.

Now, in the theory of the electromagnetic field, besides shock waves of order $n \geqslant 2$, it has also been necessary to consider the case $n = 1$, for which there are discontinuities of the first derivatives of the potential A_μ on the surface $z(x^\alpha) = 0$. The physical significance of this case lies in the fact that shock waves of the first order are produced whenever the accelerations of the bodies emitting the electromagnetic radiation vary discontinuously (e.g. if two bodies are acted upon by a pre-stressed spring which is released at a certain instant by means of a shutter mechanism). If some first derivatives of A_μ are discontinuous, then some second derivatives will become infinite on the discontinuity surface and this will in general have the result that there will be a single-layer distribution of sources on this surface. As we are interested in a pure radiation field, we must exclude such a surface distribution of sources. To do this we have to impose the condition

$$\int_\Omega \left(\sqrt{-g}\, F^{\mu\nu}\right)_{,\nu} d^4x = 0, \tag{17}$$

Ω being an infinitely thin cylinder containing an arbitrary element ΔS of the surface $z(x^\alpha) = 0$. Instead of (12) we must now write

$$A_\mu^+ = A_{\mu+}^- + z\varphi_\mu + \frac{z^2}{2}\psi_\mu \tag{18}$$

($A_{\mu+}^-$ being now a continuation of A_μ^- into V^+ which has continuous first and second derivatives). The solution of the local problem follows in this case from Eq. (17) and the structure of the discontinuity vector φ_μ is found to be given again by Eq. (14). For the propagation problem it is now sufficient to make use of equations (13) and the propagation conditions are the same as before: Shock waves of order $n = 1$ obey exactly the same laws as those of order $n \geqslant 2$.

In general relativity we do not know of any *a priori* arguments demanding the exclusion of any discontinuous variation of the accelerations of the bodies producing the gravitational field. Discontinuities of this kind will necessarily give rise to a shock wave of the order $n = 1$, as one sees immediately, e.g. by considering the case of weak gravitational fields (retarded potentials in the first approximation). It would, of course, be an important argument for excluding discontinuous variations of the acceleration, if it were to turn out that the field equations of general relativity did not allow the existence of shock waves of the first order. But this is not the case: As has been shown by the detailed discussion of this problem [3], gravitational shock waves of the order $n = 1$ are compatible with the field equations.

The discussion proceeds on lines similar to those of the corresponding problem in the theory of the electromagnetic field. We start by writing in place of (2):

$$g^{+}_{\mu\nu} = g^{-}_{\mu\nu+} + z\gamma_{\mu\nu} + \frac{z^2}{2}\,\varepsilon_{\mu\nu}. \tag{19}$$

The solution of the local problem follows from the requirement that there will be no surface-distribution of sources of the gravitational field on the discontinuity surface. The condition for the vanishing of sources of this kind is

$$\int_{\Omega} R_{\mu\nu} d^4x = 0, \tag{20}$$

the domain Ω being the same as in Eq. (17). A discussion of (20) leads to the same results as in the case $n = 2$: non-trivial shock waves of the first order can exist only on null-surfaces and the discontinuity tensor $\gamma_{\mu\nu}$ is again given by (8). The solution of the propagation problem is now obtained by the discussion of Eqs (3a) and is again given by (10), (11). We may therefore sum up by saying that gravitational shock waves of the order $n = 1$ have exactly the same properties as those of order $n \geqslant 2$.

It will be useful to point out an interesting and physically most reasonable property of gravitational shock waves of the first order: The discontinuities of the first derivatives of $g_{\mu\nu}$ mean discontinuities of the Christoffel symbols; but these discontinuities have a special structure which ensures that the same world-lines are the bi-characteristics of the gravitational field equations on both sides of the discontinuity surface $z(x^a) = 0$. In our opinion the existence of gravitational shock waves of order $n = 1$ constitutes a rather serious argument against the acceptance of the postulate of Lichnerowicz [4], according to which only gravitational fields with globally continuous first derivatives of the $g_{\mu\nu}$ ought to be physically acceptable.

Shock waves of the order $n = 1$ are also possible in the Einstein–Maxwell theory of the combined gravitational and electromagnetic field [3] and have again exactly the same properties as in the case $n \geqslant 2$.

5. In the theory of the electromagnetic field we can go a step further and consider shock waves of order $n = 0$, i.e. discontinuities of the potential A_μ itself. In this case we must replace equation (18) by

$$A^+_\mu = A^-_{\mu+} + \varphi_\mu + z\psi_\mu .$$

The solution of the problem can again be obtained formally from the field equations

$$(\sqrt{-g}\, F^{\mu\nu})_{,\nu} = 0 .$$

For the local problem one has to demand the vanishing of any double-layer distribution of sources on the discontinuity surface, which is expressed by the condition

$$\int_\Omega z(\sqrt{-g}\, F^{\mu\nu})_{,\nu} d^4x = 0 .$$

We again find that non-trivial shock waves are possible on null-surfaces only and the discontinuity vector again satisfies (14). The solution of the propagation problem, for which we now have to use Eq. (17), is not exactly the same as before. But it is not worth while to follow this discussion any further, as it is easy to see that shock waves of this kind are physically uninteresting.

We consider for this purpose the radiation field (in Minkowski space) determined by

$$A_1 = A_3 = A_4 = 0, \qquad A_2 = f(x - ct)$$

and choose the function f as follows:

$$f = \frac{1}{\varepsilon}(x - ct) f_0 \quad \text{for} \quad 0 < x - ct < \varepsilon ,$$

$$f = 0 \quad \text{for} \quad x - ct < 0, \quad f = f_0 \quad \text{for} \quad x - ct > \varepsilon$$

($f_0 = \text{const}$). We verify at once that the electromagnetic field vanishes outside the layer $0 < x - ct < \varepsilon$ and is a homogeneous radiation field inside this layer, with discontinuities of the order $n = 1$ on the null-surfaces $x - ct = 0$ or ε. The energy density of the radiation field is

$$T_{44} = \frac{1}{2}(E_y^2 + H_z^2) = \frac{f_0^2}{\varepsilon^2}.$$

For a small value of ε and any given value of t the radiation is contained, in 3-dimensional space, in a thin layer of the thickness ε and the energy per unit surface of the layer is

$$T_{44} \cdot \varepsilon = \frac{f_0^2}{\varepsilon}.$$

If we now let ε tend to zero, keeping f_0 constant, at the limit we have a shock wave of the order $n = 0$. But then the energy per unit surface of the now infinitely thin layer becomes infinitely large. This result remains valid for any other shape of the null surface and shows clearly that electromagnetic shock waves of the order $n = 0$, though compatible with Maxwell's equations, are nevertheless physically useless.

The results of the discussion of certain aspects of gravitational radiation have shown that, from the energetic point of view, this radiation does not differ essentially from electromagnetic radiation [5]. On the other side energy is a source of the gravitational field and because of this the field equations of general relativity automatically exclude, in one way or another, any case corresponding to infinite total energy. Accordingly we shall have to expect that the field equations of general relativity will not allow the existence of gravitational shock waves of the order $n = 0$. This qualitative conclusion has been confirmed by a direct calculation.(1) We have thus finally the physically satisfactory result that the field equations of general relativity allow shock waves of any order $n \geqslant 1$, but exclude shock waves of the order $n = 0$.

REFERENCES

[1] F. K. Stellmacher, *Math. Ann.* **115**, 740 (1938).
[2] H. Treder, *Ann. Phys. Lpz.* (7) **2**, 225 (1958).
[3] A. Papapetrou and H. Treder, *Math. Nachr.* **20**, 53 (1959).
[4] A. Lichnerowicz, *Théories Relativistes de la Gravitation et de l'Électromagnétisme*, Paris 1955, pp. 5–6.
[5] A. Papapetrou, *Ann., Phys. Lpz.* (7) **1**, 186 (1958).

(1) The detailed proof will be published elsewhere.

MOTION AND RADIATION OF POLE PARTICLES*

A. Peres

Department of Physics, Israel Institute of Technology, Haifa

Since the early years of the General Relativity Theory, it has been known that the linearized field equations have wave-like solutions, and that the corresponding energy-momentum pseudotensor of the gravitational field has components representing an energy flux [1]. This result, however, was treated with caution, since the field equations are really non-linear. Later, approximation methods were discovered, which took account of the non-linearity, and gave the equation of motion of particles. The situation then became quite chaotic. Some authors [2]–[4] claimed that there was no radiation reaction, others [5],[6] found a gravitational damping – which agreed, but only qualitatively, with the linearized theory – and still others [7],[8] found a gravitational "antidamping", i.e. an energy gain!

One of the main causes of this trouble doubtless was the complexity of the field equations: when extremely cumbersome expressions have to be handled, the physical meaning of the various terms becomes unclear. The first step toward the solution of this problem is therefore to develop an approximation technique which minimizes the computational labour, and thus also the risk of errors. The following one seems best fitted for our purpose.

One takes as field variables the contravariant densities $\mathfrak{g}^{\mu\nu}$ and one expands them into a series

$$\mathfrak{g}^{\mu\nu} = \underset{0}{\mathfrak{g}^{\mu\nu}} + \underset{1}{\mathfrak{g}^{\mu\nu}} + \underset{2}{\mathfrak{g}^{\mu\nu}} + \ldots$$

where each term is by one order of magnitude smaller than the previous one. One chooses quasi-Galilean coordinates ($\underset{0}{\mathfrak{g}^{\mu\nu}} = \eta^{\mu\nu}$) subjected to the harmonic condition $\mathfrak{g}^{\mu\nu}{}_{,\nu} = 0$. The solution behaving as purely outgoing waves is then unique [9].

The Einstein equations now read, in natural units:

$$\nabla^2 \mathfrak{g}^{\mu\nu} - \ddot{\mathfrak{g}}^{\mu\nu} = -16\pi \mathfrak{g} \mathcal{T}^{\mu\nu} + \Theta^{\mu\nu} \tag{1}$$

* Partly supported by the U. S. Air Force, through ARDC.

where $\mathfrak{g} = (-\mathrm{Det}\,\mathfrak{g}^{\alpha\beta})^{\frac{1}{2}}$ and $\Theta^{\mu\nu}$ is quadratic in $(\mathfrak{g}^{\mu\nu} - \eta^{\mu\nu})$. When (1) is expanded into the various orders (in order to compute $\underset{n}{\mathfrak{g}^{\mu\nu}}$) $\underset{n}{\Theta^{\mu\nu}}$ thus depends only on $\underset{m}{\mathfrak{g}^{\mu\nu}}$, $m < n$, and is a known quantity. The compatibility of (1) with the harmonic condition $\mathfrak{g}^{\mu\nu}{}_{,\nu} = 0$ follows from the equations of motion [10], which are most conveniently written as $(\mathfrak{g}\mathcal{T}^{\mu\nu})_{;\nu} = 0$, or

$$(\mathfrak{g}\mathcal{T}^{\mu\nu})_{,\nu} = \mathfrak{g}\mathcal{T}^{\alpha\beta}[\mathfrak{g}_{\alpha\gamma}\mathfrak{g}^{\gamma\mu}{}_{,\beta} + \tfrac{1}{2}\mathfrak{g}^{\gamma\mu}(\tfrac{1}{2}\mathfrak{g}_{\alpha\beta}\mathfrak{g}_{\varrho\sigma} - \mathfrak{g}_{\alpha\varrho}\mathfrak{g}_{\beta\sigma})\mathfrak{g}^{\varrho\sigma}{}_{,\gamma}] \tag{2}$$

where $\mathfrak{g}_{\mu\nu} = \mathfrak{g}^{-1} g_{\mu\nu}$.

For pole particles, localized at $\overset{A}{\xi}{}^{k} = \overset{A}{\xi}{}^{k}(t)$, one takes [11]

$$\mathfrak{g}\mathcal{T}^{\mu\nu} = \sum_{A} \overset{A}{M}\overset{A}{v}{}^{\mu}\overset{A}{v}{}^{\nu}\hat{\delta}(\overrightarrow{x - \xi}) \tag{3}$$

where $v^{\mu} = d\xi^{\mu}/dt$ and M is a function of time. (We call M the "effective gravitational mass". It can be shown [11] that the "intrinsic mass" $m_0 = M\mathfrak{g}^{-1}ds/dt$ is constant.) The equations of motion then read

$$(M{\cdot}v^{\mu}) = Mv^{\alpha}v^{\beta}[\mathfrak{g}_{\alpha\gamma}\mathfrak{g}^{\mu\gamma}{}_{,\beta} + \tfrac{1}{2}\mathfrak{g}^{\mu\gamma}(\tfrac{1}{2}\mathfrak{g}_{\alpha\beta}\mathfrak{g}_{\varrho\sigma} - \mathfrak{g}_{\alpha\varrho}\mathfrak{g}_{\beta\sigma})\mathfrak{g}^{\varrho\sigma}{}_{,\gamma}] \tag{4}$$

where the bracket has to be computed at the position of the particle under consideration, and all the singular terms in it have to be neglected.

All that remains now to do is to solve (1) at the various orders, so as to get the $\mathfrak{g}^{\mu\nu}$ which appear in the right hand side of (4). For this purpose, it is convenient to write

$$\mathfrak{g}^{\mu\nu} = \mathfrak{h}^{\mu\nu} + \mathfrak{s}^{\mu\nu}$$

where

$$\nabla^2\mathfrak{h}^{\mu\nu} - \ddot{\mathfrak{h}}^{\mu\nu} = -16\pi\mathfrak{g}\mathcal{T}^{\mu\nu} \tag{5}$$

is readily solved by the use of Liénard-Wiechert potentials, and

$$\nabla^2\mathfrak{s}^{\mu\nu} - \ddot{\mathfrak{s}}^{\mu\nu} = \Theta^{\mu\nu}. \tag{6}$$

One now has to choose the expansion parameter: the most suitable one would be the reciprocal velocity of light, but it has already been taken as unity. An equivalent choice is to assume that the velocities are small quantities of the first order. Accelerations and masses are therefore of the second order. As the only dependence of the field quantities on time is through the positions and velocities of the sources, it follows that a time derivative of a field quantity is by one order of magnitude smaller than a space derivative.

One thus expands [12]

$$\mathfrak{h}^{\mu\nu} = 4\sum_{n=0}^{\infty}\left\{\left[\frac{1}{(2n)!}\frac{d^{2n}}{dt^{2n}}\sum Mv^{\mu}v^{\nu}R^{2n-1}\right]+\right.$$
$$\left.+\,\varepsilon\left[\frac{1}{(2n+1)!}\frac{d^{2n+1}}{dt^{2n+1}}\sum Mv^{\mu}v^{\nu}R^{2n}\right]\right\} \tag{7}$$

where ε is an arbitrary constant (for pure retarded potentials, $\varepsilon = -1$).

In this expression, we suppose that the coordinates ξ^k and velocities v^k are known (initial conditions) and that the masses and accelerations have to be computed

$$M = \underset{1}{m} + \underset{2}{m} + \underset{}{m} + \ldots,$$
$$\dot{v}^k = \underset{1}{a^k} + \underset{2}{a^k} + a^k + \ldots\,.$$

Note that $\underset{n}{m}$ and $\underset{n}{a^k}$ are small quantities of order $(n+2)$.

Let us now work step by step. The lowest order term in $\mathfrak{g}^{\mu\nu}$ is

$$\underset{2}{\mathfrak{g}^{00}} = \underset{2}{\mathfrak{h}^{00}} = 4\sum (m/R)$$

where $R = \sqrt{R^kR^k}$ and $R^k = x^k - \xi^k$. Introducing this into (4) one gets the Newtonian approximation

$$\dot{m} = 0, \qquad a^k = \frac{\partial}{\partial\xi^k}\sum{}' \frac{m}{R}.$$

Next, one has $\underset{3}{\mathfrak{g}^{00}} = \underset{3}{\mathfrak{g}^{kl}} = 0$ and $\underset{3}{\mathfrak{g}^{0k}} = \underset{3}{\mathfrak{h}^{0k}} = 4\sum(mv^k/R)$, whence it follows that there is no first order correction to the Newtonian approximation ($\underset{1}{m} = \underset{1}{a^k} = 0$) and that the second order correction to mass is [12]

$$\underset{2}{m} = \tfrac{1}{2}mv^2 + 3m\sum{}' (m/R).$$

Non-linear contributions to the field appear at the fourth order [12]

$$\underset{4}{\mathfrak{g}^{00}} = 4\sum\left(\frac{\underset{2}{m}}{R} + \frac{m}{2}\ddot{R}\right) + 7\sum\frac{m^2}{R^2} + 14\sum_{A,B}{}' \overset{A}{m}\overset{B}{m}\, S^{kk},$$

$$\underset{4}{\mathfrak{g}^{0k}} = 0,$$

$$\underset{4}{\mathfrak{g}}^{kl} = 4\sum \frac{mv^k v^l}{R} + \frac{1}{2}\sum m^2\left[\frac{\delta^{kl}}{R^2} - (\log R)_{,kl}\right] + $$

$$+ \sum_{A,B}{}' \overset{A}{m}\overset{B}{m}(2\delta^{kl}S^{mn} - 4S^{kl})$$

where

$$S^{kl} = \frac{\partial}{\partial \overset{A}{\xi}{}^k}\frac{\partial}{\partial \overset{B}{\xi}{}^l}\ln(\overset{A}{R} + \overset{B}{R} + D)$$

and

$$D = \sqrt{D^k D^k}, \qquad D^k = \overset{A}{\xi}{}^k - \overset{B}{\xi}{}^k.$$

From this, we can compute the second order correction to the acceleration $\underset{2}{a}^k$ which leads, in the two-body problem, to the perihelion advance [8].

The radiation field—i.e. that part of $\mathfrak{g}^{\mu\nu}$ which is proportional to ε—appears in the fifth order. (Terms proportional to ε^2 appear only in the ninth order, and we shall not have to deal with them.) From (7), one has

$$\underset{5}{\mathfrak{h}}^{00} = 4\varepsilon\sum\left[\underset{2}{\dot{m}} + \frac{m}{6}\dddot{(R^2)}\right], \qquad \underset{5}{\mathfrak{h}}^{kl} = 4\varepsilon\sum mv^k v^l.$$

As $\underset{5}{\Theta}^{00} = \underset{5}{\Theta}^{kl} = 0$, one is tempted to write $\underset{5}{\mathfrak{s}}^{00} = \underset{5}{\mathfrak{s}}^{kl} = 0$. In fact, the situation is not so simple: at each stage of the approximation procedure, one has to solve a Poisson equation, and there is a considerable freedom of choice of solutions, each representing a possible motion and a gravitational field belonging thereto [13]. Only one of these solutions behaves at infinity as purely outgoing waves [9]; the remaining ones contain also incoming waves. It is in general difficult to determine which solution is the correct one, because the nth term of a series expansion in powers of (v/c) behaves in the wave zone as R^{n-2}, and no boundary conditions for each stage of the procedure are known.

However, a solution behaving at infinity like $f(t-R)/R$ has an expansion $f(t)/R - f'(t) + \ldots$ Therefore, if a term such as $f(t)/R$ occurs at some approximation stage, one must add $-f'(t)$ – or, more generally, $\varepsilon f'(t)$ – at the next stage [14].

Now $\underset{4}{\mathfrak{s}}^{\mu\nu}$ behaves, for large R, like

$$\underset{4}{\mathfrak{s}}^{00} \to -14\sum{}' \overset{A}{m}\overset{B}{m}/DR, \qquad \underset{4}{\mathfrak{s}}^{kl} \to -2\sum{}' \overset{A}{m}\overset{B}{m}D^k D^l/D^3 R,$$

whence

$$\underset{5}{\mathfrak{g}}^{00} = -14\varepsilon \sum{}' \overset{A}{m}\overset{B}{\dot{m}}(1/D), \qquad \underset{5}{\mathfrak{g}}^{kl} = -2\varepsilon \sum{}' \overset{A}{m}\overset{B}{\dot{m}}(D^k \dot{D}^l / D^3).$$

Further, one has [12]

$$\underset{5}{\mathfrak{g}}^{0k} = 4 \sum \left[\underset{2}{m} \frac{v^k}{R} + \frac{m}{2} (v^{\bar{k}} R) \right] + \frac{1}{2} \sum m^2 \left[15 \frac{v^k}{R} - v^l (\ln R)_{,kl} \right] +$$

$$+16 \sum{}' \overset{A}{m}\overset{B}{m} \left(\frac{3}{4} \overset{A}{v}{}^l S^{lk} + \overset{B}{v}{}^k S^{ll} - \overset{B}{v}{}^l S^{lk} \right),$$

whence, at the sixth order [15]

$$\underset{6}{\mathfrak{g}}^{0k} = 4\varepsilon \sum [(\underset{2}{\dot{m}} v^k) + \underset{2}{m} a^k + (m v^k \dddot{R}^2 / 3!)] - 2\varepsilon \sum_{A,B}{}' \overset{A}{m}\overset{B}{m} (D^k D^l \dot{v}^l / D^3).$$

We can already compute the fifth order radiative correction to the mass. From (4), one has $\underset{5}{\dot{m}} = m(\frac{3}{4}\underset{5}{\mathfrak{g}}^{00} - \frac{1}{4}\underset{5}{\mathfrak{g}}^{kk})_{,0}$. It can be shown, however, that $\underset{5}{\mathfrak{g}}^{kk} = 3\underset{5}{\mathfrak{g}}^{00}$, so that $\underset{5}{m} = 0$.

The fifth order radiative correction to the acceleration is given, by (4), as

$$\underset{5}{a}^k = \underset{6}{\mathfrak{g}}^{0k}{}_{,0} + \tfrac{1}{4}(\underset{7}{\mathfrak{g}}^{00} + \underset{7}{\mathfrak{g}}^{ll})_{,k} - \tfrac{1}{2}\underset{5}{\mathfrak{g}}^{00}\underset{2}{\mathfrak{g}}^{00}{}_{,k} - \tfrac{1}{4}\underset{5}{\mathfrak{g}}^{kl}\underset{2}{\mathfrak{g}}^{00}{}_{,l} - v^l \underset{5}{\mathfrak{g}}^{kl}{}_{,0}.$$

We thus still need $(\underset{7}{\mathfrak{g}}^{00} + \underset{7}{\mathfrak{g}}^{ll})_{,k}$. The explicit evaluation of this term is rather lengthy, and we shall refer the reader to the literature [15] where it has been performed in the special case of two masses m and M revolving on circular orbits (in the Newtonian approximation) at a distance D from each other.

The radiated energy can be taken either as the rate of work of the particles against their own radiation field:

$$U = -\sum m \underset{5}{a}^k v^k,$$

or as the rate of loss of mass [16]:

$$U = -\sum \underset{7}{\dot{m}}.$$

In the above mentioned case, both expressions are equal to

$$U = -\varepsilon \frac{32}{5} \frac{(m+M) m^2 M^2}{D^5}.$$

For purely outgoing waves ($\varepsilon = -1$), this agrees with the result obtained by the linearized theory [1].

REFERENCES

[1] L. Landau and E. Lifshitz, *The Classical Theory of Fields*, Cambridge, Mass. 1951, p. 331.

[2] L. Infeld and A. E. Scheidegger, *Canad. J. Math.* **3**, 195 (1951).

[3] A. E. Scheidegger, *Phys. Rev.* **82**, 883 (1951): *Rev. Mod. Phys.* **25**, 451 (1953).

[4] L. Infeld, *Ann. of Phys.* **6**, 341 (1959).

[5] P. Havas, *Phys. Rev.* **108**, 1351 (1957).

[6] A. Trautman, *Bull. Acad. Polon. Sci.* Cl. III, **6**, 627 (1958).

[7] N. Hu, *Proc. R. Irish Acad.* **A51**, 87 (1947).

[8] A. Peres, *Nuvo. Cim.* **11**, 644 (1959).

[9] V. A. Fock, *Teoria Prostranstva, Vremeni i Tyagotenia*, Moscow 1955, p. 441.

[10] F. Hennequin, Thèse, Paris 1956.

[11] W. Tulczyjew, *Bull. Acad. Polon. Sci.* Cl. III, **5**, 279 (1957).

[12] A. Peres, *Nuovo, Cim.* **11**, 617 (1959).

[13] A. E. Scheidegger, *Phys. Rev.* **99**, 1883 (1955).

[14] A. Peres, *Nuovo. Cim.* **13**, 670 (1959).

[15] A. Peres, *Nuovo. Cim.* **15**, 351 (1960).

[16] A. Peres, *Nuovo. Cim.* **13**, 439 (1959).

BOUNDARY CONDITIONS IN GENERAL RELATIVITY THEORY *

A. PERES and N. ROSEN

Department of Physics, Israel Institute of Technology, Haifa, Israel

THE Einstein field equations are hyperbolic, and thus need boundary conditions of the Cauchy type [1]: one gives the values of the field on a space-like hypersurface (by a suitable choice of the coordinates one can take it as $x^0 = t = 0$) and the values of the first derivatives in a direction normal to this hypersurface (time derivatives). The solution of the Cauchy problem then consists in computing the values of the higher time derivatives with the help of the field equations, thus determining their solution at some later time.

It is obvious that, in spite of the four-dimensional symmetry of the equations, it is convenient to make use of a three-dimensional formalism. We shall use Greek letters to denote the values 0, 1, 2, 3 and Latin letters the values 1, 2, 3. Beginning with the fundamental tensor $g_{\mu\nu}$ (taking $g_{00} > 0$), we define the three-dimensional contravariant metric tensor by the relation

$$e^{kl} g_{lm} \equiv \delta^k_m,$$

so that

$$e^{kl} \equiv g^{kl} - (g^{0k} g^{0l} / g^{00}).$$

We then introduce the corresponding Christoffel three-index symbols,

$$\gamma^m_{kl} \equiv \tfrac{1}{2} e^{mn} (g_{nk,l} + g_{nl,k} - g_{kl,n}),$$

and denote the corresponding covariant differentiation by a dot, e.g.

$$A_{k.l} \equiv A_{k,l} - A_m \gamma^m_{kl}.$$

Now let us write

$$\varphi_k \equiv g_{0k}, \quad \varphi^k \equiv e^{kl} \varphi_l,$$

* Partly supported by the U. S. Air Force, trough ARDC.

and let us define Ω by the relation

$$\Omega^2 \equiv \frac{1}{g^{00}} \equiv g_{00} - \varphi_k \varphi^k .$$

Finally, let us introduce

$$Z_l^k \equiv \frac{1}{2\Omega} e^{km} (\varphi_{m,l} + \varphi_{l,m} - g_{lm,0}),$$

and

$$Z \equiv Z_k^k .$$

If one writes down the field equations, one finds, as is well known, that six of them give $g_{kl,00}$ in terms of the $g_{\mu\nu}$, $g_{\mu\nu,0}$ and their spatial derivatives, so that the six g_{kl} can be considered as a convenient set of variables for Cauchy's conditions [2]. The four other equations impose conditions on the initial g_{0k} and g_{00}; they can be expressed in the following form [2]:

$$2\varkappa \Omega^4 T^{00} = \Omega^2 P + \Omega^2 (Z^2 - Z_l^k Z_k^l), \tag{1}$$

$$\varkappa \Omega T_k^0 = Z_{,k} - Z_{k,l}^l \tag{2}$$

where $\varkappa$ is the gravitational constant and where P is the scalar curvature of the metric g_{kl}. For empty space, T^{00} and T_k^0 vanish.

Consider first Eq. (1). From the definition of Z_l^k one readily verifies that the second term on the right hand side is independent of g_{00}. Since Ω^2 is linear in g_{00}, we see that this equation enables one to express g_{00} as an *algebraic* function of the other $g_{\mu\nu}$, of the $g_{kl,0}$, and of their spatial derivatives.

Now consider Eqs (2). One readily finds that these are three *spatial* second-order partial differential equations for the g_{0k}, and that they are linear in the second derivatives. If one eliminates g_{00} in (2) by the use of (1), one can first determine the g_{0k} by solving three spatial second-order differential equations, and then determine g_{00} by means of (1). The first (and higher) time derivatives of $g_{0\mu}$ remain completely undetermined by the field equations and can be chosen arbitrarily, corresponding to the possibility of arbitrary coordinate transformations.

We now come to the question of boundary conditions for g_{0k}. The three spatial differential equations are of the elliptic type, since none of the three space coordinates has a privileged role. The appropriate boundary conditions, from the mathematical standpoint, are therefore of the Dirichlet or Neumann type. If one is dealing with an infinite region, and one tries to use boundary conditions of the Cauchy type on a finite surface, one can expect that, in general, the solutions for g_{0k} will become infinite at infinity (the physical interpretation will be given later) or will have singularities elsewhere. If one has found a well behaved solution, a small change in the boundary conditions may result in a large change in the solution at large distances—the elliptic equations involve an inherent instability [1].

What makes matters even worse is the fact that g_{00} is determined from the other $g_{\mu\nu}$ and their derivatives by an algebraic relation, *without the possibility of specifying any boundary conditions*, and there is no assurance that it will be well behaved, e.g., that it will be everywhere close to unity if the other $g_{\mu\nu}$ are close to their Galilean values.

The conclusion to be drawn is that, if in the Cauchy problem the g_{kl} and $g_{kl,0}$ are chosen to be nearly Galilean everywhere at $x^0 = 0$, it will be rather exceptional for the $g_{0\mu}$ to have this property.

Although the Cauchy boundary conditions are the most appropriate for hyperbolic equations, one is sometimes interested in specifying boundary conditions at spatial infinity [3]. For example, it is sometimes stated [4] that radiation fields in general relativity should be characterized at infinity by

$$g_{\mu\nu} = \eta_{\mu\nu} + O(r^{-1}), \qquad g_{\mu\nu,\varrho} = O(r^{-1})$$

as is the case in the linearized theory which is supposed to be a good approximation for weak fields. However, from the previous argument one is aware that the results of the linear theory must be treated with considerable caution and that, in general, one cannot specify boundary conditions for all the $g_{\mu\nu}$. That the exact equations may lead to results very different from those of the linear equations can be seen from the following considerations.

By taking a suitable linear combination of the Einstein equations one obtains the relation,

$$-e^{kl}\Omega_{\cdot kl} = \varphi^k Z_{,k} - Z_{,0} + \Omega Z^k_l Z^l_k + \tfrac{1}{2}\varkappa\Omega(T^0_0 - T^k_k - 2\varphi^k T^0_k). \tag{3}$$

If we consider the field at a large distance from material sources, so the $T^\mu_\nu = 0$, this can be written

$$-e^{kl}\Omega_{.kl} = (\varphi^k Z)_{,k} - \varphi^k{}_{,k} Z - Z_{,0} + \Omega Z^k_l Z^l_k. \tag{4}$$

If we assume that the field is weak, so that the components of $g_{\mu\nu}$ are nearly equal to their Galilean values, then

$$-e^{kl}\Omega_{.kl} \approx \nabla^2\Omega.$$

Let us now suppose that the field, in addition to a static part, contains a part representing a periodic or nearly periodic wave, so that $g_{\mu\nu,\varrho} = O(r^{-1})$. Let us take the time average of Eq. (4), either over a complete cycle if the wave is periodic, or over a long time if it is nearly periodic. Denoting the time average by brackets, we have

$$-\langle e^{kl}\Omega_{,kl}\rangle = \langle \varphi^k Z\rangle_{,k} - \langle \varphi^k{}_{,k} Z\rangle + \langle \Omega Z^k_l Z^l_k\rangle .$$

From the form of this equation one can regard the right-hand member as proportional to the "source density" of Ω. One readily sees that the first term of the right-hand member corresponds to a finite source since its volume integral over a large sphere can be expressed as a surface integral having a finite limit as r tends to infinity. In the second term, both Z and $\varphi^k{}_{,k}$ fall off as r^{-1} (unless the field is static). However, one can show that, by means of an *infinitesimal* coordinate transformation, it is possible to make $\varphi^k{}_{,k}$ fall off like r^{-2}, so that the second term falls off like r^{-3}, corresponding, at most, to a logarithmically divergent source. The last term is positive definite and falls off like r^{-2} (unless the field is static). This is then the dominant term, and we see that, when r goes to infinity, it represents an infinite source of Ω. It follows therefore that Ω cannot approach unity as r increases, but rather tends to infinity [5], [6]. We have thus arrived at a contradiction with the original assumption that all the components of the metric tensor tend to their Galilean values at infinity.

From the physical standpoint, this result is not difficult to understand. Not only the energy of the matter creates a gravitational field, but also the energy of the gravitational field itself, and, with a reasonable definition, the latter is infinite in the case under discussion, and leads to an infinite field at infinity.

REFERENCES

[1] P. Morse and H. Feshbach, *Methods of Theoretical Physics*, New York 1953, p. 706.
[2] A. Peres and N. Rosen, *Nuovo Cim.* **13**, 430 (1959).
[3] A. Trautman, *Bull. Acad. Polon. Sci.* Cl. III **6**, 403 (1958).
[4] A. Trautman, *Bull. Acad. Polon. Sci.* Cl. III **6**, 407 (1958).
[5] A. Papapetrou, *Ann. Phys., Lpz.* (6) **20**, 399 (1957); (7) **1**, 186 (1958); (7) **2**, 87 (1958).
[6] A. Peres and N. Rosen, *Phys. Rev.* **115**, 1085 (1959).

INVARIANT CLASSIFICATION OF GRAVITATIONAL FIELDS

A. Z. PETROV

Kazan State University, USSR

WHILE investigating any problem in general relativity theory or in one of the existing versions of the unified field theory, invariant values and correlations which are independent of the choice of the coordinate system are of the greatest interest. In particular, the introduction of any special coordinate system (including the "privileged" one, if such a system exists) is motivated by the desire to determine such invariant values and facts in the simplest way. If geometrical objects or tensors entering into the equations of the field permit invariant division into different types, then there appears an invariant classification of the field under investigation. In studying any problem in the light of field classification, two questions inevitably arise: (1) For which of the possible types of fields does the formulation of the given problem have any meaning? and (2) How can this problem be solved by using the peculiarities of the given type of field?

Such an invariant classification, of course, may be carried out in various ways, but it must be connected with the investigation of the tensors or the objects which determine the given field.

Since every unified field theory is constructed as a generalization of Einstein's gravitational theory, it is primarily important to classify the gravitational fields using the field equations

$$R_{\alpha\beta} - \tfrac{1}{2}Rg_{\alpha\beta} = \varkappa T_{\alpha\beta} \qquad (1)$$

where $R_{\alpha\beta}$ is the Ricci tensor, R is the curvature scalar, $T_{\alpha\beta}$ is the energy-momentum tensor, and $\varkappa$ is a constant.

The simplest and most essential properties of the tensors determining the field are connected with their *algebraic structure*. Thus it is important to make a *local* classification of the gravitational field at a given point in space-time.

§ 1. SPECIAL CASE ($T_{\alpha\beta} = \nu g_{\alpha\beta}$)

First, let us consider the particular case of the field equations (1) which arises if we assume that the energy-momentum tensor of the matter differs from the metric tensor only by the scalar factor

$$T_{\alpha\beta} = \nu g_{\alpha\beta}. \tag{2}$$

Examination of this special case is interesting in itself and, as will be shown in § 2, the solution of the general problem can be reduced to the solution of this particular case.

It results from (1) and hypothesis (2) that the equations of the field will be:

$$R_{\alpha\beta} = \varkappa g_{\alpha\beta} \tag{3}$$

where $\varkappa$ is a constant. Since the field equations (3) are constructed with the help of the curvature tensor and the metric tensor, the problem of classification is reduced to a combined study of the algebraic structure of these two tensors. For this purpose it is convenient to map a 4-dimensional space on to a 6-dimensional *bi-vectoral* space in a manner which is based on the following considerations.

The curvature tensor $R_{\alpha\beta\gamma\delta}$ possesses the following properties: (1) The number of indices is even, and (2) the indices are divided into *anti-symmetrical* pairs $\alpha\beta$ and $\gamma\delta$. Any tensor possessing such properties we shall call a *bi-tensor*. By accepting every anti-symmetrical pair as one *collective* index and introducing the numbering

$$14-1,\ 24-2,\ 34-3,\ 23-4,\ 31-5,\ 12-6,$$

it is possible to fix a correspondence between every given space-time point and a 6-dimensional space, the centred affine space $\mathscr{E}_6$. This mapping determines the *isomorphism* concerning the operations of addition, subtraction and multiplication of the bi-tensors (without contraction). A more thorough mathematical discussion of such a mapping is considered in [1] [2, pp. 26–40].

Under such a mapping the curvature tensor and the tensor

$$g_{\alpha\beta\gamma\delta} \equiv g_{\alpha\gamma} g_{\beta\delta} - g_{\alpha\delta} g_{\beta\gamma}$$

considered at the given space-time point in $\mathscr{E}_6$ correspond to the symmetrical tensors

$$R_{ab},\ g_{ab} \quad (a, b = 1, \ldots, 6).$$

Note that this kind of construction can be carried out for any Riemann space V_n.

If, now, the tensor g_{ab} is chosen as a metric tensor (which is quite possible since $|g_{ab}| \neq 0$ if $|g_{\alpha\beta}| \neq 0$) then $\mathscr{E}_6$ is converted into a 6-dimensional *metric* space R_6. Considering the matrix in R_6 constructed from the symmetrical tensors R_{ab} and g_{ab}

$$(R_{ab} - \lambda g_{ab}) \tag{4}$$

and reducing this matrix to a canonical form with the help of real operations we shall obtain the required classification of the fields of gravitation (3) with regard to the algebraic structure of the curvature tensor.

It should be noted that in R_6 not every linear coordinate transformation can be used, but only those that are *real* and are induced by Lorentz transformations at the given space-time point [2, pp. 27]. Reduction of the matrix (4) to a canonical type is not essential for the classification, but since in deductions it is extremely important to have a canonical type of the curvature component tensor at the given point in space, this reduction has basic significance. The reduction of this matrix to a canonical form may be carried out in different ways. It is possible to carry out investigations within the limits of the bi-vectoral space R_6 [2, pp. 45–60] or else it may first be mapped on the three-dimensional complex space $\mathscr{E}_3$ [3] with the help of the formulas

$$R_{ab} + iR_{ab+3} = \overset{*}{R}_{ab} \ (a, b < 3),$$

making use of the fact that the group of Lorentz transformations is isomorphic to the group of rotations of the complex three dimensional "Euclidean" space. We refer the reader to the works mentioned above for strict proofs and formulate here the main result in the form of the two following theorems: (1) *There exist three and only three types of gravitational fields* ($R_{\alpha\beta} = \varkappa g_{\alpha\beta}$) *with the signature* $(- - - +)$, with regard to the algebraic structure of the curvature tensor; this theorem introduces the classification of the gravitational fields of the type mentioned; the concrete content of this classification is determined by the second theorem: (2) *We are able to determine one and only one orthonormal system of coordinates with respect to which the components of the curvature tensor are determined by the matrix*:

$$(R_{ab}) = \begin{pmatrix} M & N \\ N & -M \end{pmatrix}$$

where M and N, for each of the possible types, have the form:

$$T_1\colon\ M = \begin{pmatrix} \alpha_1 & & \\ & \alpha_2 & \\ & & \alpha_3 \end{pmatrix}, \qquad N = \begin{pmatrix} \beta_1 & & \\ & \beta_2 & \\ & & \beta_3 \end{pmatrix}, \quad \sum \alpha_i = -\varkappa, \ \sum \beta_i = 0,$$

$$T_2\colon\ M = \begin{pmatrix} \alpha_1 & 0 & 0 \\ 0 & \alpha_2+1 & 0 \\ 0 & 0 & \alpha_2-1 \end{pmatrix}, \quad N = \begin{pmatrix} \beta_1 & 0 & 0 \\ 0 & \beta_2 & 1 \\ 0 & 1 & \beta_2 \end{pmatrix}_1 \quad \begin{matrix} \alpha_1 + 2\alpha_2 = -\varkappa, \\ \beta_1 + 2\beta_2 = 0, \end{matrix} \tag{5}$$

$$T_3\colon\ M = \begin{pmatrix} \sigma & 1 & 0 \\ 1 & \sigma & 0 \\ 0 & 0 & \sigma \end{pmatrix}, \qquad N = \begin{pmatrix} 0 & 0 & 0 \\ 0 & 0 & -1 \\ 0 & -1 & 0 \end{pmatrix}, \qquad \sigma = -\frac{\varkappa}{3}.$$

Here $\lambda_s = \alpha_s \pm i\beta_s$ are bases of elementary divisors of the matrix (4) and hence are *invariant* under every affine transformation at the space-time point. Furthermore the *characteristics* of the matrix (4) will be invariant. They register simple and non-simple elementary divisors and thus *non-isotropic* and *isotropic eigenvectors* of the tensor R_{ab} in the bi-vectoral space. The characteristics will have, respectively, the following form:

$$T_1\colon [111, \overline{111}], \quad T_2\colon [21, \overline{21}], \quad T_3\colon [3, \overline{3}];$$

where the numbers with a line above them determine the elementary divisors with bases which are complex-conjugates of the bases of the elementary divisors corresponding to the unmarked numbers. The invariants of λ_s and the characteristics give a *full invariant picture* determining each of the three possible types of the gravitational fields. Thus the classification of gravitational fields shown above is *invariant*. Of course, formulas (5) will be affected by changes of coordinates. It is not difficult for us to obtain for *the tetrad* (5) the expression for the *eigenvectors* and to investigate their structure for each of the three possible cases [2, p. 26].

In particular, assuming $\varkappa = 0$ in (5), we obtain the canonical types of the curvature tensor at the point in the *free* space-time case ($R_{\alpha\beta} = 0$).

This result was achieved by me in 1949 [4], [1]. In 1954 I found another method of demonstrating the main theorem and determining the matrices (5), and the same result was arrived at by A. Norden [5]. A fourth method of investigation was suggested by Géhéniau in 1957 [6] (with $\varkappa = 0$ and without canonical forms (5)). We shall dwell on certain applications of this result in § 3.

§ 2. THE GENERAL CASE

Let us assume that there are no limitations for the energy-momentum tensor $T_{\alpha\beta}$ except the conditions that (1) $T_{\alpha\beta} = T_{\beta\alpha}$ and (2) $T_{\alpha\beta}$ satisfies field equations (1). First let us note that the canonical forms (5) of the special case were obtained *only* as a consequence of the conditions

$$R_{(\alpha\beta)\gamma\delta} = R_{\alpha\beta(\gamma\delta)} = R_{\alpha[\beta\gamma\delta]} = 0, \qquad R_{\alpha\beta} = \varkappa g_{\alpha\beta}; \tag{6}$$

the condition $\varkappa =$ const, was not used. Therefore, for every four-index tensor satisfying conditions (6), a canonical tetrad may be found to which formulas analogous to (5) will be applicable. Thus, since in the general case field equation (1) is constructed with the help of the curvature tensor, the metric tensor and the energy-momentum tensor, it is no longer possible to base the classification on an investigation of the algebraic structure based only on the curvature tensor. It is necessary to choose as the object of investigation a tensor which depends on the curvature tensor and the energy-momentum tensor; such that as $T_{\alpha\beta} \to \nu g_{\alpha\beta}$ it leads to the conclusions of paragraph 1 and the classification must be given by the canonical forms (5).

Let us call the new geometrical object the *space-time-matter* tensor, designate it by $P_{\alpha\beta\gamma\delta}$ and define it by the equation

$$P_{\alpha\beta\gamma\delta} \stackrel{\text{def}}{=} R_{\alpha\beta\gamma\delta} + \varkappa(g_{\alpha[\delta}T_{\gamma]\beta} + g_{\beta[\gamma}T_{\delta]\alpha}) + \sigma g_{\alpha[\delta}g_{\gamma]\beta}. \tag{7}$$

This tensor possesses the following properties: (1) from (1) and (7) it follows that

$$P_{(\alpha\beta)\gamma\delta} = P_{\alpha\beta(\gamma\delta)} = P_{\alpha[\beta\gamma\delta]} = 0, \qquad P_{\alpha\beta} \equiv P^{\sigma}{}_{\alpha\sigma\beta} = \omega g_{\alpha\beta}, \tag{8}$$

i.e. all the properties (6) hold; (2) If the distribution and the motion of the matter are given, so that $T_{\alpha\beta}$ is known, and if $P_{\alpha\beta\gamma\delta}$ is known (for some specified choice of σ and $\varkappa$) then the curvature tensor $R_{\alpha\beta\gamma\delta}$ is uniquely determined; (3) If the metric tensor is given, and $P_{\alpha\beta\gamma\delta}$ (again for some specified choice of σ and $\varkappa$) is given, then $T_{\alpha\beta}$ is determined; (4) If $T_{\alpha\beta}=0$ then $P_{\alpha\beta\gamma\delta}$ determines $R_{\alpha\beta\gamma\delta}$; (5) The tensor $P_{\alpha\beta\gamma\delta}$ is a bi-tensor.

Let us note that the scalar ω is expressed linearly by the scalar curvature of the space R and by the scalar σ, and it is convenient not to specify its choice for the time being.

As a result of formulas (8) and the above-mentioned note we automatically obtain the following two theorems which solve the question of classification of the gravitational fields in the general case. (1) *As far as the algebraic structure of the tensor $P_{\alpha\beta\gamma\delta}$ is concerned, there exist three and only three types of gravitational fields. For each of these three possible types of gravitational fields it is possible to determine a tetrad with respect to which the matrix (P_{ab}) $(a, b = 1, \ldots 6)$ is determined by type* (5) *formulas, if in* (5) *we substitute*

$$R_{ab} \to P_{ab}, \ \varkappa \to \omega;$$

or in other words:

$$(P_{ab}) = \begin{pmatrix} M & N \\ N & -M \end{pmatrix}.$$

For each of the possible types we obtain, respectively:

$$T_1\colon M = \begin{pmatrix} A_1 & & \\ & A_2 & \\ & & A_3 \end{pmatrix}, \qquad N = \begin{pmatrix} B_1 & & \\ & B_2 & \\ & & B_3 \end{pmatrix}, \ \sum A_i = -\omega, \sum B_i = 0;$$

$$T_2\colon M = \begin{pmatrix} A_1 & 0 & 0 \\ 0 & A_2+1 & 0 \\ 0 & 0 & A_2-1 \end{pmatrix}, \ N = \begin{pmatrix} B_1 & 0 & 0 \\ 0 & B_2 & 1 \\ 0 & 1 & B_2 \end{pmatrix}, \tag{9}$$

$$A_1+2A_2 = -\omega, \ B_1+2B_2 = 0;$$

$$T_3\colon M = \begin{pmatrix} \varrho & 1 & 0 \\ 1 & \varrho & 0 \\ 0 & 0 & \varrho \end{pmatrix}, \qquad N = \begin{pmatrix} 0 & 0 & 0 \\ 0 & 0 & -1 \\ 0 & -1 & 0 \end{pmatrix}, \ \varrho = -\frac{\omega}{3}$$

where the invariants $A_s \pm iB_s$ have the same value and correspond to the same characteristics of the matrix $(P_{ab} - \lambda g_{ab})$ as in the case of formulas (5).

If $T_{\alpha\beta} \to \nu g_{\alpha\beta}$ then $A_s \to \alpha_s$, $B_s \to \beta_s$, $P_{ab} \to R_{ab}$ and we obtain case (5). With $T_{\alpha\beta} = 0$ we obtain the classification of the gravitational fields in *free* space.

It is possible, of course, to make a more detailed classification, marking out, for instance, cases of identical λ_s, of real λ_s etc. The choice of the scalars ω, σ, $\varkappa$ can be naturally connected with physical considerations. Note that because of the freedom in our choice of σ we can always make ω zero.

§ 3. SOME PHYSICAL APPLICATIONS

1. Among the physical theories where the classification of the gravitational fields and the canonical forms (5) have been successfully applied, an important and modern gravitational radiation theory is that developed by Pirani [7], who proceeded from some of the results obtained by Lichnerowicz. Similar results have been obtained by L. Bel [8] and this theory, while not final, bears examination. An interesting idea proposed by Joseph may be noted [9] though thus far it is illustrated by only one example.

2. The great majority of solutions known from the literature on the field equation $R_{\alpha\beta} = 0$ [see 2, pp. 201–11] belong to the fields T_1. The simplest example is Minkowski space. The first example of a field T_2 given in the literature is the well-known solution with cylindrical waves [10] by Einstein–Rosen. We can demonstrate rigorously that any solution of the Einstein–Rosen type will determine either a field T_1 or a field T_2 [2, pp. 210]. It is possible to give a solution of this type in a closed form in which the metric is determined with a certain functional arbitrariness. The simplest such solution which is of type T_2 has the metric

$$ds^2 = 2dx^1dx^4 - \sin^2 x^4 (dx^2)^2 - \sinh^2 x^4 (dx^3)^2. \tag{10}$$

This space T_2, permitting the group of motions G_6, is of the sixth order, which determines the maximum mobility for T_2.

In case of the gravitational fields T_3 the simplest examples are the fields determined by the metric

$$ds^2 = -e^{x^2}\left(e^{-2x^4}(dx^1)^2 + (dx^2)^2\right) + x^2(x^3 + e^{x^2})(dx^4)^2 - 2dx^3dx^4 \tag{11}$$

with the group of motions G_2 of maximum mobility for T_2.

3. While integrating the field equations and determining the equations of motion, the hypothesis is often introduced that at spatial infinity, as one moves away from the source of gravitation, the field potentials $g_{\alpha\beta}(x)$ come as close as desired to the corresponding potentials $\overset{*}{g}_{\alpha\beta}(x)$ determining Minkowski space within some system of coordinates. Thus, for example, in Schwarschild's well known static spherically-symmetric field the metric approaches the Minkowski metric as we go radially outwards from the singularity (θ, φ, and $t =$ constants, $r \to \infty$ in spherical coordinates). However, it is possible to demonstrate rigorously that *if one excludes from considerations the points at which the metric is degenerate* (that is $|g_{\alpha\beta}| \neq 0$), *then in no allowed coordinate system can the metric of gravitational fields of the T_2 and T_3 types approach the Minkowski*

metric; in other words, *if the metric does not degenerate then the type of the space does not change.* This can easily be seen from the example of the T_2 metric of type [10]. This fact is very interesting as it brings us to the alternatives: (a) either it is necessary to set up *boundary conditions* for T_2 and T_3 different from those for the gravitational fields T_1; or (b) the fields T_2 and T_3 can exist (without degeneration of the metric) only in the case of closed (e.g. spherical) space, when the boundary conditions become superfluous. It seems natural to try to solve this problem of boundary conditions, which disturbed Einstein [11], in accordance with alternative (a) above. In this case the following *principle of imposing boundary conditions* seems the most natural [2, pp. 267–74]: let us assume the gravitational field T_i $(i = 1, 2, 3)$; *then in regions where the action of the matter is small, the metric can be made to differ as little as desired from the space metric determined by the conditions*:

(1) *It is a space of the same type* T_i *as the one that is given*, and

(2) *It permits a group of motions of the maximum order, which is possible for* T_i, *of the given type.*

Thus, for T_1 the space of maximum mobility will be the Minkowski space with the group G_{10}, for T_2 the space with the metric (10) which permits the group of motions G_6 and for T_3 a space with the metric (11) with the group of motions G_2. Of course all these considerations require further investigation and the physical interpretation of the gravitational fields T_2 and T_3.

REFERENCES

[1] A. Z. PETROV, *Dokl. Akad. Nauk SSSR,* **81,** N 2, 1951.
[2] A. Z. PETROV, Einsteinian Space, dissert. 1956.
[3] A. Z. PETROV, *Dokl. Akad. Nauk SSSR,* **105,** N 5, 1955.
[4] A. Z. PETROV, *Sci. Not. Kazan State Univ.* **110,** 55, 1950.
[5] A. Z. PETROV, *Sci. Not. Kazan State Univ.* **114,** v. 8 1954.
[6] I. GÉHÉNIAU, *C. R. Acad. Sci., Paris* **244,** N 6, 1957.
[7] P. A. E. PIRANI, *Phys. Rev.* **105,** 1957.
[8] L. BEL, *C. R. Acad. Sci., Paris* **247,** N 15, 1958.
[9] V. JOSEPH, *Proc. Camb. Phil. Soc.* **53,** N 4, 1957.
[10] A. EINSTEIN and N. ROSEN, *J. Franklin. Inst.* **223,** 1937.
[11] A. EINSTEIN, *S. B. Preuss. Akad. Wiss.* p. 142(**1917**).

GRAVITATIONAL FIELD GEOMETRY AS THE GEOMETRY OF AUTOMORPHISMS

A. Z. PETROV

Kazan State University, USSR

GRAVITATIONAL field geometry, i.e. the whole complex of invariant values and correlations in the general theory of relativity, is completely determined by the space-time metric

$$ds^2 = g_{\alpha\beta}(x)\, dx^\alpha dx^\beta. \tag{1}$$

The distribution and the motion of the matter determining the field is characterized, in particular, by the energy-momentum tensor $T_{\alpha\beta}(x)$ which is determined by the metric tensor $g_{\alpha\beta}$ with the help of the Einstein field equations

$$R_{\alpha\beta} - \tfrac{1}{2} R g_{\alpha\beta} = \lambda T_{\alpha\beta}. \tag{2}$$

Generally, if we do not make any additional hypotheses, to any distribution and motion of matter corresponds an arbitrary tensor $g_{\alpha\beta}$ obeying only the following conditions: (1) the metric signature at each point is of the form $---+$; (2) the components $g_{\alpha\beta}(x)$ are functions of class C^2 at least; (3) $|g_{\alpha\beta}| \neq 0$. Thus it is suggested that in the general theory of relativity the matter which produces the field can be described by six functions of four variables $x^a (a = 1, \ldots, 4)$, provided these functions meet the conditions just given.

We shall not discuss here the possibility of the existence of "privileged" coordinate systems, and we suppose that for some reason a certain system of coordinates has been chosen to describe the given gravitational field. Let us consider the complex of all point transformations

$$\overset{*}{x}{}^a = f_a(x^1, \ldots, x^4; a^1, \ldots, a^r) \tag{3}$$

depending on r *essential* parameters $a^1, \ldots, a^r$ which *preserve* the space-time metric (1), i.e.

$$g_{\alpha\beta}(\overset{*}{x})\, d\overset{*}{x}{}^{\alpha} d\overset{*}{x}{}^{\beta} = g_{\alpha\beta}(x)\, dx^{\alpha} dx^{\beta}. \tag{4}$$

These transformations determine *the group of motions* G_r *of the given space.* With every such transformation a point mapping of the space-time into itself takes place, i.e. we have here a group of *automorphisms.*

As a result of the automorphism the matter and the geometry of the gravitational field will be described by the same functions and equations as before the automorphism, since it follows from (4) that the functions which determine the components of the metric tensor $g_{\alpha\beta}$ remain invariant. If the space-time geometry is given, then all its properties are conserved under automorphisms, including the structure of the formulas and of the functions. Thus any description of the gravitational field is given with some arbitrariness which corresponds to the automorphisms of motion of the space-time. *The geometry of any gravitational field is the geometry of automorphisms of motion of the space-time.*

Every gravitational field has its own corresponding group of motions G_r, where $0 \leqslant r \leqslant 10$. If $r = 0$, the space permits only the identity transformation $\overset{*}{x}{}^{\alpha} = x^{\alpha}$ and the group of automorphisms coincides with the *unity* of the group.

This idea has been stated before [1] [2, pp. 60–201] [3] and the question reduced to its realization and a practical study of the geometry of the gravitational field from a group point of view.

§ 1. FREE SPACE

It is interesting to apply the above considerations to the case of Einstein's free space when equations (2) may be written in the following way:

$$R_{\alpha\beta} = 0 \tag{5}$$

where $R_{\alpha\beta}$ is a Ricci tensor. It is known[(1)] that there are precisely three types of spaces, classified according to the algebraic structure of their curvature tensors, which obey Eq. (5). Let these types be T_i $(i = 1, 2, 3)$. It is natural to set the following two problems:

---

(1) See the article "Invariant Classification of Gravitational Fields" by the same author in this book.

(1) To determine which groups are permissible for each of the three possible types of spaces T_i; (2) To determine the space-time metrics which permit a given group of automorphisms. The solution to the first of these two problems in terms of the "order of the possible group" can be given with the help of the following scheme [2].

the group order \ Type	T_1	T_2	T_3
G_{10}	1 (Minkowski Space)		
$G_7, G_8, G_9,$			
G_6	Lacune	1 (Maximum mobility Space)	
G_5		1	
G_4	6	Lacune	
G_3	7	3	
G_2	4	2	1 (Maximum mobility Space)
G_1	2	2	2
G_0	1	1	1

Here single hatching ("lacune") means that such a T_i with a group of such an order automatically permits a group with order one unit higher (thus, in the case of T_1 it is the group G_{10}, which corresponds to plane space-time; in the case of T_2 it is the group G_5). Double hatching means that no spaces of this type exist with a group of motions of the given order. There are no other "lacunes" except those that are given in the scheme. In each box are shown the number of different classes of spaces of the given type which permit a group of motions of the given order. The classes are considered different if the groups related to them either have the same order but a different group structure or have the same group structure and have respectively *isotropic* and *nonisotropic surfaces of transitiveness.*

An important fact follows directly from this scheme—namely that *the spaces T_2 and T_3 cannot be flat* (the curvature tensor always differs from zero).

We shall give the solution of the second problem with the help of the following summary of the possible metrics. For the sake of brevity we shall limit ourselves to the cases $r \geqslant 4$ for T_1; $r \geqslant 5$ for T_2, and $r = 2$ for T_3. The metrics are written down in special systems of coordinates.

Space T_1

Group G_{10}

$$ds^2 = -dx^{1^2} - dx^{2^2} - dx^{3^2} + dx^{4^2}.$$

$$G_r \ (r = 5, 6, 7, 8, 9).$$

If the space T_1 permits a group of motions of this order then it permits the group G_{10} and therefore is a flat space.

Group G_4

$$1.\ \ ds^2 = -(c_1x^2+c_2)(dx^1)^2 - \frac{c_1(c_1x^2+c_2)}{x^2+c_3}(dx^2) - \frac{x_2+c_3}{c_1(c_1x^2+c_3)}(dx^3)^2 + \\ +(c_1x^2+c_2)^2\cos x^1(dx^4)^2.$$

A static solution of the field equations with an *unsolvable* group with the structure:

$$[X_1X_2] = X_1,\ [X_1X_3] = 2X_2,\ [X_2X_3] = X_3,\ [X_iX_4] = 0$$

$$(i = 1, 2, 3),\ c_i = \text{const}.$$

$$2.\ \ ds^2 = -\frac{c_1(c_1x^1+c_2)}{x^1+c_3}dx^{1^2} - (c_1x^1+c_2)^2dx^{2^2} - (c_1x^1+c_2)\sin^2x^2dx^{3^2} + \\ + \frac{x^1+c_3}{c_1(c_1x^1+c_2)}dx^{4^2}.$$

A static solution. The group is *unsolvable* and has the structure

$$[X_1X_2] = X_3,\ [X_3X_1] = X_2,\ [X_2X_3] = X_1,$$

$$[X_i\,X_4] = 0 \quad (i = 1, 2, 3);$$

when $c_1 = 1$, $c_2 = 0$, $c_3 = -2a$ we obtain Schwarzschild's central-symmetric static solution; when $c_1 = 1$, $c_2 = -2a$, $c_3 = 0$ a Buchdahl *mutual* solution [4]. In metrics 1. and 2. the number of essential parameters can be reduced to one.

$$3.\ \ ds^2 = -(kx^3+1)^2dx^{1^2} - (kx^3+1)\,dx^{2^2} - \frac{1}{kx^3+1}dx^{3^2} + (kx^3+1)^2dx^{4^2},$$

$$k = \text{const}.$$

A static solution: when $k \to 0$, we obtain a flat space. The group is solvable, with the structure $[X_1 X_2] = 0$, $[X_1 X_3] = X_2$, $[X_2 X_3] = X_1, \ldots$

4. $ds^2 = -\nu^{4/3}(dx^{1^2} + dx^{2^2}) - \nu^{-2/3}dx^{3^2} + dx^{4^2}, \quad \nu = kx^4 + 1.$

A *nonstatic* solution of the field equations.

5. $ds^2 = -\nu^{4/3}(dx^{1^2} + dx^{2^2}) - dx^{3^2} + \nu^{-2/3}dx^{4^2}, \quad \nu = kx^3 + 1.$

A *static* solution.

6. $ds^2 = -\nu^{4/3}dx^{1^2} - \nu^{-2/3}dx^{2^2} - dx^{3^2} + \nu^{4/3}dx^{4^2}, \quad \nu = kx^3 + 1.$

A *static* solution. Metrics 5. and 6., in the same system of coordinates, were found by Kasner [5] and by Narlikar and Karmarkar [6]. Metrics 4., 5. and 6. have a *solvable* group

$$[X_i X_j] = 0 \ (i,j = 1,2,3), \ [X_1 X_4] = l_1 X_2, \ [X_2 X_4] = l_2 X_1,$$
$$[X_3 X_4] = 0, \ l_1 = l_2 = 0, \pm 1.$$

The group G_4 includes the Abelian subgroup G_3.

7. $$ds^2 = -e^{\nu}[\cos(\sqrt{3}\nu)dx^{1^2} - 2\sin(\sqrt{3}\nu)dx^1 dx^4 - \cos(\sqrt{3}\nu)dx^{4^2}] - $$
$$-dx^{2^2} - e^{-2\nu}dx^{3^2}, \quad \nu = kx^2.$$

A *static* solution with the structure

$$[X_i X_j] = 0 \ (i,j = 1,2,3), \ [X_1 X_4] = -\frac{1}{2}X_1 - \frac{\sqrt{3}}{2}X_3,$$
$$[X_2 X_4] = X_2, \ [X_3 X_4] = \frac{\sqrt{3}}{2}X_1 - \frac{1}{2}X_3.$$

Having integrated the Killing equation it is easy to determine Killing vectors $\underset{s}{\xi}^a$ $(s = 1, \ldots, r)$ which determine the motion operators: $X_i = \underset{i}{\xi}^a \partial_a$ where

$$\underset{i}{\xi}_{(\alpha,\beta)} = 0$$

for each of these spaces. Let us note that the groups of motions allowed by metrics 1.–6. are *intransitive* (i.e. the rank of the matrix $\|\underset{s}{\xi}^a\|$ is 3) and only in the case of metric 7. do we obtain a *simply-transitive* group (the rank of the matrix $\|\underset{s}{\xi}^a\|$ is 4). The surfaces of transitiveness of the G_3 subgroups *are in all cases non-isotropic*.

Space T_2

Group G_6

$$ds^2 = 2dx^1dx^4 - \sin^2 x^4 dx^{2^2} - \sin^2 x^4 dx^{3^2}.$$

A *transitive* group, *solvable* with the structure

$$[X_1X_i] = [X_2X_j] = [X_4X_k] = 0, \ (i = 2, \ldots, 6, \ j = 3, 5, \ k = 3, 5),$$

$$[X_2X_4] = X_1, \ [X_2X_6] = X_4, \ [X_3X_5] = X_1, \ [X_3X_6] = X_5,$$

$$[X_4X_6] = X_2, \ [X_5X_6] = -X_3.$$

This metric determines the *space of maximum mobility* T_2.

Group G_5

I. $ds^2 = 2dx^1dx^4 + \alpha dx^{2^2} + 2\beta dx^2dx^3 + \gamma dx^{3^2}$,

where α, β, γ are functions of x^4 satisfying the equation

$$\gamma\alpha'' - 2\beta\beta'' + \alpha\gamma'' + \frac{1}{2g}[\gamma^2\alpha'^2 + \alpha^2\gamma'^2 + 2\alpha\gamma\beta'^2 + 2\beta^2(\alpha'\gamma' + \beta'^2) -$$

$$-4\beta\gamma\alpha'\beta' - 4\alpha\beta\beta'\gamma'] = 0, \qquad g = |g_{\alpha\beta}|.$$

The group has the structure

$$[X_iX_j] = [X_sX_4] = [X_kX_5] = 0,$$

$$(i, j = 1, 2, 3; \ s = 1, 3, 5; \quad k = 1, 2),$$

$$[X_2X_4] = [X_3X_5] = X_1.$$

The fact that subgroups as a rule act on isotropic surfaces of the space is characteristic for spaces T_2 (i.e. they determine $|g_{ij}| = 0$ $(i, j = 1, \ldots, s; \ s < 4)$, where g_{ij} is a metric tensor on the surface).

Space T_3

Group G_2

$$ds^2 = -e^{x^2}(e^{-2x^4}dx^{1^2} + dx^{2^2}) - 2dx^3dx^4 + x^2(x^3 + e^{x^2})dx^{4^2}.$$

This is the space of *maximum mobility* T_3. The group is *non-abelian* (structure $[X_1X_2] = X_1$) and acts on *non-isotropic* surfaces of transitiveness whose signature is of the $--$ type.

§ 2. GENERAL CASE. INVARIANT IMAGES

In the general case, when the field equations (2) hold, the number of possible classes of spaces permitting some group of motions greatly increases. The problem reduces to the determination of Riemannian spaces V_4 with the signature $---+$ permitting some group of motions. This has been considered by many authors [7] [8] [9] and has now been completely solved.(1)

All known solutions of the field equations in the literature are found in such classifications and are essentially invariant.

Any type of group transformation, if it is *intransitive*, results in the space-time points being reflected on a point lying on some certain surface of transitiveness. The whole space-time divides into such surfaces and physically they represent invariant images. In the case of a *transitive* group (e.g. metric 7., T_1) such surfaces do not exist; any point of the space-time may be mapped onto any other with the help of a transformation of the group. But in this case an *imprimitive system* of the group may exist, i.e. the totality of varieties which change into one another during the transformation of the group. The system of imprimitiveness as well as the system of surfaces of transitiveness may consist of *non-isotropic* surfaces (the case of space T_1), but also may include *isotropic* surfaces of various number of dimensions, on which the metric degenerates (the case of space T_2).

A physical interpretation of these invariant images and other group conceptions would be very useful in the study of gravitational fields, and such a study would be very desirable.

It should be noted that all the many special solutions of the field equations (1) or (5) known in the literature are easily classified according to the geometry of automorphisms. A great number of solutions coincide or repeat one another as they differ only in the choice of the coordinate system. For instance, Kotler's solution [10] has the same group as metric 2. of the space T_1 with group G_4; a static solution with axial symmetry of the Weyl and Levi-Cività type [11] [12] permit the Abelian group G_2 acting on non-isotropic surfaces of transitiveness; a special case is the solution by Mitter [13] and Lewis [14] and Delsarte [15] with the same group of motions;

(1) A general solution of the problem and a summary of results will be given in a series of articles by A. Z. Petrov, V. R. Kaigorodov and V. I. Abdullin, to be published in "The WUZ proceedings. Mathematics" Kazan. U.S.S.R. (in Russian).

the solution given by Choy [16] is reduced either to Schwarzschilds's or Kasner's solution or to the space T_1, with G_4 and metric 2. Any *reduced* space, the metric of which is split into two binary forms

$$ds^2 = \mathrm{I}(x^1, x^2) + \mathrm{II}(x^3, x^4)$$

which satisfy the equation $R_{\alpha\beta} = \varkappa g_{\alpha\beta}$, permits (with $\varkappa \neq 0$) a six parameter group of motions (and with $\varkappa = 0$, the group G_{10}). The well known cylindrical waves of Einstein and Rosen [17], which are solutions of the field equations (5), permit an Abelian group G_2.

Thus the general algebraic classification of gravitational fields and the classification of automorphisms together allow us to give an *invariant characterization of gravitational fields*. It would be interesting to have physical interpretations of the quantities and concepts which arise when we carry out such an invariant characterization.

REFERENCES

[1] E. Cartan, *L'Enseignement Mathématique,* p. 20–225 (1927).
[2] A. Z. Petrov, Dokt. dissert., Moscou 1956.
[3] H. Keres, *Phys. Astr. Inst. Proc.*, 5, Tartu 1957.
[4] H. A. Buchdahl, *Quart. J. Math.* **5**, 18 (1954).
[5] E. Kasner, *Amer. J. Math.* **43**, 1921.
[6] V. V. Narlikar and K. K. Karmarkar, *Curr. Sci.* **15**, 1946.
[7] G. Fubini, *Ann. di mat.* (3) **8**, 1903.
[8] G. Fubini, *Ann. di mat.* (3) **9**, 1904.
[9] G. I. Kruckowic, *Mat. collect* **41**, issue 2 (1957).
[10] F. Kottler, *Ann. Phys., Lpz.* (4), **56**, 1918.
[11] Levi-Civita, *R.C. Acad. Lincei* **27**, 7–8 (1918).
[12] H. Weyl, *Ann. d. Phys.* **54**, 1917; **59**, 1919.
[13] O. K. Mitter, *Těhaxy math. J.*, **34**, 1931.
[14] T. Lewis, *Proc. Roy. Soc.* **136**, 1932.
[15] M. Delsarte, *Sur les ds² d'Einstein a symetrie axiale,* Paris 1934.
[16] P. Y. Choy, *Amer. J. Math.* **59**, 1937.
[17] A. Einstein and N. Rosen, *J. Franklin Inst.* 223 (1937).

INTERPRETATION OF RAINICH GEOMETRY *

G. Rosen

Institute for Theoretical Physics, Stockholm

Abstract—Rainich geometries are analyzed in terms of the invariants associated with the Ricci vierbein of principal directions. At any point the four unit vectors of the vierbein pair off into two blades which contain the maxima and minima directions of mean curvature. The blades mesh into smooth integral surfaces for certain electromagnetic fields. In general, neighbouring blades are related by only two independent differential conditions.

INTRODUCTION

The Einstein–Maxwell equations govern the gravitational behaviour of classical electromagnetic radiation. Considerable interest attaches itself to electromagnetic fields which are *non-null*, in the sense that the square of the Maxwell stress tensor is greater than zero,[(1)]

$$\varrho^2 \equiv \tfrac{1}{4} R^{\varrho}{}_{\sigma} R^{\sigma}{}_{\varrho} > 0. \tag{1}$$

When this non-null condition is satisfied, the whole content of source-free electrodynamics and Einstein gravitation theory is contained in the statement that the space-time geometry satisfies the following *Rainich conditions* ([1], [2]):

* Essential results in this paper are taken from the author's publication, "Geometrical Significance of the Einstein–Maxwell Equations", *Phys. Rev.* **114** (May 15, 1959).

(1) In the idealization for which space-time is treated as approximately flat, the electromagnetic form of (1) requires that $(\boldsymbol{E}^2 - \boldsymbol{H}^2)$ and $(\boldsymbol{E} \cdot \boldsymbol{H})$ do not both vanish. This *non-null* requirement is satisfied by a general superposition of waves travelling in various directions. An outstanding exception, however, is the case of a pure monochromatic wave travelling in a single direction. It is not known whether this *null* case has a rigorous correspondent which satisfies the Einstein–Maxwell equations.

The Maxwell stress tensor has zero trace, or

$$R = 0. \tag{2}$$

The square of the stress tensor is proportional to the unit matrix, or

$$R^{\mu}{}_{\sigma} R^{\sigma}{}_{\nu} = \varrho^2 \delta^{\mu}{}_{\nu}. \tag{3}$$

The electromagnetic energy density is positive definite, or

$$R_{00} > 0. \tag{4}$$

A certain vectorial combination of the Ricci curvature components and their first derivatives shall have zero curl; that is to say, this prescribed combination shall be expressible in the form of a gradient,

$$\frac{g_{\mu\sigma}\, \varepsilon^{\sigma\varrho\nu\lambda} R^{\varkappa}{}_{\varrho} R_{\varkappa\nu;\lambda}}{4\varrho^2 \sqrt{-g}} = \alpha_{,\mu} \tag{5}$$

where α is a scalar invariant, the "complexion" of the electromagnetic field [2]. The Levi-Civitá symbol $\varepsilon^{\sigma\varrho\nu\lambda}$ is skew-symetric in all pairs of indices, with $\varepsilon^{0123} \equiv 1$.

Whenever the non-null condition (1) is satisfied, *Rainich geometries* [2]–[5] are entirely equivalent to Einstein's original description of gravitation and electromagnetic radiation. In this paper we seek to determine the geometrical meaning of Rainich's system of equations. First, we proceed to reduce [2]–[5] to an equivalent, but more tractable, set of geometrical conditions.

RAINICH GEOMETRY IN TERMS OF THE RICCI VIERBEIN

The local canonical form of a non-null Rainich–Ricci tensor ([1], [2]) available to any point through an appropriate coordinate transformation, guarantees the existence of the Ricci *vierbein* of principal directions (see [3], p. 113). The sixteen vierbein components are established by the set of equations:

$$(R_{\mu\nu} - \varrho_a g_{\mu\nu}) \lambda_{a|}{}^{\nu} = 0 \qquad (a = 0, 1, 2, 3) \tag{6}$$

$$g_{\mu\nu} \lambda_{a|}{}^{\mu} \lambda_{b|}{}^{\nu} \equiv \lambda_{a|\nu} \lambda_{b|}{}^{\nu} = e_a \delta_{ab}, \tag{7}$$

$$e_0 = -1, \qquad e_1 = e_2 = e_3 = +1. \tag{8}$$

Relations (7) and (6) imply

$$g_{\mu\nu} = \sum_{a=0}^{3} e_a \lambda_{a|\mu} \lambda_{a|\nu}, \tag{9}$$

$$R_{\mu\nu} = \sum_{a=0}^{3} e_a \varrho_a \lambda_{a|\mu} \lambda_{a|\nu}. \tag{10}$$

Substituting (10) into (3), we find the Ricci invariants

$$\varrho_a = f_a \varrho \tag{11}$$

where each

$$f_a^2 = 1. \tag{12}$$

Then from (2) it follows that

$$\sum_{a=0}^{3} f_a = 0. \tag{13}$$

Now without loss of generality we can satisfy (12) and (13) by putting

$$f_0 = f_1 = -1, \quad f_2 = f_3 = +1. \tag{14}$$

These values for f_a pair the vierbein legs into a negative and a positive blade. The particular numerical assignment to f_0 in (14) fixes the sign of ϱ according to (4),

$$\varrho > 0. \tag{15}$$

The Ricci tensor (10) with (11), (14) and (15),

$$R_{\mu\nu} = \varrho \sum_{a=0}^{3} e_a f_a \lambda_{a|\mu} \lambda_{a|\nu}, \tag{16}$$

satisfies the first three requirements of a Rainich geometry.

A geometrical interpretation of the Ricci tensor (16) goes as follows. Let n^μ denote any unit vector which lies in the positive blade at a point. Then the mean curvature [3] of the space in the direction n^μ, defined by geometries as $R_{\mu\nu} n^\mu n^\nu$, is equal to ϱ. This is the maximum value attainable for all directions at the point. Furthermore, the minimum mean curvature $(-\varrho)$ is associated with any unit vector which resides in the negative blade at a point.

Let us denote the intrinsic derivative in the direction of a vierbein leg by

$$\partial_a \equiv \lambda_{a|}{}^{\nu} \frac{\partial}{\partial x^\nu}. \tag{17}$$

The *structure coefficients* are introduced in the commutation relations

$$[\partial_a, \partial_b] \equiv \partial_a \partial_b - \partial_b \partial_a = \sum_{c=0}^{3} C_{cab} \partial_c. \tag{18}$$

In analogy to a hydrodynamic flow, these structure coefficients may be called "the projected vorticities" of the Ricci vierbein,

$$C_{cab} = -C_{cba} \equiv e_c(\lambda_{c|\mu,\nu} - \lambda_{c|\nu,\mu})\lambda_{a|}^{\mu}\lambda_{b|}^{\nu}. \tag{19}$$

With the aid of this intrinsic notation, Rainich's final condition, equation (5), can be drastically simplified. Substituting (16) into (5) and performing a few manipulations establishes the relation

$$\eta_a = \partial_a \alpha \tag{20}$$

in which four structure coefficients appear as

$$\begin{aligned} \eta_0 &\equiv C_{123}, & \eta_2 &\equiv C_{310}, \\ \eta_1 &\equiv C_{032}, & \eta_3 &\equiv C_{201}. \end{aligned} \tag{21}$$

The integrability conditions equivalent to (20) are easily found with the help of (18)

$$\Omega_{ab} = 0, \tag{22}$$

$$\Omega_{ab} \equiv \partial_a \eta_b - \partial_b \eta_a - \sum_{c=0}^{3} C_{cab}\,\eta_c. \tag{23}$$

Before looking at the geometrical content of (22) in the general case, we consider Rainich geometries for which the blades "mesh".

THE BLADES CAN MESH

Let us investigate the existence of two sets of integral surfaces which contain the blades at every point. The integral surfaces are defined by the intersections of pairs of σ-hypersurfaces $[\sigma = \sigma(x^0, x^1, x^2, x^3)]$:

$$S_{(-)} = \begin{Bmatrix} \sigma_0 = \text{const} \\ \sigma_1 = \text{const} \end{Bmatrix} \quad \text{such that} \quad \begin{Bmatrix} \partial_0\sigma_0 = \partial_1\sigma_0 = 0 \\ \partial_0\sigma_1 = \partial_1\sigma_1 = 0 \end{Bmatrix} \tag{24}$$

and

$$S_{(+)} = \begin{Bmatrix} \sigma_2 = \text{const} \\ \sigma_3 = \text{const} \end{Bmatrix} \quad \text{such that} \quad \begin{Bmatrix} \partial_2\sigma_2 = \partial_3\sigma_2 = 0 \\ \partial_2\sigma_3 = \partial_3\sigma_3 = 0 \end{Bmatrix} \tag{25}$$

By virtue of (18) and (21), the integrability conditions which admit the existence of the negative blade integral surfaces $S_{(-)}$ are

$$\eta_2 = \eta_3 = 0. \tag{26}$$

Similarly, the necessary and sufficient conditions for the positive blade integral surfaces $S_{(+)}$ are

$$\eta_0 = \eta_1 = 0 . \tag{27}$$

In view of (20), we have the theorem:

The negative blade integral surfaces exist if and only if the normal to the $\alpha =$ const hypersurface is contained in the negative blade at every point; similarly, the positive blade integral surfaces exist if and only if normal to the $\alpha =$ const hypersurfaces is contained in the positive blade at every point. Finally, both sets of integral surfaces exist if and only if α is identically constant.

The case of α identically constant, characteristic of the Reissner-Nordstrom ([4], [5]) solution and most Rainich geometries presently known to us, is physically significant in that it describes an electromagnetic field which is purely electrical. This does not mean that the geometry is necessarily static, since $\alpha \equiv$ const is *not* sufficient to guarantee a group of motions in the direction of $\lambda_{0|\mu}$.

Notice that if the normal to the $\alpha =$ const hypersurface is contained in the negative blade, not only does the negative blade integral surface exist, but also the positive blades are contained in a set of hypersurfaces, namely, $\{\alpha = \text{const}\}$. We are thus tempted to consider whether the general content of Rainich's fourth condition (20) amounts to the statement, "Two sets of hypersurfaces exist which contain the positive and negative blades, respectively". This possibility was studied and found to require more than the content of (20) or its equivalent equation (22).

THE GENERAL CONTENT OF RAINICH'S FOURTH EQUATION

At first glance, the integrability conditions (22) comprise six independent conditions which must be satisfied by the geometry. However, since the Ricci vierbein is not uniquely determined, these conditions are not all independent. An *internal gauge* exists which can Lorentz-transform blade partners in the vierbein in a way which preserves (9), (16) and all relations which follow from them. Under the internal gauge transformations, the components of (23) within the blades (Ω_{01} and Ω_{23}) remain unchanged — they are gauge-invariant. The cross-components of (23) (Ω_{02}, Ω_{03}, Ω_{12}, Ω_{13}) suffer mixing with the two arbitrary internal gauge functions. The Rainich conditions (22) for the cross-components reduce to a pair of internal gauge conditions, and a pair of bonafide geometrical conditions. Hence, (22) states *two* and not four geometrical conditions on the cross-components.

What is the nature of the two conditions in (22) which require the gauge-invariant components within the blades (Ω_{01} and Ω_{23}) to vanish? We shall prove that the conditions

$$\Omega_{01} = \Omega_{23} = 0 \tag{28}$$

are trivially satisfied, as a consequence of the algebraic form of the Ricci tensor (16). Thus, the components of (22) within the blades express nothing that we do not already know about Rainich geometry.

The proof starts with the Poisson operator identity,

$$[\partial_c, [\partial_a, \partial_b]] + [\partial_a, [\partial_b, \partial_c]] + [\partial_b, [\partial_c, \partial_a]] \equiv 0 . \tag{29}$$

We substitute (18) into this identity and find

$$\partial_c C_{eab} + \partial_a C_{ebc} + \partial_b C_{eca} + \\ + \sum_{d=0}^{3} (C_{dab} C_{ecd} + C_{dbc} C_{ead} + C_{dca} C_{ebd}) \equiv 0 . \tag{30}$$

Equating c and e in this expression and summing, we have

$$\Psi_{ab} \equiv \sum_{c=0}^{3} (\partial_c C_{cab} + \partial_a C_{cbc} + \partial_b C_{cca}) + \sum_{c,d=0}^{3} C_{ccd} C_{dab} \equiv 0 . \tag{31}$$

Next, observe that the contracted Bianchi identities and (2) state that

$$R_{\mu\ ;\sigma}^{\ \sigma} = 0 . \tag{32}$$

Substituting (16) into this expression, we eventually obtain

$$\partial_a (\ln \varrho) = 2\xi_a \tag{33}$$

where

$$\begin{aligned} \xi_0 &\equiv C_{202} + C_{303} , \\ \xi_1 &\equiv C_{212} + C_{313} , \\ \xi_2 &\equiv C_{020} + C_{121} , \\ \xi_3 &\equiv C_{030} + C_{131} . \end{aligned} \tag{34}$$

The intrinsic curl of (33) is

$$\Phi_{ab} \equiv \partial_a \xi_b - \partial_b \xi_a - \sum_{c=0}^{3} C_{cab} \xi_c = 0 . \tag{35}$$

Now it is readily seen by referring to the definitions (23), (21), and (34), as well as the definition parts of (31) and (35), that

$$\begin{aligned} \Omega_{01} &= \Psi_{32} - \Phi_{32}, \\ \Omega_{23} &= \Psi_{01} - \Phi_{01}. \end{aligned} \tag{36}$$

Hence, (31) and (35) prove the assertions made in (28). The Rainich conditions (22) *within* the blades are trivially satisfied. However, the geometrical significance of the two gauge-free cross-components of (22) still remains a mystery.

REFERENCES

[1] G. Y. RAINICH, *Trans. Amer. Math. Soc.* **27**, 106 (1925).
[2] C. W. MISNER and J. A. WHEELER, *Ann. Phys.* **2**, 525 (1957).
[3] L. P. EISENHARD, *Riemannian Geometry*, Princeton University Press, 1949.
[4] K. REISSNER, *Ann. Phys.* (4) **50**, 106 (1916).
[5] L. NORDSTROM, *Proc. Amsterdam Acad.* **20**, 1238 (1918).

DISTANCE AND THE ASYMPTOTIC BEHAVIOUR OF WAVES IN GENERAL RELATIVITY

R. SACHS*

Hamburg University, Hamburg

Abstract—It is shown that in electromagnetic null, gravitational null, or vacuum gravitational type III waves that spread out, there are universal algebraic relations between the parallax distance, the electromagnetic luminosity distance, the preferred parameter distance along the rays, and the rotation of the rays; when the rotation vanishes all three kinds of distance are equal. The dependence of the electromagnetic field or Riemannian tensor on the distance is calculated explicitly and the waves interpreted as pure retarded fields seen at large distances from some source. The results can be extended to all vacuum metrics except the algebraically most general, non-degenerate type I, metrics. The question of whether fields that are not type I but do spread out actually exist is left open.(1)

I. INTRODUCTION

IN linearized gravitational theory, the Riemannian tensor of the retarded field coming from a time-dependent multipole source at rest is null (vacuum degenerate type II [1], [2]), in the far-field region [3] and type III in the semi-far-field region [4]. Thus there is some reason to assume that in the exact theory null or type III waves are the appropriate idealizations of actual retarded radiation fields seen at large distances from the source. The main purpose of this paper is to show without approximations that if there are any metrics which are null or vacuum type III and spread out they automatically have the expected type of behavior: up to certain corrections for the rotation of the rays, the Riemannian

* It is an honour to be able to dedicate this paper to Professor L. Infeld, whose work on so many topics, especially on the equations of motion in general relativity, has greatly enriched our knowledge of the physical universe.

(1) This existence question has meanwhile been solved by Robinson and Trautman (note added in proof).

tensor of a null metric falls off inversely as the distance, while the Riemannian tensor of a type III wave splits (uniquely, covariantly, and additively) into two portions that fall off as $1/r$ and $1/r^2$ respectively. In order to formulate our results precisely we first discuss the notion of distance. To indicate how our results fit into a broader framework we include, without proof, some results on vacuum non-degenerate type II and degenerate type I fields.

Our basic viewpoint is invariant-theoretical: electromagnetic and gravitational fields define in a natural, covariant way certain scalars, plane elements, etc. ([1], [2]); these preferred elements are subject to differential conditions by the field equations and Bianchi identities; we assume that such absolute quantities and conditions are *ipso facto* interesting and set ourselves the problem of interpreting them geometrically and physically [5]. We shall complete a small portion of this general task.

Latin indices run from 1 to 4; the metric g_{ab} has the signature $+2$; $G_{ab}{}^{cd}_{..} = \delta^c_{[a}\delta^d_{b]}$; the duality operation on a pair of antisymmetric indices ([6], [7]) is denoted by a star and chosen to be real, $\overset{*}{w}_{ab} = E_{ab}{}^{cd}_{..} w_{cd} = (\sqrt{-g}/2)\, e_{ab}{}^{cd}_{..} w_{cd}$, where e_{abcd} is the alternating symbol. We assume that all quantities introduced are three times differentiable.

The electromagnetic and gravitational fields we shall consider define a wave vector field ([4], [8], [9]) k^a with the properties

$$k^a k_a = k^a{}_{;b} k^b = 0. \tag{1}$$

The wave vector is unique up to the "restricted parameter transformations" induced by real scalar functions $\underset{0}{A} \neq 0$:

$$k'^a = \underset{0}{A} k^a, \qquad \operatorname{Prop} \underset{0}{A} \equiv \underset{0}{A}{}_{;a} k^a = 0. \tag{2}$$

Here and throughout we use "Prop" for the covariant derivative in the k^a direction and use the subscript "0" directly underneath only for quantities whose Prop vanishes. The null geodesics with tangent k^a will be called "rays". $\underset{0}{u}{}^a$ always denotes an auxiliary four-velocity field, $\underset{0}{u}{}^a \underset{0}{u}{}_a = -1$, Prop $\underset{0}{u}{}^a = 0$.

II. THE FIELD EQUATIONS AND BIANCHI IDENTITIES

In order to make full use of the information that we are dealing with a normal-hyperbolic four-dimensional space we shall rewrite the electromagnetic field equations $F^{ab}{}_{;b} = \overset{*}{F}{}^{ab}{}_{;b} = 0$ and the gravitational vacuum Bianchi identities, $R_{ab..;d}^{\ \ cd} = 0$, $\overset{*}{R}{}_{ab..;d}^{\ \ cd} = 0$, as sets of scalar equations.

With a given metric and k^a fixed up to the transformations (2), we can define ∞^4 tetrad systems at any point by the equations:

$$g^{ab} = 2k^{(a}m^{b)} + v^a v^b + w^a w^b = 2k^{(a}m^{b)} + 2\bar{t}^{(a}\bar{t}^{b)};\ t^a = (1/\sqrt{2})(v^a + iw^a). \quad (3)$$

Here v^a, w^a and m^a are real vectors; $\bar{t}^a$ is the complex conjugate of t^a.(1) With the convention (3), $k^a m_a = \bar{t}_a t^a = 1$ and all other contractions of vectors in the (k, m, t) tetrad are zero. With any tetrad (3) we associate two simple bivectors v_{ab} and m_{ab}:

$$v_{ab} = 2k_{[a}v_{b]}, \qquad m_{ab} = 2k_{[a}m_{b]}. \quad (4)$$

Given an electromagnetic null field F_{ab} whose wave vector is k^a and any vector v^a obeying Eq. (3)

$$F_{ab} = \mathrm{Re}(\varphi)v_{ab} - \mathrm{Im}(\varphi)v^*_{ab} \quad (5)$$

for a suitably chosen complex scalar function φ with real and imaginary parts $\mathrm{Re}(\varphi)$ and $\mathrm{Im}(\varphi)$. Similarly, a Riemannian tensor N_{abcd} has the algebraic form of a null conformal tensor with wave vector k^a if and only if there is a complex scalar θ such that

$$N_{abcd} = [\mathrm{Re}(\theta)G_{ab..}^{\ \ ef} - \mathrm{Im}(\theta)E_{ab..}^{\ \ ef}](v_{ef}v_{cd} - v^*_{ef}v^*_{cd}).^{(2)} \quad (6)$$

Finally, a vacuum type III Riemannian tensor III_{abcd} with wave vector k^a has the form

$$\mathrm{III}_{abcd} = [\mathrm{Re}(\sigma)G_{ab..}^{\ \ ef} - \mathrm{Im}(\sigma)E_{ab..}^{\ \ ef}](m_{ef}v_{cd} + v_{ef}m_{cd} - m^*_{ef}v^*_{cd} - v^*_{ef}m^*_{cd}), \quad (7)$$

for suitably chosen m^a and σ. The tetrad defined by Eq. (3) and one of the Eqs (5), (6) or (7) is arbitrary up to the "4-screw" [10] induced by the $\underset{0}{A}$ considered in Eq. (2) and any complex function C of unit magnitude ($C\bar{C} = 1$),

$$k'^a = \underset{0}{A}k^a,\quad m'^a = \underset{0}{A}{}^{-1}m^a,\quad t'^a = Ct^a,\quad \bar{t}'^a = \bar{C}t^a,\quad \varphi' = C\underset{0}{A}{}^{-1}\varphi,$$
$$\theta' = C^2\underset{0}{A}{}^{-2}\theta,\quad \sigma' = C\underset{0}{A}{}^{-1}\sigma, \quad (8)$$

(1) This complex notation is closely related to the spinor notation; compare [10] and [11].

(2) More elegant defining properties than Eqs (6) and (7) are those in terms of minimal equations [7] and the powerful criteria of Lichnerowicz and Bel [12].

and certain reflections. Eqs (3), (5) and (6) are invariant under "m-rotations":

$$m'^a = m^a + Bt^a + \bar{B}\bar{t}^a - B\bar{B}k^a, \quad t'^a = t^a - \bar{B}k^a, \quad \bar{t}'^a = \bar{t}^a - Bk^a. \quad (9)$$

By means of a suitable m-rotation we can show that the addition, with fixed metric, of a tensor (6) to a tensor (7) having the same wave vector, results in another type III tensor (7).(1) We shall see presently that this addition theorem, which seems at first to be a mere algebraic curiosity because of the non-linearity of the theory, has an important analogue for Riemannian tensors that are type III throughout some region.

Using Eqs (3), (4) and (5), (6) or (7) to evaluate the electromagnetic field equations or vacuum Bianchi identities in some one of the preferred anholonomic coordinate systems (m, k, t) gives scalar conditions on these frames and the scalars φ, θ, and σ. Two (complex) conditions are the same in all three cases considered:

$$k_{a;b} t^a k^b = 0, \quad (10)$$

$$k_{a;b} t^a t^b = 0. \quad (11)$$

The others are given in Table I, where we have introduced the 4-screw affinity in the natural way; the equations for the two types of null fields are identical.

Eq. (10) is the relation that allows us to impose Eq. (1) without loss of generality. Eq. (11) then implies that $k_{a;b}$ has the form:

$$k_{a:b} \equiv k_{a;b} - k_a k_{c;b} m^c = z t_a \bar{t}_b + y t_a k_b + \text{complex conjugate}; \quad (12)$$

the complex scalar function z defined by Eq. (12),

$$z = k_{a;b} \bar{t}^a t^b, \quad (13)$$

plays a basic role in the following; when $z \neq 0$ its real part turns out to be the inverse parallax distance. Using Eqs (1) and (12) we can rewrite Eq. (11) in the equivalent, manifestly covariant, form due to Robinson [13]:

$$k_{(a;b)} k^{a;b} = (1/2)(k^a{}_{;a})^2. \quad (14)$$

III. ROBINSON'S EQUATION AND DISTANCE IN GENERAL RELATIVITY

We now interpret Eq. (14) and the quantity z and derive consequences of Eqs (1) and (14). The main idea is to think of

(1) For more elegant proofs and generalizations see [11] and [12].

spatial distance as being meaningful precisely for those observers who are instantaneously located on the same ray.[1] The main result is that when we require not only Eq. (1) but also (14) for the rays of a wave we find that the relationship between the preferred parameter distance s [14], parallax distance r_P,

TABLE I

Differential conditions

Type No.	A. Electromagnetic Null	B. Gravitational Null	C. Gravitational Type III
1.	$\Phi_{:a}k^a = -z\varphi$	$\theta_{:a}k^a = -z\theta$	$\sigma_{:a}k^a = -2\sigma k_{a;b}\bar{t}^a t^b \equiv -2z\sigma$
2.	$\Phi_{:a}\bar{t}^a = +y\varphi$	$\theta_{:a}\bar{t}^a = +y\theta$	$\sigma_{:a}\bar{t}^a = -2\sigma\bar{t}_{a;b}k^a m^b \equiv +2y\sigma$
3.	—	—	$\sigma_{:a}t^a = -4\sigma t_{a;b}m^a k^b$
4.	—	—	$\sigma_{:a}m^a = -4\sigma m_{a;b}t^a\bar{t}^b$

These are scalar equations which, together with Eqs (1) and (11), are equivalent to the electromagnetic field equations (A.) or the vacuum Bianchi identities (B., C.). The colon derivative is defined as follows: If the quantity Q transforms under a 4-screw (8) according to the law $Q' = C^M \mathring{A}^N Q$ and has a tensor transformation law under coordinate transformations, then $Q_{:a} \equiv Q_{;a} + t_{b;a}t^b N + m_{b;a}k^b M$ transforms as a tensor under coordinate transformations and according to the same law as Q under a 4-screw. In addition to their invariance properties under transformations (8) and (9) all three sets of equations are invariant under the rigid duality rotations $t'^a = Ct^a$, $\bar{t}'^a = \bar{C}\bar{t}^a$ where C is a complex constant of unit magnitude, $C_{,a} = 0$, $C\mathring{C} = 1$.

$$r_P^{-1} = k^a{}_{;a}/2\,,^{(2)} \tag{15}$$

and the rotation of the rays,

$$\omega = \sqrt{(1/2)\,k_{[a;b]}k^{a;b}}\,, \tag{16}$$

becomes surprisingly simple. We shall treat these three quantities

---

(1) Even in Lorentz covariant theories it is natural to introduce spatial distance in this way provided we are dealing with a pure-retarded (or pure-advanced) wave. Compare Appendix B in [10].

(2) When $k^a = 0$ we set $r_P = \infty$; the justification of the name parallax distance is given below.

and the electromagnetic luminosity distance r_L as "parameter densities", e.g. under a transformation (2):

$$s' = \underset{0}{A}^{-1}s, \quad r'_P = \underset{0}{A}^{-1}r_P, \quad r'_L = \underset{0}{A}^{-1}r_L, \quad \omega' = \underset{0}{A}\omega. \qquad (17)$$

For s this transformation corresponds to a change of preferred parameter along each ray; for the other three quantities it corresponds to a correction for the total red- and Doppler-shift [10], [15]–[17].

Equation (14) can be interpreted by a procedure whose main features are familiar from hydrodynamics [18]–[20]. Introduce any timelike vector field $\underset{0}{u}^a$—the final results hold for any $\underset{0}{u}^a$ whose Prop vanishes – and a vector δx^a orthogonal to $\underset{0}{u}^a$ and k^a at one point of some particular ray L. Require that: (a) δx^a is propagated along k^a in such a way that it remains orthogonal to $\underset{0}{u}^a$ and k^a; (b) δx^a differs from some vector Lie propagated along k^a only by a term $f(s)k^a$. The second condition insures that δx^a is "dragged along" the ray L, e.g., it is propagated as if its origin and endpoint were constrained to move in L and some one neighboring ray respectively [21]. Conditions (a) and (b) together lead to the unique propagation law:

$$\mathrm{Prop}\,\delta x^a = [k^a{}_{;b} - (k_d \underset{0}{u}^d)^{-1} k^a \underset{0}{u}^c k_{c;b}]\,\delta x^b \equiv A^a_{.b}\delta x^b. \qquad (18)$$

$A^a_{.b}$ can be chosen orthogonal to $\underset{0}{u}^a$ and k^a. Just as in hydrodynamics we now divide the linear transformation $A^{\;a}_{.b}$ into an expansion $(1/2)h^a_b A^c_{.c}$, a rotation $A_{[ab]}$, and a shear $A_{(ad)} - (1/2)h_{ab}A^c_{.c}$; here h^a_b is the projection operator into the two-space orthogonal to k^a and $\underset{0}{u}^a$. Robinson's equation (14) implies precisely that, for any choice of $\underset{0}{u}^a$, the shear vanishes; the waves cast shadows that may be enlarged or rotated but reproduce shape exactly. For z we find from Eqs (3), (13), (15), (16) and (18)

$$z = (1/2)A^a_{.a} + i\sqrt{(1/2)A_{[ab]}A^{ab}} = r_P^{-1} + i\omega. \qquad (19)$$

The geometrical interpretation (18) of $A^a_{.b}$ justifies the name parallax distance for r_P. The rotation ω is seen to be the rate at which the rays spiral around each other in the set of two spaces considered above. If k^a is hypersurface orthogonal, ω vanishes:

$$k_{[a,b}k_{c]} = 0 \Longleftrightarrow \omega = 0 \Longleftrightarrow z = \bar{z}. \qquad (20)$$

Having interpreted Robinson's equation and the quantity z, we now ask how z varies along a given ray.[1] By means of a straightforward calculation using Eqs (3), (12), (13) and (1), the Ricci identity [14], and $R_{ab}k^b = 0$ we find

$$(\mathrm{Prop}+z)z = 0. \tag{21}$$

Eq. (21) can be integrated outright. We obtain: Either $z = 0$ or

$$z = 1/(s - i\underset{0}{n}), \quad \overline{\underset{0}{n}} = \underset{0}{n}, \quad \mathrm{Prop}\,\underset{0}{n} = 0. \tag{22}$$

As a convention we here require that the function $\underset{0}{n}$ be real. If $z \neq 0$ the convention fixes the origin of s along each ray so that s becomes a function of space-time unique up to transformations (17). When $z \neq 0$ Eqs (19) and (22) imply a universal relation between s, r_P, and ω:

$$r_P/[1+(\omega r_P)^2] = s. \tag{23}$$

In particular, if $\omega = 0$ then $r_P = s$; in the general case $r_P = s + \underset{0}{n}^2/s$.[2] We shall see in Section V that the electromagnetic luminosity distance is also related to r_P and ω by universally valid algebraic equations.

IV. THE ASYMPTOTIC BEHAVIOUR OF WAVES

We now use Table I and the results of the previous section to investigate the asymptotic behavior of waves. Let us associate with the scalar z the tensor $Z_{ab..}^{\ \ \ cd} = r_P^{-1}G_{ab..}^{\ \ \ cd} - \omega E_{ab..}^{\ \ \ cd}$ and agree to sum over adjacent pairs of antisymmetric indices in tensor equations with suppressed indices. We look for propagation equations for the electromagnetic field or the Riemannian tensor similar to equation (21). We find: An electromagnetic null field F_{ab} obeys the equation

$$(\mathrm{Prop}+Z)F = 0, \tag{24}$$

e.g., $F_{ab;c}k^c = -r_P^{-1}F_{ab} + \omega F^*_{ab}$; a gravitational null Riemannian tensor N_{abcd} obeys

$$(\mathrm{Prop}+Z)N = 0; \tag{25}$$

---

(1) This calculation, on which all the following results depend, was suggested by Dr E. T. Newmann (private communication).

(2) Equations (1) and (14), and all the results of this section remain valid in vacuum metrics that are non-degenerate type II or degenerate type I.

a type III vacuum Riemannian tensor always obeys the equation

$$(\mathrm{Prop} + 3Z)^3 \mathrm{III} = 0 \tag{26}$$

and when $z = \bar{z}$ it also satisfies

$$(\mathrm{Prop} + 2Z)^2 \mathrm{III} = 0^{(1)}. \tag{27}$$

As a sample proof we discuss Eq. (27). Equations (1), (3), (7), and (I.1.C) imply

$$(\mathrm{Prop} + 2Z)\mathrm{III} = N' \tag{28}$$

where N' has all the algebraic properties of a null conformal tensor. Operating on Eq. (28) with $(\mathrm{Prop} + 2Z)$ we find that the only term that causes difficulty is $\mathrm{Prop}(m_{a;b} t^a k^b)$. However, using Eqs (I.2.C) and (I.3.C), we can show that this term vanishes when $z = \bar{z}$; Eq. (27) then follows.

Using Eq. (22), Eqs (24)–(27) can again be explicityl integrated. The "constants" of integration are tensors parallelly displaced along the rays; they can be evaluated, modulo restricted parameter transformations, in terms of the fields and at most two of their derivatives on some spacelike or timelike hypersurface that cuts each ray at a point. The results are given in Table II; the positions in the table for which the non-emptiness of our results is guaranteed by the existence of known exact solutions, are indicated by check marks. For comparison, the expansion of a non-degenerate type II (or degenerate type I) Riemannian tensor II_{abcd} and of the retarded field due to a time dependent multipole source at rest in the linearized theory is included in the table. Each term in each box is uniquely defined by the metric.

V. INTERPRETATIONS

A satisfying—though rather startling—conclusion to be drawn from our results is that waves with $z \neq 0$, if they exist at all, have an asymptotic behaviour which is similar to and hardly more complicated than that implied by Lorentz covariant electrodynamics or the linearized theory: up to corrections for the rotation ω the null fields fall off as $1/r_P$, as suggested by Trautman [3], [23], while the type III waves split into two terms that fall off as $1/r_P$ and

(1) A vacuum non-degenerate type II or degenerate type I Riemannian tensor R_{abcd} always satisfies $(\mathrm{Prop} + 5Z)^5 R = 0$. When $z = \bar{z}$ it also satisfies the simpler equation $(\mathrm{Prop} + 3Z)^3 R = 0$.

$1/r_P^2$ respectively. The fact that the expansion of any one of the fields in powers of z (or, when $z = 0$, s) contains not an infinite number but at most 3 terms suggests that such waves are the generally covariant analogues of pure retarded or pure advanced solutions. The linear superposition theorems in row 3 of Table II mean that we have given a unique and covariant prescription for separating out the "asymptotic null" portion $Z\underset{0}{N}$, $\underset{0}{N}/s$, or $\underset{0}{N}s$ from a given type III wave by examining the behavior of the wave at finite distances. To what extent such superposition theorems can replace the far more powerful and general superposition principles of linear theories is an open question.

Table II

Expansions of the Fields

Type	A. $\bar{z} \neq z = r_P^{-1} + i\omega$	B. $z = \bar{z} = r_P^{-1} = s^{-1} \neq 0$	C. $z = 0$
1. Electromagnetic Null	$F = Z\underset{0}{N}$	$F = \underset{0}{N}/s$	$F = \underset{0}{N}$
2. Gravitational Null	$N = Z\underset{0}{N}$	$N = \underset{0}{N}/s$	$N = \underset{0}{N}$
3. Gravitational Type III	$\text{III} = Z\underset{0}{N} + Z^2\underset{0}{\text{III}}^+ + Z^3\underset{0}{N}'$	$\text{III} = \underset{0}{N}/s + \underset{0}{\text{III}}/s^2$	$\text{III} = \underset{0}{\text{III}}^+ + \underset{0}{N}s$
4. Gravitational Type II	$\text{II} = Z\underset{0}{N} + Z^2\underset{0}{\text{III}}^+ + Z^3\underset{0}{\text{II}} + Z^4\underset{0}{\text{III}}'^+ + Z^5\underset{0}{N}'$	$\text{II} = \underset{0}{N}/s^+ + \underset{0}{\text{III}}/s^2 + \underset{0}{\text{II}}/s^3$	$\text{II} = \underset{0}{\text{II}}^+ + \underset{0}{\text{III}}s^+ + \underset{0}{N}s^2$
5. Linearized Multipole	—	$R = \underset{0}{N}/s + \underset{0}{\text{III}}/s^2 + + \underset{0}{\text{II}}/s^3 + O(s^{-4})$	$(R = \underset{0}{N})$

Expansions are along the rays, in powers of the parallax distance r_P and rotation ω or the preferred parameter distance s, of an electromagnetic null field F_{ab}, a gravitational null field N_{abcd}, a vacuum type III Riemannian tensor III_{abcd}, a vacuum type II Riemannian tensor II_{abcd}, and the Riemannian tensor R_{abcd} in a linearized multipole solution. Tensors with subscript "0" are parallel transferred along the rays and have either the algebraic structure indicated by the letter used for them or a structure lower on the Penrose diagram [11]. Written out explicitly, a term like $Z^2\underset{0}{\text{III}}$ means $(r_P^{-2} - \omega^2)\underset{0}{\text{III}}_{abcd} - 2r_P^{-1}\omega\underset{0}{\text{III}}^*_{abcd}$.

We shall now give a more detailed discussion of the first three rows in Table II, considering both information that is polarization independent and information that involves the vectors m^a, t^a.

(*a*) *Electromagnetic Null Fields.* The information independent of the direction of the electric field is contained in the stress-energy tensor $T^{ab} = R^{ab}$:

$$T^{ab} = \underset{0}{\mu}(z\bar{z})^{-1}k^a k^b, \qquad \mathrm{Prop}\,\underset{0}{\mu} = 0. \tag{29}$$

The action conservation law [22], [24] $[\underset{0}{\mu}(z\bar{z})^{-1}k^a\sqrt{-g}]$ follows from Eq. (29) and Eq. (21). Equations (22) and (29) imply that the electromagnetic luminosity distance obeys the universal relationships

$$r_L^2 = (z\bar{z})^{-1} = r_P s = r_P^2/[1+(r_P\omega)^2] \tag{30}$$

when $z \neq 0$; the first and last terms in Eq. (30) involve only quantities that are in principle measurable.

As we go along a given ray, the electric field in any reference frame $\underset{0}{u}^a$, $E^a = F_{b\cdot}{}^a \underset{0}{u}^a$, rotates in the same direction and at the same rate ω as the rays spiral around each other.(1) This rotation is an effect seen by different observers on the same ray and not, like circular polarization in the usual sense, an effect seen by one observer who encounters a succession of rays.

If $z = 0$ the wave does not spread out and F_{ab} itself is parallel displaced along the rays. In this case, neither luminosity distance nor parallax distance are well defined.

(*b*) *Gravitational Null Fields.* These are very similar to electromagnetic null fields. The action conservation law [22], [24] again follows. If $\underset{0}{h}^a k_a = \underset{0}{h}^a \underset{0}{u}_a = 0$, then the vector of relative accelerations [4] $E^d_{(g)} = \underset{0}{u}^a \underset{0}{h}^b \underset{0}{u}^c N_{abc\cdot}{}^d$ is non-zero and rotates at the rate ω. The statement that the vector of relative accelerations does not rotate when $\omega = 0$ is a reformulation of Stellmacher's second conservation law [26].

(*c*) *Gravitational Type III Waves.* The asymptotic null portion $Z\underset{0}{N}$ does not in general obey the full Bianchi identities but along a fixed

(1) More generally, it can be shown that F^{ab} is surface forming and F^{ab} is surface orthogonal and Lie transferred along k^a. In gravitational null fields the quantity $F^{ab}_{(g)} = \underset{0}{u}^c \underset{0}{h}^d N_{cd\cdot\cdot}{}^{ab}$ where $\underset{0}{u}^a$ and $\underset{0}{h}^b$ are any fields chosen as in the next sub-section, has the same three properties. Compare [21] and [25].

ray it behaves exactly like the Riemannian tensor of a null metric. In particular, the action and vector of relative acceleration associated with $\underset{0}{Z}N$ behave exactly as in (*b*) above. In this sense a null wave with $z \neq 0$ could be regarded as a type III wave seen at very large distances from the source.

The density of characteristic length [4] $\sqrt{-g}\,|\sigma|\,k^a$ formed from the semi-asymptotic portion $P_{abcd} = Z_{ab..}^{\ \ \ ef} Z_{ef..}^{\ \ \ gh} \underset{0}{\mathrm{III}}_{ghcd}$ according to Eqs (3) and (7) equals that formed from the full Riemannian tensor and obeys the usual conservation law $(\sqrt{-g}\,|\sigma|\,k^a)_{,a} = 0$. The vector $\underset{0}{m}^a$ associated with $\underset{0}{\mathrm{III}}$ is parallel displaced along the rays although the vector m^a associated with the full Riemannian tensor is not in general so displaced. Two interesting spacelike vectors are obtained by letting $\underset{0}{u}^{[a}\underset{0}{m}^{b}k^{c]} = 0$, $\underset{0}{h}^a$ be as above, and $\underset{0}{f}^{[a}m^b k^{c]} = \underset{0}{f}^a \underset{0}{u}_a = 0$. Then the vector $\underset{0}{u}^a \underset{0}{h}^b \underset{0}{u}^c P_{abc.}^{\ \ \ \ d}$ is either zero or lies in the same direction as the spatial projection of the wave vector into the three-space orthogonal to $\underset{0}{u}^a$ and does not rotate; the vector $\underset{0}{u}^a \underset{0}{f}^b \underset{0}{u}^c P_{abc.}^{\ \ \ \ d}$ is orthogonal to k^a and $\underset{0}{u}^a$ and rotates at the rate 2ω.

If $z \neq \bar{z}$ then the relations so far investigated permit a non-zero term Z^3N' in the Riemannian tensor, whose significance is obscure. A comparison of row 3 with row 4 in Table II suggests that in a physically realistic metric this term may not by itself have any particular significance, since it falls off at the same rate as other terms we neglect when we consider the metric to be of type III rather than of type II.

VI. CONCLUSION

We have shown that the asymptotic behaviour of electromagnetic null fields, gravitational null fields, and gravitational type III fields with a vanishing Ricci tensor is extremely simple and fully in accordance with the intuitive picture of such fields as pure retarded waves seen at large distances from the source. We have stated that all the results can be extended to all vacuum type II and degenerate type I metrics. Can the results also be extended to some of the really general fields — vacuum metrics that are non-degenerate type I and non-null electromagnetic fields? The following calculation, while very minor in itself, is quite interesting because it suggests that our results can be extended at least to those non-null electromagnetic fields and type I metrics which correspond in some sense to retarded waves. Suppose in Lorentz covariant electrodynamics we consider the retarded field of a vibrating dipole at rest and neglect terms in the field strengths that fall off faster than $1/r_P^2$ along the "rays", e.g., along the null geodesics in Minkowski space leading from the source at the retarded time to the observation point. Then the field is not a null field but it does have one very special property: one of its two principal null vectors [10], say k^a, is tangent to a congruence of geodesics and obeys Robinson's equation. If we now examine in general relativity any non-null electromagnetic field that happens to have this special property, we find that the associated complex scalar q obeys the equation (Prop $+2z)q = 0$. On integrating we find that q falls off as $1/r_P^2$ up to possible corrections for the rotation ω.

Insofar as they are novel almost all the ideas in this paper were worked out jointly by Dr J. Ehlers and the author. The author wishes to thank Professor Pascual Jordan and the members of his seminar on general relativity at Hamburg, especially Dr E. Schücking, Dr W. Kundt and M. Trumper for many detailed discussions. Conversations with I. Robinson, Dr L. Bel, and Dr E. T. Newmann were very helpful. The financial support of the Flick Exchange Fellowship is gratefully acknowledged.

REFERENCES

[1] A. S. Petrov, *Kazan Univ. Rep.* **114**, 8, 55 (1954).
[2] F. A. E. Pirani, *Phys. Rev.* **105**, 1089 (1957).
[3] A. Trautman, *C. R. Acad. Sci., Paris* **246**, 1500 (1958).
[4] R. Sachs, Propagation Laws for Null and Type III Gravitational Waves, *Z. Phys.* **157**, 462 (1960).
[5] T. Y. Thomas, *Differential Invariants of Generalized Spaces,* London 1934 (Chapt. 1).
[6] C. W. Misner and J. A. Wheeler, *Ann. Phys.* **2**, 525 (1957).
[7] P. Jordan, W. Kundt and J. Ehlers, *Ber. Akad. Wiss. Mainz,* No. 2 (1960).
[8] A. Lichnerowicz, *C. R.Acad. Sci., Paris* **246**, 3015 (1958).
[9] L. Bel, *La radiation gravitationelle,* Paris 1959.
[10] J. L. Synge, *Relativity: The special theory,* Amsterdam 1956 (Sections IV. 7, IV. 11, V. 12, and Chapter IX).
[11] R. Penrose, *Report to the Royaumont Conference* (1959).
[12] L. Bel, *Report to the Royaumont Conference* (1959).
[13] I. Robinson, *Report to the Royaumont Conference* (1959).
[14] L. P. Eisenhart, *Riemannian Geometry,* Princeton 1949 (Sections 11 and 17).

[15] E. Schrödinger, *Expanding Universes,* Cambridge 1956.
[16] H. Bondi, *Cosmology*, Cambridge 1952 (Section 10.4).
[17] E. T. Newmann and J. Goldberg, *Distance in General Relativity,* Wright-Patterson Air Force Base, Ohio, U. S. A., 1958.
[18] J. L. Synge, *Proc. Lond. Math. Soc.* **43**, (1937).
[19] A. Lichnerowicz, *Théories relativistes de la gravitation et de l'éléctromagnétisme,* Paris 1955.
[20] J. Ehlers, Article in this book.
[21] J. A. Schouten, *Ricci-Calculus,* Berlin 1954 (Sections II.5, II. 10).
[22] A. Lichnerowicz, Report to the Royaumont Conference (1959).
[23] A. Trautman, *Lectures on General Relativity,* King's College, London 1958 (pp. 14 and 15).
[24] J. Ehlers and R. Sachs, *Z. Phys.* **155**, 498 (1959).
[25] M. Kohler, *Z. Phys.* **148**, 443 (1957).
[26] K. Stellmacher, *Math. Ann.* **115**, 741 (1938).

CONSERVATIVE GRAVITATIONAL THEORIES OF WHITEHEAD'S TYPE*

A. SCHILD

The University of Texas

1. INTRODUCTION

WHITEHEAD'S theory of gravitation [1] is an action-at-a-distance theory[(1)] in flat Minkowski space-time, where mass particles interact through retarded gravitational tensor potentials. In this note, a theory of Whitehead's type is examined which embodies the principle of equal action and reaction in the sense that conservation laws hold for energy, linear and angular momentum.

The theory is obtained from a single action principle which is symmetric in all the particles of a system. The Lorentz invariance of the action integral leads directly to conservation laws. The symmetry between the particles leads to interactions which are half-advanced plus half-retarded, rather than purely retarded.

2. THE ACTION PRINCIPLE

Units are chosen such that the velocity of light and twice the Newtonian constant of gravitation are each unity ($c = 1$, $2G = 1$). Greek suffixes range over 1, 2, 3, 4 and label space-time components; Latin suffixes range over $1, 2, \ldots, N$ and label the different particles of the system. The summation convention applies to Greek suffixes but not to Latin suffixes; summations over particles are always

* This research was supported by the United States Air Force under Contract No. AF 33(616)-5832, monitored by the Aeronautical Research Laboratory, Wright Air Development Center.

(1) A very readable summary of the theory is given in [2]. Modifications of the theory were discussed in [3].

shown explicitly. Space-time is flat Minkowski space with the line element

$$d\tau^2 = \eta_{\mu\nu} dx^\mu dx^\nu = -(dx^1)^2 - (dx^2)^2 - (dx^3)^2 + (dx^4)^2. \tag{1}$$

Tensor suffixes will be raised and lowered by means of the Minkowski metric tensor $\eta_{\mu\nu} = \eta^{\mu\nu}$.

The motion of the ath particle of the system is described by the functions $x_a^\mu(u_a)$, where u_a is a parameter along the world line of the particle; the physical meaning of u_a will be defined later (Eq. 10). Differentiation with respect to u_a is denoted by a dot, e.g., $\dot{x}_a^\mu \equiv dx_a^\mu / du_a$.

The Action integral of the theory is

$$J = \sum_a \int_{-\infty}^{\infty} \dot{x}_{a\mu} \dot{x}_a^\mu du_a +$$

$$+ \tfrac{1}{2} \sum_{ab}' \int_{-\infty}^{\infty} \int_{-\infty}^{\infty} \delta(y_{ab\varrho} y_{ab}^\varrho) [\alpha \dot{x}_{a\mu} \dot{x}_a^\mu \dot{x}_{b\nu} \dot{x}_b^\nu + \beta (\dot{x}_{a\mu} \dot{x}_b^\mu)^2] du_a du_b \tag{2}$$

where α and β are constants, where δ is the Dirac delta function and

$$y_{ab}^\mu = x_a^\mu - x_b^\mu, \tag{3}$$

and where the prime on the double summation sign indicates that the summation is to be carried out over distinct particle labels only ($a \neq b$).

The gravitational equations of motion are determined by the action principle:

$$\delta J = 0 \tag{4}$$

for arbitrary variations $\delta x_a^\mu(u_a)$ which vanish identically outside arbitrary but finite intervals $(\bar{u}_a, \bar{\bar{u}}_a)$ on their respective world lines.

To find the equation of motion of the ath particle, consider that part J_a of the action which contains the coordinates x_a^μ. By performing one of the integrations in the double integral of Eq. (2), we obtain

$$J_a = \int_{-\infty}^{\infty} g_{a\mu\nu} \dot{x}_a^\mu \dot{x}_a^\nu du_a, \tag{5}$$

$$g_{a\mu\nu} = \eta_{\mu\nu} + \frac{1}{2} \sum_b{}' \left\{ \left[\frac{\alpha \eta_{\mu\nu} \dot{x}_{b\varrho} \dot{x}_b^\varrho + \beta \eta_{\mu\varrho} \eta_{\nu\sigma} \dot{x}_b^\varrho \dot{x}_b^\sigma}{y_{ab\alpha} \dot{x}_b^\alpha} \right]_- + \right.$$

$$\left. + \left[\frac{\alpha \eta_{\mu\nu} \dot{x}_{b\varrho} \dot{x}_b^\varrho + \beta \eta_{\mu\varrho} \eta_{\nu\sigma} \dot{x}_b^\varrho \dot{x}_b^\sigma}{-y_{ab\alpha} \dot{x}_b^\alpha} \right]_+ \right\}. \tag{6}$$

Here the prime on the summation again indicates that the term $b = a$ is omitted. The $-$ and $+$ suffixes indicate that the expressions must be evaluated at the events u_{b-} and u_{b+} on b's world line, which are respectively retarded and advanced relative to x_a^μ. These events are determined by

$$(y_{ab\mu} y_{ab}^\mu)_\pm \equiv (x_{a\mu} - (x_{b\mu})_\pm)(x_a^\mu - (x_b^\mu)_\pm) = 0,$$
$$(y_{ab}^4)_- > 0, \quad (y_{ab}^4)_+ < 0. \tag{7}$$

Thus, with the motion of all other particles regarded as given, $g_{a\mu\nu}$ is a function of the coordinates x_a^μ.

The action principle, applied to Eq. (5), gives the differential equation of motion of particle a:

$$g_{a\mu\nu} \ddot{x}_a^\nu + [\varrho\sigma, \mu]_a \dot{x}_a^\varrho \dot{x}_a^\sigma = 0, \tag{8}$$

$$[\varrho\sigma, \mu]_a = \frac{1}{2}\left(\frac{\partial g_{a\sigma\mu}}{\partial x_a^\varrho} + \frac{\partial g_{a\varrho\mu}}{\partial x_a^\sigma} - \frac{\partial g_{a\varrho\sigma}}{\partial x_a^\mu}\right). \tag{9}$$

These equations are formally identical to those of a geodesic in a Riemannian space with $g_{a\mu\nu}$ as metric tensor. They have a first integral $g_{a\mu\nu} \dot{x}_a^\mu \dot{x}_a^\nu = \text{const.}$ It is by means of this constant of the motion that we introduce the mass m_a of particle a, by defining

$$m_a^2 = g_{a\mu\nu} \dot{x}_a^\mu \dot{x}_a^\nu. \tag{10}$$

The equations (6), (8), and (10) constitute the equations of motion of the system.

3. THE ONE BODY PROBLEM

In this section only two interacting particles are considered and, instead of particle labels, the variables which describe their motions are denoted by capital and small letters: M, X^μ, U and m, x^μ, u.

If M is much larger than m, so that M/m can be neglected compared to 1, M will be at rest in a suitable inertial frame, and its motion can be shown to be given by

$$X^1 = X^2 = X^3 = 0, \quad dX^4/dU = M. \tag{11}$$

For particle m, the $g_{\mu\nu}$ of Eq. (6) are then given by

$$g_{\mu\nu} = \left(1 + \alpha \frac{M}{r}\right)\eta_{\mu\nu} + \beta \frac{M}{r} \eta_{\mu 4} \eta_{\nu 4},$$
$$r^2 = (x^1)^2 + (x^2)^2 + (x^3)^2. \tag{12}$$

If M/r is small, the equations of motion (8) give in first approximation the usual Newtonian planetary motion, provided that

$$\alpha+\beta = -1. \tag{13}$$

This is now assumed; it can then be shown that for a general system of slowly moving particles, whose masses are small compared to their distances, the action principle of Eqs (2) and (4) reproduces Newtonian gravitational motion.

In the second approximation, a rotation of the perihelion is obtained through an angle

$$\frac{2(\alpha+1)\pi M}{a(1-e^2)} \tag{14}$$

per revolution, where a is the semi-axis major and e the eccentricity of the elliptic orbit of particle m. The perihelion rotation agrees with that given by general relativity theory if $\alpha = 1/2$, so that, by Eq. (13),

$$\alpha = 1/2, \quad \beta = -3/2. \tag{15}$$

4. THE CONSERVATION LAWS

The conservation laws follow from the invariance properties of the action integral, those of energy and linear momentum from invariance under infinitesimal translations in space-time, those of angular momentum from invariance under infinitesimal rotations. The method for obtaining these laws is straightforward and is essentially that described in a previous paper on electrodynamics [4].

Along each world line of the particles of the system choose an event u_a. Then, as a consequence of the equations of motion of the system, the vector

$$P_\mu(u_1, u_2, \ldots, u_N) = \sum_a [g_{a\mu\nu}\dot{x}_a^{\nu}]u_a + \tag{16}$$

$$+\sum_{ab}{}' \Big(\int_{u_a}^{\infty}\int_{-\infty}^{u_b} - \int_{-\infty}^{u_a}\int_{u_b}^{\infty}\Big) \delta'(y_{ab\nu}y_{ab}^{\nu})x_{a\mu}[\alpha\dot{x}_{a\sigma}\dot{x}_a^{\sigma}\dot{x}_{b\varrho}\dot{x}_b^{\varrho} + \beta(\dot{x}_{a\sigma}\dot{x}_b^{\sigma})^2]du_a du$$

is constant, in the sense that P_μ is independent of the choice of the events $u_1, u_2, \ldots, u_N$. This is the law of conservation of energy and linear momentum. The law of conservation of angular momentum has a similar structure and will not be stated here. Because the delta functions and their derivatives occur in the integrations, the momentum 4-vector and the angular momentum tensor of the system are completely determined by suitably chosen finite arcs of the particle world lines.

In Whitehead's original theory of gravitation the mass centre of a two-body system has a secular acceleration [5]. In the present theory there is a conservation law for linear momentum, but it does not have the classical Newtonian form, and the consequences for the motion of the mass centre are not obvious. A calculation of the two-body problem is in progress.

It is a pleasure to contribute this paper to a volume dedicated to Leopold Infeld, who taught me the principles of relativity theory and of research.

REFERENCES

[1] A. N. WHITEHEAD, *The Principle of Relativity*, Cambridge University Press 1922.
[2] J. L. SYNGE, *Proc. Roy. Soc.* A**211**, 303 (1952).
[3] A. SCHILD, *Proc. Roy. Soc.* A**235**, 202 (1956).
[4] J. W. DETTMAN and A. SCHILD, *Phys. Rev.* **95**, 1057 (1954).
[5] G. L. CLARK, *Proc. Roy. Soc. Edinb.* A**64**, 49 (1954).

ON THE ANALOGY BETWEEN CHARGE AND SPIN IN GENERAL RELATIVITY

D. W. Sciama

King's College, London

Summary—In general relativity the energy-momentum tensor of a material system is defined as the quantity coupled to the metric in the material Lagrangian. We here suggest that the spin tensor of a material system should be defined as the quantity coupled to the (vierbein) affine connexion $o_p(\alpha\beta)$. It follows from this definition that (*a*) spin gives rise to a skew part of the affine connexion Γ^p_{qr}, (*b*) a particle with spin is acted on by a gravitational force which depends on the spin and on the curvature tensor (as first shown in another way by Mathisson).

The existence of this gravitational force shows that the principle of equivalence needs careful discussion. A weak form of the principle is favoured, namely, that inertial forces are gravitational in origin. However, this form is too weak to account for the result of the Galileo–Eötvös experiments, even for non-spinning particles. We need in addition the principle of minimal gravitational coupling, which states that the entire gravitational coupling is obtained from the material Lagrangian of special relativity by replacing ordinary by covariant derivatives. This principle implies that there is no additional direct coupling of matter to curvature and thereby accounts for the Galileo–Eötvös experiments.

The main purpose of this paper is to point out that the theory of spin in general relativity is closely analogous to the theory of charge in electromagnetism. For the charge-current vector can be defined as the quantity coupled to the vector potential (or phase connexion) in the (phase covariant) material Lagrangian. It follows that a particle with charge is acted on by an electromagnetic force which depends on the charge and on the electromagnetic field. Moreover, there is a minimal coupling principle which states that the Lagrangian should contain no direct coupling of matter to electromagnetic field (that is, there should be no Pauli terms). Gell-Mann has pointed out that this principle of minimal electromagnetic coupling predicts that strangeness should be conserved in electromagnetic transitions of strange particles — a prediction which is in agreement with experiment. This experimental result is thus the electromagnetic analogue of the Galileo–Eötvös result.

In view of the close analogy between spin and the vierbein connexion on the one hand, and charge and the phase connexion on the other, we believe that the phase connexion should be made part of the geometrical structure of space (through the so-called holonomy group). An attempt to do this has already been described elsewhere. It seems likely that it could be extended so as to incorporate other fields (e.g. the meson field) into the geometrical structure of space.

1. INTRODUCTION

THE aim of this paper is to describe the close analogy that exists between the charge and spin of a material system in general relativity. This analogy is of some intrinsic interest, but its main importance is that it suggests why and how one should geometrize electromagnetism, and perhaps other aspects of nature (isotopic spin etc.). I am happy to dedicate this paper to Professor Infeld, whose first published work was about the geometrization of electromagnetism [1].

There are, of course, well-known analogies between charge and quantities occurring in gravitational theory. The most familiar is that between charge and gravitational mass, arising from the formal similarity between Coulomb's and Newton's inverse square laws. More important for us is the analogy between charge and the energy-momentum tensor of general relativity. This analogy is also well-known, but we shall recall it here since it introduces a basic idea which we shall need in discussing spin.

Let us suppose that we have a (non-quantized) material system ψ whose behaviour is described in terms of some Lagrangian-density $\mathcal{L}$ $(\psi, \psi_{,i})$. We begin by assuming that $\mathcal{L}$ transforms as a scalar-density under Lorentz transformations. The invariance of $\mathcal{L}$ under space-time displacements, together with the field equations $\delta\mathcal{L}/\delta\psi = 0$, then imply the existence of a second-rank tensor $T^j{}_i$ which is conserved, namely $T^j_{i,j} = 0$ where

$$T^j_i = \frac{\partial\mathcal{L}}{\partial\psi_{,j}}\psi_{,i} - \mathcal{L}\delta^j_i. \tag{1}$$

This tensor $T^j{}_i$ is known as the canonical energy-momentum tensor. It is not uniquely defined by the requirement of having a vanishing divergence, since in general there exist other tensors whose divergence vanishes identically which could be added to the canonical tensor. By contrast with a later definition, we shall call the present one (that of having vanishing divergence) a *kinematic* definition, and the associated group of rigid space-time displacements a kinematic group.

We see then that the kinematic definition of the energy-momentum tensor does not determine this tensor uniquely. In order to resolve this ambiguity we now make the further assumption that $\mathfrak{L}$ transforms as a scalar density under arbitrary (well-behaved) co-ordinate transformations. In conjunction with this step, we assume that we should use the metric tensor g_{ij} as the variables which describe the gravitational field. The energy-momentum tensor of the material system can now be defined *dynamically* as the tensor which is directly coupled to g^{ij} in $\mathfrak{L}$, that is,

$$\sqrt{-g}\, T_{ij} = \frac{\delta \mathfrak{L}}{\delta g^{ij}}.$$

In this way, T_{ij} is defined dynamically as the *source* of the gravitational field in Einstein's field equations

$$\frac{\delta(\sqrt{-g}\,R + \mathfrak{L})}{\delta g^{ij}} = 0$$

and not just kinematically as something that is conserved. Moreover, we can now resolve the ambiguity in the kinematical definition, since the invariance of $\mathfrak{L}$ under the (dynamic) group of arbitrary co-ordinate transformations leads to an identity [2] which tells us that one particular kinematical tensor is equal to the dynamical one [3] (see Section 2.4).

A similar procedure was introduced for charge and the electromagnetic field by Weyl [4]. He assumed that $\mathfrak{L}$ is invariant under the rigid phase transformation

$$\psi \to e^{ie\lambda}\psi, \qquad \psi^* \to e^{-ie\lambda}\psi^*$$

where e and λ are constants (λ will later be allowed to vary with position in space-time). This assumption, together with the field equations, implies the existence of a vector J^i which is conserved, namely

$$J^i{}_{,i} = 0$$

where

$$J^i = -ie\left(\frac{\partial \mathfrak{L}}{\partial \psi_{,i}}\psi - \frac{\partial \mathfrak{L}}{\partial \psi^*{}_{,i}}\psi^*\right).$$

This, then, is the kinematic definition of the charge-current vector. In order to justify it dynamically, we further assume that $\mathfrak{L}$ is invariant under non-rigid phase transformations in which λ is allowed to vary with position in space-time. This leads one to introduce a phase-connexion A_i which is identified with the electromagnetic vector potential (see Section 4). The charge-current vector can then be defined dynamically as the vector which is coupled to A^i in $\mathcal{L}$, that is,

$$J_i = \frac{\delta \mathcal{L}}{\delta A^i}.$$

In this way, J^i is defined dynamically as the source of the electromagnetic field in Maxwell's field equations

$$\frac{\delta (F_{jk} F^{jk} + \mathcal{L})}{\delta A^i} = 0.$$

Moreover, there is an identity which shows that the kinematical charge-current vector is equal to the dynamical one (cf. [5], p. 77).

We see then that there is a close analogy between the charge-current vector and the energy-momentum tensor. Each arises from both kinematic and dynamic invariance groups, and there are identities which relate the kinematic quantities to the dynamic ones. In this paper we point out that there exists a similar but still closer analogy between charge and spin. We begin with a detailed discussion of the spin of a material system in general relativity (Section 2). This discussion shows that a particle with spin is acted on by a gravitational force which depends on the spin and on the curvature tensor. Accordingly, one needs a more careful statement of the principle of equivalence than is usually given. Two different aspects of this principle are distinguished (Section 3). We then point out the close analogy between our discussion of spin and Weyl's theory of electromagnetism (Section 4). In particular, we shall see that the second aspect of the principle of equivalence has an analogue in electromagnetic theory. The existence of this analogue, and of the gravitational force on a spinning particle, removes the main argument against attempting to geometrize the electromagnetic field (e.g. [6]). Such an attempt [7], along the lines laid down in this paper, is briefly mentioned, and will be further developed elsewhere.[1]

---

[1] See J. *Math. Phys.*, July – August 1961.

2. THE SPIN OF A MATERIAL SYSTEM IN GENERAL RELATIVITY

2.1. *Introduction*

The literature contains several discussions of spin angular momentum in general relativity (e.g. [8]–[12]). These discussions treat the conservation of angular momentum as a by-product of the conservation of energy-momentum. This is certainly possible, since Noether's theorem [13] implies that the law of energy-momentum conservation, which follows from the invariance of the theory under arbitrary coordinate transformations, already contains all the independent conservation laws. Nevertheless, it would make the physical significance of spin much clearer if it could be defined autonomously in terms of its own transformation group. This is done here. The technique is to combine Palatini's [14] idea of regarding the metric and affine connexion as independent variables, with Weyl's [4] idea of writing Einstein's theory in terms of vierbeins. This will lead to a general definition of spin, and also to a slight change from the purely metric theory (first pointed out by Weyl in [15]). We begin by recalling the vierbein formalism (2.2, 2.3) and then use it to define the spin of a material system (2.4, 2.5).

2.2. *The Vierbein Formalism for Reimannian Space*

The starting-point of this formalism is the introduction of four linearly independent real vectors $\boldsymbol{e}(\alpha)$ at each point of space-time (vierbeins). These vectors do not form a preferred set; they are subject to linear transformations depending arbitrarily on position. In practice we shall restrict the transformations so that the vectors depend analytically on position in some neighbourhood of each point. When a coordinate system is introduced, the vectors will have components $e_i(\alpha)$[(1)]. The metric tensor g_{ij} can then be written in the form

$$g_{ij} = \eta(\alpha\beta)\, e_i(\alpha)\, e_j(\beta)$$

where $\eta(\alpha\beta)$ is a real symmetric matrix of Minkowskian signature.

Tensor quantities can now be referred to their vierbein-components, e.g. for a vector A^i we have

$$A(\alpha) = e_i(\alpha)\, A^i.$$

(1) In what follows, Greek indices always number the vectors, Latin indices refer to the coordinate system. The summation convention is used for both sets of indices.

In this sense, $\eta(\alpha\beta)$ is the metric tensor expressed in vierbein-components.

We now introduce a process of parallel-transfer in terms of a symmetric affine connexion Γ^i_{jk}. To begin with we place no restriction on this connexion, in particular, we do not yet assume the Christoffel relations. If we transfer in a parallel manner the vierbein at one point P to a neighbouring point P', the transferred vierbein will in general differ infinitesimally from the local vierbein at P. We assume that the two vierbeins differ by a linear transformation $O(\alpha\beta)$ given by $O(\alpha\beta) = \delta(\alpha\beta) + đo(\alpha\beta)$ where $\delta(\alpha\beta)$ is the Kronecker delta and $đo(\alpha\beta)$ is an infinitesimal matrix (and not a perfect differential unless space-time is flat). We further assume that $đo(\alpha\beta)$ depends linearly on the displacement PP' $(= dx^p)$; that is,

$$đo(\alpha\beta) = o_p(\alpha\beta)\,dx^p.$$

These assumptions are summarized in the equation

$$\frac{\partial e^p(\alpha)}{\partial x^q} + \Gamma^p{}_{rq} e^r(\alpha) + o_q(\alpha\beta) e^p(\beta) = 0. \tag{2}$$

We emphasize that the quantity $o_p(\alpha\beta)$ is the basic element in terms of which the formalism will be constructed. It is the affine connexion for a quantity expressed in vierbein-components.[1] Under coordinate transformations it transforms like a covariant vector, and under arbitrary linear transformations $O(\alpha\beta)$ of the vierbeins it transforms like a matrix with the addition of the term $-O(\beta\gamma)\dfrac{\partial O(\alpha\gamma)}{\partial x^p}$.

Since Γ^p_{rq} is symmetric we can eliminate it from (2) and obtain

$$e^q(\alpha)o_q(\beta\gamma) - e^q(\beta)o_q(\alpha\gamma) = e_p(\gamma)\left\{e^q(\beta)\frac{\partial e^p(\alpha)}{\partial x^q} - e^q(\alpha)\frac{\partial e^p(\beta)}{\partial x^q}\right\}. \tag{3}$$

Thus, although Γ^p_{rq} is arbitrary, $o_p(\alpha\beta)$ must satisfy (3). This is not surprising, since $o_p(\alpha\beta)$ represents the effect of an infinitesimal displacement, and (3) is just the first-order integrability condition for the infinitesimal displacement-group generated by $e^p(\alpha)$ [16]. If $\Gamma^p{}_{rq}$ were not symmetric, successive parallel displacements in the p and q directions would yield different end points, depending on the order of the displacements. In this case the first-order integra-

---

(1) We shall use a semi-colon for the complete covariant derivative. Thus (2) can be written $e^p(\alpha)_{;q} = 0$.

bility condition would not be satisfied—a fact which is obvious from (2).

We can define a curvature tensor in terms of $o_p(\alpha\beta)$ by considering the change in an arbitrary vector $A(\alpha)$ when it is parallely transferred around an infinitesimal closed circuit $dx^p \delta x^q$. The result is

$$\delta A(\alpha) = R_{pq}(\alpha\beta)\, dx^p \delta x^q A(\beta)$$

where

$$R_{pq}(\alpha\beta) = \frac{\partial o_q(\alpha\beta)}{\partial x^p} - \frac{\partial o_p(\alpha\beta)}{\partial x^q} + o_p(\alpha\gamma)\, o_q(\gamma\beta) - o_q(\alpha\gamma)\, o_p(\gamma\beta) \tag{4}$$

which is skew in p and q. By comparing the changes in the vectors A^i, $A(\alpha)$, we get the relation

$$R_{pq}(\alpha\beta) = R^i{}_{jpq}\, e_i(\alpha)\, e^j(\beta) \tag{5}$$

where $R^i{}_{jpq}$ is the Riemann–Christoffel curvature tensor. It follows from this that the curvature scalar R can be written

$$R = e^p(\alpha)\, e^q(\beta)\, R_{pq}(\alpha\beta). \tag{6}$$

We now examine the effect of assuming the Christoffel relations for Γ^i_{jk}. This assumption implies that lengths and angles are preserved by parallel transfer. It is then natural to choose vierbeins that are orthonormal at each point, so that $\eta(\alpha\beta)$ becomes the Kronecker–Minkowski delta, and the vierbeins are subject only to a Lorentz rotation varying arbitrarily with position. This is natural because orthonormality is a property which will now be preserved if a vierbein is parallely transferred around a closed loop. Moreover, after parallel transfer to a neighbouring point, a vierbein will differ from the local vierbein by at most an infinitesimal Lorentz rotation. This means that $O(\alpha\beta)$ is now a skew matrix, and $o_p(\alpha\beta)$ will be skew in α and β. As a result of this skewness, $o_p(\alpha\beta)$ can be eliminated from (2), and we retrieve the Christoffel relations for Γ^i_{jk}. Furthermore, (3) now determines $o_p(\alpha\beta)$ in terms of the vierbeins. For by using the skewness of $o_p(\alpha\beta)$, and by cyclically interchanging the Greek indices and combining the resulting equations, we obtain

$$2e^p(\gamma)\, o_p(\alpha\beta) = [e(\gamma), e(\alpha)](\beta) + [e(\beta), e(\gamma)](\alpha) - [e(\alpha), e(\beta)](\gamma) \tag{7}$$

where

$$[e(\gamma), e(\alpha)](\beta) = e_p(\beta)\left(e^q(\alpha)\,\frac{\partial e^p(\gamma)}{\partial x^q} - e^q(\gamma)\,\frac{\partial e^p(\alpha)}{\partial x^q}\right).$$

Finally we may note that if we transfer in a parallel manner a vector around an infinitesimal closed circuit, it can change by only an infinitesimal Lorentz rotation, so that $R_{pq}(\alpha\beta)$ is now skew in α and β, a result which is also obvious from (4). Hence (5) implies that R_{ijpq} is skew in i and j, a well-known result in Riemannian geometry which here finds its true meaning.

It will be convenient for later purposes to re-state this discussion in the following way. If we are given a function of position $o_p(\alpha\beta)$ with the correct transformation properties under arbitrary transformations of both coordinates and vierbeins, the associated affine connexion Γ^i_{jk} will not be symmetric unless the integrability condition (3) is satisfied. Similarly, if $o_p(\alpha\beta)$ is skew lengths will be preserved by parallel transfer, but the associated affine connexion will not be symmetric and so will not satisfy the Christoffel relations unless (3) holds, or equivalently (7). When (3) does hold, the statement that $o_p(\alpha\beta)$ is skew is equivalent to the statement that the Γ^i_{jk} satisfying (2) is the Christoffel connexion—this property of Γ^i_{jk} does not have to be assumed or derived separately.

2.3. *General Relativity in Terms of Vierbeins*

We shall now express the theory of the pure gravitational field in terms of $e_i(\alpha)$ and $o_p(\alpha\beta)$ instead of g_{ij} and Γ^i_{jk}. As mentioned in the introduction, we shall take $e_i(\alpha)$ and $o_p(\alpha\beta)$ as independent variables in the variational principle of the theory. We shall also assume that $o_p(\alpha\beta)$ is skew, so that if the integrability condition (3) is satisfied, there will exist a Christoffel connexion Γ^i_{jk}. In fact, the condition (3) will follow from the vanishing of the variation of the Lagrangian with respect to $o_p(\alpha\beta)$.

The Lagrangian is the same as in the conventional theory, namely

$$\varepsilon R$$

where R is given by (6) and ε is the determinant of $e_i(\alpha)$, which is equal to $\sqrt{-g}$ for orthonormal vierbeins. The vanishing of the variation of εR with respect to $e_i(\alpha)$ gives the field equations

$$e^j(\beta)R_{ij}(\alpha\beta) = 0$$

or

$$R(\alpha\beta) = 0$$

where

$$R(\alpha\beta) = e^i(\beta)e^j(\gamma)R_{ij}(\alpha\gamma).$$

The vanishing of the variation with respect to $o_p(\alpha\beta)$ gives

$$X^p(\alpha\beta) = 0 \tag{8}$$

where

$$X^p(\alpha\beta) = -\big(\varepsilon e^q(\alpha)e^p(\beta) - \varepsilon e^p(\alpha)e^q(\beta)\big)_{,q} + \big(\varepsilon e^q(\gamma)e^p(\beta) - \\ - \varepsilon e^p(\gamma)e^q(\beta)\big)o_q(\gamma\alpha) + \big(\varepsilon e^p(\alpha)e^q(\gamma) - \varepsilon e^q(\alpha)e^p(\gamma)\big)o_q(\beta\gamma). \tag{9}$$

The field equation (8) can be simplified by noting that it implies that

$$X^p(\alpha\beta)e_p(\beta) = 0.$$

If the left hand side of this equation is subtracted from $X^p(\alpha\beta)$ as given by (9), we find from (8) that

$$e^q(\alpha)\frac{\partial e^p(\beta)}{\partial x^q} - e^q(\beta)\frac{\partial e^p(\alpha)}{\partial x^q} + \\ + e^p(\gamma)e^q(\beta)o_q(\gamma\alpha) - e^p(\gamma)e^q(\alpha)o_q(\gamma\beta) = 0 \tag{10}$$

which is just the integrability condition (3). The field equations (8) thus implies that the associated Γ^i_{jk} is just the symmetric Christoffel connexion.

It must be emphasized that the normal Palatini formalism is rather different from the present one. There it is assumed from the outset that there is a symmetric connexion Γ^i_{jk}, and the fact that it is the Christoffel connexion is deduced from the vanishing of the variation of the Einstein Lagrangian with respect to Γ^i_{jk}. Here the existence of a *symmetric* affine connexion Γ^i_{jk} is itself deduced from the vanishing of the variation with respect to $o_p(\alpha\beta)$. The fact that this connection is the Christoffel one then follows immediately from the symmetry condition imposed from the outset on $o_p(\alpha\beta)$. This symmetry condition ensures that we have all the field equations we need, since if $o_p(\alpha\beta)$ is skew, it is completely determined in terms of $e_i(\alpha)$ by (3), (see (7)), and correspondingly Γ^i_{jk} is determined by (2).

Let us now assume that there is matter present in addition to gravitation, and that this matter is described by a Lagrangian density $\mathcal{L}$. In this section we shall restrict ourselves to the case where $\mathcal{L}$ does not depend explicitly on $o_p(\alpha\beta)$. As we shall see, this implies that we are dealing with a material system whose spin density is zero. The energy-momentum tensor of the system will be given by

$$t_i(\alpha) = \frac{\delta\mathcal{L}}{\delta e^i(\alpha)}$$

and the gravitational field equations will be

$$2R(\alpha\beta)-R\delta(\alpha\beta) = -\frac{1}{\varepsilon}t(\alpha\beta)$$

$$\big(\text{where } t(\alpha\beta) = t_i(\alpha)e^i(\beta)\big)$$

and

$$X^p(\alpha\beta) = 0 \tag{11}$$

$\big($since $\mathfrak{L}$ contributes nothing to the variation with respect to $o_p(\alpha\beta)\big)$. The field equations (11) show that we can still introduce a symmetric Christoffel connexion Γ^i_{jk}.

As usual, there will be conservation laws arising from the invariance properties of the Lagrangian. Its invariance under arbitrary coordinate transformations leads to the conservation of energy and momentum, in the form

$$\big(t^j(\alpha)e_i(\alpha)\big)_{,j}-t^p(\alpha)\frac{\partial e_p(\alpha)}{\partial x^i} = 0.$$

The invariance of $\mathfrak{L}$ under arbitrary Lorentz rotations of the vierbeins which reduce to the identity outside a certain domain D leads to

$$\delta\int_D \mathfrak{L}\,d\tau = \int_D t_p(\alpha)\delta e^p(\alpha)\,d\tau+\int_D \frac{\delta\mathfrak{L}}{\delta o_p(\alpha\beta)}\,\delta o_p(\alpha\beta)\,d\tau+\int_D\frac{\delta\mathfrak{L}}{\delta\psi}\,\delta\psi\,d\tau = 0.$$

Assuming that $\mathfrak{L}$ is independent of $o_p(\alpha\beta)$ and that the material field equations hold ($\delta\mathfrak{L}/\delta\psi = 0$), we have

$$\int_D t_p(\alpha)\,\delta e^p(\alpha) = 0. \tag{12}$$

Now for an infinitesimal Lorentz rotation,

$$\delta e^p(\alpha) = do(\alpha\beta)e^p(\beta)$$

where $do(\alpha\beta)$ is an infinitesimal skew matrix depending arbitrarily on position. It follows from (12) that $t_p(\alpha)e^p(\beta)$, that is, $t(\alpha\beta)$, must be symmetric in α and β. Hence also $t(\alpha\beta)e_i(\alpha)e_j(\beta)$ or t_{ij} is symmetric in i and j. A further identity following from invariance under coordinate transformations now shows (cf. [2]) that this symmetric t_{ij} is just equal to the canonical energy-momentum tensor, that is

$$t_i^j = \frac{\delta\mathfrak{L}}{\delta e^i(\alpha)}\,e^j(\alpha) = \frac{\partial\mathfrak{L}}{\partial\psi_{,j}}\,\psi_{,i}-\mathfrak{L}\delta_i^j.$$

Finally, the invariance of R under arbitrary Lorentz rotations of the vierbeins leads to

$$\delta \int_D R\,d\tau = \int_D 2R_p(\alpha)\,\delta e^p(\alpha)\,d\tau + \int_D X^p(\alpha\beta)\,\delta o_p(\alpha\beta)\,d\tau = 0 .$$

Hence (11) implies that $R(\alpha\beta)$ is symmetric in α and β, which corresponds to the well-known result that the Christoffel relations for Γ^i_{jk} imply that the Ricci tensor R_{ij} is symmetric (cf. [17], p. 70).

It will be seen that this discussion, and its equivalence to Einstein's original formulation, depends at various points on our assumption that $\mathfrak{L}$ does not depend explicitly on $o_p(\alpha\beta)$, that is, that

$$\frac{\delta \mathfrak{L}}{\delta o_p(\alpha\beta)} = 0 .$$

We shall now examine the consequences of rejecting this assumption. As we shall see, this is equivalent to supposing that our material system has spin, so that we have at last reached the main topic of this paper. However, the subsequent discussion will be clearer if we begin by reminding the reader of the conventional theory of spin in special relativity. The general theory is given in Section 2.5.

2.4. *The Spin of a Material System in Special Relativity*

In this section we assume that the Lagrangian density $\mathfrak{L}(\psi, \psi_{,i})$ is invariant under the rigid Lorentz transformations of special relativity. As we have already pointed out, the invariance of $\mathfrak{L}$ under displacements, together with the field equations $\delta L/\delta\psi = 0$, imply that the canonical energy tensor T_{ij} defined in (1) is conserved:

$$T_{ij,j} = 0 . \tag{13}$$

Of more immediate interest is the implication of the invariance under Lorentz rotations, which is (cf. [5], p. 71)

$$J^{ijk}{}_{,k} = 0 \tag{14}$$

where

$$J^{ijk} = \frac{\partial L}{\partial \psi_{,k}} S^{ij}\psi + x^i T^{jk} - x^j T^{ik}$$

and S^{ij} is the skew tensor defining the transformation properties of ψ under the infinitesimal Lorentz rotation $\delta_{ij} + O_{ij}$, that is

$$\psi' = (1 + \tfrac{1}{2} O_{ij} S^{ij})\psi . \tag{15}$$

The conservation equation (14) can be written [using (13)]

$$S^{ijk}{}_{,k} = T^{ij} - T^{ji} \tag{16}$$

where

$$S^{ijk} = \frac{\partial L}{\partial \psi_{,k}} S^{ij} \psi . \tag{17}$$

The two sides of this equation do not in general vanish unless ψ transforms as a scalar under Lorentz rotations (that is $S^{ij} = 0$).

We now consider the physical interpretation of these equations. Since T_{ij} is conserved, it is natural to regard it as the energy-momentum tensor of the material system. However, the energy-momentum tensor is not defined uniquely by the conservation requirement since in general there exist other tensors whose divergence vanishes identically which could be added to the canonical tensor. If, in particular, we add to T_{ij} a tensor which is itself a divergence, the integrated energy and momentum of a finite system will be unaltered – only the detailed distribution of energy and momentum will be affected. Belinfante [3] and Rosenfeld [2] were thus led to consider the symmetric tensor T'_{ij} given by

$$T'_{ij} = T_{ij} - R_{ijk,k}$$

where

$$R_{ijk} = \tfrac{1}{2}(S_{kji} + S_{kij} + S_{ijk}) = -R_{ikj}$$

as the "correct" energy momentum tensor. The justification for this choice lies in the fact that when $\mathcal{L}$ is made covariant under general coordinate transformations, there is an identity which states that

$$\sqrt{-g}\, T'_{ij} = \frac{\delta \mathcal{L}}{\delta g^{ij}} .$$

This means that T'_{ij} is the tensor coupled to g^{ij} in $\mathcal{L}$ and is thus the source of gravitation in Einstein's field equations. As stated in the introduction, this is a dynamical criterion for resolving an ambiguity that exists at the kinematical level.

We must now investigate the physical interpretation of the quantity S_{ijk}. Equations (14) and (17) suggest that S_{ijk} is the spin tensor of the material system. However, we are again faced with an ambiguity, for we can add to S_{ijk} any tensor which is skew in i and j, has vanishing divergence, and is itself a divergence, without altering the total spin of a finite system or destroying the conservation equations. For instance, as suggested by Corson ([5], p. 72), we could define a new spin tensor S'_{ijk} by the equation

$$S'_{ijk} = S_{ijk} + (x_i R_{jkl} - x_j R_{ikl})_{,l}. \tag{18}$$

In order to resolve this ambiguity, we need a dynamical definition of spin. Such a definition is proposed in the next section.

2.5. The Spin of a Material System in General Relativity

In order to obtain a dynamical definition of spin we proceed by analogy with the dynamical treatment of the energy-momentum tensor. There we extended the invariance of the Lagrangian by considering not just rigid space-time displacements depending on a set of fixed parameters, but also arbitrary non-linear transformations of coordinates depending on a set of functions of position. In a similar way, we shall now assume that the material Lagrangian is invariant not only under rigid Lorentz rotations depending on a set of fixed parameters O_{ij}, but also under non-rigid Lorentz rotations, that is, rotations whose parameters vary with position.(1) These rotations can be specified by their effect on a set of orthonormal vectors $e_i(\alpha)$ defined at each point of space (which at this stage of the discussion is still Minkowskian). For infinitesimal rotations we have

$$\delta e_i(\alpha) = o(\alpha\beta) e_i(\beta).$$

Since derivatives of ψ appear in the Lagrangian $\mathcal{L}$ the effect of a non-rigid Lorentz rotation will be to introduce into $\mathcal{L}$ derivatives of the functions $o(\alpha\beta)$ which specify the Lorentz rotations. Thus we will have

$$\begin{aligned} \psi &\to [1 + \tfrac{1}{2} s(\alpha\beta) o(\alpha\beta)]\psi, \\ \psi_{,p} &\to [1 + \tfrac{1}{2} s(\alpha\beta) o(\alpha\beta)]\psi_{,p} + \tfrac{1}{2} s(\alpha\beta)\psi o(\alpha\beta)_{,p}. \end{aligned} \tag{19}$$

The transformed Lagrangian will thus contain additional terms representing a "coupling" between ψ and $o(\alpha\beta)_{,p}$.

We see, then, that as originally defined, $\mathcal{L}$ is not in fact invariant under non-rigid Lorentz rotations. In order to obtain this invariance we adopt the following device. We assume that there exists in nature, in addition to the material field ψ, another field $o_p(\alpha\beta)$ with the following properties:

(i) It is skew in α and β,

(1) Cf. Utiyama, *Phys. Rev.* **101**, 1597 (1956).

(ii) It transforms like a covariant vector under coordinate transformations, and its change under the infinitesimal Lorentz rotation generated by $o(\alpha\beta)$ is given by

$$\delta o_p(\alpha\beta) = o(\alpha\gamma)\,o_p(\gamma\beta) + o(\beta\gamma)\,o_p(\alpha\gamma) - o(\alpha\beta)_{,p} \tag{20}$$

that is, its transformation law differs from that of a tensor by the last term of (20).

(iii) It is coupled to matter in the same way as $o(\alpha\beta)_{,p}$, resulting in a new Lagrangian density $\mathcal{L}'$, say. With these assumptions the theory is invariant under non-rigid Lorentz rotations, since the extra terms in the Lagrangian density $\mathcal{L}'$ implied by (19) are now cancelled by the extra terms arising from the non-tensorial transformation law of $o_p(\alpha\beta)$.

The existence of this non-tensorial law gives rise to the possibility that the $o_p(\alpha\beta)$ field could be made to vanish everywhere by a suitable choice of vierbeins. The necessary and sufficient condition that this be possible is that

$$R_{ij}(\alpha\beta) = 0\,.$$

(cf. (4)). If this condition is satisfied, our new field can be eliminated from the theory, at the cost of restricting the choice of possible vierbeins. However, this would contradict the spirit of the idea that all sets of orthonormal vierbeins are essentially equivalent. We therefore impose the further condition on the $o_p(\alpha\beta)$ field:

(iv) $$R_{ij}(\alpha\beta) \neq 0\,.$$

Now that we have a new irreducible field, we must add to the Lagrangian density a term representing this field in the free state, in addition to the coupling term (iii). We shall assume that this free field term is εR (see (6)). The total Lagrangian density is thus

$$\mathcal{L}' + \varepsilon R\,.$$

It differs from the Lagrangian density of Section 2.3 by the terms in $\mathcal{L}'$ involving $o_p(\alpha\beta)$. By analogy with the dynamical definition of the energy-momentum tensor as the quantity coupled to $e_i(\alpha)$ in the material Lagrangian density, we now define the dynamical spin tensor $s^p(\alpha\beta)$ as *the quantity coupled to* $o_p(\alpha\beta)$ *in the material Lagrangian density*, that is

$$s^p(\alpha\beta) = \frac{\delta\mathcal{L}'}{\delta o_p(\alpha\beta)}\,.$$

It is immediately clear that $s^p(\alpha\beta)$ is skew in α and β, and is a function of ψ, $\psi_{,i}$ and $s(\alpha\beta)$ (cf. (19) and (iii)). Its further significance and, in particular, its conservation law and its relation to the kinematical spin tensor, will now be elucidated from an examination of the field equations and the identities arising from our new Lagrangian.

We shall again assume that $e_i(\alpha)$ and $o_p(\alpha\beta)$ are independent in all variations. The vanishing of the variation with respect to $e_i(\alpha)$ yields the field equations

$$2R(\alpha\beta)-R\delta(\alpha\beta) = -\frac{1}{\varepsilon}t(\alpha\beta) \tag{21}$$

where

$$t(\alpha\beta) = \frac{\delta\mathfrak{L}'}{\delta e^i(\alpha)}e^i(\beta).$$

The vanishing of the variation with respect to $o_p(\alpha\beta)$ yields the field equations

$$X^p(\alpha\beta) = -\frac{\delta\mathfrak{L}'}{\delta o_p(\alpha\beta)} = -s^p(\alpha\beta). \tag{22}$$

We call these relations "field equations" although $X^p(\alpha\beta) = 0$ is equivalent to the Christoffel relations, since now the spin tensor of the material field is involved in the relation between $o_p(\alpha\beta)$ and $e_i(\alpha)$. This result is important because it means that $o_p(\alpha\beta)$ no longer satisfies the integrability conditions (3). It follows that the associated affine connexion Γ^p_{qr} defined in (2) is not symmetric. In other words, *spin gives rise to a skew part of* Γ^p_{qr}.

To find the precise relation between $s^p(\alpha\beta)$ and $\Gamma^p_{\check{qr}}$ we manipulate (22) in the same way as (8). If we write (10) as $I^p(\alpha\beta) = 0$, we now find

$$I^p(\alpha\beta) = \frac{1}{\varepsilon}[s^p(\alpha\beta)-\tfrac{1}{2}e_q(\gamma)e^p(\beta)s^q(\alpha\gamma)+\tfrac{1}{2}e_q(\gamma)e^p(\alpha)s^q(\beta\gamma)]$$

$$= Y^p(\alpha\beta), \text{ say.}$$

Then we have from (2)

$$\Gamma^p_{\check{qr}} = \tfrac{1}{2}Y^p(\alpha\beta)e_q(\alpha)e_r(\beta).$$

It is clear that these results differ from those of the purely metric theory where the Christoffel relations are assumed *a priori*. The physical significance of this difference can be seen as follows. First we observe that $o_p(\alpha\beta)$ is now given by

$$2e^p(\gamma)o_p(\alpha\beta) = [e(\gamma), e(\alpha)](\beta) + [e(\beta), e(\gamma)](\alpha) - \\ - [e(\alpha), e(\beta)](\gamma) + Y(\gamma\alpha, \beta) + Y(\beta\gamma, \alpha) - Y(\alpha\beta, \gamma)$$

where

$$Y(\alpha\beta, \gamma) = Y^p(\alpha\beta)e_p(\gamma).$$

Hence the quantity $o'_p(\alpha\beta)$ defined by

$$2o'_p(\alpha\beta) = 2o_p(\alpha\beta) - Y_p(\gamma\alpha) - Y_p(\beta\gamma) + Y_p(\alpha\beta)$$

will satisfy the integrability conditions (3). The affine connexion associated with $o'_p(\alpha\beta)$ will thus be the Christoffel connexion. It follows that if we re-write our theory in terms of $o'_p(\alpha\beta)$, the resulting geometrical relations will be the same as those of the purely metric theory. On the other hand, a difference from the metric theory will arise since covariant derivatives of quantities expressed in vierbein components must now involve $o'_p(\alpha\beta)$ rather than $o_p(\alpha\beta)$. When the material Lagrangian density $\mathcal{L}'$ is re-written in this way, it will contain terms in which $s_p(\alpha\beta)$ and $Y_p(\alpha\beta)$ are coupled together. These terms give rise to a spin-spin interaction which does not exist in the purely metric theory [15].

We shall now derive further properties of $s^p(\alpha\beta)$ by using the invariance of $\mathcal{L}'$ under non-rigid Lorentz rotations. This invariance leads to the identities [(1)]

$$s^p(\alpha\beta)_{;p} = t(\alpha\beta) \tag{23}$$

and

$$s^p(\alpha\beta) = \frac{\partial\mathcal{L}'}{\partial\psi_{,p}} s(\alpha\beta)\psi.$$

The first of these identities shows that our dynamical spin tensor $s^p(\alpha\beta)$ satisfies the expected conservation law for angular momentum (cf. (16)).

The second identity resolves the ambiguity in the kinematical definition of the spin tensor by showing that it is the original kinematical spin tensor s_{ijk} which is the same as the dynamical one, [(2)] rather than the tensor s'_{ijk} (see (18)) proposed by Corson.

---

(1) The technique of obtaining identities is discussed in detail by Rosenfeld [2]. Our results are straightforward applications of this technique, so we shall not go into detail here.

(2) This justifies our notation for the dynamical spin tensor.

The first identity also reminds us that in general $\underset{\vee}{t}(\alpha\beta)$ is not zero, that is, if a material system has spin, its dynamically defined energy-momentum tensor is not symmetric. It follows from the field equations (21) that in this case $R(\alpha\beta)$ is not symmetric either. This is not surprising, since, as we have already mentioned, in Riemannian geometry the Ricci tensor is symmetric only by virtue of the Christoffel relations (e.g., [17], pp. 51, 70), whereas here these relations do not hold [1]. In fact, one can show from the invariance of R under non-rigid Lorentz rotations or directly from the definition of the Ricci tensor in terms of $o_p(\alpha\beta)$, that

$$2\underset{\vee}{R}(\alpha\beta) = \frac{1}{\varepsilon} X^p(\alpha\beta)_{;p}.$$

On the other hand, because of the Lorentz invariance of the theory, the field equations for $\underset{\vee}{R}(\alpha\beta)$ implied by (21) are not independent of the field equations (22). Indeed, we have from (22)

$$X^p(\alpha\beta)_{;p} = -s^p(\alpha\beta)_{;p} = -\underset{\vee}{t}(\alpha\beta)$$

from (23). This gives us the field equations for $\underset{\vee}{R}(\alpha\beta)$, namely

$$2\underset{\vee}{R}(\alpha\beta) = -\frac{1}{\varepsilon}\underset{\vee}{t}(\alpha\beta).$$

These results are of interest in connexion with a previous suggestion by Costa de Beauregard [18] and the author [19] that in the presence of spinning matter the Ricci tensor and the energy-momentum tensor should be non-symmetric. This asymmetry was there derived from the assumption that the metric tensor g_{ij} is also non-symmetric. It is clear from the present discussion that this assumption about the metric tensor is unnecessary, since the asymmetry arises automatically if one works simultaneously in the vierbein and Palatini formalisms.

We now come to the most important consequence of this treatment of spin, namely, its implications for the equations of motion of the material system. Since the material Lagrangian density contains a term which couples $s_p(\alpha\beta)$ and $o_p(\alpha\beta)$, there will be a corresponding force-density f_p in the equations of motion. This force-density can be easily derived from a variational principle in which $o_p(\alpha\beta)$ is kept fixed and the world-lines of matter are varied (cf. [20], § 47

(1) Of course the Ricci tensor constructed from $o'_p(\alpha\beta)$ is symmetric, and corresponds to the Ricci tensor of the purely metric theory.

for the corresponding electromagnetic calculation). It can also be obtained from the conservation identities for t_{pq} which now contain the extra term $R_{pq}(\alpha\beta)S^q(\alpha\beta)$. We thus find that f_p is given by[1]

$$f_p = R_{pq}(\alpha\beta)s^q(\alpha\beta).$$

This means that *a material system with spin is acted on by a gravitational force which depends on its spin and on the curvature.*

This result has the important consequence that orbits in a purely gravitational field are not the same for all types of matter, independent of their internal properties. At first sight this appears to conflict with the basic ideas underlying general relativity, especially with the principle of equivalence. We shall therefore give a detailed discussion of this principle. Much of this discussion will be found to have an analogue in electromagnetic theory (Section 4).

3. THE PRINCIPLE OF EQUIVALENCE

The principle of equivalence is often stated in the following form: a gravitational field is equivalent in its effects to a suitably chosen acceleration of the frame of reference. In this form of the principle one must add the proviso that one is considering regions so small that the gravitational field (that is, the connexion Γ^i_{jk}) is sensibly constant. This proviso is not usually regarded as a serious limitation on the significance of the principle of equivalence, since, for instance, the length-scale of the earth's gravitational field is far larger than the size of the apparatus used to confirm the principle (Galileo–Eötvös experiments).

In the usual discussions of the principle of equivalence, the proviso is taken to mean that we must ignore the geodesic deviation of neighbouring geodesics. This is a reasonable procedure when applied, say, to the Einstein lift experiment at the surface of the earth, but it cannot be applied to the behaviour of spinning particles, since they do not even move on geodesics. The proviso can perhaps be saved by the following argument. The orbits of spinning particles deviate from geodesics because of the action of a force depending on an internal property of the particles (their spin) and on the Riemann tensor. The existence of such a gravitational force can be intuitively understood in the following way. A spinning particle

---

(1) An equivalent result was first obtained by Mathisson [8] who worked entirely in terms of the energy momentum tensor of the material system. The present method appears to be a simpler and more natural one.

has a minimum "size" associated with it which depends on its spin (cf. [21], p. 173). Such a particle can "feel" the change in the gravitational field, that is, in Γ^i_{jk}, across it, and so is subject to a tidal force depending on its spin and on the Riemann tensor. It could thus be argued that a spinning particle is too large for the principle of equivalence to apply to its motion in a gravitational field. Unfortunately, this would mean that the principle is practically empty, since even protons and electrons would be too large for it to apply. It would be preferable to adopt a weaker formulation of the principle which would be rigorously true for all particles.

The most obvious suggestion for such a formulation is the following well-known statement: inertial forces are gravitational in origin. This formulation of the principle of equivalence is very attractive. It accounts for inertial forces in the spirit of Mach's principle, and it corresponds to the fact that the non-interacting material Lagrangian $\mathcal{L}$ of special relativity, which describes the inertial behaviour of matter, is also the interacting Lagrangian between matter and gravitation ($\sqrt{-g}\,T_{ij} = \delta\mathcal{L}/\delta g^{ij}$). Its only drawback is that in this form the principle of equivalence is so weak that *it does not enable one to predict the result of the Galileo–Eötvös experiments, even for non-spinning matter.*

The reason for this is that when we made assumption (iii) about the $o_p(\alpha\beta)$ field, we could have included in $\mathcal{L}'$ a further coupling term of the form

$$R_{ij}(\alpha\beta)f^{ij}(\alpha\beta)$$

where $f^{ij}(\alpha\beta)$ is a function of ψ. The assumption that such a term exists would not be in conflict with special relativity (which holds only when $R_{ij}(\alpha\beta) = 0$). So far as our weak formulation of the principle of equivalence is concerned, such a term could be characteristic of the coupling between gravitation and matter, and indeed could appear in the Lagrangian with such a large coefficient as to be grossly inconsistent with the Galileo experiment, even though the value of $R_{ij}(\alpha\beta)$ for the earth is very small. Hence, in order to predict the observed result of this experiment, we must assume, in addition to the weak principle of equivalence, that the coefficient of such a term is less than some upper limit (related to the accuracy of the experiment).

It is natural to go further and to assume that this coefficient is actually zero. In other words, we shall assume that the entire coupling between matter and gravitation is deducible from the invariance arguments of Section 2.5—there is no additional term in the Lagrangian directly coupling curvature with matter.[1] We shall call this version of the principle of equivalence the principle of minimal gravitational coupling. Physically it means that the coupling is of two types only:

(i) The coupling between energy and metric, which by itself would lead to a geodesic equation of motion.

(ii) The coupling between spin and affine connexion, which gives rise to a gravitational force that deflects a spinning particle from a geodesic.

It is interesting to note that this principle of minimal gravitational coupling may not have to be postulated independently of the empty space gravitational field equations. The reason for this is that if matter is regarded as a singularity of the gravitational field, its motion is completely prescribed by the field equations—no further coupling principles are needed. Unfortunately, it takes an infinity of parameters to characterize a singularity [22], and it is not clear how these parameters should be chosen. In the absence of a satisfactory theory of matter, it may be more useful to accord the principle an independent status.

So far we have been concerned entirely with the pure gravitational field. Nevertheless, the real importance of the principle of minimal gravitational coupling lies in the fact that, as we shall see, it has an analogue in other field theories based on invariance groups. Moreover, these other fields are like gravitation in that the forces they exert on matter depend on the internal properties of matter. We therefore take the view that gravitation is *not* so fundamentally different from other fields that it alone should be geometrised. These points will now be examined in detail in connexion with the electromagnetic field.

4. THE ELECTROMAGNETIC FIELD

We have seen that the dynamic group underlying the interaction between spin and affine connexion is the Lorentz group, and that this interaction implies the existence of a purely gravitational force which depends on the spin of a particle and on the curvature of the gravitational field. It is well known that a similar situation exists for the electromagnetic field. In this case it is the dynamic

[1] If the material Lagrangian is a function of the second derivative of ψ, the curvature might appear explicitly in the Lagrangian. In this case, we can still assume that the entire coupling is deducible from the invariance arguments of Section 2.5.

group of phase transformations which underlies the interaction between charge and the electromagnetic vector potential, resulting in an electromagnetic force depending on the charge of a particle and on the electromagnetic field. As we have already stated, there is also an electromagnetic analogue of the principle of minimal gravitational coupling. Before explaining this analogue, we shall recall the group theoretical foundations of electromagnetic field theory.

It was pointed out in the Introduction that one is led to consider the non-rigid phase transformations

$$\psi \to \psi' = e^{ie\lambda}\psi \qquad \psi^* \to \psi^{*\prime} = e^{-ie\lambda}\psi^*$$

(where λ is an arbitrary function of position) as an invariance group of the material Lagrangian. Under these transformations the gradient of ψ transforms as follows:

$$\psi_{,i} \to e^{ie\lambda}\psi_{,i} + ie\lambda_{,i}\psi', \qquad \psi^*_{,i} \to e^{-ie\lambda}\psi^*_{,i} - ie\lambda_{,i}\psi^{*\prime}. \tag{24}$$

Since the gradient of ψ appears in the Lagrangian, this Lagrangian will only be invariant if we assume the existence in nature of a field A_i with the following properties (cf. the introduction of the $o_p(\alpha\beta)$ field in section 2.5).

(i) It transforms like a covariant vector under coordinate transformations, while under phase transformations it behaves like a connexion, namely

$$A'_i = A_i - i\lambda_{,i} \tag{25}$$

(ii) It is coupled to ψ exactly like $\lambda_{,i}$, resulting in a modified Lagrangian density $\mathcal{L}'$. This Lagrangian density is invariant since the extra terms in (24) are compensated by the extra terms arising from the non-tensorial transformation law (25).

If A_i were the gradient of a scalar, we could make it vanish throughout a domain by a suitable phase transformation. The necessary and sufficient condition for this to be possible is

$$F_{ij} = A_{j,i} - A_{i,j} = 0.$$

If this condition were satisfied it would imply the existence of a set of preferred "phase-frames". To avoid this situation, we assume

(iii) $$F_{ij} \neq 0.$$

Since the curvature F_{ij} does not vanish we have a new irreducible field. We must therefore add to $\mathcal{L}'$ a term representing this field in the free state, and of course we shall adopt the Maxwellian Lagrangian density.

The total Lagrangian density is thus

$$\mathfrak{L}' + eF_{ij}F^{ij}.$$

This Lagrangian density gives rise to familiar field equations and also to the identity

$$\frac{\delta \mathfrak{L}}{\delta A_i} = J^i$$

where

$$J^i = -ie\left(\frac{\partial \mathfrak{L}}{\partial \psi_{,i}}\psi - \frac{\partial \mathfrak{L}}{\partial \psi^*_{,i}}\psi^*\right)$$

J^i is the kinematically defined charge-vector, and is conserved ($J^i{}_{,i} = 0$). Since $\delta\mathfrak{L}/\delta A_i$ is the source term in Maxwell's equations, we have here a dynamic definition of the charge vector which justifies the kinematic one.

Since the material Lagrangian density contains a term which couples J^i and A_i, there will be a corresponding force-density f_i in the equations of motion of the material system. This force-density can be easily derived from a variational principle in which A_i is kept fixed and the world-lines of matter are varied (cf. [20], § 47). The result is the Lorentz force-density

$$f_i = F_{ik}J^k.$$

It is clear that we have here an exact analogy between the charge and spin of a material system ψ.

(i) They are defined by the transformation properties of ψ under kinematic invariance groups.

(ii) They are coupled to the connexions introduced to preserve invariance under the corresponding dynamic groups.

(iii) The material system is acted on by a force depending on them and on the curvature of the connexion.

This analogy can be extended by introducing into electromagnetic theory the analogue of the principle of minimal gravitational coupling. This would mean that there is no term in the Lagrangian of the form

$$F_{ij}f^{ij}$$

where f^{ij} is a function of ψ. A term of this form was once proposed by Pauli in order to account for the anomalous magnetic moments of nucleons, but this phenomenon is nowadays attributed to the virtual meson cloud which surrounds them.

The principle that the Lagrangian should contain no Pauli term has actually already been proposed by elementary particle theorists, and Gell-Mann [23] has called it the principle of minimal electromagnetic coupling (which indeed suggested the name of our gravitational principle). It is interesting to note that he also pointed out a piece of evidence in favour of this principle—*this evidence is thus the electromagnetic analogue of the Galileo experiment.* It consists in the observed fact that strangeness is always conserved in electromagnetic transitions of strange particles. This would be hard to understand if Pauli terms were allowed, since such terms can be written down connecting particles of different strangeness with the electromagnetic field. On the other hand, it would be automatically accounted for if the entire electromagnetic interaction is derived from a strangeness-conserving Lagrangian in accordance with assumption (ii). This evidence is not very strong, but nor is that implied by the Galileo experiment, which sets only a rather high upper limit for the coefficient of the coupling term $R_{ij}(\alpha\beta)f^{ij}(\alpha\beta)$.

5. CONCLUSIONS

Our discussions of spin and charge have shown that there is a close analogy between them and also between the vierbein affine connexion and the vector potential, their differences arising from the differences in structure of the underlying dynamic groups. However, this analogy is not complete since the vierbein affine connexion is treated as part of the geometrical structure of space, whereas the vector potential is not. Since the analogy between these two quantities appears to be a deep one, it seems natural to complete it by making also the vector potential part of the structure of space. In other words, we should geometrize the electromagnetic field.

Various attempts have, of course, been made to do just this. Some of them are based on ideas quite different from those described in this paper—for instance some completely ignore the dynamic group of phase transformations. Because of analogies of the type described in this paper, I believe that dynamic groups are of fundamental importance in physics, and that geometrical field theories should be based on them. This means that the various dynamic groups must be subgroups of the so-called holonomy group of space [24]. The corresponding connexions then become part of the geometrical structure of space. A preliminary attempt to carry out this programme for the electromagnetic field has already been described [7], and will be developed elsewhere. The next step would be to introduce still larger dynamic fields ([25], [24]). These possibilities, perhaps combined with topological considerations, show that non-quantum field theory is far from being exhausted as a means of attacking the fundamental problems of physics.(1)

REFERENCES

[1] L. Infeld, *Phys. Z.* **29**, 145 (1928).
[2] L. Rosenfeld, *Mem. Acad. Roy. Belg.* **18**, 6 (1940).
[3] F. J. Belinfante, *Physica* **7**, 449 (1940).
[4] H. Weyl, *Proc. Nat. Acad. Sci.,Wash.* **15**, 323 (1929); *Z. Phys.* **56**, 330 (1929).
[5] E. M. Corson, *Introduction to Tensors, Spinors and Relativistic Wave Equations*, London 1953.
[6] W. Pauli, *Theory of Relativity*, London 1958, p. 227.
[7] D. W. Sciama, *Nuovo Cim.* **8**, 417 (1958).
[8] M. Mathisson, *Acta Phys. Polon.* **6**, 163 (1937).
[9] M. Schonberg, *Phys. Rev.* **59**, 616 (1941).
[10] A. Papapetrou, *Proc. R. Irish Acad.* **52**, 11 (1948).
[11] A. Papapetrou, *Proc. Roy. Soc.* **209**, 248 (1951).
[12] P. G. Bergmann and R. Thomson, *Phys. Rev.* **89**, 400 (1953).
[13] E. Noether, *Nachr. Ges. Wiss. Göttingen* **235** (1918).
[14] A. Palatini, *R. C. Circ. Mat. Palermo* **43**, 203 (1919).
[15] H. Weyl, *Phys. Rev.* **77**, 699 (1950).
[16] L. P. Eisenhart, *Continuous Groups of Transformations*, Princeton 1933, p. 22.
[17] E. Schrödinger, *Space-Time Structure,* Cambridge 1950.
[18] O. Costa de beauregard, *J. Math.* **22**, 85 (1943).

---

(1) *Note added in proof.* Since this paper was written there have been several developments. T. W. B. Kibble (*J. Math. Phys.* **2**, 212 (1961)) has independently proposed a similar theory of spin. It is more general than the present theory in that coordinate transformations are considered as well as Lorentz transformations of vierbeins. The geometrization of the phase connexion has been studied by me in a paper to appear in the July–August (1961) issue of the *Journal of Mathematical Physics*. The geometrization can be carried out, but the underlying holonomy group contains the phase group as an *invariant* sub-group. The resulting theory is thus not a unified one. To obtain a unified theory the holonomy group should be a simple group. An obvious candidate is the symplectic group, but this possibility remains to be investigated. Meanwhile, elementary particle theorists have been investigating dynamical groups following the lead of Yang and Mills [25]. As typical references we quote J. J. Sakurai, *Ann. Phys.* **11**, 1 (1960), and A. Salam and J. C. Ward, *Nuovo Cim.* **19**, 165 (1961). Despite the elegance of this approach it has not yet been rewarded by the obtaining of a significant new result.

[19] D. W. SCIAMA, *Proc. Camb. Phil. Soc.* **54**, 12 (1958).
[20] V. FOCK, *The Theory of Space, Time and Gravitation,* London 1959.
[21] C. MØLLER, *The Theory of Relativity,* Oxford 1952.
[22] P. G. BERGMANN, *Phys. Rev.* **112**, 287 (1958).
[23] M. GELL-MANN, *Nuovo Cim. Supp.* **4**, 848 (1956).
[24] D. W. SCIAMA, *Ann. Inst. H. Poincaré,* to be published 1960.
[25] C. N. YANG and R. L. MILLS, *Phys. Rev.* **96**, 191 (1954).

RELATIVITY BASED ON CHRONOMETRY

J. L. SYNGE

Dublin Institute for Advanced Studies, Dublin, Ireland

IN a book now being written for the North Holland Publishing Co., I have developed the general theory of relativity on a chronometric basis, and in this paper I outline some of the methods and results.

We start with the concept of a Riemannian space-time of events, the meaning of the metric ds being purely chronometric: for a timelike element dx^i, $ds = (-g_{ij}dx^i dx^j)^{\frac{1}{2}}$ is the measure of time by a standard (atomic) clock with a world line including the element dx^i. The geodesic hypothesis for free particles and photons is accepted. The *distance* between two adjacent timelike world lines, C and C', is defined chronometrically as half the time, measured by a clock on C, between the emission of a photon from C and its return to C after bouncing off C'. In general, this distance is of course not constant. There are no yardsticks, and if there is any *rigidity* (in the sense of Born) it is a chronometric rigidity. Since an interferometer compares path-times, there is actually little essential novelty in the reduction of the measurement of distance to the measurement of time.

The techniques employed involve

(i) the use of a general coordinate system throughout, so that the machinery of tensor calculus may be employed, and approximations for weak fields (where they occur) are based directly on the smallness of the Riemann tensor R_{ijkm} and not on an approximation of the metric tensor to the diagonal form $(1, 1, 1, -1)$;

(ii) Fermi transport of vectors along curves in space-time, a fundamental relativistic operation which is little known;[1]

(iii) a 2-point function $\Omega(PP')$, which I call the *world-function*

---

[1] I owe my own acquaintance with it to Dr F. A. E. Pirani.

and which, to within a sign, is $\frac{1}{2}PP'^2$ where PP' is the measure of the geodesic PP'.

Every attempt is made to make the theory factual and realistic, and the observations made by a terrestrial observer are considered in some detail. He has a clock, and so can measure the time of any observation, but to measure *direction* he needs a frame of reference consisting of three unit vectors orthogonal to one another and to his world line. If his world line were a geodesic, he would undoubtedly make this frame of reference undergo parallel transport along his world line. But the world line of a terrestrial observer is certainly not a geodesic (he is not falling freely), and there are two choices of frame of reference which are natural from a mathematical standpoint:

(i) a triad of vectors which undergo Fermi transport;

(ii) the triad of principal normals to his world line.

The mathematical definition of Fermi transport [1] of a vector F^i reads

$$DF^i = A^i F_j DA^j \tag{1}$$

where $A^i = dx^i/ds$, the unit tangent vector to the world line, and $D = \delta/\delta s$, the operator of absolute differentiation. This law conserves the orthogonality of F^i and A^i, and also conserves the scalar product of any two vectors orthogonal to A^i. This simple mathematical definition admits also a simple chronometric interpretation in the following way.

The observer whose world line is the curve of transport fires a photon at some near object and receives back a scattered photon. Using an arbitrary reference triad, he measures the apparent direction cosines of the emitted photon and the direction from which the scattered photon appears to come. If s is the (small) time recorded by his clock between emission and return of the photon, the two sets of direction cosines will differ in general by amounts of order s. But if he uses a frame of reference which undergoes Fermi transport, these changes in direction cosines are negligible in comparison with s, being of order s^2. There is no assumption here—it is a matter of exact calculation—and we are led to say that Fermi transport defines a *non-rotating frame*. Thus the vexed question of rotation in relativity takes on a simple operational (chronometric) meaning, for the observations employed in measuring direction are given, without difficulty, chronometric meanings.

As for the triad of principal normals, they are given mathematically by the well known Frenet–Serret formulae. To identify this triad physically, the observer lets a body fall freely, and observes the deviation of its (geodesic) world line from his (non-geodesic) world line. Calculation shows that the deviation takes place in the direction $-B^i$ where B^i is the unit first normal to the observer's world line, and the initial acceleration is b, the first curvature of that world line. However, a more detailed calculation of the deviation of the falling body shows that it bends in the direction of C^i, the second normal to the observer's world line. The relative trajectory is in fact a semi-cubical parabola involving as parameter the quantity c^2/b where c is the second curvature of the observer's world line. Thus by simple dynamical experiment an observer can determine the directions of the first two normals to his world line, and hence the third by orthogonality; he also determines the first two curvatures b, c. If he combines these observations with the optical observations described above, he can get the third curvature d also.

Now the behaviour of a freely falling body relative to the rotating earth is well known. It starts to fall vertically down with an acceleration $g = 980 \text{ cm sec}^{-2}$ approximately, the value depending on latitude. We can then at once identify the first normal B^i of the world line of a terrestrial observer: it points straight up, against the plumb line. As for the first curvature b, we have $b = g = 980 \text{ cm sec}^{-2}$ approx. Furthermore, we know that on the earth a falling body deviates to the east, falling in a semi-cubical parabola. Thus the second normal C^i points east, and the third normal D^i north in consequence. As for the second curvature c, we evaluate it by comparison with a well known Newtonian formula. The third curvature d is given as mentioned above, and we get the values

$$c = \omega \cos \lambda, \qquad d = \omega \sin \lambda \tag{2}$$

where ω is the angular velocity of the earth and λ the latitude of the observer.

When relativity is approached chronometrically, there is only one unit—the period of a standard atom (say the cadmium red line). But this is a very short time, and we prefer to work with the *second*, a conventional multiple of the fundamental period. The centimetre is purely artificial, since we have defined distance chronometrically and no reference is ever made, except incidentally, to the speed of light. If we wish to bring in the ordinary units, we write

$$1 \text{ cm} = 3{\cdot}336 \times 10^{-11} \text{ sec}, \qquad 1 \text{ sec} = 2{\cdot}998 \times 10^{10} \text{ cm}. \tag{3}$$

Mass, as is well known, is a length in relativity. But for us a length is a time, and we get the formula

$$1 \text{ gm} = 2{\cdot}476 \times 10^{-39} \text{ sec.} \tag{4}$$

In fact, everything appears in seconds or powers of seconds. This is very convenient because it gives us an instant comparison of magnitudes of the same dimensions but apparently dissimilar. We are accustomed to think of the acceleration of gravity as fairly large and the angular velocity of the earth as small; however the dimensionless ratio is

$$g/\omega = 4{\cdot}475 \times 10^{-4}. \tag{5}$$

This means that the world line of a terrestrial observer on the equator is a curve for which the second curvature is more than a thousand times the first curvature.

Ordinary geodetic measurements of gravity do not really measure the gravitational field at all. These measurements give the first curvature of the observer's world line, whereas the gravitational field consists in the components of the Riemann tensor R_{ijkm}. To give a clear description of the field, the terrestrial observer should decide on some tetrad of reference, and he would probably select the tetrad composed of the three principal normals and his 4-velocity. If this tetrad is denoted by $\lambda^i_{(a)}$ (i tensorial, a a label), then the quantities which the geodesist should record are the invariants

$$R_{(abcd)} = R_{ijkm} \lambda^i_{(a)} \lambda^j_{(b)} \lambda^k_{(c)} \lambda^m_{(d)}. \tag{6}$$

It is rather curious that, although these quantities *are* the gravitational field, and Einstein's theory is now over forty years old, no one seems to have thought about the measurement of the components of the Riemann tensor. But it is still more curious that geodesists have actually measured some of these components without knowing what they were doing! This is worth going into, viewing the matter from two standpoints—the practical and the mathematical.

A man is equipped with a spring balance and a unit mass suspended from it. The value of g is the reading of the spring balance, and this reading varies with the position of the man in latitude and height. Let him take two readings, one in the basement of his house and the other in his attic at a height dh above the basement. Comparison of the readings gives the gradient of gravity, dg/dh. The strange thing is that while the value of g has nothing to do with the gravitational field (it is a mere acceleration effect), the value of dg/dh is truly gravitational.

However, as long as we use words carelessly we shall never reach a clear understanding as to what is due to what. Clarity demands that we refer the whole situation to the background of the Riemannian geometry of space-time. In space-time we see two world lines representing the history C of the man in the cellar and the history C' of the man in the attic. How are they related to one another? Very simply. We draw the first normals to C and proceed along them a distance dh; the events so obtained make up C'. The acceleration g is simply the first curvature of C, and so dg/dh is the rate of change of this curvature with respect to displacement along the normal. The calculation of dg/dh is a straightforward calculation in Riemannian geometry, and it is not necessary to make any approximations at all: the result is

$$db/dh = R_{(1414)} - b^2 - c^2 \tag{7}$$

where b is the first curvature ($b = g$), c the second curvature, and $R_{(1414)}$ is the component of Riemannian curvature, as in (6), for the pair of vectors representing the direction of the first normal to C and the tangent to C (i.e. the observer's 4-velocity).

We see that (7) does not give the gravitational field alone—it is mixed with the curvatures b and c. However, they are already known by dynamical experiments as mentioned earlier.

The formula analogous to (7) in Newtonian theory for the rotating earth is

$$dg/dh = -d^2V/dh^2 - \omega^2 \cos^2 \lambda \tag{8}$$

where V is the Newtonian potential. Hence, by (2), we have

$$R_{(1414)} = -d^2V/dh^2 - g^2. \tag{9}$$

But the ratio of g^2 to the preceding term is very small, about 7×10^{-10}, and so this component of the Riemann tensor is to be identified with the second derivative of the Newtonian potential; numerically,

$$R_{(1414)} = -3{\cdot}07 \times 10^{-6}\ \text{sec}^{-2}, \tag{10}$$

which value agrees with that obtained from the Schwarzschild field. (The argument leading to (7) does not involve the field equations at all.)

The above method of measuring a gravitational field is rather special—it yields only one component of the Riemann tensor.

It is proposed that the systematic measurement of gravitational fields should make use of the well known formula:

$$\frac{\delta^2 V^i}{\delta p \delta q} - \frac{\delta^2 V^i}{\delta q \delta p} = R_{ijkm} V^i \frac{\partial x^k}{\partial p} \frac{\partial x^m}{\partial q} \tag{11}$$

where V^i is a vector field given over a 2-space $x^i = x^i(p, q)$ and δ is the symbol of absolute differentiation. To use this formula physically, all we need is a physical (chronometric) meaning for absolute differentation, and that can be supplied. To employ (11) to best advantage, we should take, not a 2-space, but a congruence of time-like world lines and assign parameters $y_{(a)}$ with the first three constant along each of the world lines. Then, if we define

$$X^i_{(a)} = \frac{\partial x^i}{\partial y_{(a)}}, \tag{12}$$

we can write the invariant components of the Riemann tensor in the form

$$\begin{aligned} R_{(abcd)} &= R_{ijkm} X^i_{(a)} X^j_{(b)} X^k_{(c)} X^m_{(d)} \\ &= g_{ij} X^i_{(a)} \left(\frac{\delta^2 X^j_{(b)}}{\delta y_{(c)} \delta y_{(d)}} - \frac{\delta^2 X^j_{(b)}}{\delta y_{(d)} \delta y_{(c)}} \right). \end{aligned} \tag{13}$$

This is to be regarded as the fundamental formula for the measurement of gravitational fields.

It remains to say something about the world-function $\Omega\ (PP')$, without which the calculations needed in this chronometric treatment of relativity would lose all beauty and become a tedious mess. This function occurs in the work of Hadamard [2], but it was Ruse [3] who first developed the idea along the required lines. The essential point is that, while it is not permitted to compare vectors and tensors at different points and hence development in power series is not a permitted procedure in the domains of ordinary tensor techniques, this difficulty is overcome by means of the world-function. It is a *2-point invariant* and its covariant derivatives with respect to either or both points are *2-point tensors*. It is convenient to denote these covariant derivatives by subscripts without special signs, the subscripts being primed for P' and unprimed for P. Thus we have such symbols as

$$\Omega_i, \quad \Omega_{i'}, \quad \Omega_{ij}, \quad \Omega_{ij'}, \quad \Omega_{ijk}, \quad \Omega_{ijkm}, \quad \Omega_{ijkm'}, \tag{14}$$

each having with respect to transformation of the coordinates of P the tensor character indicated by the unprimed subscripts, and likewise for P' and the primed subscripts.

As noted earlier, the world-function $\Omega\ (PP')$ is, to within a sign, half the square of the measure of the geodesic PP'. The squaring of the measure gives a smooth function, and when we let P' approach P the values of the *coincidence limits* of the covariant derivatives are independent of the path by which the limit is attained. These limits play an important part in the calculations and are indicated by the notation

$$[\Omega\ldots] = \lim_{P'\to P} \Omega\ldots \tag{15}$$

Here are some of the values:[1]

$$\begin{gathered}[\Omega] = 0, \quad [\Omega_i] = 0, \quad [\Omega_{i'}] = 0, \\ [\Omega_{ij}] = g_{ij}, \quad [\Omega_{ij'}] = -g_{ij}, \\ [\Omega_{ijk}] = 0, \quad [\Omega_{ijkm}] = S_{ijkm}\end{gathered} \tag{16}$$

where S_{ijkm} is the symmetrized Riemann tensor

$$S_{ijkm} = -\tfrac{1}{3}\,(R_{ikjm} + R_{imjk}). \tag{17}$$

In working in the small, one uses power series and these coincidence limits. But in the large too the world-function is very useful, particularly in the case of weak fields. For in flat space-time we have the following tensor equations

$$\Omega_{ij} = g_{ij}, \quad \Omega_{ijk} = 0, \quad \Omega_{ijkm} = 0, \tag{18}$$

and therefore we know intuitively that these equations will be satisfied approximately in a weak field. It is possible to carry out evaluations of these and other quantities with the small deviations from the flat values displayed in the form of integrals involving the Riemann tensor to the first degree, all expressions being completely tensorial.

The world-function also enables us to write down exact integral conservation laws in tensorial form.

---

(1) Cf. J. L. Synge [4]; these matters were treated in lectures on "The Geometry of Space-Time" at the International Summer Centre, Sestriere, 1958, and published by Istituto Matematico dell'Università, Roma.

REFERENCES

[1] E. Fermi, *R.C. Acad. Lincei* **31**, 21, 51 (1922).
[2] J. Hadamard, *Lectures on Cauchy's problem in linear partial differential eqations*, Yale University Press, 1923; Dover Publications, New York 1952.
[3] H. S. Ruse, *Proc. Lond. Math. Soc.* **32**, 87 (1931); *Quart. J. Math.* **2**, 190 (1931).
[4] J. L. Synge, *Proc. Lond. Math. Soc.* **32**, 241 (1931).

ON SPHERICALLY SYMMETRIC DISTRIBUTIONS OF INCOMPRESSIBLE FLUIDS

A. H. TAUB*

University of Illinois, Digital Computer Laboratory, Urbana, Illinois

1. INTRODUCTION

IN a recent paper [1] the equations governing small isentropic motions of a spherically symmetric distribution of a perfect fluid in the general theory of relativity were derived. In that paper it was assumed that the fluid in question was characterized by its caloric equation of state which defined the specific rest internal energy ε as a function of the pressure, p, and the rest density ϱ, namely

$$\varepsilon = \varepsilon(p, \varrho).$$

It was further assumed that ε was not identically zero.

The purpose of this paper is to discuss the case where

$$\varepsilon \equiv 0. \tag{1.1}$$

Fluids satisfying this equation will be said to be incompressible. For such fluids it is possible to deal with the Einstein field equations directly and the restriction to small motions need not be made. Such motions may be obtained from the results given below by suitably restricting various parameters which will enter into the discussion.

It will be shown that the time-dependent interior solutions of the Einstein field equations for a spherically symmetric incompressible fluid at constant density (entropy) lead to singular metric tensors. If one rules out singular line-elements, as one should, one is lead to the conclusion that an incompressible fluid cannot undergo time-dependent motions. This result is a satisfactory one in that it rules

* Dedicated to Leopold Infeld.

out a motion whose classical analogue would involve an infinite propagation velocity, namely the velocity of sound in an incompressible fluid. The velocity of sound does enter into the discussion of the small isentropic motions of a fluid for which $\varepsilon(p, \varrho) \neq 0$ in a manner described in reference [1].

It should be emphasized that the impossibility of having an incompressible fluid in motion is connected with the non-admissibility of singularities in the line element. Thus singular line-elements allow the existence of infinite velocities of propagation of signals.

For an incompressible fluid the stress-energy tensor is given by the equation

$$T^{\mu\nu} = (\varrho + p/c^2)u^\mu u^\nu - \frac{p}{c^2} g^{\mu\nu} \tag{1.2}$$

where p is the pressure and u^μ is the four-velocity vector of the fluid and it satisfies the equation

$$u^\mu u_\mu = g_{\mu\nu} u^\mu u^\nu = 1. \tag{1.3}$$

The specific enthalpy of the fluid is given by

$$i = p/\varrho. \tag{1.4}$$

As in the compressible case, the temperature T and the entropy S of the fluid are defined as functions of p and ϱ by the requirement that

$$dS = \frac{1}{T}\left[d\varepsilon + p d\left(\frac{1}{\varrho}\right)\right] = \frac{1}{T}\left(di - \frac{1}{\varrho} dp\right) \tag{1.5}$$

be a perfect differential. In view of Eq. (1.1) the requirement that the motion be isentropic is equivalent to the requirement that

$$\varrho = \text{const} = \varrho_0. \tag{1.6}$$

It is a consequence of the isentropy assumption and the conservation laws

$$T^{\mu\nu}_{;\nu} = 0 \tag{1.7}$$

that the conservation of mass equation holds. This latter equation is

$$(\varrho u^\mu)_{;\mu} = 0.$$

In view of Eq. (1.6) it reduces to

$$u^\mu_{;\mu} = 0. \tag{1.8}$$

It is well known that for a spherically symmetric space-time we may write the line-element as

$$ds^2 = e^{2\varphi}dt^2 - \frac{1}{c^2}e^{2\psi}dr^2 - \frac{1}{c^2}e^{2\mu}(d\theta^2 + \sin^2\theta d\chi^2). \tag{1.9}$$

It was shown in [1] that for isentropic motions in such a space-time we may write

$$u_\mu = \frac{1}{\left(1+\frac{i}{c^2}\right)}\frac{\partial\theta}{\partial x^\mu} \tag{1.10}$$

where θ is a scalar function. It was further shown that we may write in the coordinate system in which Eq. (1.9) holds

$$\theta = at$$

where a is a constant. It then follows from Eqs (1.3), (1.6) and (1.10) that

$$a e^{-\varphi} = (1 + p/\varrho c^2), \tag{1.11}$$

$$u_\mu = e^{\varphi}\delta^4_\mu. \tag{1.12}$$

The coordinate system in which Eqs (1.9) and (1.12) hold may be regarded as the general relativistic analogue of a Lagrangian coordinate system in classical mechanics. The function $\mu(r, t)$ may always be chosen to satisfy the condition

$$\mu(r, 0) = \log r. \tag{1.13}$$

If this equation is not satisfied, a transformation of r alone may make it satisfied. With this normalization e^μ represents the position at time t of the particle which was at r at $t = 0$.

2. THE EINSTEIN FIELD EQUATIONS

The Einstein field equations

$$R^\mu_\nu - \tfrac{1}{2}\delta^\mu_\nu R = -8\pi G T^\mu_\nu$$

where G is the Newtonian constant of gravitation, T^μ_ν is given by Eqs (1.2), and R^μ_ν and R are the Ricci tensor and scalar curvature respectively reduce to a system of equations for φ, ψ and μ alone in virtue of Eqs (1.6), (1.11) and (1.12).

For the line-element given by Eq. (1.9) and for the energy

tensor given by Eq. (1.2) with Eqs (1.11) and (1.12) holding, the field equations reduce to

$$e^{-2\varphi}(2\mu_{tt}+3\mu_t^2-2\mu_t\varphi_t)-c^2e^{-2\psi}\mu_r(\mu_r+2\varphi_r)+c^2e^{-2\mu}=-\frac{8\pi Gp}{c^2} \tag{2.1}$$

$$\mu_{rt}-\mu_t\varphi_r-\mu_r\psi_t+\mu_t\mu_r=0 \tag{2.2}$$

and

$$e^{-2\varphi}(\mu_t^2+2\mu_t\psi_t)-c^2e^{-2\psi}(2\mu_{rr}+3\mu_r^2-2\mu_r\psi_r)+c^2e^{-2\mu}=8\pi G\varrho_0 \tag{2.3}$$

where ϱ_0 is a constant because of the isentropy assumption and the subscripts denote derivatives with respect to the variable listed. Equations (2.1) and (2.2) are to be fulfilled in a neighborhood of $t=0$ and Eq. (2.3) need only be satisfied for $t=0$.

These equations are to be satisfied interior to a hypersurface

$$r=r_0^*. \tag{2.4}$$

Exterior to this hypersurface we demand that the Eqs (2.1) to (2.3) with the right-hand sides set equal to zero be satisfied. Across the hypersurface we require that φ, ψ and μ be continuous and that their derivatives with respect to t also be continuous. The functions φ and μ must also have continuous derivatives with respect to r, however, ψ_r need not be continuous. Further we require that

$$p(r_0^*,t)=0.$$

3. THE STATIC SOLUTION

The static interior and exterior solutions of Eqs (2.1) to (2.3) for the incompressible fluid are due to Schwarzschild [2] and are well known. They are given below for use in later sections. We use the subscript zero to denote the static solution and we may write

$$\mu_0=\log r$$

and Eq. (2.2) is satisfied. Equation (2.3) becomes

$$-c^2e^{-2\psi_0}\left(\frac{1}{r^2}-\frac{2}{r}\psi_0\right)+\frac{c^2}{r^2}=8\pi G\varrho_0. \tag{3.1}$$

If we now write

$$e^{-2\psi_0}=1-\frac{2Gm_0(r)}{c^2r}, \tag{3.2}$$

Eq. (3.1) reduces to

$$m_{0r} = 4\pi\varrho_0 r^2.$$

Since ϱ_0 is a constant, we must have

$$m_0(r) = \frac{4\pi}{3}\varrho_0 r^3 \tag{3.3}$$

where the constant of integration has been chosen to be zero in order that the line-element be non-singular at the origin $r = 0$. Thus we have

$$e^{-2\varphi_0} = 1 - \frac{8\pi G\varrho_0}{3c^2} r^2 = 1 - r^2/R^2 \tag{3.4}$$

where

$$1/R^2 = 8\pi G\varrho_0/3c^2. \tag{3.5}$$

Equation (2.1) now becomes

$$\varphi_{0r} = \frac{r}{2R^2}\frac{(3P+1)}{1-r^2/R^2}$$

where

$$P = \frac{p}{\varrho_0 c^2}.$$

However, it is a consequence of Eq. (1.11) that

$$(1+P)\varphi_r = -P_r. \tag{3.6}$$

Hence, we have

$$P_r = -\frac{r}{2R^2}\frac{(3P+1)(1+P)}{1-r^2/R^2}. \tag{3.7}$$

The solutions of Eqs (3.7) and (3.6) are

$$p = \varrho_0 c^2 \frac{\sqrt{1-r^2/R^2} - \sqrt{1-r_0^2/R^2}}{3\sqrt{1-r_0^2/R^2} - \sqrt{1-r^2/R^2}} \tag{3.8}$$

$$e^{\varphi_0(r)} = \tfrac{1}{2}(3\sqrt{1-r_0^2/R^2} - \sqrt{1-r^2/R^2}). \tag{3.9}$$

The constants of integration have been chosen so that $p_0(r_0) = 0$ and

$$e^{\varphi_0(r_0)} = \sqrt{1-r_0^2/R^2} = \sqrt{1-\frac{2Gm_0(r_0)}{r}} \tag{3.10}$$

where

$$m_0(r_0) = \frac{4\pi}{3} \varrho_0 r_0^3. \tag{3.11}$$

For the exterior solution ($r > r_0$) we have the well-known solution

$$\mu_0 = \log r \tag{3.12}$$

$$e^{-2\psi_0} = \left(1 - \frac{2Gm_0(r_0)}{rc^2}\right) = e^{2\varphi_0}. \tag{3.13}$$

It may be verified that the above solution satisfied the boundary conditions given in the preceding section. Note that the derivative of ψ_0 is not continuous across the hypersurface $r = r_0$ nor is it required to be by the boundary conditions.

4. EQUATION (2.2)

We now turn our attention to non-static solutions of Eqs (2.1) to (2.3). In view of Eq. (1.12), Eq. (1.8) may be written as

$$(e^{-\varphi}\sqrt{g})_t = (e^{\psi+2\mu})_t = 0$$

where g is the determinant of the metric tensor. Hence we must have

$$\psi_t = -2\mu_t \tag{4.1}$$

or

$$\psi(r, t) = -2\mu(r, t) + \psi(r, 0) + 2\log r \tag{4.2}$$

where we have made use of Eq. (1.13).

When equation (4.1) is substituted into Eq. (2.2) the latter equation becomes

$$\mu_{rt} - \mu_t\varphi_r + 3\mu_r\mu_t = 0.$$

This may be integrated to give

$$e^{3\mu}\mu_t = K(t)e^{\varphi}$$

where $K(t)$ is an arbitrary function of t. It may be chosen to be a constant for a transformation of coordinates involving t alone sends φ into φ plus a function of t. Hence we may write

$$e^{3\mu}\mu_t = \frac{Ke^{\varphi}}{\sqrt{3}} \tag{4.3}$$

where K is a constant and the $\sqrt{3}$ is introduced for later convenience.

5. EQUATIONS (2.3)

In view of Eq. (4.1), Eq. (2.3) may be written as

$$-3e^{-2\varphi}\mu_t^2 - c^2e^{-2\psi}(2\mu_{rr} + 3\mu_r^2 - 2\mu_r\psi_r) + c^2e^{-2\mu} = 8\pi G\varrho_0.$$

Substituting from Eq. (4.3) we find that the above equation may be written as

$$-K^2e^{-6\mu} - c^2e^{-2\psi}(2\mu_{rr} + 3\mu_r^2 - 2\mu_r\psi_r) + c^2e^{-2\mu} = 8\pi G\varrho_0. \qquad (5.1)$$

Equation (5.1) will hold for all values of t if it holds for $t = 0$ and Eqs (2.1) and (2.2) are satisfied. We use Eq. (1.13) and still write ψ for $\psi(r, 0)$ and obtain

$$-c^2e^{-2\psi}\left(\frac{1}{r^2} - \frac{2}{r}\psi_r\right) + \frac{c^2}{r^2} = 8\pi G\varrho_0 + \frac{K}{r^6}.$$

If we now write

$$e^{-2\psi(r,0)} = 1 - \frac{2Gm(r)}{c^2r} \qquad (5.2)$$

we obtain

$$m(r) = \frac{4\pi}{3}\varrho_0 r^3 - \frac{K^2}{6Gr^3} + L \qquad (5.3)$$

where L is a constant of integration.

If the constants K and L are non-zero it follows from Eq. (5.2) that the metric tensor at $t = 0$ is singular. Such singularities might be allowed if it could be shown that for $t > 0$ the metric tensor is non-singular. Actually the opposite can be shown as a consequence of Eq. (4.2). That equation may be written as

$$e^{-2\psi(r,t)} = \left(\frac{e^{\mu}}{r}\right)^4\left(1 - \frac{2Gm(r)}{c^2r}\right)$$

where $m(r)$ is given by Eq. (5.3). If $e^{-2\psi(r,t)}$ is to be well-behaved at the origin e^{μ} must be proportional to r^{α} ($\alpha > 1$) near the origin. In that case the coefficients g_{22} and g_{33} in the line element given by Eq. (1.9) will have an essential singularity at the origin for all t.

Hence if we are have a non-singular line element for an interval in t we must take $K = 0$. In that case it follows from Eq. (4.3) that $\mu_t = 0$ and from Eq. (4.1) that $\psi_t = 0$. Thus we must have

$$\mu(r,t) = 2\log r,$$

$$\psi(r,t) = \psi(r,0)$$

and this function is given by Eqs (5.2) and (5.3). Equations (2.1) to (2.3) then reduce to those treated in Section 3. The general solutions of these equations are given by Eqs (3.8), (3.9), (3.12) and (3.13) except for an additive function of t in the definition of φ in Eq. (3.9). It has already been pointed out that such a function may be set equal to zero without any restriction.

If the quantity occurring in Eqs (3.8) and (3.9) is a function of t, all the conditions as yet imposed are satisfied. However there is still another boundary condition on the hypersurface

$$r - r_0(t) = 0 \tag{5.4}$$

which must be imposed if this hypersurface is to be the boundary between an interior solution and an exterior one. The condition is that

$$u^\mu \lambda_\mu = 0 \tag{5.5}$$

where λ_μ are the covariant components of the normal to the hypersurface given by (5.4) and u^μ is the velocity vector of the fluid on the hypersurface. Equation (5.5) follows from the requirement of conservation of mass across the hypersurface and the condition that the density vanished in the exterior region (see [3], p. 385). It follows from Eqs (1.12), (5.4) and (5.5) that

$$\frac{dr_0}{dt} = 0.$$

Hence we have shown that the only non-singular solutions of the Einstein field equations for a spherically symmetric distribution of an incompressible fluid at constant density (entropy) are the static ones found by Schwarzschild.

The method used for solving the field equations for a plane-symmetric distribution of an incompressible fluid at a constant density (entropy) in an earlier paper [4] may be used to determine the singular solutions of Eqs (2.1) to (2.3). It should be pointed out that the non-static solutions given in that paper correspond to line elements with singularities.

REFERENCES

[1] A. H. TAUB, Small Motions of a Spherically Symmetric Distribution of Matter, to be published in the Proceedings of Colloque International sur les Theories Relativistes de la Gravitation held in June 1959 at Royaumont, France.

[2] K. SCHWARZSCHILD, *Berl. Ber.*, p. 189 and p. 424 (1916).

[3] A. H. TAUB, Singular Hypersurfaces in General Relativity, *Ill. Math.*, **1**, 370–88 (1957).

[4] A. H. TAUB, Isentropic Hydrodynamics in Plane Symmetric Space-Times, *Phys. Rev.* **103**, 454–67 (1956).

ON THE PROPAGATION OF INFORMATION BY WAVES

A. TRAUTMAN

Institute of Physics, Polish Academy of Sciences, Warsaw

1. INTRODUCTION

GRAVITATIONAL waves are usually defined by their geometric properties. For example, plane waves are invariant under a 5-parameter group of motions [1]. Pirani's definition of pure radiation fields refers to the algebraic structure of the Riemannian tensor [2]. However, the elegant geometrical approach cannot easily be applied to the problem of spherical gravitational waves. In this case no more than axial symmetry can be assumed. The Riemannian tensor of a spherical wave is expected to be of type I.

There is another important property of waves, both linear and gravitational: *waves can propagate information*. This means that wave-like solutions depend on arbitrary functions, the shape of which contains the information carried by the wave. This is obviously true of both linear waves and the known gravitational waves. The dependence on these arbitrary functions can be very simple, as in the case of plane waves, or more complicated as in the case of cylindrical waves.

We shall show how one can deduce certain properties of waves from the fact that they carry information. We shall begin with very simple remarks on linear waves. In the gravitational case we have only been able to rederive Robinson's line-element for plane-fronted waves [3], [4]. However, it may be possible to obtain some information about spherical waves by the method outlined in this note.

2. WAVES IN LINEAR THEORIES

Let us start with scalar waves in Minkowski space. We shall consider solutions of the wave equation

$$(g^{\mu\nu}\partial_\mu\partial_\nu + \varkappa^2)\varphi = 0, \qquad g^{00} = 1, \qquad g^{0k} = 0, \qquad g^{ik} = -\delta^{ik}, \qquad (1)$$

which have the form

$$\varphi = \varphi(x, F(\sigma)) \tag{2}$$

where $F(\sigma)$ is an *arbitrary* (twice differentiable) function of the scalar $\sigma = \sigma(x)$. The form (2) includes plane and spherical but not cylindrical waves. Derivatives with respect to F will be denoted by primes. A comma followed by an index will denote differentiation with respect to the x's which appear in φ explicitly; for instance:

$$\partial_\nu \varphi = \varphi_{,\nu} + \varphi' F' \sigma_{,\nu}, \qquad \sigma_{,\nu} \equiv \partial_\nu \sigma.$$

The function F being arbitrary, we obtain from (1):

$$g^{\mu\nu} \sigma_{,\mu} \sigma_{,\nu} = 0, \tag{3a}$$

$$g^{\mu\nu} (2\varphi'_{,\mu} \sigma_{,\nu} + \varphi' \sigma_{,\mu\nu}) = 0, \tag{3b}$$

$$g^{\mu\nu} \varphi_{,\mu\nu} + \varkappa^2 \varphi = 0. \tag{3c}$$

The surfaces $\sigma =$ const turn out to be null. Equation (3b) is a typical propagation equation (cf., for example, [5]) and the meaning of (3c) is obvious.

It is easy to write down equations analogous to (3) in Maxwell's theory. In order to include both plane and some spherical waves let us take for the electromagnetic tensor:

$$f_{\mu\nu} = {}^0f_{\mu\nu}(x) F(\sigma) + {}^1f_{\mu\nu}(x) F'(\sigma) + {}^2f_{\mu\nu}(x) F''(\sigma). \tag{4}$$

Maxwell's equations give:

$${}^2f^{\mu\nu} \sigma_{,\nu} = 0, \tag{5a}$$

$${}^1f^{\mu\nu} \sigma_{,\nu} + {}^2f^{\mu\nu}{}_{,\nu} = 0, \tag{5b}$$

$${}^0f^{\mu\nu} \sigma_{,\nu} + {}^1f^{\mu\nu}{}_{,\nu} = 0, \tag{5c}$$

$${}^0f^{\mu\nu}{}_{,\nu} = 0, \tag{5d}$$

and similar equations with the f's replaced by their duals. If follows that $\sigma_{,\nu}$ is null and ${}^2f$ is a null bivector which satisfies a propagation equation identical in form to (3b). This means ${}^2fF''$ is the pure radiation part of the wave; if $\sigma_{,\nu}$ satisfies Robinson's equation [3] and $g^{\mu\nu}\sigma_{,\mu\nu} \neq 0$ then ${}^2f$ falls off like $1/r$ [5]. The propagation equations for ${}^0f$ and ${}^1f$ are

$$2\,\mathrm{Prop}\,{}^0f + {}^0f \Box \sigma + \Box\, {}^1f = 0,$$

$$2\,\mathrm{Prop}\,{}^1f + {}^1f \Box \sigma + \Box\, {}^2f = 0.$$

(We have suppressed the indices and introduced the operators $\mathrm{Prop} = g^{\mu\nu} \sigma_{,\mu} \partial_\nu$ [3], $\Box = g^{\mu\nu} \partial_\mu \partial_\nu$.)

We can easily write down the electromagnetic potentials corresponding to the field given by q. (4). The potentials of a typical spherical wave produced by a Hertz dipole are of the form:

$$A_\mu = {}^0A_\mu(x)F(\sigma)+{}^1A(x)F'(\sigma)\sigma_{,\mu}+{}^2A(x)F''(\sigma)\sigma_{,\mu}. \tag{6}$$

In this case we have [5]:

$$\sigma_{,\varrho}{}^1f^\varrho{}_{[\mu}\sigma_{,\nu]} = 0$$

and Robinson's equation follows from Eqs (5). For the potentials of a plane wave depending on one arbitrary function of σ we can choose the expression

$$A_\mu = A(x)F(\sigma)\sigma_{,\mu}. \tag{7}$$

Electromagnetic potentials are not interesting from the point of view of the theory but their form may suggest possible metrics corresponding to gravitational waves.

3. GRAVITATIONAL WAVES

It is not quite easy to apply our method to the gravitational field. Arbitrary functions can be introduced into every metric by coordinate transformations. Metrics containing only arbitrary functions which can be removed by a change of coordinates do not carry information and cannot be called waves. We do not know, however, how to distinguish beforehand between spurious and genuine arbitrary functions. We are therefore forced to check the character of a metric only after the field equations have been solved.

The second difficulty is of a technical character but is by no means less serious. Suppose we take for $g_{\mu\nu}$ a simple function of F, say a polynomial in F and its derivatives up to a certain order. However, the corresponding inverse tensor $g^{\mu\nu}$ need not be simple; in general it will be an infinite series in F and its derivatives. The field equations will split into an infinite and overdetermined set of equations and the whole procedure will closely resemble an approximation method.

In order to avoid this difficulty we shall investigate only the simplest case, when both $g_{\mu\nu}$ and $g^{\mu\nu}$ depend linearly on F alone. We can show that the metric must then be of the form:

$$g_{\mu\nu} = \underset{0}{g}_{\mu\nu}(x)+F(\sigma)h_\mu(x)h_\nu(x) \tag{8}$$

where h_ν is a null vector with respect to the background metric $\underset{0}{g}_{\mu\nu}$:

$$\underset{0}{g}^{\mu\nu} h_\mu h_\nu = 0, \quad \underset{0}{g}^{\mu\varrho} \underset{0}{g}_{\varrho\nu} = \delta^\mu_\nu. \tag{9}$$

The metric tensor with upper indices has the form:

$$g^{\mu\nu} = \underset{0}{g}^{\mu\nu} - F h^\mu h^\nu$$

where

$$h^\mu = \underset{0}{g}^{\mu\nu} h_\nu .$$

In the following we shall use $\underset{0}{g}^{\mu\nu}$ to raise the indices. Covariant differentiation with respect to the background metric will be denoted by a semicolon. The operators Prop and $\square$ will also be understood to be taken with respect to $\underset{0}{g}_{\mu\nu}$.

Einstein's field equations $R_{\mu\nu} = 0$ lead to the following conditions on $\underset{0}{g}_{\mu\nu}$, h_ϱ and σ:

(a) the Riemann space defined by the background metric must by empty, $\underset{0}{R}_{\mu\nu} = 0$;

(b) $\underset{0}{g}^{\mu\nu}\sigma_{,\mu}\sigma_{,\nu} = 0$;

(c) $h^\nu\sigma_{,\nu} = 0$, therefore $h_\nu = h\sigma_{,\nu}$;

(d) $\square\sigma = 0$;

(e) $(\mathrm{Prop})^2 H = 0$, where $H = h^2$;

(f) $2(\mathrm{Prop}\, H_{,(\alpha}\sigma_{,\beta)}) - (\mathrm{Prop}\, H)_{,(\alpha}\sigma_{,\beta)} + \mathrm{Prop}(H\sigma_{;\alpha\beta}) - \frac{1}{2}\square H\sigma_{,\alpha}\sigma_{,\beta} = 0$.

If we choose the flat metric for $\underset{0}{g}_{\mu\nu}$, we can take

$$\sigma_{;\alpha\beta} = 0, \quad \sigma_{,\alpha} \neq 0, \quad x^0 \equiv \sigma$$

and x^1 as the preferred parameter along rays. The general solution of (e) and (f) is of the form:

$$H = M(x^0, x^2, x^3) + x^1 N(x^0)$$

with M satisfying

$$M_{,22} + M_{,33} = 0. \tag{10}$$

The arbitrary function N is spurious, i.e., it can be transformed away. The line-element reduces to that of plane-fronted waves,

$$ds^2 = M(x^0, x^2, x^3)(dx^0)^2 + 2\,dx^0 dx^1 - (dx^2)^2 - (dx^3)^2$$

with M restricted by equation (10) only and $F(x^0)$ absorbed into M.

Spherical gravitational waves will be more complicated than plane waves in several respects. First of all, we cannot expect both

$g_{\mu\nu}$ and $g^{\mu\nu}$ to be simple functions of F. Secondly, the simplest gravitational spherical wave may be described as a "quadrupole" wave. Therefore, it will probably be necessary to introduce into the metric derivatives of F of a higher order than in equation (4).

REFERENCES

[1] H. Bondi, F. A. E. Pirani and I. Robinson, *Proc. Roy. Soc.* A **251**, 519 (1959).

[2] F. A. E. Pirani, *Phys. Rev.* **105**, 1089 (1957).

[3] I. Robinson, Lectures at the Institute of Physics in Warsaw, 1959 (unpublished).

[4] I. Robinson, Report to the International Colloquium on Gravitation, Royaumont 1959.

[5] R. Sachs, Distance and the Asymptotic Behaviour of Waves in General Relativity p. 397 (in this work)..

ON MULTIPOLE FORMALISM IN GENERAL RELATIVITY

B. TULCZYJEW and W. TULCZYJEW

Chair of Physics, Main School of Agriculture, Warsaw
Institute of Physics, Polish Academy of Sciences, Warsaw

1. IN most problems concerning test bodies, such as planets, we are interested in their orbits and not in internal processes. The description of bodies by means of the energy-momentum density is not suitable for these problems. In Newtonian dynamics the bodies are usually represented by point masses or described by moments of inertia and internal angular momenta in addition to masses and momenta. In General Relativity a body may also be treated as a point particle or described by few multipole moments of its energy-momentum density. A method of describing bodies by multipole moments was proposed by Papapetrou [1]. It was a noncovariant method. A covariant description by means of parameters similar to multipole moments was given by Mathisson [2]. In the present paper we shall show the possibility of describing test bodies in a covariant way in terms of a set of parameters that can be interpreted as multipole moments in a special coordinate system.

2. If the internal processes, such as heat exchange, are not taken into account, one can expect the motion of a body to be determined by the dynamical equations

$$\nabla_\nu \theta^{\mu\nu} = \partial_\nu \theta^{\mu\nu} + \theta^{\varkappa\lambda} \Gamma^\mu_{\varkappa\lambda} = 0\,, \tag{2.1}$$

where $\theta^{\mu\nu}$ is the energy-momentum density.

Let us assume that the gravitational field $g_{\mu\nu}$ can be written in the form of a power series in the spatial coordinates x^m:

$$g_{\mu\nu} = \overline{g_{\mu\nu}(t)} + x^m \overline{\partial_m g_{\mu\nu}(t)} + \tfrac{1}{2} x^m x^n \overline{\partial_m \partial_n g_{\mu\nu}(t)} + \ldots,$$

$$t = x^0.$$

We shall show that in this case the dynamical properties of a body are characterized completely by the multipole moments of its energy-momentum density:

$$t^{m_1\ldots m_r \varkappa\lambda} = \int \theta^{\varkappa\lambda} x^{m_1}\cdots x^{m_r} d_{(3)}x .$$

In fact equations (2.1) may be replaced by an infinite set of equations

$$\int \nabla_\nu \theta^{\mu\nu} d_{(3)}x = 0 ,$$

$$\int \nabla_\nu \theta^{\mu\nu} x^m d_{(3)}x = 0 ,$$

$$\cdots\cdots\cdots\cdots$$

$$\int \nabla_\nu \theta^{\mu\nu} x^{m_1}\cdots x^{m_r} d_{(3)}x = 0 ,$$

$$\cdots\cdots\cdots\cdots\cdots$$

By inserting power series developments for the Christoffel symbols and carrying out the integrations one obtains a set of ordinary differential equations

$$\frac{d}{dt} t^{\mu 0} + t^{\varkappa\lambda}\overline{\Gamma^\mu_{\varkappa\lambda}} + t^{k\varkappa\lambda}\overline{\partial_k \Gamma^\mu_{\varkappa\lambda}} + \tfrac{1}{2} t^{kl\varkappa\lambda}\overline{\partial_k\partial_l \Gamma^\mu_{\varkappa\lambda}} + \ldots = 0 ,$$

$$\frac{d}{dt} t^{m\mu 0} - t^{m\mu} + t^{m\varkappa\lambda}\overline{\Gamma^\mu_{\varkappa\lambda}} + t^{mk\varkappa\lambda}\overline{\partial_k \Gamma^\mu_{\varkappa\lambda}} + \tfrac{1}{2} t^{mkl\varkappa\lambda}\overline{\partial_k\partial_l \Gamma^\mu_{\varkappa\lambda}} + \ldots = 0 ,$$

$$\cdots\cdots\cdots\cdots\cdots\cdots\cdots\cdots\cdots\cdots$$

$$\frac{d}{dt} t^{m_1\ldots m_r \mu 0} - r t^{(m_1\ldots m_r)\mu} + t^{m_1\ldots m_r \varkappa\lambda}\overline{\Gamma^\mu_{\varkappa\lambda}} +$$

$$+ t^{m_1\ldots m_r k\varkappa\lambda}\overline{\partial_k \Gamma^\mu_{\varkappa\lambda}} + \tfrac{1}{2} t^{m_1\ldots m_r kl\varkappa\lambda}\overline{\partial_k\partial_l \Gamma^\mu_{\varkappa\lambda}} + \ldots = 0 ,$$

$$\cdots\cdots\cdots\cdots\cdots\cdots\cdots\cdots\cdots\cdots \tag{2.2}$$

in which the energy-momentum density of the body appears only through its moments $t^{m_1\ldots m_r \mu\nu}$.

The description of bodies by means of multipole moments does not simplify the problem of motion. In various physical problems, however, a satisfactory representation of a body by a few of its first multipole moments can be obtained. Such simplified representatives of bodies will be called multipole particles. The motion of these particles can be determined from Eqs (2.2) of which only a finite number have to be taken into account, the rest being satisfied trivially.

The method of describing bodies and the definition of multipole particles given here are due to Papapetrou [1].

3. The description used in the last section was noncovariant.

In order to obtain a covariant formalism we choose an arbitrary world line $x^\varkappa = \xi^\varkappa(s)$ and introduce a special coordinate system

$$x^\varkappa = \xi^\varkappa(s) + \underset{a}{e}^\varkappa(s) y^a - \frac{1}{2!}\widetilde{\Gamma^\varkappa_{\lambda\mu}} \underset{a}{e}^\lambda \underset{b}{e}^\mu y^a y^b - \frac{1}{3!}\widetilde{\Gamma^\varkappa_{\lambda\mu\nu}} \underset{a}{e}^\lambda \underset{b}{e}^\mu \underset{c}{e}^\nu y^a y^b y^c + \ldots,$$

$$s = y^0,$$

$$\Gamma^\varkappa_{\lambda\mu\nu} = \partial_{(\lambda}\Gamma^\varkappa_{\mu\nu)} - 2\Gamma^\varkappa_{\omega(\lambda}\Gamma^\omega_{\mu\nu)}, \ldots \tag{3.1}$$

where $\underset{a}{e}^\varkappa$ is a Fermi propagated tetrad [3]:

$$\underset{\alpha}{e}^\mu \underset{\beta}{e}_\mu = \begin{cases} 1 & \alpha = \beta = 0 \\ -1 & \alpha = \beta = 1, 2, 3, \\ 0 & \alpha \neq \beta \end{cases} \qquad \underset{0}{e}^\mu = \dot{\xi}^\mu,$$

$$\frac{\delta \underset{a}{e}^\mu}{ds} = (\eta^\mu \dot{\xi}_\nu - \dot{\xi}^\mu \eta_\nu)\underset{a}{e}^\nu, \qquad \eta^\mu = \frac{\delta \dot{\xi}^\mu}{ds}. \tag{3.2}$$

The system (3.1) is a kind of normal coordinate system based on orthogonal axes that are Fermi propagated along the line $x^\varkappa = \xi^\varkappa(s)$. The multipole moments with respect to this coordinate system contain the most objective information on the structure of the body. Instead of the moments $t^{a_1 \ldots a_n \alpha\beta}$ with respect to the special coordinate system their covariant continuations

$$t^{\varkappa_1 \ldots \varkappa_n \mu\nu} = \underset{a_1}{e}^{\varkappa_1} \ldots \underset{a_n}{e}^{\varkappa_n} \underset{\alpha}{e}^\mu \underset{\beta}{e}^\nu t^{a_1 \ldots a_n \alpha\beta}$$

will be used.

Equations (2.2) can now be written in the covariant form

$$\frac{\overset{F}{\delta}}{ds}(\dot{\xi}_\mu t^{\mu\varkappa}) + t^{\mu\nu}\overset{F}{N}{}^\varkappa_{\mu\nu} + t^{\varrho\mu\nu}\overset{F}{N}{}^\varkappa_{\varrho\mu\nu} + \tfrac{1}{2} t^{\varrho_1\varrho_2\mu\nu}\overset{F}{N}{}^\varkappa_{\varrho_1\varrho_2\mu\nu} + \ldots = 0,$$

$$\frac{\overset{F}{\delta}}{ds}(\dot{\xi}_\mu t^{\lambda\mu\varkappa}) - \varepsilon^\lambda_\mu t^{\mu\varkappa} + t^{\lambda\mu\nu}\overset{F}{N}{}^\varkappa_{\mu\nu} + t^{\lambda\varrho\mu\nu}\overset{F}{N}{}^\varkappa_{\varrho\mu\nu} + \ldots = 0,$$

$$\ldots\ldots\ldots\ldots\ldots\ldots\ldots\ldots\ldots\ldots$$

$$\frac{\overset{F}{\delta}}{ds}(\dot{\xi}_\mu t^{\lambda_1 \ldots \lambda_r \mu\varkappa}) - r\varepsilon^{(\lambda_1}_\mu t^{\lambda_2 \ldots \lambda_r)\mu\varkappa} + t^{\lambda_1 \ldots \lambda_r \mu\nu}\overset{F}{N}{}^\varkappa_{\mu\nu} + \ldots = 0$$

$$\ldots\ldots\ldots\ldots\ldots\ldots\ldots\ldots\ldots\ldots \tag{3.3}$$

with

$$\overset{F}{\frac{\delta}{ds}}\, a^{\mu\nu\dots}(s) = \underset{\alpha}{e}^{\mu}\underset{\beta}{e}^{\nu}\dots \frac{d}{ds}\, a^{\alpha\beta\dots}(s); \qquad \varepsilon^{\lambda}_{\mu} = \underset{a}{e}_{\mu}\underset{b}{e}^{\lambda}\delta^{ab} = \delta^{\lambda}_{\mu} - \dot{\xi}^{\lambda}\dot{\xi}_{\mu}$$

and

$$\overset{F}{N}{}^{\varkappa}_{\varrho_1\dots\varrho_r\mu\nu} = \underset{\alpha}{e}^{\varkappa}\, \overset{\beta_1}{e}_{\varrho_1}\dots \overset{\beta_r}{e}_{\varrho_r}\overset{\gamma}{e}_{\mu}\overset{\delta}{e}_{\nu}\,\overline{\partial_{\beta_1}\dots\partial_{\beta_r}\Gamma^{\alpha}_{\gamma\delta}}\,.$$

The quantities last introduced are a kind of normal tensors. Examples of the calculation of these tensors are given in the Appendix. The derivative $\overset{F}{\frac{\delta}{ds}}$ is related to the ordinary absolute derivative $\frac{\delta}{ds}$ by

$$\overset{F}{\frac{\delta}{ds}}\, a^{\mu\nu\dots} = \frac{\delta}{ds}\, a^{\mu\nu\dots} - \dot{\xi}^{\varkappa}\overset{F}{N}{}^{\mu}_{\varkappa\lambda}a^{\lambda\nu\dots} - \dot{\xi}^{\varkappa}\overset{F}{N}{}^{\nu}_{\varkappa\lambda}a^{\mu\lambda\dots} - \dots \tag{3.4}$$

The covariant representation of the bodies that has been obtained is still unsatisfactory because the parameters $t^{\varkappa_1\dots\varkappa_n\mu\nu}$ are not determined by the energy-momentum distribution alone, being dependent on the choice of the world line. A further improvement of the formalism would consist in finding a satisfactory definition of the centre of mass of the body and taking the world line of the centre as the line $x^{\varkappa} = \xi^{\varkappa}(s)$.

4. We shall now derive the equations of motion of a pole-dipole particle. The equations of a single pole particle will be obtained as a special case.

A pole-dipole is characterized by unipole moments $t^{\mu\nu}$ and dipole moments $t^{\varkappa\mu\nu}$. The nontrivial equations from the set (3.3) in this case are

$$\overset{F}{\frac{\delta}{ds}}\,(\dot{\xi}_{\mu}t^{\mu\varkappa}) + t^{\mu\nu}\overset{F}{N}{}^{\varkappa}_{\mu\nu} + t^{\varrho\mu\nu}\overset{F}{N}{}^{\varkappa}_{\varrho\mu\nu} = 0, \tag{4.1.a}$$

$$\overset{F}{\frac{\delta}{ds}}\,(\dot{\xi}_{\mu}t^{\lambda\mu\varkappa}) - \varepsilon^{\lambda}_{\mu}t^{\mu\varkappa} + t^{\lambda\mu\nu}\overset{F}{N}{}^{\varkappa}_{\mu\nu} = 0, \tag{4.1.b}$$

$$-2\varepsilon^{(\lambda_1}_{\mu}t^{\lambda_2)\mu\varkappa} = 0. \tag{4.1.c}$$

The tensors $t^{\mu\nu}$ and $t^{\varkappa\mu\nu}$ can be written as a sum of their time-like and space-like components:

$$t^{\mu\nu} = m\dot{\xi}^{\mu}\dot{\xi}^{\nu} + m^{\mu}\dot{\xi}^{\nu} + m^{\nu}\dot{\xi}^{\mu} + m^{\mu\nu},$$

$$t^{\varkappa\mu\nu} = n^{\varkappa}\dot{\xi}^{\mu}\dot{\xi}^{\nu} + n^{\varkappa\mu}\dot{\xi}^{\nu} + n^{\varkappa\nu}\dot{\xi}^{\mu} + n^{\varkappa\mu\nu}$$

with

$$m = t^{\varrho\sigma}\dot{\xi}_\varrho\dot{\xi}_\sigma, \qquad m^\mu = t^{\varrho\sigma}\dot{\xi}_\varrho\varepsilon^\mu_\sigma, \qquad m^{\mu\nu} = t^{\varrho\sigma}\varepsilon^\mu_\varrho\varepsilon^\nu_\sigma,$$

$$n^\varkappa = t^{\varkappa\varrho\sigma}\dot{\xi}_\varrho\dot{\xi}_\sigma, \qquad n^{\varkappa\mu} = t^{\varkappa\varrho\sigma}\dot{\xi}_\varrho\varepsilon^\mu_\sigma, \qquad n^{\varkappa\mu\nu} = t^{\varkappa\varrho\sigma}\varepsilon^\mu_\varrho\varepsilon^\nu_\sigma.$$

Equations (4.1.c) now give

$$n^{(\lambda_1\lambda_2)\varkappa} + n^{(\lambda_1\lambda_2)}\dot{\xi}^\varkappa = 0.$$

Hence

$$n^{\lambda_1\lambda_2\varkappa} = 0, \qquad n^{(\lambda_1\lambda_2)} = 0.$$

The dipole structure of the particle is thus described by a space-like antisymmetric tensor $2n^{\lambda_1\lambda_2}$ and a space-like vector $n^\varkappa$. These should be interpreted as the internal angular momentum and the static moment, respectively, since in the special coordinate system

$$2n^{a_1a_2} = \int (y^{a_1}\theta^{0a_2} - y^{a_2}\theta^{0a_1})\, d_{(3)}y$$

and

$$n^a = \int y^a\theta^{00} d_{(3)}y.$$

Both these quantities can be conveniently represented by a bivector:

$$S^{\mu\nu} = 2n^{\mu\nu} + n^\mu\dot{\xi}^\nu - n^\nu\dot{\xi}^\mu.$$

Equation (4.1.b) now reads[1]

$$\frac{1}{2}\frac{\overset{F}{\delta}}{ds}(S^{\lambda\varkappa} + S^{\lambda\mu}\dot{\xi}_\mu\dot{\xi}^\varkappa + S^{\varkappa\mu}\dot{\xi}_\mu\dot{\xi}^\lambda) - m^\lambda\dot{\xi}^\varkappa - m^{\lambda\varkappa} +$$

$$+ S^{\lambda\mu}\dot{\xi}_\mu\eta^\varkappa - S^{\lambda\mu}\eta_\mu - S^{\mu\nu}\dot{\xi}_\nu\eta_\mu\dot{\xi}^\lambda\dot{\xi}^\varkappa = 0. \qquad (4.2)$$

The antisymmetrization of the last equation gives

$$\frac{\overset{F}{\delta}}{ds}S^{\lambda\varkappa} - m^\lambda\dot{\xi}^\varkappa + m^\varkappa\dot{\xi}^\lambda + S^{\lambda\mu}\dot{\xi}_\mu\eta^\varkappa - S^{\lambda\mu}\eta_\mu\dot{\xi}^\varkappa - S^{\varkappa\mu}\dot{\xi}_\mu\eta^\lambda +$$

$$+ S^{\varkappa\mu}\eta_\mu\dot{\xi}^\lambda = \frac{\delta S^{\lambda\varkappa}}{ds} - m^\lambda\dot{\xi}^\varkappa + m^\varkappa\dot{\xi}^\lambda = 0,$$

which results in

$$m^\lambda = \frac{\delta S^{\lambda\varkappa}}{ds}\dot{\xi}_\varkappa \qquad (4.3)$$

---

(1) The normal tensors $\overset{F}{N}$ are calculated in the Appendix.

and

$$\frac{\delta S^{\lambda\varkappa}}{ds}+\frac{\delta S^{\mu\lambda}}{ds}\dot{\xi}_{\mu}\dot{\xi}^{\varkappa}+\frac{\delta S^{\varkappa\mu}}{ds}\dot{\xi}_{\mu}\dot{\xi}^{\lambda}=0. \tag{4.4}$$

The symmetrization of the space-like part of (4.2) leads to

$$m^{\lambda\varkappa}=\tfrac{1}{2}S^{\lambda\mu}\dot{\xi}_{\mu}\eta^{\varkappa}+\tfrac{1}{2}S^{\varkappa\mu}\dot{\xi}_{\mu}\eta^{\lambda}. \tag{4.5}$$

The last term of (4.1.a) can be written in the following form:

$$n^{\varrho}\overline{R_{\varrho\mu\nu}}^{\varkappa}\dot{\xi}^{\mu}\dot{\xi}^{\nu}-n^{\varrho}\eta_{\varrho}\eta^{\varkappa}-n^{\varrho}\frac{\delta\eta_{\varrho}}{\delta s}\dot{\xi}^{\varkappa}+n^{\varrho\mu}\overline{R_{\varrho\mu\nu}}^{\varkappa}\dot{\xi}_{\nu}$$

$$=\tfrac{1}{2}S^{\varrho\mu}\overline{R_{\varrho\mu\nu}}^{\varkappa}\dot{\xi}^{\nu}-S^{\varrho\sigma}\dot{\xi}_{\sigma}\eta_{\varrho}\eta^{\varkappa}-S^{\varrho\sigma}\dot{\xi}_{\sigma}\frac{\delta\eta_{\varrho}}{ds}\dot{\xi}^{\varkappa},$$

and the whole Eq. (4.1.a) gives

$$\frac{\overset{F}{\delta}}{ds}\left(m\dot{\xi}^{\varkappa}+\frac{\delta S^{\varkappa\mu}}{ds}\dot{\xi}_{\mu}\right)+m\eta^{\varkappa}-2\frac{\delta S^{\nu\mu}}{ds}\dot{\xi}_{\mu}\eta_{\nu}\dot{\xi}^{\varkappa}-$$

$$-S^{\nu\mu}\dot{\xi}_{\mu}\eta_{\nu}\eta^{\varkappa}-S^{\nu\mu}\dot{\xi}_{\mu}\frac{\delta\eta_{\nu}}{ds}\dot{\xi}^{\varkappa}+\tfrac{1}{2}S^{\varrho\mu}\overline{R_{\varrho\mu\nu}}^{\varkappa}\dot{\xi}^{\nu}$$

$$=\frac{\delta}{ds}\left(m\dot{\xi}^{\varkappa}+S^{\mu\nu}\dot{\xi}_{\mu}\eta_{\nu}\dot{\xi}^{\varkappa}+\frac{\delta S^{\varkappa\mu}}{ds}\dot{\xi}_{\mu}\right)+\tfrac{1}{2}S^{\varrho\mu}\overline{R_{\varrho\mu\nu}}^{\varkappa}\dot{\xi}^{\nu}=0. \tag{4.6}$$

Equations (4.3) and (4.5) reduce the number of independent unipole moments to one. Thus the pole-dipole particle is described by seven independent parameters m and $S^{\mu\nu}$. The number of independent Eqs (4.4) and (4.6) also is seven. The choice of the world line is not restricted by these equations.

Next the centre of mass of a pole-dipole particle should be defined. The definition should be of the form

$$S^{\mu\nu}p_{\nu}=0 \tag{4.7}$$

with p_{ν} a suitably defined four-momentum vector. In the case of flat space-time we can take $p^{\varkappa}$ to be the expression in brackets in (4.6). Multiplying (4.4) by p_{λ} and using (4.7) and (4.6) we obtain

$$\frac{\delta S^{\mu\lambda}}{ds}\frac{\delta S_{\lambda}^{\ \nu}}{ds}\dot{\xi}_{\mu}\dot{\xi}_{\nu}\dot{\xi}^{\varkappa}+(m+S^{\mu\nu}\dot{\xi}_{\mu}\eta_{\nu})\frac{\delta S^{\varkappa\varrho}}{ds}\dot{\xi}_{\varrho}=0. \tag{4.8}$$

Hence

$$\frac{\delta S^{\mu\nu}}{ds}\dot{\xi}_{\nu}=0$$

and

$$S^{\mu\nu}\dot{\xi}_{\nu}=0 \tag{4.9}$$